CONTENTS

COMPUTER
AND
INFORMATION
SCIENCES

COLLECTED PAPERS ON LEARNING, ADAPTATION
AND CONTROL IN INFORMATION SYSTEMS

Edited by
JULIUS T. TOU
Northwestern University

and

RICHARD H. WILCOX
Office of Naval Research

SPARTAN BOOKS, INC.
1106 Connecticut Avenue, N. W.
Washington, D. C. 20036

1964

Library of Congress Catalog Card Number 64-25585

Sole Distributors in Great Britain, The British Commonwealth and the Continent of Europe:

Cleaver-Hume Press
10-15 St. Martins Street
London W.C. 2

Printed in the United States of America

PREFACE

The demands of World War II resulted in the introduction of many scientists and engineers to the knowledge and practice of automatic control; with their help (and that of their subsequent students) the associated theory and techniques were pushed forward at an increasing rate in an effort to keep up with the newer demands of the space age. A slightly younger but even faster-growing discipline is represented by digital computing technology, whose birth was heralded in 1944 by the Harvard Mark I relay machine and slightly later by the vacuum tube ENIAC at the University of Pennsylvania, and whose final stature is not yet achieved. Finally, the last five years have witnessed phenomenal growth of interest in methods of emulating with machines many of the functions formerly ascribed solely to human intellect, such as general pattern recognition, game playing, theorem proving, and learning.

Certainly these three technical areas have regions of overlap. But in general they are populated by separate groups of scientists and engineers who use somewhat different vocabularies. Consider the fact that each year sees a Joint Automatic Control Conference, Eastern and Western Joint Computer Conferences, and special symposia devoted to such topics as Self-Organizing Systems and Bionics. Fortunately, however, more and more leaders of modern technology are coming to realize that these three fields are in reality all specialties of one macro-discipline which we choose to call the computer and information sciences.

To lend support to this unified view, and to provide an arena for the exchange of current results and conjectures among active representatives of the various specialties, the Office of Naval Research joined with the Northwestern University Technological Institute in holding a first Computer and Information Sciences Symposium. Devoted particularly to Learning, Adaptation, and Control, this Symposium was held on 17 and 18 June 1963 at the Northwestern Technological Institute in Evanston, Illinois. Approximately 300 people from industry, government, and universities throughout the United States and several foreign countries represented an unusually wide variety of scientific and engineering disciplines. Judging from the numerous intense discussions in the lobby and coffee rooms, the objective of fostering information exchange was achieved with considerable success.

v

This book comprises the official Proceedings of the Symposium. It is intended not only to reach those who could not attend the meeting but also to serve as a permanent reference. To this latter end the papers are arranged is logical groups and an index is provided to help the reader locate items of particular interest.

The papers appearing here were prepared by active investigators who were selected because of their contributions to a representative sample of the appropriate specialized areas of the computer and information sciences. It is recognized that many other research workers have made or are making highly significant contributions to the understanding of learning, adaptation, and control. Unfortunately, the omnipresent tyranny of time and space prohibited the inclusion of their work in the Symposium and these subsequent Proceedings.

Credit for any success achieved with the Symposium rests to a major extent with the authors of the individual papers. However, in making the many necessary arrangements the Co-chairmen, Professor Tou and Mr. Wilcox, were aided materially by the contribution of significant time and talent by personnel from both sponsoring institutions. In particular, the planning committee included also Margo A. Sass of the Office of Naval Research, and Roger R. Jeness and Gilbert K. Krulee of Northwestern University. Additional thanks are due Mrs. Dorothy Wagner and Mrs. Gerta Houston of Northwestern, and Gordon D. Goldstein, Mrs. Judy E. Caesar, and Mrs. Judy A. Hetrick of ONR for their invaluable assistance in arranging and running the Symposium, not to mention the effort put into these resulting Proceedings. To all of these goes the heartfelt appreciation of the editors.

Richard H. Wilcox, Head,
Information Systems Branch,
Office of Naval Research.

WELCOME ADDRESS

H. B. GOTAAS

Dean of The Technological Institute
Northwestern University

I am delighted to have the opportunity to welcome you to this Symposium on behalf of The Technological Institute, Northwestern University. I am indeed very happy that The Technological Institute has the opportunity to work with the Office of Naval Research in organizing this Symposium on what I personally consider a timely topic of utmost importance. Computer and information science is one of the most exciting classes of scientific study today. The 1950s can be regarded as the computer decade, in which many of man's menial mental tasks were taken over by computers in offices and laboratories. By the same token, the 1960s and 1970s may well be known to future historians as the age of the intelligent machine.

During the past decade there have been a great many remarkable and important advances in the development of computer techniques and control theories and in the capabilities of information-processing equipment. No doubt these significant advances have stimulated growing interest in the study of learning and cognitive systems, and in intelligent machines. In recent years a number of new groups have been formed across the country to do research which would lead toward an understanding of learning, adaptation, and control in information science. We at The Technological Institute have organized the Computer Sciences Laboratory for pursuing research in this important area and have introduced a graduate program in computer and information science to train teachers and research workers in this ever-growing field.

We feel that this is the time for leading scientists who have been actively working in this field at university laboratories, industrial concerns, and government institutions to get together and review their research accomplishments and discuss their research problems. This is the main objective of the Symposium. I hope that as the well-selected papers of this Symposium are given, starting this morning, you will find opportunity to discuss new and significant problems. I hope that the talks and discussions of this Symposium will prove useful and stimulating, and that you will find your visit to Northwestern University and the City of Evanston an enjoyable one.

Thank you.

WELCOME ADDRESS

THE NEXT TEN YEARS

Keynote Address

W. R. ASHBY

It is now ten years since the last of the MACY Conferences on Cybernetics ended the process of getting the subject of "brainlike mechanisms" well launched. Where are we today, and what will come in the next ten years?

The chief difference today, from our outlook ten years ago, is, I think, a much better sense of what is realistic. Although we still face a largely undeveloped subject in which there is plenty of room for exciting developments, we are today beginning to grasp that our subject is dominated by quantitative laws that must be respected if our activities are not to be futile.

I was myself sobered (and therefore probably improved) by Banerji's recent observation (if I quote him rightly) that information theory is, basically, just counting—nothing more mysterious than that. The man who says "you can't get three maneuvers out of a satellite with only two signals" has the basic idea. Where Shannon showed his skill was not in formulating a new mystery but in showing how the simple process of counting could be extended to cases such as the sequence with constraints, or the continuous waveform limited in bandwidth, in which direct counting could no longer be performed by the untrained person. Ultimately, we count causes and effects: signals sent to a satellite, maneuvers executed. What is peculiar to our science today is that we study processes in which causes and effects, instead of being considered one pair at a time as in classic science, are now handled in great aggregates. A program on a digital computer, for instance, evokes millions of cause-effect pairs, linked into a long chain. "Feedback" considers long chains circulating around a single pair of variables. In a network, large numbers of cause-effect pairs act simultaneously over many variables, in parallel.

QUANTITY OF INTELLIGENCE

Once one applies the quantitative approach one can, I think, see the topic of Artificial Intelligence in better perspective. As I have maintained before, all intelligence (of active type) is shown essentially by appropriate

2

selection, and the process is therefore *homologous with that of the removal of noise from a message.* If the goal is given, the "message" is from a set of entropy zero, and the whole of the intelligent activity corresponds to the activity of the correction channel, as treated in Shannon's tenth theorem. From that theorem it follows that the intensity of intelligent activity cannot exceed the quantity of information transmitted by the correction channel.

It seems to me today that the whole nature of artificial intelligence was once quite misconceived. Twenty years ago it was regarded as something essentially mysterious and semidivine, regarded rather as the savage sees lightning. Today we know that both electricity and intelligence are essentially ordinary in their nature—stroke a cat and you will evoke a small quantity of both—but neither becomes important until it is available in substantial quantities. Thus the difficulty with artificial intelligence is not to get it, but to get enough of it.

There are some problems that, though they look difficult, are in fact trivial unless they are supplemented by a detailed specification. "Making a musical instrument," for instance, is trivially easy in this form, for all one needs to do is to pick up the nearest object and strike it. It will emit some vibration and will thus pass the basic test. The difficulty starts when the sponsor says, "Yes, but I don't like that particular vibration." Then comes the question "what vibration *do* you want?" followed by the quite difficult work of actually achieving the demanded vibration-pattern.

"Make a map" is another such problem. As it stands, this directive can be satisfied by any scribbled marks on paper, for the pattern is sure to be isomorphic with some region of the earth—or perhaps of the moon. Only when the sponsor says "I want a map of this country showing such and such features" does the task become a major one.

Here I am suggesting that "making a brainlike mechanism" is equally trivial, for almost any object or mechanism will have some feature in common with the brain. Anything that is wet is brainlike, and so is anything that undergoes ion surges, or electric pulses, or loses information, and so on. Only when a substantial further specification is added—that the mechanism is to do thus and so—does the problem cease to be easy and trivial, and become tough and worthwhile.

In the last ten years the center of interest has thus shifted from the mere making of something that shows a trace of intelligence to the making of something that shows intelligence in large degree. This is why I would like to see a serious attempt made to build a chess-playing machine that would beat the World Champion. The building would be trivial from one point of view, for it would teach us nothing about the principles, which are already clear; but the actual struggling with the actual problems encountered would be most instructive, and might well serve as a textbook example for years to come.

One remembers here, of course, that the principle of the rocket was known for centuries, but the big rocket was not understood realistically until the engineers had actually managed to get one to achieve its assignment.

The knowledge we need today in building an artificial intelligence is not of principles but of practical efficiency. The rocket engineers know today a great deal about the efficiencies of their devices; today we know appallingly little about the efficiencies—or rather, the inefficiencies—of the methods we use. It took us about ten years to realize, through Neil Miller, that if we have to search for a goal through an expanding tree of trials, branching at every step, then if we don't also search backwards from the goal so as to meet in the middle we raise the number of operations not to double but to the *square* of the number. Thus an operation that requires a million operations may today have a trillion expended on it. Or consider using a nerve cell, that can change significantly in a millisecond, as a reverberating circuit to carry one bit as a memory for ten years. Its efficiency would be about 0.000,000,03 percent. It is the elimination of this sort of nonsense that would be the chief virtue of the serious and practical attempt to build a top chess player. One might say that it would force us to stop being information theorists and to become information engineers.

THE NUMBER CEILING

The practical attempt to build such an advanced chess player would, I am sure, force into prominence an aspect of the subject that is at present seldom noticed in general theoretical studies. The attempt would soon run into inconveniently big numbers, and then one would be tempted to say: "Let's wait a year or two—there's a new diode coming up that's ten times as fast." This attitude, I suggest, is utterly inappropriate, and seeing why is well worth a few minutes' consideration.

How fast do these numbers get big? Without fussing for exact solutions, we know that, as a whole is made from parts, the number of states goes up exponentially with the number of parts; so the number of *properties* possible over the states (i.e., the number of subsets) goes up as the exponential *of* an exponential. What does this mean? Try a simple example. Suppose we have a block of lamps, 20 × 20, each of which can be lit or not lit. The number of states of this block is 2^{400}, i.e., about 10^{120}. Suppose now we want to specify some "property" over these states, saying "this has it, that does not." How many properties are there to choose from? Obviously there are $2^{(10^{120})}$. This number is $10^{(10^{119.5})}$ so we can think of it, without serious error, as $10^{(10^{120})}$

How big is this number? We can get some faint impression of its size by the following device. First notice that $10^{10} - 10^7$ is practically 10^{10}, for it is actually 9,990,000,000. Thus, subtraction from 10^k has no appreciable effect unless the other exponent is within a unit or two of k. Now consider the number $10^{(10^{80})}$. Written out in full it would be a 1 followed by 10^{80} zeros. But there are only 10^{73} atoms in the whole visible universe. Thus, this number is so large that there is not material enough to get it written in our universe. It can certainly claim to be a big number. But now what is $10^{(10^{120})}$ divided by this huge thing? The exponent will be $10^{120} - 10^{80}$, and, as we saw, this is practically 10^{120}. Thus the number $10^{(10^{120})}$ is so large that division by a number too big to be written in our universe does not touch it! These huge numbers are *immune to division* (unless the divisor is close to their own size). This is the number that comes up when we consider a mere 20×20 block of lamps and the patterns that can be defined over its states.

The point here, of course, is that the number 20, which catches our eye, is in fact of practically no importance. What matters is the collecting into a *whole* and then thinking about *subsets*. Each of these topics has the effect of lifting the number from its direct value to that of an exponent, and the result is a numerical explosion.

In fact, by looking at the elementary combinatorial properties we can soon satisfy ourselves that every topic in the following list (in no way exhaustive) raises the number (approximately) either to an exponential or to a factorial function—and the latter grows even faster than the exponential.

System	Order
Net	Subset
Assembly	Property
Automaton	Constraint
Organization	Relation
Pattern	

Each of these terms is well defined in our work, and every one is numerically explosive.

Learning and memory must be added to the list. To use these two topics we require a primary set of variables, and then we must add their values at past times. Now these values are themselves variables in another sense, so the primary set—say $x(t)$, $y(t)$ and $z(t)$—is increased by the addition of $x(t - 1)$, $x(t - 2)$, ..., $y(t - 1)$, ..., etc. Adding in memory is equivalent to adding more variables, so far as the number of possibilities is concerned, and it has an equally explosive effect.

Thus, the very topics that interest us in this Symposium are those that generate these tremendous numbers.

At this point the astronomer may well ask: "Who's afraid of big numbers?"—but his comment, I suggest, misses the point. The "astronomical" numbers, the physically existent and actually realizable numbers—are all below 10^{100}. The number of microseconds since the earth solidified is 10^{23}. As we have seen above, the total number of atoms in the visible universe is about 10^{73}. Again, Bremermann has shown that the fundamental properties of matter make it impossible for any physical system, even if it uses individual atomic states as its symbols, to process more than 2×10^{47} bits/gram/sec, so that if a computer the size of the earth had computed through all time since the earth cooled, it could not by now have processed more than 10^{93} bits.

Again: if we take 10^{-10} sec as an average time for an atomic event, then the total number of atomic events that have occurred anywhere in the whole universe, in all time, is about 10^{100}. Thus, we can epitomize with:

Everything material stops at 10^{100}

Ceilings are not new. Aircraft for fifty years have had to be designed with a proper respect for their aerodynamic ceilings, and though the designer has always been looking beyond he has shown his skill, not by aiming at the Sun as did Icarus, but by adapting his resources skilfully to get fairly close to the actual ceiling of his year. We in the computer world, I suggest, having tried a few flights to the sun, should now advance to the more realistic task of deliberately working under a known ceiling of 10^{100}

THE NEXT COMPUTER

If we are to progress further in the world of adapting and self-organizing systems we must explore the possibilities of new types of computer, for the two present types of digital and analog are grossly specialized as well as seriously defective in some respects. If example is needed, the lack is shown with special clarity when we attempt to use today's machines for such a task as chess playing.

The typical analog is grossly hampered by the fact that all its variables are continuous, so that the highly important step-type change can be embodied only clumsily and in small degree. Related to this feature is its inability to hold any memory for long: all effects tend to decay exponentially, so that holding information for an indefinite term is as difficult as producing a step-function trajectory. These properties make it unfit in practice to be used as basis for a chess player.

The digital computer can, of course, theoretically carry out every defined operation, but this generality is in fact vetoed by the Number Ceiling. The computer's main faults are worth notice, for they suggest lines of improvement.

Its major shortcoming, as has been recognized for a long time, is that it has typically only one center for operations, to which everything must be brought. The computer's organization, if used in the Air Force, would treat the atmosphere as something to be occupied now by this airplane, now by that, but never by two simultaneously! In the Army, the same mode of organization would bring into action one and only one man at a time, all the others waiting their turn! In an industry, the same organization would force everything to be done by one general "workman"! Why, one wonders, do we tolerate this mode of organization in the computer?

There are an abundance of cases when the one-at-a-time method is not appropriate. Take the chess player again as example. Of every position, many facts will be required before action can be considered:

Is my King in check?

Can the opponent's King and Queen be forked by a Knight?

Have I a Pawn near Queening?

and so on. Either such well-known questions will have to be answered, or other more recondite functions of the position will have to be formed—but in either case the bulk of the questions can be answered independently, i.e., *the answer to one does not have to wait for the answer to another to be given first.* I take it as axiomatic that if a process need not wait, then any method that makes it wait is self-condemned.

Here, of course, we must not allow ourselves to be misled by talk about nanoseconds. Nanoseconds or not, any job that involves 10^{12} operations or more is going to take centuries, if it is done by the digital's one-at-a-time rule. Nanosecond operations do not alter the basic fact that as the demanded work *allows* more and more simultaneous operations, so does the digital computer's one-at-a-time method become less and less efficient.

Related to this peculiarity—that it has only one site of action—is the necessary corollary that it must store its memories away from the site. So the computer keeps its memory store in the next room, and has to do quite a lot of work keeping track of where the various memories are at any given instant. If the machine, for instance, has a million-bit store, then 1 bit stored in an arbitrary position requires no less than 19 bits for the record of where it is! And the law of diminishing returns holds: every increase in size, to cure the wastage, increases the proportion of wastage. Already, in the average-sized computer, a 30-bit instruction, which obviously should refer to the main process, has to divert 15 of its bits to deal with the question "where is it in the store?"

These considerations, with the chess-playing process as type-problem to keep us focused, seem to indicate another type of computer, a type well suited to learnings and adaptations of chess-playing type.

Its main feature is that it would be composed of many units, each capable of carrying out a simple task and capable of achieving this independently of the other units. Each unit would keep its memories not at a central or common store but in itself. Memories would thus be stored at their sites of action. "Access time" would practically disappear, for each memory would be actually in the working machinery. Such a system might be described as having "distributed" memory.

The many units would, of course, require the main problem ·to be distributed among them, so a distributing system, or a distributing method, would be necessary. Such a system could be designed in detail, but since we are concerned in this Symposium with methods of self-organization, and as I am permitted to talk of the future, I would like to sketch the way in which such a system could be organized to build itself. Though the ideas are somewhat speculative, I hope to show that they have some plausibility, and that such a machine might well appear within the next ten years.

THE POLYSTABLE SYSTEM

A system with lots of memory must be, in some sense, a system with lots of states of equilibrium, for the persistence of memory must be a consequence of some event (or value or state) persisting in the system. Yet if we ask what is known about such systems we find the answer to be: practically nothing. A great deal is known, of course, about statistical mechanics, but most of this knowledge is based on an assumption that the system is conservative. Liouville's theorem, for instance—the starting point of many studies—assumes that energy is strictly conserved. But the systems we are thinking of as computers may use energy as freely as they please; so this assumption would be far too restrictive for us. Then again, much is known of complex dynamics, of star clusters, for instance; but most of these systems have very few equilibria, often none. What is already known in science about the nonconservative system with many states of equilibrium is very little.

Yet there can be little doubt that there are many interesting things to be discovered, and many remarkable processes available as models for computation. Had we known only atoms, for instance (with their properties and equations), we would hardly have suspected that so peculiar a phenomenon as the liquid state could exist. Here we have a phenomenon of the highest interest and of unique properties, offering facilities not readily obtainable in any other way, yet hardly to be detected in the basic equations. It is evidently not a special property of atoms, or molecules, for almost all compounds show it, regardless of their molecular details. Fortunately, we encounter it in daily experience, otherwise we might never suspect its existence. What I know of dynamic systems in general makes me incline strongly to the belief that other phenomena, equally peculiar yet equally usable, remain to be discovered.

Suppose then that we have a system before us, defined only insofar as we know it to have lots of states of equilibrium. How are we going to program it? By "programming" it, I mean acting on it with some particular input so that it will subsequently behave in some particular way and emit the desired output.

Now it is a peculiarity of the system with lots of equilibria that the mere act of programming requires no special method or setup. Any well-defined sequence of operations, whether thought of as input or as a change of external conditions, will move the system around in its phase space. Where the system is left by the treatment—i.e., where it begins on a computation—will be a function of the previous treatment.

At this point we can see that though the first stage of our work is easy enough, there still remains a very great deal to be done in detail. Here we may be helped by a fact that I believe to have great potentialities.

First we have the well-established fact (ignoring for the moment any question of why it happens) that although the infant is born with no preformed pattern of behavior, nevertheless, as he lives in contact with the world, he gradually takes into himself something of the pattern of that world. The physical chemist, speaking metaphorically, might say that the pattern in the infant's world "diffuses" into the infant's nervous system. It shows itself later by the developing coherence of the infant's movements, both as muscular coordination in a three-dimensional Euclidean world and as behavioral coordination (shown, for instance, by the thirsty child reaching for a cup rather than for a stone.) Jean Piaget has given a great deal of study to this transfer of pattern from the outside world into the nervous system. (That the developing internal pattern is formed by experience and not by genetic control is shown by the child with a damaged arm who develops an appropriately different pattern.)

Lest the process seem wholly miraculous we should remember that we do see something of the process in less complex ways. One of the simplest examples of a system with many equilibria is a dish of sand, in which the grains can rest in a great variety of combinations. Put your finger in a dish of sand and make a few circular writing movements with the finger; take the finger away, and the dish will be found to show something of "circularity." Here is the phenomenon actually at work, though not yet at an economically valuable level!

It can be shown, in fact, that if any system with many equilibria is subjected to an input that is consistently constrained in the transitions that it can undergo (so that the input's behavior is, in this sense, "patterned"), and if the input is continued until the system has arrived at a region of its phase space that is *stable under this input* (i.e., further continuation of the input will not drive it out), then the pattern of the transitions the *system* undergoes will be related to the pattern present in the input. And this relation can be stated rigorously and unambiguously. The relation is weaker than isomorphism, but it is present, and only adjustment of the parameters is necessary for the relation to be made stronger.

Suppose, then, that our understanding and technical facility in this matter were somewhat advanced. What sort of computer would we have?

Let it be clear that I am not suggesting the replacement of the present analog or the present digital types. If the computation consists of one extremely long thread, in which each action can be performed only after the earlier stages have been completed, the present digital is the natural form. But there are more computations than those of this type. Consider again the chess-playing machine. The necessarily sequential feature of the game amounts only to a mere 100 moves or so, and counts for little against the millions of necessarily sequential operations that are the digital computer's *natural* task. In chess-playing, as I said earlier, a great deal of simultaneous work is required, and the computer should be able to advance its operations, as it were, on a broad front.

Playing chess also reminds one that there are many real problems that, though difficult enough, do not demand the absolute precision achieved by the digital. Routing problems, for instance, are often well answered if the answers are persistently *near* the optimum: seeking the absolute optimum is often an unrealistic and time-wasting refinement. Sometimes the problem becomes: "Find a way (any way) that satisfies the following conditions . . . ," and a computer that has some random element in its construction or behavior may be well suited to such a problem.

The possibility of the introduction of randomness should persistently be borne in mind. Doubtless the makers of the big digitals are very proud of the fact that everything is just so, but the practical man may well keep searching for methods that are less demanding. Computers must obviously become both smaller and cheaper. To make them both precise and small simply increases the cost, as the engineer becomes a jeweller. Statistically built types, however, have no limit for cheapness and almost no limit in smallness. They can be made in various ways, and might eventually be made by a simple cooking-type formula applied to a mixture of flour and sand. The general outlines are clear, and I would like to list them for definiteness:

1. Prepare units with *many states of equilibrium* (their details are of little importance: they will become invisible when the system gets large).
2. Control the connections or connection-patterns *statistically* so as to get a balance between too much connection and too little.
3. Relate the pattern of a repetitive input to the region of the phase-space eventually arrived at under the repetitive input.
4. Relate local movements in the phase space to the type of behavior shown externally.
5. Couple the system to a vetoing system to make the whole selective for the unvetoed property.

In this way we can move towards a computer that is self-organizing, learning, and adaptive. Something of what I have suggested is, of course, already going on, in the researches of Rosenblatt, Farley, Selfridge, and others. Here I wish only to suggest that much remains to be done, and that our work, for the next decade at least, is clearly defined.

REFERENCES

1. Bremermann, H. J., "Optimization Through Evolution and Recombination," in *Self-organizing Systems, 1962*, M. C., Yovits, G. T. Jacobi, and G. D. Goldstein, (eds.), Spartan, Washington, D.C., 1962.
2. Piaget, J., and B. Inhelder, *The Child's Conception of Space*, London, Routledge, 1956.

INTRODUCTION

Julius T. Tou

Computer Sciences Laboratory
The Technological Institute
Northwestern University

Computer and information science is a relatively young field of modern engineering and is rapidly becoming a very important and glamorous subject. This field of scientific study covers a great variety of extremely interesting topics such as advanced automatic programming, artificial intelligence and neurocybernetics, automata theory and sequential machines, computer organization and control, decision theory, information retrieval, language translation, learning and cognitive systems, modern control theory, pattern identification, simulation of human behavior, and applications of digital computers to solve complex military, industrial, government, and business problems. Computer and information science may be regarded as the science of extending man's intellect.

In similar fashion, these Proceedings also cover a great variety of topics, ranging from dynamic programming to automata theory, from pattern recognition to learning control, from perceptron theory to artificial intelligence, from adaptive logic to feature detection. So many fields are covered that very few can claim to be expert in all of them. This widely-inclusive volume may therefore be welcomed by many as an antidote to the ever-growing specialization of technical fields. To maintain a better coherence between the papers and to improve the organization of the material, the papers in this book are not in the same sequence as originally presented. Furthermore, the paper by Michael J. Pedelty was add D to enlarge the coverage in automata theory.

One of the most persistent problems in the theory of brain mechanisms has been the requirement for a model capable of storing and recapitulating the sequence of experience which may occur in the duration of a human lifetime. Rosenblatt proposes a mathematical model for long-term sequential memory, which appears to be of sufficient capacity to record an entire life history of sensory experience with a high probability of permitting correct judgments and decision in retrospect. His model is also consistent in size and structural organization with the known constraints of the human nervous system. The fundamental theorems of perceptron-learning theory of Rosenblatt and Block were developed by ingenious analytic constructions and bounding techniques whose motivation and restrictiveness may be unclear. Charnes presents new proofs of the fundamental theorem by an intuitive geometric approach, together with extensions which include a necessary and sufficient condition for possibility. His discussion clarified the motivation and restrictiveness of earlier work. By considering a pattern on a discrete retina to be the set of active retinal points, Block, Nilsson, and Duda study the problem of determining a small number of features for a given set of patterns. They also develop an algorithm for finding features of restricted sets of patterns and consider the implementation of this algorithm by adaptive neural networks.

Pattern identification plays an important role in the design of learning systems. One of the important approaches to pattern recognition is the statistical-decision theory approach. Pattern identification may be viewed as a problem in statistical classification wherein an n-dimensional space is partitioned into category regions with decision boundaries. Cooper discusses the concept of hyperplanes, hyperspheres, and hyperquadrics as decision boundaries, and introduces techniques for determining the actual optimum boundary from known samples and for efficiently reducing the dimensionality. Learning from experience may be viewed as a process of computing estimates of probability measure from sample data during a conditioning phase. Based upon this point of view, Brick and Owen treat an intelligent pattern recognizer as a learning and classification problem in a multidimensional characteristic feature or measurement space, and introduce the concept of using nonparametric probability estimation techniques and Bayes risk analysis for the investigation of pattern-recognition and self-organization problems. Griffin, King, and Tunis describe a character-recognition system using adaptive linear decision functions. The system is made up of the transducer, processor, and categorizer. It is different from the IBM 1210 Reader-sorter in that the 1210 categorizer is based upon Boolean logic and this system works with linear decision functions. Kamentsky and Liu present a theoretical and experimental study of a model for pattern recognition. They derive some equations for the performance of a recognition system as a function of the type of classifier used and the number and power of the measurements. Gamba discusses the concept of establishing probability weights for statistical inference and the principles involved in the automatic programmer and probability analyzer (PAPA), and the papistor.

The theory of automata and semi-groups appears to provide a useful tool in the synthesis of learning systems and adaptive processes. Weeg reviews some general properties of an automaton and the structural properties of

Rabin-Scott automata, and discusses the structure-preserving function of automata, input semi-groups associated with strongly connected automata, and divisible semi-groups. Pedelty points out the essential behavioral equivalence between combinatorial switching networks or threshold-logic circuits operating in a "spatial domain" and those employing pulse-interval modulation. He also describes a particular type of temporally organized automaton which is referred to as a P-machine. Klaczko-Ryndzium discusses a procedure for recognition of normalized, connected patterns by using a threshold-conditioned adaptive template. A software representation of digital two-dimensional pattern is used as a template for pattern recognition.

An important advancement in modern control theory is the introduction of learning, adaptation, and pattern identification to control processes. The theories of automata, of threshold logic, and of statistical decision have found may important applications in modern synthesis of control systems. Several papers emphasizing this new approach to control system design are presented. Tou and Ivanenko discuss the design of a learning system for control based upon pattern-recognition principles. The design is treated as the problem of decision making on the basis of information obtained from the control process. The observed data is transformed into special types of multidimensional information pattern from which a proper decision is made. In a survey paper, Widrow and Smith emphasize the use of adaptive-logic networks in optimum control and review the applications of pattern classification principles to such system problems as weather forecasting, speech recognition, and vector-cardiogram diagnosis. Fu approaches the learning-control problems from the point of view of statistical decision and introduces the method of state-space partition for system design. Kuck and Krulee describe an interesting model which has the same input-output characteristics as a person solving simple physics problems. The proposed system is a part of a larger system which accepts inputs in the form of descriptive statements in natural language. Emphasis is placed upon the design of the subsystem which takes a descriptive formalism derived from natural language as its input and proceeds deductively to attempt a solution.

Dynamic programming has been recognized as a very useful technique for the study of learning, adaptation and control in information systems. Bellman points out some of the major problems in the study of learning and adaptation processes, and some of the ways in which dynamic programming furnishes a natural bridge between classical and modern theories. Some directions of research and further study are suggested. Andrew discusses prerequisites of self-organization and general system properties conducive to self-organization. Mesarovic introduces a unified approach to learning and information theory. In a review paper, Greene considers some problems in designing highly adaptive systems and the problem of identifying the behavioral structures. Ledley reports the interesting idea of simulation of a billion-gate computer on a thousand-gate computer. Fein proposes and clarifies the terminology concerned with natural and artifical intelligence.

In conclusion, it is clearly evident that computer and information science covers a rather broad spectrum. Although this volume presents a collection of some 22 technical papers in this area, it has scratched only a small surface of this vast field. The practical design of intelligent machines is not yet here. The purpose of this volume is to provide a ready source of reference material to the widest possible audience. It is hoped that the Proceedings will stimulate a great deal of interest in this exciting field of scientific study, so that the days of physical realization of intelligent machines may be brought nearer.

A MODEL FOR EXPERIENTIAL STORAGE IN NEURAL NETWORKS*

F. ROSENBLATT

Cornell University

INTRODUCTION

This is a preliminary exposition of a model for long-term sequential memory in the brain. The model was first formulated about a year ago, and has since been subjected to a series of numerical studies which have revealed a capacity considerably beyond our original expectations. A more comprehensive treatment of the theory, with emphasis on its biological and biochemical aspects, is currently in preparation.[46] The objective of this paper is to summarize the main quantitative results (particularly those which may be of engineering interest) and to suggest some of the possible applications of this model to the problems of memory, recall, and the learning of heuristic programs and algorithms. This seems, in fact, to be the first instance of a model of the perceptron variety which is sophisticated enough to learn computerlike programs employing stored data and stored instructions.

The reader will find that an introductory knowledge of perceptron theory is essential for an adequate understanding of the following presentation. A general orientation can be obtained from Block,[4] or from the first eight chapters of Rosenblatt.[44] To bring the perceptual aspects of the theory up to date, the summary of recent work in Ref. 45 might prove helpful. The present paper assumes some knowledge of the pattern recognition and discrimination capabilities of perceptrons, and concentrates entirely on the question of how a record of such sensory experience can be stored and

* The work reported in this paper has been supported jointly by the Information Systems Branch of the Office of Naval Research, and by the National Science Foundation.

recalled, for periods comparable in duration to a human lifetime, by a biologically plausible network of neurons.

An adequate theory of memory must satisfy at least two criteria:

1. It must employ a recording mechanism (or "trace mechanism") which is physically, mathematically, and biologically plausible.

2. It must provide a demonstration that this trace mechanism, when incorporated into a biologically plausible neural network, can in fact account for the basic psychological phenomena of memory and recall.

In order to motivate the particular trace mechanism which is proposed, we shall undertake a demonstration of the second point first, introducing a detailed biochemical mechanism only after its required characteristics have been clarified.

The problem of memory as a physiological phenomenon has, of course, been dealt with in a vast volume of literature. Recent reviews by Gerard[21,22] Morell,[40,41] John,[31] and Eccles,[13] and some of the recent symposia[17,50] are helpful in indicating the directions of current research. The variety of specific theories which have been proposed in recent years are exemplified by those of Hebb,[24,26] Lashley,[35] Culbertson,[9] Hydén,[28] Wechsler,[58] Briggs and Kitto,[6] Gaito,[20] Smith,[55] Milner,[39] and Roy.[47] These theoretical treatments vary widely in mathematical rigor and in the range of memory phenomena which they attempt to encompass. Unfortunately, those which attempt to treat the psychological phenomena most comprehensively, such as Hebb's theory, are apt to be lacking in rigor, while the most rigorous of them (such as Roy's ingenious model) are apt to be superficial and unconvincing psychologically. Many of these "theories" are in fact, no more than suggestions of a possible approach, while others, such as the imaginative and currently fashionable notion of a "tape recorder molecule" in the cellular RNA, seem to do such violence to our basic conceptions of both physics and physiology (without, in fact, satisfactorily explaining any phenomena of memory) that they can only be regarded as a desperate attempt to fill a theoretical vacuum.

The experimental literature on memory physiology, which used to be concerned chiefly with the effects of lesions and surgical ablation of brain tissue, has recently begun to yield a number of interesting reports on electrophysiological and neurochemical influences in conditioning and learning experiments. Some of this literature is covered by the reviews mentioned in the last paragraph. Representative of recent contributions are those of Gerard, Chamberlain, and Rothschild,[23] Hebb,[25] Scoville and Milner,[51] and Milner and Penfield.[38] The psychological literature, much of which is clearly relevant to the problem, is too extensive to summarize here. Instead, we shall present a brief list of empirical phenomena which an adequate theory should be able to account for. This list, while far from exhaustive, gives us something to aim for in evaluating a proposed model. Since our primary interest is in human memory, the phenomena listed are all to be found in man; it seems likely that if we can account for these, then a simplified or modified version of the model is likely to prove applicable to memory phenomena in simpler nervous systems as well.

The primary phenomena which we would like to explain include the following:

1. Ability to recapitulate past experience in proper temporal order.
2. Selective recall; effects of "cognitive set," attention, and suggestion.
3. "Free association" (dreams; transitions and jumps between remembered events).
4. Retention and subsequent recall of originally "unnoticed" events.
5. Poor memory for sequences with low diversity (e.g., strings of digits), in contrast to sequences of nonrepetitive events.
6. Modification of stored information (cf. Bartlett[2]).
7. Effect of practice on accuracy of sequential recall.
8. Effects of "reinforcement" (pleasure, pain, reward, punishment) on memory.
9. Forgetting (transient and permanent).
10. "Repression," psychogenic amnesias, and subsequent recovery of memory.
11. Heightened accessibility of memory under hypnosis.
12. Posthypnotic suggestion.
13. Extra-high stability of early memory.
14. Low stability of recent memory in senility.
15. Lapse of memory during sleep or unconsciousness.
16. Retrograde amnesia (due to shock, cold, concussion, epileptic convulsion).
17. Recovery from retrograde amnesia in original temporal order.
18. Consolidation time (brief period following an event during which shock or trauma leads to irrecoverable loss of memory).
19. Hallucinatory recall of sequences under temporal lobe stimulation (Penfield[42]).
20. Effects of localized lesions and electrical stimulation in aphasia, agnosia, and related disorders (cf. Penfield and Roberts[43]).
21. Distributed memory and functional equivalence of cortical regions (cf. Lashley[35]).
22. Incapacity for retention of new experience, without interference with recall of old experience, temporary memory, or motor learning, following hippocampal lesions (cf. Milner and Penfield,[38] and Scoville and Milner[51]).

In examining the above list, it can be seen that the phenomena have been arranged in a rough sequence from purely psychological to primarily physiological ones. The list emphasizes qualitative, rather than quantitative, phenomena. On some of the most important quantitative questions, such as the total amount of information stored in human memory, investigators are hopelessly at odds, ranging from estimates of 1.5×10^6 bits (Miller,[37]) to 10^{21} bits for a model which assumes storage in protein molecules (von Foerster[57]). An interesting review of these estimates has been presented by Schaefer,[49] while some of the theoretical considerations are discussed by Brown.[7] Until recently, it seemed to this writer unlikely that such a thing as continuous and complete recording of sensory experience could be made physically plausible. The model proposed by Culbertson, for example,[9] would require about 3×10^9 modifiable connections to record one second of visual experience, or about 10^{19} connections to record continuously for the duration of a human lifetime (taking this to be about 100 years). Nonetheless, the results of the present theory force us to reconsider the possibility of almost complete recording, as will be seen from the numerical results in the following sections.

Despite the many unanswered questions which may be raised in connection with the above items, few investigators would be likely to deny that these are empirically well-established phenomena; consequently, a brain model which seems intrinsically incapable of dealing with them must be judged inadequate as a theory. It will clearly be impossible to deal with all of this evidence satisfactorily in the short space of this paper; a more comprehensive discussion will be forthcoming in Ref. 46. Nonetheless, even in this brief space we hope to show that a considerable number of the phenomena on our checklist can find plausible explanations in terms of the proposed model.

Before concluding these introductory remarks, a word is in order concerning different types of memory. The word "memory" has been used to cover a wide range of empirical observations, including conditioned reflexes, perceptual learning, the learning of goal-directed behavior, the temporary storage of information (such as telephone numbers), and the retention of experience from the remote past. It has become increasingly clear to those working in the field that we are probably dealing not with a single mechanism but with a variety of different mechanisms. We should not necessarily expect that the mechanism which enables a flatworm to modify a tropic reaction to light[30] is the same mechanism which enables an actor to recite *Hamlet*. In particular, the work of Milner, Penfield, and others on the effects of hippocampal lesions (mentioned in Item 22 of the preceding list) suggests that a clear distinction should be made between the mechanisms of experiential recording, experiential recall, short-term memory, and the learning of motor skills in man, since it is possible to completely obliterate one of these capabilities without, in any way, interfering with the others. The distinction between "short-term" and "long-term" memory has now been rather widely accepted among psychologists (cf. Hebb,[25] Milner,[39] and Konorski[34]). There is, in fact, a popular belief that some form of temporary "dynamic storage" (e.g., a reverberating trace system) is a necessary precondition for the establishment of a permanent recording. This belief has been fostered by the idea that a permanent change (such as synaptic growth) must take a considerable time to establish, and by the consolidation period (Item 18 on the above list) which is revealed by studies of amnesia. Actually, the evidence for such a dependent relationship between temporary and permanent storage mechanisms seems much too scanty to be assumed without question— particularly in view of the persistence of temporary memory after the long-term recording mechanism has been incapacitated by hippocampal ablation. In the present theory we shall not require an "active" short-term memory mechanism to precede permanent recording; the consolidation time, in this system, comes about as a result of slow chemical reactions which do not require an "active trace" to support them.

This paper, then, will concentrate on the problem of the long-term storage of experience, and the mechanism which enables us to retrieve information about past events. Some of the more "primitive" types of memory (such as the association of responses to stimuli, and certain types of perceptual learning) have been demonstrated in earlier work on perceptron theory.[5,44,45] Up to this time, however, none of these networks have met the challenge of being able to recapitulate a sequence of experienced events, no matter how well the events may have been "recognized" at the time they occurred. The model which is proposed for this will now be considered in detail in the following section.

DESCRIPTION OF THE MODEL

A neural network, capable of learning to give recognition responses to sensory patterns with some degree of generalization to "similar" stimuli, may take the form shown in Fig. 1. For the sake of explicitness, we shall take this model (representing a fairly general perceptron) as the starting point for the development of a sequential memory. It should be borne in mind, however, that the basic principles of the memory model could work equally well with a number of other "neural networks" (such as Widrow's Adaline or Madaline[59]) as the perceptual part of the system. Networks of the type shown here have successfully learned such tasks as alphabet character recognition and speech recognition. In its simplest form (the "simple perceptron") the model shown in Fig. 1 is reduced to a three-layer network, with a single response unit, and a "retina" of sensory points connected directly to the set of internuncial neurons, or A-units (association units). The A-units are threshold elements, which respond to any combination of input signals whose sum exceeds the A-unit threshold. In more sophisticated models, the intervening network (stimulus-transformation network) acts as a recoding system, which may detect such features as straight lines or edges in the stimulus pattern, transmitting only information about these important features to the A-units.[45] Short-time sequences, rather than momentary stimuli, may form the input patterns; these may be encoded in the association system as a nontemporal (spatial) pattern by means of a distribution of transmission delays in the S to A network, or by means of a closed-loop cross-coupled network (either in the A-system itself or prior to it), or else by means of a combination of "On" and "Off" neurons in the early layers which signal the onset and termination of the activity induced by a moving or changing stimulus.[44] There is increasing evidence that the last of these three mechanisms may be largely responsible for motion detection in the cat's visual system (Hubel and Wiesel[27]).

Whatever the preliminary transformations may be, we shall be chiefly concerned with the succession of states induced in the association system by the sequence of stimuli from the environment. Each activity state of the A-units (represented by the set of units which are "on" or active at the time) bears information about the stimulus, or recent succession of stimuli, which has just occurred. It is now well established that this information is sufficient to permit an arbitrary identifying response to be associated either to a particular stimulus or to a class of similar stimuli, if the network is properly designed.[44] When an R-unit receives a superthreshold signal from the set of active A-units, it emits a signal which serves to identify the current stimulus.

The assignment of discriminating responses to stimulus classes is generally carried out by means of an "error-correction procedure" in which

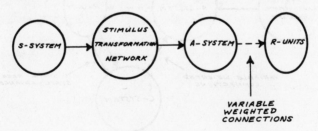

Figure 1

the weights of connections from the A-units to the R-unit (or R-units) are modified, whenever an "error" occurs in the response of the perceptron. The "motivational system" which is responsible for recognizing such errors and applying the necessary reinforcement to the connections may consist of an outside experimenter or trainer, or it may be built into the network itself, as a "reinforcement-control system".[44] In any case, it is not shown in Fig. 1 or in any of the subsequent figures; the memory processes with which we will be chiefly concerned are automatic, and do not depend on the "reinforcement-control system" in any necessary way. An alternative training procedure (the S-controlled procedure) assumes that reinforcement will be supplied continuously, modifying the weights of the A- to R-unit connections for each stimulus in a direction which will tend to give the correct response for that stimulus. For this S-controlled procedure, a detailed mathematical analysis of the resulting distribution of R-unit input signals is now available (Joseph,[32] and Rosenblatt[44]). Since the signal distributions resulting from the error-correction procedure have been less well analyzed than the signal distributions in the S-controlled procedure, Joseph's analysis of the S-controlled procedure will be used in this paper to describe the signal distribution to the R-units which might be expected to exist after a period of training.

The sequential memory model will operate, basically, by reconstituting the succession of A-unit activity states which occurred when the original experience took place. This reconstitution is, generally, far from perfect, but it will be shown that it can be made close enough to the original activity states to permit the previously learned responses to occur, or, alternatively, to learn new responses to stimuli in retrospect, which will then generalize satisfactorily to stimuli appearing in the environment. In order to do this, an auxiliary network is necessary, as shown in Fig. 2.

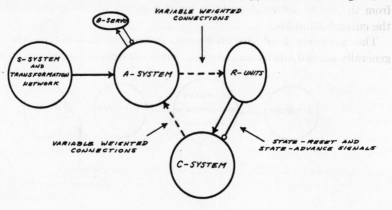

Figure 2

In this figure, as in the subsequent ones, broken arrows are used to represent adaptive connections (with variable weights), while solid arrows represent fixed connections. The circles represent sets of "neurons" or functionally analogous units. A normal arrowhead generally represents excitatory connections (or mixtures of excitatory and inhibitory connections), while a small circle in place of the arrowhead represents inhibitory connections.

The two main additions to the system shown in the previous figure are the threshold servomechanism for the association system, and the C-system, or clock network, which has variable connections to the A-units, and input connections from the R-units. The θ-servo is simply a negative feedback system which tends to maintain a constant level of activity in the association system. It might consist, physiologically, of a set of cells whose input connections are drawn from the whole of the association network, and whose output connections deliver an inhibitory signal to all A-units, which increases with the magnitude of the input signal. With such a control mechanism the association system will tend to find and maintain a constant level of activity despite changes in the distribution or intensity of input signals. Such mechanisms have been proposed previously by Beurle[3] and Rosenblatt.[44]

The A-units may receive signals from two sources, apart from the servo system itself. Normally, their chief input source would be the sensory network, which is assumed to send strong signals to the A-units whenever sensory events occur. The second source is the set of adaptive connections from the C-network (the functioning of which will be elaborated shortly). These connections, however, are assumed to be limited to weights which are considerably smaller in magnitude than the weights of the S- to A-connections. Consequently, as long as sensory signals are arriving at the A-units, the state of the association system will be "S-determined," the signals which might be coming in simultaneously from the C-system constituting only a negligible perturbation in the total input signals. Under the action of the θ-servo, the A-units will act essentially like high-threshold units in a simple perceptron, and the C-system will have little or no influence on the operation of the primary information channel, from S to A to R. In this state (as long as sensory inputs continue) the perceptron can be trained or interrogated in the usual fashion, and all previous analyses of such performances remain applicable. On the other hand, when sensory signals cease (either due to lack of environmental stimulation or due to an active cutoff mechanism in the perceptron itself, which might be controlled by one of the R-units) the θ-servo will immediately act to lower the thresholds of the A-units until previous activity levels are restored. Under these conditions, the relatively weak signal component coming from the C-system becomes the primary determinant of the state of the A-system, and the A-units will respond to the C-network as if it were an alternate sensory field.

We must now consider the C-system itself in greater detail. Several alternative organizations are illustrated in Fig. 3. The C-network, as its name suggests, operates as a "clock" for the memory of sequences. This clock may either be synchronous (progressing through a sequence of states at a rate which is independent of external events) or asynchronous, in which case it advances from one state to the next only when a suitable trigger-event occurs to make it do so. A synchronous clock is exemplified by a simple cross-coupled network (Fig. 3a) which will advance through a succession of states, each determined by the preceding state, with a speed which depends only on the transmission time of the connections and synaptic delays. The θ-servo acts to prevent "blowups" or extinction of activity. Random networks of this type have been analyzed in Chap. 18 of Ref. 44, and elsewhere. While it would be quite possible for our model to operate with such a simple mechanism, the asynchronous clock, which permits the events constituting the recorded sequence to occur at one rate and to be recalled later at a different rate, is inherently of much greater interest.

Two variations of the asynchronous clock are shown in Figs. 3b and 3c. In each case, the C-network is subdivided into two sets (or layers) of neurons. One layer consists of "On" neurons, which deliver a sustained burst of impulses in response to an excitatory input signal; the second layer

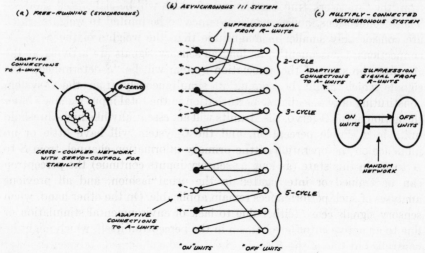

Figure 3

consists of "Off" neurons, which are effectively inhibited during an input signal, but deliver a brief burst of high-frequency impulses when the input ceases. Such "On" and "Off" neurons are known to exist in the cerebral cortex, and extensive recordings of their activity are available (cf. Jung,[33] Florey,[19] Hubel and Wiesel,[27] Sandel and Kiang[48]). The physiological mechanism underlying the Off responses is not well understood. In some cases it is possible that the cell is part of a more complex network which, in fact, delivers excitatory signals to it upon the termination of a stimulus. A more plausible explanation in most cases, however, is that there is an intracellular servomechanism tending to keep the membrane potential at its normal, resting level, despite the effect of transmitter substances which either hyperpolarize or depolarize the membrane. Such a cell would tend to deliver a brief burst after an excitatory stimulus began, which would terminate as the servomechanism began to operate, and would similarly deliver a burst after the cessation of an inhibitory input signal, since its membrane would suddenly be left under the depolarizing influence of the servo system, in the absence of the hyperpolarizing effect which it was combating. The observations of Sandel and Kiang[48] are particularly suggestive of such a mechanism. A particular type of long-lasting after-discharge following stimulation has been studied by B. D. Burns,[8] who attributes it to a network of "Type B" neurons. It seems likely that these cells, once stimulated, will continue to discharge indefinitely until some inhibitory signal occurs to cut them off. The mechanism is likely to depend on differential rates of repolarization in different parts of the cell, which Burns has demonstrated could lead to a continuing volley of impulses. It is quite tempting, although not essential, to identify the "On" units in Fig. 3 with Burns' Type B neurons.

The manner of operation of the asynchronous clock network can best be understood from Fig. 3b. Assume that those "On" units which are filled in solidly in the diagram are active at the present time. They will continue to emit impulses (if they are of the Burns Type B variety) until some inhibitory signal arrives to cut them off. This inhibitory signal is provided by an "On" burst or "Off" burst of short duration, from any of the R-units, signaling some change in the response of the perceptron, and thus the beginning or end of a distinguishable event. If we assume that the coupling from the R-units to the C-network is dense enough and powerful enough, then any change in response will momentarily quench the activity of the On units in the C-system. During all of the time that these On units have been firing, however, they have not only been transmitting signals back to the A-units (by way of the variable connections, which will soon be discussed in detail); they have also been sending "priming signals" to the Off units, which thus begin to fire as soon as the On units are cut off. This

Off burst occurs only in the subset of cells which were connected to the active On units. These cells will immediately transmit excitatory signals back to the On layer, activating a new subset of On units, which will then continue to fire until it is finally quenched by the next change in the R-units. Thus the C-system will advance through a deterministic succession of states, changing abruptly to a new state whenever the response of the perceptron is altered in a significant fashion.

Ultimately, since the number of C-units must be finite, the network must return to its initial state, and the cycle will repeat. It can readily be seen that the activity configuration shown in the network of Fig. 3b will repeat every thirty steps, since it factors into prime-numbered cycles of durations 2, 3, and 5, respectively. Such a network organization can easily yield cycles of immense duration with only a small number of neurons. Its cycle-time will be equal to the product of all of its prime subloops which are not "silent" (no units active) or "saturated" (all units active). Moreover, a large number of different initial conditions are possible which will lead to totally different "life histories" for the state sequence of the network. For example, an initial state with only one active neuron in each loop will yield a cycle which must be distinct, in all its states, from that which results from an initial condition with two active neurons in one or more of the loops.

While a network of this sort would be quite useful for engineering purposes, and quite satisfactory so far as the operation of the memory system is concerned, it is clearly unbiological in its requirement of successive prime numbers for the order of its subcycles, and in its 1-to-1 connectivity. A slightly more plausible network results if we retain the 1 : 1 constraint, but allow the connections between On and Off units to be made at random. A number of computer studies have been made by Trevor Barker and the writer to determine the expected cycle times for initially random activity states of such 1 : 1 networks. Based on samples of 1,000 networks of each size, with 50 percent of the units active, the following cycle times were obtained:*

Number of "On" units in network (N_c)	Mean cycle time	Variance of cycle times	Minimum cycle time	Maximum cycle time
10	8.91	4.96	1	30
100	30,677	164,370	~ 40	$\sim 4 \times 10^6$
200	1,518,299	10,057,894	~ 150	$\sim 3 \times 10^8$
400	114,963,471	93,358,746	~ 250	$> 2 \times 10^9$

* The numbers in the first line are exact theoretical values; the subsequent lines are estimated from samples of 1,000 cases.

Thus it is clear that with a network of biological size, numbering at least a few thousand C-units, the probability that a state would repeat during a long period is very slight indeed, despite the random choice of connections and starting state.

A more plausible biological model is shown in Fig. 3c. Here each On-unit may be connected to many Off-units, and vice-versa, the only important constraint being that On-units should not be connected to one another (or at least not strongly) in order to prevent the activity pattern from spreading to all units in the network. A θ-servo could again be employed to govern the level of activity. Unlike the 1 : 1 network there is the possibility with the multiply-connected model that two different starting states might lead into the same activity state of the network. This and other complexities make the cycle times exceedingly hard to estimate, but from previous observations of cross-coupled systems in computer simulation programs (e.g. Farley and Clark[16]) as well as from theoretical considerations, it seems likely that cycles will tend to be at least as long as in the 1 : 1 network, and possibly much longer. In all that follows, it will be assumed that the C-system is of sufficient size that the likelihood of a state repeating itself, without the network having been deliberately reset, is entirely negligible.†

Although the successive states of the C-system form a deterministic sequence, each state being a predictable consequence of the preceding one, their interrelationships (particularly the measure of the intersections of active sets at different times) are, generally, indistinguishable from those that would pertain to a collection of randomly chosen states. Thus, if the initial state in a 1 : 1 network, for example, is selected at random (with a probability P of any unit being on or off) the measure of the intersection between the initially active set and any following active set will have an expected value of P^2. Such a sequence, then, can be considered a "quasi-random-state sequence," since the measures of all active sets and their intersections will have a distribution which is indistinguishable (except in specially contrived cases) from a random-state sequence. This property will be seen to be of great importance in the subsequent analysis of the memory system.

It now remains to see how the states of the C-system can be made to induce a succession of states in the A-system corresponding to a recorded

† Despite the arguments given above for its plausibility, the writer is convinced that the C-system, in its present form, is the least plausible part of the model. At the present time a more "realistic" form of C-system is being investigated, which makes use of a statistically homogeneous network containing only one kind of neuron, with states represented by frequency modes rather than On/Off activity states. This will be reported in Ref. 46.

sequence of stimuli. For this we must specify more precisely the modification mechanism of the C-unit to A-unit connections.

We assume that each A-unit receives connections from a fraction M of the "On" units in the C-network. The connection system from C to A is a many-to-many system, the only important constraint being that the choice of connections to particular A-units should be statistically independent of the particular sets of C-units which are likely to be active in different "clock states." To be explicit, it will be assumed that the connections to each A-unit originate from a set of MN_c points chosen at random with a uniform probability distribution (where N_c is the total number of units in the "On" layer of the C-system). Thus, if a fraction Q_c of the C-units are active in any given state, it is expected that a fraction MQ_c are actually transmitting signals to any particular A-unit.

The modification of connections takes place according to a rule which has been called the gamma-system in perceptron terminology. Chiefly because it permits us to obtain more rigorous equations, the gamma-system will be employed for the A- to R-unit connections as well as the C- to A-unit connections. For the A-R connections, however, the simpler alpha-system, which changes only the weights of connections from active units, would undoubtedly work equally well.[44]

The γ-system reinforcement procedure is conservative in the weights of connections to a given unit; that is, the sum of the weights of all input connections to any A-unit (or R-unit) must remain constant. Therefore, if the active connections should gain in weight at time t, the inactive connections must lose a compensating amount. γ-systems have been defined and analyzed in detail for simple perceptrons in Ref. 44. In the case of the C- to A-unit connection weights, the "reinforcement procedure" operates as follows:

Let w_{ij} = weight of connection from the ith C-unit (c_i) to the jth A-unit (a_j).

$c_i^*(t)$ = activity state of c_i at time t. $c_i^* = 1$ if c_i is active, 0 otherwise.

$a_i^*(t)$ = activity state of a_i at time t. $a_i^* = 1$ if a_i is active, 0 otherwise.

η = unit of reinforcement, generally taken as 1.

Q_c = fraction of C-units active.

Two variations of the reinforcement rule will be considered: the *asymmetric model*, which modifies only connections to active association units, and the *symmetric model*, which modifies connections to inactive A-units as well as to active ones.

For the asymmetric model, the change in the weight w_{ij} at time t takes the form

$$\Delta w_{ij}(t) = w_{ij}(t + \Delta t) - w_{ij}(t)$$

$$= \eta \cdot a_j^* (t) \left[c_i^* (t) - \frac{1}{MN_c} \sum_{i=1}^{MNc} c_i^* (t) \right] \qquad (1a)$$

$$E\Delta w_{ij}(t) = \eta \cdot a_j^* (t)[c_i^* (t) - Q_c] \qquad (2a)$$

The index i in this equation ranges over the set of C — units connected to a_j.

For the symmetric model, the corresponding equations are

$$\Delta w_{ij}(t) = \eta \cdot (-1)^{a_j^* (t)+1} \left[c_j^* (t) - \frac{1}{MN_c} \sum_{i=1}^{MNc} c_i^* (t) \right] \qquad (1b)$$

$$E\Delta w_{ij}(t) = \eta \cdot (-1)^{a_j^* (t)+1}[c_i^* (t) - Q_c] \qquad (2b)$$

That is, for an active A-unit, the change in weights is the same in both models, but for an inactive A-unit (in which case there is no change in the asymmetric model) Δw_{ij} is the negative of what it would be for an active unit.

In the recording of a memory sequence, the following succession of events occurs. It is assumed that the C-system is set to some initial activity state, by any one of several mechanisms which will be discussed in more detail later. This could be achieved, in the simplest case, by activating one of the R-units which forces the on-units of the C-network to the desired starting condition. This R-unit, in turn, could be trained to respond to a starting command, such as the name of the recorded sequence. A starting mechanism of this sort is suggested in Fig. 2. The initial weights of C-to-A connections are assumed to be zero.

With the C-system in its initial state, the first stimulus pattern of the sequence appears in the sensory system, and induces a corresponding activity state in the association units. Say, for example, the first stimulus is a triangle. The set of A-units responding to this triangle will then have their connections from the active C-units augmented in value, according to equation (1a) or (1b). As long as the triangle remains on the "retina," signals transmitted from the C-units to the A-units will tend to be ignored, due to the action of the Θ-servo, and the relatively high weights of connections from the sensory system. On the other hand, if the same C-state should recur, without the presence of a retinal input, the Θ-servo will lower the effective thresholds of the A-units, and the augmented connection weights to the previously active A-units will tend to reactivate the same set of units which responded to the triangle. In the case of the asymmetric model, there will be no systematic attempt to turn off the "improper units," which did not respond to the triangle, but the Θ-servo will tend to find a level at which only the units receiving the strongest input signals will be reactivated, which has essentially the same effect. In the case of the symmetric model, there is an additional tendency to turn off the improper units, due to the negative weights which have been acquired by the connections from active C-units to inactive A-units, Eq. (1b).

As soon as the triangle is replaced by the next stimulus (say a square) which is sufficiently different so that the response of the perceptron changes, the C-system will advance to its second state, which we have seen to be statistically independent of the first, although it is a deterministic consequence of it. Due to this statistical independence and the use of the γ-system, it will be shown in the following section that the expected value of the signal now received by any A-unit from the C-system is equal to zero. Consequently, the modifications of the connections which now take place to the set of A-units responding to the square will have the same effect (except for a slight noise effect) as if no previous memory had been recorded.

If the square, in turn, is replaced by another triangle the change in response (whether correct or not is immaterial) will cause the C-system to advance to its third state, from which the expected signal to the A-units will again be zero. A new change in weights then occurs as before. This process continues indefinitely until the C-system either recycles (an unlikely possibility) or is deliberately reset.

To see how the system acts in recall, suppose the response which resets the C-system is evoked, followed by a "silent period," during which no sensory inputs occur. The Θ-servo, striving to normalize the activity level in the A-system, now lowers the thresholds to the point where the A-units begin to respond to the C-unit signals. As we have seen, the first state of the C-system will tend to reactivate the set of A-units responding to the first triangle (without any interference, other than random-noise effects, from any subsequently recorded memory). As soon as this state is, in fact, reconstituted in the association system, however, the triangle response should occur, and this response will advance the C-system to its next state. This state induces the A-unit activity pattern corresponding to the square, and as soon as this is responded to, the C-system is advanced again. Thus the association states corresponding to the entire sequence of sensory events tends to be reconstituted, in proper temporal order. If the states are reconstituted accurately enough they can be used for teaching the perceptron new discriminations, in retrospect, or for applying subsequently learned discriminations to events which were improperly recognized at the time they occurred. None of this interferes with the sequential memory system, which is independent of changes in the A- to R-unit network.

Due to the fact that the expected interaction between recorded events is zero, the sequences which can be stored may be extremely long. Ultimately, noise effects, which show up as a gradually increasing variance in the transmitted signals, grow to such a degree that they effectively mask the residual traces of previous memory, and the system saturates. Before this happens, the accuracy with which the association states are reconstituted gradually diminishes, and consequently the discriminatory responses which occur to remembered stimuli become less and less accurate. In evaluating the performance of this model, the most important question is the probability that a discriminatory response to a remembered stimulus is correct, after a long history of experience has been recorded. The estimation of this probability is the task which is undertaken in the following section.

ANALYSIS OF PERFORMANCE PROBABILITIES

The measurement of memory performance will be based upon the following experiment:

Assume that the perceptron sees a long sequence of stimulus patterns, $S_1, S_2, S_3 \ldots, S_t$. Each stimulus persists for an equal period of time, Δt, which for convenience is set equal to unity. Among these n stimuli, there is at least one occurrence of a stimulus S_x which the perceptron has been taught to recognize by emitting the response R_x. It is assumed that the perceptron has been taught to suppress the response R_x for all stimuli other than S_x. The level of performance of the perceptron in discriminating S_x from other stimuli is to be treated as a parameter of the problem. At the start of the sequence of n stimuli, the C-system is initialized, and recording goes on throughout the sequence. The C-system is then set back to its initial state, with no external stimuli present, so that the perceptron begins to recapitulate the remembered sequence. Suppose the stimulus S_x originally occurred at time t_x (measured from the start of the sequence). Then when the C-system has advanced to the t_x-th state, the response R_x should occur. We wish to calculate the probability $P(R_x)$ that this response does, in fact, occur at the appropriate point in the recapitulated sequence.

The perceptron is characterized by the choice of the symmetric or asymmetric reinforcement rule [Eqs. (1a) or (1b)] and by the following parameters:

N_a = number of A-units
N_c = number of C-units in the "on" layer
M = fraction of C-units connected to each A-unit $(0 < M \leq 1)$

Q_a = proportion of A-units activated by a stimulus (i.e., the measure of the A-unit activity level maintained by the Θ-servo).

Q_c = proportion of C-units active in any given clock state.

For a plausible biological system, we would require N_a and $N_c \leq 10^9$, MN_c (the number of connections to an A-unit) $\leq 1,000$, and Q_a and Q_c probably no greater than 0.1 or 0.2.

In the analysis of S-controlled reinforcement procedures,[44] it was shown that the probability of a correct response could be very closely approximated by assuming a normal distribution of input signals to the R-unit. The probability of a correct response to stimulus S_x (when S_x is actually present on the retina) is then given by

$$P(R_x|S_x) = \Phi\left[E(u_x)/\sigma(u_x)\right] \tag{3}$$

where $E(u_x)$ = expected value of signal to R-unit when S_x is present

$\sigma(u_x)$ = standard deviation of the signal u_x

$\Phi(z)$ = cumulative normal distribution function, from $-\infty$ to z, i.e.,

$$\Phi(z) = \frac{1}{\sqrt{2\pi}} \int_{-\infty}^{z} e^{-x^2/2} \, dx$$

The above distribution of signals may be taken over a collection of different perceptrons, or over a set of training sequences, or over a set of possible choices of the test stimulus, S_x. For any given perceptron and training sequence, of course, the actual signal is deterministic, and, assuming the response to be correctly learned, we could set $E(u_x)/\sigma(u_x) = \infty$, in applying the above equation. Since we are interested in studying the effects of imperfect recognition, or low levels of discrimination performance, upon recall, however, we will permit an arbitrary choice of the ratio $E(u_x)/\sigma(u_x)$ to characterize the initial performance level of the perceptron. The computation of this ratio for a number of different kinds of discrimination experiments with γ-system reinforcement is presented in Chap. 8 of Ref. 44.

A special case which is likely to be of interest is that of a perceptron which has been trained on only two stimuli, S_x and S_y, where the perceptron is taught to give the response R_x for S_x, but to suppress this response for S_y. In this case, if S_x and S_y are not identical or nearly identical stimuli, correct performance is virtually certain, and it is safe to take $E(u_x)/\sigma(u_x)$ = ∞.

Suppose, then, that the perceptron has been trained to some level of performance for which $E(u_x)$ and $\sigma(u_x)$ are known. When the memory sequence has been recorded and the state of the C-system is restored to the conditions which existed when S_x appeared on the retina, some set of A-units, more or less similar to those activated by S_x, will be activated by the signals from the C-units. In particular, suppose the stimulus originally activated a set of $N^+ = Q_a N_a$ "proper units," the remaining $N^- = N_a - N^+$ units being designated "improper units." Of the N^+ proper units, the C-system now activates n^+ proper units; it also activates n^- improper units. If $n^+ = N^+$, and $n^- = 0$, this means that the original A-unit state has been reconstituted exactly, and the probability of a correct response would be just what it was if the stimulus actually appeared on the retina. In general, however, this condition is not likely to occur. For a given set of n^+ proper units reactivated, and n^- improper units activated, we must determine the new probability of obtaining a correct response.

To estimate this probability, we assume, first of all, that the set of proper A-units reactivated are not systematically related, in any way, to the weights of their A-R connections. In this case, the n^+ proper units would be expected to receive a fraction n^+/N^+ of the total signal from the proper set, $E(u_x)$. Similarly, the n^- improper units activated are assumed to be unrelated to the weights of their A-R connections, so that they will be expected to receive a fraction n^-/N^- of the total weight of the N^- improper A-units. But, if we assume that a γ-system has been employed for training the A-R network, the expected sum of the weights of the improper set must be equal to $-E(u_x)$, so that the expected value of the regenerated signal to the R-unit will be

$$\left[\frac{n^+}{N^+} - \frac{n^-}{N^-} \right] E(u_x) \tag{4}$$

By the same reasoning which was just applied to the expected value of the regenerated signal, the variance will likewise be expected to redistribute in a uniform fashion over the active units. (This will be rigorously true if the sets of A-units activated by different stimuli are statistically independent of one another, as occurs in a "binomial model" simple perceptron in an environment of random stimuli. In that case, the variance of the weight of any given A-unit a_i will be the same as the variance for any other A-unit, a_j.) For the n^+ units of the proper set, the new variance will be $(n^+/N^+) \sigma^2(u_x)$. The N^- improper units are inferred to have a total variance of $(N^-/N^+) \sigma^2(u_x)$, and consequently the variance of the n^- units which are actually active will be $(n^-/N^+) \sigma^2(u_x)$. Combining these components, the variance of the reconstituted signal becomes

$$\frac{n^+ + n^-}{N^+} \sigma^2(u_x) \tag{5}$$

and, taking the ratio of Eq. (4) and the square root of Eq. (5) we obtain the expression

$$
Z(n^+, n^-) = \frac{\dfrac{n^+}{N^+} - \dfrac{n^-}{N^-}}{\sqrt{\dfrac{n^+ + n^-}{N^+}}} \cdot \frac{E(u_x)}{\sigma(u_x)}
$$

$$
= \frac{\dfrac{n^+}{Q_a N_a} - \dfrac{n^-}{(1 - Q_a) N_a}}{\sqrt{\dfrac{n^+ + n^-}{Q_a N_a}}} \cdot \frac{E(u_x)}{\sigma(u_x)}
$$

and consequently (given n^+ and n^-), the probability of a correct response is

$$
P(R_x) = \Phi [Z(n^+, n^-)] \tag{6}
$$

Actually, however, any combination of $n^+ \leq N^+$ and $n^- \leq N^-$ might possibly occur. Let $P(n^+, n^-)$ be the probability that some particular set of n^+ proper units and n^- improper units is activated. This probability should be the same for any choice of the n^+ proper units and the n^- improper units, due to symmetry considerations. There are $\binom{N^+}{n^+}$ ways of choosing the proper set, and $\binom{N^-}{n^-}$ ways of choosing the improper set. Thus the general equation for $P(R_x)$ takes the form:

$$
P(R_x) = \sum_{n^+=0}^{N^+} \sum_{n^-=0}^{N^-} \binom{N^+}{n^+}\binom{N^-}{n^-} P(n^+, n^-) \, \Phi[Z(n^+, n^-)] \tag{7}
$$

The only unknown quantity in this equation is $P(n^+, n^-)$, which must now be analyzed.

Let us consider two extreme possibilities. First, the signals to different A-units from the C-system may be totally uncorrelated with one another, in which case $P(n^+, n^-)$ will be the product of the probabilities of activating each of the n^+ proper units and the n^- improper units individually. At the other extreme, the signals might all be perfectly correlated with one another, in which case either every A-unit will be turned on, or every A-unit will be turned off jointly, the probability of activating the entire set being the same as the probability of activating any one individually. In the first of these cases, due to a sort of "majority decision" effect, performance will be greatly improved by having a large number of A-units, while in the second case the probability of a correct response from a great number of units will be no better than the probability of a correct response with only one or two units in the system. Thus the correlation between the signals to different A-units, transmitted from the C-system, is seen to be a consideration of prime importance. The correlation between the signals to units a_i and a_j, measured over the set of C-system states, will be called ρ_{ij}. This correlation is, in general, nonzero, and will be different for the symmetric and asymmetric models as will be seen shortly.

Assuming that the correlations can be obtained, it will still be necessary to know the probability of turning on a given proper unit or improper unit, a_j, in order to develop an equation for $P(n^+, n^-)$. If we again assume a Gaussian distribution for the input signals to the A-units from the C-system (which will, in fact, be an extremely close approximation, since the signals consist of sums of a great number of increments and decrements which are added or subtracted at random (or pseudo-random) times during the recorded sequence) we have an analogous expression to Eq. (3),

$$P\{a_j^* = 1\} = \Phi\left[\frac{E(u_j) - \theta_j}{\sigma(u_j)}\right] = \Phi(h) \qquad (8)$$

where u_j = signal to a_j from the C-system
$\quad\ \theta_j$ = threshold of a_j

The expected value $E(u_j)$ can be considered to consist of two contributions, the first due to the reinforcement which occurred at the time of stimulus S_x, and the second due to all other stimuli in the recorded sequence. Each connection to a_j which is active at the time of recapitulation was also active at the time S_x originally occurred, since the state of the C-system is presumed to be identical. There are a total of $Q_c M N_c$ such connections. Consequently, the expected signal contribution from S_x is

$$Q_c M N_c \cdot E(\Delta w_{ij}|c_i^* = 1). \qquad (9)$$

From any other state of the C-system, however, only a fraction Q_c of the active units will be common with those which are active at the present time, since the quasi-independence of different C-states guarantees that the measure of any intersection will be Q_c. Thus from any such state other than the one previous occurrence of the present state, the expected contribution to the signal to a_j will be

$$Q_c^2 M N_c \cdot E(\Delta w_{ij}|c_i^* = 1) + (Q_c - Q_c^2) M N_c \cdot E(\Delta w_{ij}|c_i^* = 0). \qquad (10)$$

Taking the magnitude of the reinforcement increment η to be unity, and substituting in (10) for the asymmetric model, from Eq. (2a), we obtain

$$Q_c^2 MN_c\, a_i^*\, (1 - Q_c) - (Q_c - Q_c^2)\, MN_c\, a_i^*(Q_c) = 0.$$

Similarly, substituting in Eq. (10) for the symmetric model, from Eq. (2b), yields

$$Q_c^2 MN_c(-1)^{\overset{*}{a_j}+1}\, (1 - Q_c) - (Q_c - Q_c^2)\, MN_c(-1)^{\overset{*}{a_j}+1}\, (Q_c) = 0.$$

Thus the only contribution to $E(u_j)$ which survives is that given in Eq. (9). Substituting for the expectations, and taking $\eta = 1$, we obtain

$$E(u_j) = Q_c MN_c a_i^*(S_x)(1 - Q_c) \qquad \text{(Asymmetric case)} \quad (11a)$$

$$E(u_j) = Q_c MN_c(-1)^{\overset{*}{a_j}(S_x)+1}\, (1 - Q_c) \qquad \text{(Symmetric case)} \quad (11b)$$

where $a_j^*(S_x)$ = activity state of a_j in response to stimulus S_x.

The variance $\sigma^2(u_j)$ of the signal to a_j will receive an increment for every stimulus for which the connections to a_j are reinforced. In the asymmetric model, such reinforcements occur only when a_j is active; in the symmetric model, they occur for every stimulus, being equal in their expected magnitude but opposite in sign, depending upon whether $a_j^* = 1$ or 0. These differences in sign will not affect the variance, however, which will receive a fixed positive increment for every stimulus. An exact expression for the variance which results from a series of γ-system reinforcements has been obtained by Joseph,[32] and can also be found in Chap. 8 of Ref. 44. We assume here that Q_c is constant for all C-states, that the intersection between the active sets in two C-states has measure Q_c^2, and the triple intersection between three active C-sets has measure Q_c^3. For these conditions (which would apply with randomly chosen C-sets with large values of N_c) Joseph's formula for the γ'-system is applicable [Eq. (8.8) in Ref. 44]. Specifically, with appropriate changes in symbols, and assuming each C-state to occur only once, this equation becomes

$$\sigma^2(u_j) = MN_c \sum_{i=1}^{\tau} \sum_{k=1}^{\tau} r_i r_k[(Q_{ikx} - Q_c^3) - 2Q_c(Q_{ix} - Q_c^2)$$

$$- (Q_{ix} - Q_c^2)(Q_{kx} - Q_c^2)] \qquad (12)$$

where the indices i and k range over the set of C-states for which the connections to a_j were reinforced, τ = the number of such states, and r_i (the sign of the reinforcement) is always $+1$ for the asymmetric model and $(-1)^{a_j^*(S_j)+1}$ for the symmetric model. Q_{ij} = the measure of the intersection between the ith and jth C-states ($= Q_c{}^2$ if $i \neq j$ and Q_c if $i = j$). Q_{ijk} = measure of the intersection between the ith, jth, and kth C-states ($= Q_c{}^3$ if $i \neq j \neq k$, $Q_c{}^2$ if exactly two indices are identical, and Q_c if $i = j = k$). Counting the number of terms with similar and dissimilar indices, assuming $x \neq i$ or k, and taking account of the signs r_i, it can be seen that all terms for $i \neq k$ vanish, and we are left with the expression

$$\sigma^2(u_j) = MN_c \sum_{i=k} [Q_c^2 - Q_c^3] = MN_c \tau (Q_c^2 - Q_c^3). \tag{13}$$

If $x =$ some i or k, then we must add the increment

$$\Delta \sigma^2(u_x) = MN_c[Q_c - 3Q_c^2 + 3Q_c^3 - Q_c^4]$$

to Eq. (13). For large values of τ, this increment will obviously be negligible, and Eq. (13) will be taken as the estimate of the variance throughout the following.

For the symmetric model, since reinforcement occurs regardless of the activity states of the A-units, $\tau = t$ (the total number of stimuli recorded). For the asymmetric model, τ depends on the number of stimuli by which the unit a_j was activated; specifically, $\tau = \varrho_a t$, where $\varrho_a =$ the fraction of stimuli activating a_j. In a nonrepetitive random environment, we can assume that $\varrho_a = Q_a$, but in a systematic environment (for example, one with only two stimuli constituting a long sequence) this will not generally be true. Thus, from Eq. (11) and (13), for the two cases of interest, we have

$$\frac{E(u_j) - \theta}{\sigma(u_j)} = \begin{cases} \sqrt{\dfrac{MN_c(1 - Q_c)}{\hat{Q}_a t}} \, [a_j^*(S_x)] - \dfrac{\theta}{\sigma(u_x)} & \text{(Asymmetric case)} \\[4mm] \sqrt{\dfrac{MN_c(1 - Q_c)}{t}} \, [(-1)^{a_j^*(Sx)+1}] - \dfrac{\theta}{\sigma(u_x)} & \text{(Symmetric case)} \end{cases} \tag{14}$$

Note that for the symmetric case, the ratio $E(u_j)/\sigma(u_j)$ for a "proper" unit is equal in magnitude, but opposite in sign to the ratio for an "improper" unit. We can assume, then, that the θ-servo will set the threshold at a level close to zero, which would provide the best cutting-point between the units receiving high input signals and those receiving low input signals. The threshold will therefore be assumed to be exactly zero, in this model, for the following analysis. For the asymmetric case, on the other hand, the ratio $E(u_j)/\sigma(u_j)$ will be 0 for an improper unit, while for a proper unit it will have the value of the left-hand term in Eq. (14). In this case, the θ-servo will tend to find a level halfway between the 0 signal which is expected as the input to improper units, and the signal expected by proper units. But this yields a distribution for the probability of activating proper or improper units which is entirely equivalent to assuming a zero threshold, and a Gaussian distribution with $E(u_j)/\sigma(u_j)$ of exactly half of the magnitude shown in Eq. (14), with $E(u_j)$ having opposite signs for proper and improper units. Since this treatment permits both the symmetric and asymmetric models to be handled in an identical fashion, it will be adopted in the following analysis. Thus, the probability of activating the unit a_j is given by

$$P\{a_j^* = 1\} = \Phi(h) \tag{15}$$

where

$$h = \begin{cases} \pm \sqrt{\dfrac{MN_c(1 - Q_c)}{4\hat{Q}_a t}} & \text{(Asymmetric case)} \\[4mm] \pm \sqrt{\dfrac{MN_c(1 - Q_c)}{t}} & \text{(Symmetric case)} \end{cases} \tag{16}$$

The sign of h is positive for proper units, and negative for improper units.

For the case in which the correlation between A-unit input signals, P_{ij}, can be assumed to be zero for all $i \neq j$, we would immediately be able to obtain the probability

$$P(n^+, n^-) = \Phi(+h)^{n^+} \cdot \Phi(-h)^{n^-}.$$

For the correlated case, however, we will have to face the problem of calculating the probability that each of $(n^+ + n^-)$ correlated Gaussian variables is positive. In general, this is known to be an insoluble problem. For the particular case in hand, fortunately, a solution is possible. In order to deal with this, however, we must first estimate the values of the correlation coefficients, P_{ij}.

It can be seen that there are two possible sources of correlation effects. One is the set of C-units which is connected both to a_i and to a_j. If the origins of the connections to the A-units are selected at random, this set will have an expected measure equal to M^2. (By selecting disjoint C-sets for the connections to each A-unit, the correlation can, in fact, be reduced to zero, but with only a limited number of C-units available, this leads to a reduction of h which more than compensates for any advantages which might acrue.) The other possible source of correlation comes from the joint activity of the A-units a_i and a_j themselves. The probability that $a_i^* = a_j^*$ will be designated q_{ij}. Thus if a_i and a_j are always either both on or both off (as might occur if they both respond to some stimulus S_x and to no other stimuli) q_{ij} will be equal to 1. If they are always in opposite states, $q_{ij} = 0$. If they are each activated independently, with a probability $Q_a = 0.5$, then $q_{ij} = 0.5$. For any other value of Q_a, however, q_{ij} must be either greater than or less than 0.5. For notational convenience in the following discussion, let $q_{ij} = q$.

We will first compute ρ_{ij} for the symmetric case. By definition,

$$\rho_{ij} = \frac{\text{cov }(u_i, u_j)}{\sigma(u_i)\,\sigma(u_j)} \tag{17}$$

The value of $\sigma(u_i)$ has already been obtained, but we must still compute the covariance of the signals. For this we have

$$\text{cov}(u_i.u_j) = \frac{1}{t}\sum_{k=1}^{t} (u_i(k) - \underset{k}{E}(u_i),\ (u_j(k) - \underset{k}{E}(u_j))$$

$$= \frac{1}{t}\sum_{k=1}^{t} [\tilde{u}_i(k) + u_{ij}(k) - E(\tilde{u}_i) - E(u_{ij})][\tilde{u}_i(k)$$

$$+ u_{ji}(k) - E(\tilde{u}_j) - E(u_{ji})]$$

where $\tilde{u}_i(k)$ = signal to a_i from the kth C-state

$\tilde{u}_i(k)$ = signal to a_i from the set of C-units connected to a_i and not to a_j

$u_j(k)$ = signal to a_j from the set of C-units connected to a_j and not to a_i

$u_{ij}(k)$ = signal to a_i from the set of C-units connected to both a_i and a_j

$u_{ji}(k)$ = signal to a_j from the set of C-units connected to both a_i and a_j.

It can easily be shown that the terms coming from the "unique" connections to a_i and to a_j will cancel out of the above expression, only the "common" set of connections contributing to the covariance. Thus we obtain

$$\text{cov }(u_i, u_j) = \frac{1}{t}\sum_{k=1}^{t} [u_{ij}(k) - E(u_{ij})][u_{ji}(k) - E(u_{ji})] \tag{18}$$

Now let $\Delta_i{}^\nu(k)$ = contribution to $[u_{ij}(k) - E(u_{ij})]$ from the νth stimulus

$\Delta_j{}^\nu(k)$ = contribution to $[u_{ji}(k) - E(u_{ji})]$ from the νth stimulus.

Note that $|\Delta_i{}^\nu| = |\Delta_j{}^\nu|$ since the same set of C-units is involved for both a_i and a_j. Also, note that the sign of $\Delta_i{}^\nu$ always agrees with the sign of the total signal increment for the νth stimulus.* For convenience, we can let

---

* Actually, it is easy to show that $E(u_{ij}) = 0$, so that $\Delta_i{}^\nu$ is actually equal to the signal increment.

sgn Δ_i^ν = sgn Δ_j^ν for the first qt stimuli, and let the signs be opposite for the remaining stimuli in the sequence. Thus,

$$u_{ij}(k) - E(u_{ij}) = \sum_{\nu=1}^{qt} \Delta_i^\nu(k) + \sum_{\nu=qt+1}^{t} \Delta_i^\nu(k)$$

$$u_{ji}(k) - E(u_{ji}) = \sum_{\nu=1}^{qt} \Delta_i^\nu(k) - \sum_{\nu=qt+1}^{t} \Delta_i^\nu(k)$$

and

$$\text{cov }(u_i, u_j) = \frac{1}{t}\sum_{k=1}^{t}\left[\left(\sum_{\nu=1}^{qt}\Delta_i^\nu(k)\right)^2 - \left(\sum_{\nu=qt+1}^{t}\Delta_i^\nu(k)\right)^2\right]$$

$$= \frac{1}{t}\sum_{k=1}^{t}\left(\sum_{\nu=1}^{qt}\Delta_i^\nu(k)\right)^2 - \frac{1}{t}\sum_{k=1}^{t}\left(\sum_{\nu=qt+1}^{t}\Delta_i^\nu(k)\right)^2$$

which can be seen to be a difference between two variances. The first term represents the contribution to the variance $\sigma^2(u_{ij})$ due to the first qt stimuli, and the second term represents the contribution to the variance due to the remaining $(1 - q)t$ stimuli. Since each stimulus in the sequence contributes an equal increment to the variance of the signal, this becomes

$$\text{cov }(u_i, u_j) = q\sigma^2(u_{ij}) - (1 - q)\,\sigma^2(u_{ij})$$

$$= (2q - 1)\,\sigma^2(u_{ij}).$$

But since the intersection of the sets of C-units connected to a_i and a_j is a fraction of the set connected to either A-unit alone (for $i \neq j$), it can readily be seen that $\sigma^2(u_{ij}) = M\sigma^2(u_i)$. Thus, substituting in Eq. (17), we obtain (for $i \neq j$)

$$\rho_{ij} = \frac{(2q - 1)\,M\sigma^2(u_i)}{\sigma(u_i)\,\sigma(u_j)} = (2q_{ij} - 1)\,M \quad \text{(Symmetric case)}$$

$$(19a)$$

For the asymmetric case, Eq. (17) and (18) still apply. $\Delta_i^\nu(k)$ and $\Delta_j^\nu(k)$ are defined as before. Note, however, that in this case the sign of these increments is always positive, of magnitude Δu whenever a reinforcement occurs, and of magnitude 0 when the A-unit in question is inactive. Suppose both a_i and a_j are active for $\varrho_a t$ stimuli. Then we have

$$u_{ij}(k) - E(u_{ij}) = \hat{Q}_a t\,\Delta u = u_{ji}(k) - E(u_{ji}).$$

Consequently, Eq. (18) becomes

$$\text{cov }(u_i, u_j) = \frac{1}{t}\sum_{k=1}^{t}[u_{ij}(k) - E(u_{ij})]^2 = \sigma^2(u_{ij})$$

and we obtain (for $i \neq j$)

$$\rho_{ij} = \frac{\sigma^2(u_{ij})}{\sigma(u_i)\,\sigma(u_j)} = M \qquad \text{(Asymmetric case)} \qquad (19b)$$

Note that in the symmetric model, it is theoretically possible to guarantee a zero correlation by guaranteeing that $q_{ij} = 0.5$ for $i \neq j$. This would be true if the environment consists of random stimuli, and Q_a is kept at 0.5 by the θ-servo. These conditions, however, are quite implausible biologically, and the high value of Q_a would be far from optimum in most discrimination experiments. In the asymmetric model, on the other hand, ρ_{ij} is entirely independent of q and consequently of Q_a, depending only on M. This corresponds to the worst possible case of the symmetric model, in which $2q - 1 = 1$. These relatively high correlations are compensated' however, by the appearance of Q_a in the expression for h [Eq. (16)]. Here it is clear that by keeping Q_a small, the probability of activating any given A-unit correctly becomes correspondingly large, which tends to offset the effects of the increased correlation between signals, as we shall see.

At this point, we have established all of the necessary prerequisites for the analysis of $P(n^+, n^-)$. This probability (that a particular set of n^+ proper units and n^- improper units and no others are activated) can be rephrazed as follows: Given N_a normally distributed random variables with unit variance and mean 0, and a matrix R of correlation coefficients ρ_{ij}, we require the probability that the first n^+ variables are $< h$, the next n^- variables are $< -h$, the next $N^+ - n^+$ are $< -h$, and the remaining $N^- - n^-$ variables are all $< h$, where the quantity h is defined in Eq. (16) and ρ_{ij} is defined by Eq. (19), for $i \neq j$. For $i = j$, ρ_{ij} is obviously equal to 1. The method which was finally obtained for achieving a tractable solution to this problem was suggested by Milton Sobel, and has been described by Curnow and Dunnet in Ref. 10. The method is applicable to any case in which the correlation matrix, R, has the structure $\rho_{ij} = \alpha_i \alpha_j$ for $i \neq j$, where $-1 \leq \alpha_i \leq +1$. This condition is clearly satisfied for the asymmetric model, where $\alpha_i = \sqrt{M}$. It is also satisfied for the symmetric case, if we assume q_{ij} to be equal for all pairs i and j ($i \neq j$).

For the above conditions the following analysis is applicable.* Let $Z_1, Z_2, \ldots, Z_n$ be n standardized normal variables with correlation coefficients ρ_{ij} satisfying the above constraint. Then the variables Z_i can be generated from $n + 1$ independent normal variables $(X_1, X_2, \ldots, X_n, Y)$ by substituting

$$Z_i = \sqrt{1 - \alpha_i^2}\, X_i + \alpha_i Y. \qquad (20)$$

---

* This treatment follows that of Curnow and Dunnet. It is also possible to reduce the multivariate normal distribution, in this case, to a sum of products of Hermite polynomials, but the resulting equation becomes quite unmanageable for large n.

original training of the perceptron permits) due to the growth of h. As the length of the recorded sequence, t, becomes large, on the other hand, h diminishes and the probability of a correct response approaches 0.5.

Of greater interest is the asymptotic behavior of the amount of information stored in the C-system as the recorded sequence grows in length. To estimate this, assume that the stimulus sequence activates random A-states, with $Q_a = .5$, and M small, so that $\rho_{ij} \approx 0$ for both the symmetric and asymmetric models. Then we have the following:

Information content of original stimulus $= N_a$ bits.
Information in S-sequence of t stimuli $= tN_a$ bits.
Information content of reconstituted A-state $= x$ bits.

$$x = H(S) - H_n(S)$$

where $H(S) =$ entropy of stimulus representation $= N_a$ bits
$\quad H_n(S) =$ equivocation (measure of uncertainty in the stimulus, given the reconstituted A-state)
Information stored in C-network $= tx$ bits.

Minimum information stored per C-A connection $= H_c = tx/$total number of connections $= tx/N_aMN_c$.

Lower bound for number of distinguishable weight levels required per connection (with optimal coding) to achieve the obtained storage capacity $= 2^{H_c}$.

The only quantity in the above equations for which we still lack an explicit expression is $H_n(S)$ But this is given by the expression

$$H_n(S) = -\sum_i P(S_i|S) \log P(S_i|S) \equiv -\sum_i P_i(S) \log P_i(S) \quad (29)$$

where $P(S_i|S) =$ probability of obtaining the A-state for stimulus S_i when the correct state is S. This is symbolized by $P_i(S)$.

Therefore the information content of the reconstituted (remembered) A-state is

$$x = N_a + \sum_i P_i(S) \log P_i(S).$$

After Shannon,[54] for the above case, if $P = \Phi(h) =$ probability that the activity state of a given A-unit is correctly reconstituted, the equivocation is given by

$$H_n(S) = -N_a[P \log_2 P + (1 - P) \log_2 (1 - P)] \quad (30)$$

and x is given by

$$x = N_a[1 + P \log_2 P + (1 - P) \log_2 (1 - P)] \quad (31)$$

Thus, substituting back in the previous expressions, we obtain the following formula for the minimum density of information stored per C-connection (for random stimuli):

$$H_c = \frac{t[1 + P \log_2 P + (1 - P) \log_2 (1 - P)]}{MN_c}$$

$$= \frac{t}{MN_c}\left[1 + \frac{1}{\ln (2)} (P \ln P + (1 - P) \ln (1 - P)) \right] \quad (32)$$

We are interested in determining the limit of this quantity as $t \to \infty$. Call this limit H_∞. Note that as $t \to \infty$, $P = \Phi(h) \to (0.5 + \phi'(0) \cdot h) = \left(0.5 + \frac{h}{\sqrt{2\pi}} \right)$ Let $C = MN_c/t$. Then $h = k\sqrt{C}$, where, for the symmetric model, $k = \sqrt{1 - Q_c}$, and for the asymmetric model, $k = \sqrt{\frac{1 - Q_c}{4Q_a}}$.

As $t \to \infty$, C goes to zero. Let $g = k/\sqrt{2\pi}$. Thus, substituting in Eq. (32), we obtain:

$$H_\infty = \operatorname*{Lim}_{C \to 0} \frac{1}{C} \left\{ \frac{1}{\ln 2} [(0.5 + g\sqrt{C}) \ln (0.5 + g\sqrt{C}) \right.$$

$$\left. + (0.5 - g\sqrt{C}) \ln (0.5 - g\sqrt{C})] \right\}$$

$$= \frac{1}{C} + \frac{1}{2C \ln 2} \ln (0.5 + g\sqrt{C}) + \frac{g}{\sqrt{C} \ln 2} \ln (0.5 + g\sqrt{C})$$

$$+ \frac{1}{2C \ln 2} \ln (0.5 - g\sqrt{C}) - \frac{g}{\sqrt{C} \ln 2} \ln (0.5 - g\sqrt{C})$$

$$= \frac{1}{C} + \frac{1}{2C \ln 2} \left\{ \ln (0.5) + 2\left[\frac{g\sqrt{C}}{1 + g\sqrt{C}} + \frac{1}{3}\left(\frac{g\sqrt{C}}{1 + g\sqrt{C}} \right)^3 + \cdots \right] \right\}$$

$$+ \frac{g}{\sqrt{C} \ln 2} \left\{ \ln (0.5) + 2\left[\frac{g\sqrt{C}}{1 + g\sqrt{C}} + \frac{1}{3}\left(\frac{g\sqrt{C}}{1 + g\sqrt{C}} \right)^3 + \cdots \right] \right\}$$

$$+ \frac{1}{2C \ln 2} \left\{ \ln (0.5) - 2\left[\frac{g\sqrt{C}}{1 - g\sqrt{C}} + \frac{1}{3}\left(\frac{g\sqrt{C}}{1 - g\sqrt{C}} \right)^3 + \cdots \right] \right\}$$

$$-\frac{g}{\sqrt{C}\ln 2}\left\{\ln(0.5)-2\left[\frac{g\sqrt{C}}{1-g\sqrt{C}}+\frac{1}{3}\left(\frac{g\sqrt{C}}{1-g\sqrt{C}}\right)^3+\cdots\right]\right\}$$

Since the higher power terms in the series become negligible as C goes to zero, this reduces to the form

$$H_\infty = \operatorname*{Lim}_{C\to 0}\left\{\frac{g}{\sqrt{C}\ln 2}\left(\frac{1}{1+g\sqrt{C}}\right)+\frac{2g^2}{\ln 2}\left(\frac{1}{1+g\sqrt{C}}\right)\right.$$

$$\left.-\frac{g}{\sqrt{C}\ln 2}\left(\frac{1}{1-g\sqrt{C}}\right)+\frac{2g^2}{\ln 2}\left(\frac{1}{1-g\sqrt{C}}\right)+\epsilon\right\}$$

$$= \operatorname*{Lim}_{C\to 0}\left\{\frac{1}{1-g^2C}\left[\frac{2g^2}{\ln 2}\right]+\epsilon\right\}$$

$$= \frac{2g^2}{\ln 2}.$$

Thus, substituting for g, we have

$$H_\infty = \frac{1-Q_c}{\pi\cdot\ln 2} \qquad \text{(Symmetric case)} \qquad (33a)$$

$$H_\infty = \frac{1-Q_c}{4Q_a\cdot\pi\cdot\ln 2} \qquad \text{(Asymmetric case)} \qquad (33b)$$

Note that this represents quite a low density of information in the network; for Q_c close to zero and Q_a close to 0.25, H_∞ for both models is 0.45922 bits per connection. Note also that with $Q_a < 0.25$ the asymmetric model is capable of storing more information than the symmetric model. Thus we see that as t becomes large, the saturation of the memory is represented by an asymptotic approach to a limiting information density. This fixed amount of stored information as the number of stored stimuli increases is, of course, a direct reflection of the diminishing probability of correct recall.

In the above case it has been assumed that the original association state actually contains N_a bits of information, which will be true only if the stimulus sequence is sufficiently heterogeneous so that each A-unit may be active independently. It was further assumed that the A-units were reactivated independently by the C-system, with probability P of being correct. If the correlation coefficients ρ_{ij} are not equal to zero, this assumption is no longer accurate. In the extreme case, where only two stimuli can occur in the environment, the information content of the A-state is only 1 bit instead of N_a bits, and with perfect correlation of signals from the C-system to the A-system the N_a A-units act, in effect, as a single A-unit. Thus the analysis takes the same form as the above case, but with N_a reduced to 1. This yields limits which are only $1/N_a$ times as large as those for the heterogeneous environment. This again bears out our conclusion that memory of a diverse environment will be better than memory of a repetitious environment.

Before leaving this topic, one final exercise may prove to be illuminating. If we assume that the human brain functions in the manner of our asymmetric memory model, and that there are 10^9 neurons (or about 10 percent of the brain's population) functioning as C-units, each having 1,000 connections to A-units, and if we set $Q_c = Q_a = 0.01$, then Eq. (33b) gives us one more estimate of the information capacity of the brain. Specifically, this would predict that in its saturated condition, the brain would be capable of storing approximately 1.2×10^{13} bits of information, from a sufficiently heterogeneous environment. This fits comfortably in between the two extremes estimated by Miller and von Foerster, which were mentioned in the Introduction.

NUMERICAL RESULTS

Equation (26) has been integrated numerically for a number of cases of interest, using an IBM 7090 computer.* This has yielded estimates for the probability of a correct discriminatory response to a remembered stimulus, $P(R_x)$, for values of t ranging from 10^3 through 10^{11}, and for values of N_a and N_c ranging from 10^3 through 10^9. It was assumed that preliminary training on the discrimination of the test stimulus, S_x, was perfect, i.e., $E(u_x)/\sigma(u_x) = \infty$. MN_c (the number of input connections to each A-unit) was taken as 1,000 in all cases. This would make the A-units roughly comparable to large pyramidal cells in the cerebral cortex. Q_c was assumed to be negligibly small. N_a was assumed to be equal to N_c.

The main calculations completed to date are for the symmetric model, but preliminary calculations of performance for the asymmetric model show

---

* The writer is indebted to Robert Tuttle for his assistance in programming this problem, and to the Atomic Energy Commission for making its facilities at the Courant Institute available for the computation.

Under these conditions, it follows that the Z_i are normally distributed with zero means, unit variances, and correlation coefficients $\rho_{ij} = \alpha_i\alpha_j$ $(i \neq j)$.

Let $f(Z_1, Z_2, \ldots, Z_n)$ represent the joint frequency function of the variables Z_i. The cumulative distribution function is then defined by:

$$F_n(h_i) = P\{Z_i < h_i, \text{ for all } i\}$$

$$= \int_{-\infty}^{h_1} \int_{-\infty}^{h_2} \cdots \int_{-\infty}^{h_n} f(Z_1, Z_2, \ldots, Z_n)\, dZ_1, dZ_2, \ldots, dZ_n$$

We can clearly multiply this expression by $\int_{-\infty}^{\infty} \phi'(Y)\, dY = 1$ without changing its value, (where ϕ' is the normal density function). This yields

$$F_n(h_i) = \int_{-\infty}^{\infty} \left[\int_{-\infty}^{h_1} \int_{-\infty}^{h_2} \cdots \int_{-\infty}^{h_n} f(Z_1, Z_2, \ldots, Z_n)\, \phi'(Y) \right.$$
$$\left. dZ_1, dZ_2, \ldots, dZ_n \right] dY.$$

Now substitute $Z_i = \dfrac{X_i - \alpha_i Y}{\sqrt{1 - \alpha_i^2}}$ for all Z_i.

Since the X_i are mutually independent, the resulting integral can be factored, and we obtain

$$F_n(h_i) = \int_{-\infty}^{\infty} \prod_{i=1}^{n} \left[\int_{-\infty}^{h_i} \phi'\left(\frac{X_i - \alpha_i Y}{\sqrt{1 - \alpha_i^2}} \right) dX_i \right] \phi'(Y)\, dY$$

$$= \int_{-\infty}^{\infty} \prod_{i=1}^{n} \Phi\left(\frac{h_i - \alpha_i Y}{\sqrt{1 - \alpha_i^2}} \right) \phi'(Y)\, dY \tag{21}$$

For the particular case with which we are concerned, $\alpha_i = \sqrt{\rho}$ where $\rho = $ the value of ρ_{ij} for $i \neq j$, and the h_i are all $\pm h$, for the appropriate sets of variables. This yields

$$P(n^+, n^-) = \int_{-\infty}^{\infty} \Phi^{n^+ + N^- - n^-}\left(\frac{x\sqrt{\rho} + h}{\sqrt{1 - \rho}} \right)$$

$$\left[1 - \Phi\left(\frac{x\sqrt{\rho} + h}{\sqrt{1 - \rho}} \right) \right]^{n^- + N^+ - n^+} \phi'(x)\, dx \tag{22}$$

The expression $\dbinom{N^+}{n^+} \dbinom{N^-}{n^-} P(n^+, n^-)$ which appears in Eq. (7), representing the probability of any arbitrary set of n^+ proper units and n^- improper units being active, can then be written in the form

$$G(n^+, n^-) = \int_{-\infty}^{\infty} \binom{N^+}{n^+} F^{n^+} (1 - F)^{N^+ - n^+} \binom{N^-}{n^-} F^{N^- - n^-}$$

$$(1 - F)^{n^-} \phi'(x) \, dx \qquad (23)$$

where $F = \Phi\left(\dfrac{x\sqrt{\rho} + h}{\sqrt{1 - \rho}}\right)$. This integrand evidently includes the product

of two binomial probability functions. For large N^+ and N^- (such as we will always be dealing with) it is possible to approximate this by the product of two Gaussian probabilities as follows:

$$G(n^+, n^-) \approx \int_{-\infty}^{\infty} \phi'\left(\frac{n^+ - N^+F}{\sqrt{N^+F(1 - F)}}\right) \phi'\left(\frac{n^- - N^-(1 - F)}{\sqrt{N^-F(1 - F)}}\right) \phi'(x) \, dx \qquad (24)$$

and thus, substituting in Eq. (7), we obtain

$$P(R_x) = \sum_{n^+ = 0}^{N^+} \sum_{n^- = 0}^{N^-} G(n^+, n^-) \, \Phi[Z(n^+, n^-)]$$

$$= \int_{-\infty}^{\infty} \sum_{n^+ = 0}^{N^+} \sum_{n^- = 0}^{N^-} \phi'\left(\frac{n^+ - N^+F}{\sqrt{N^+F(1 - F)}}\right) \phi'\left(\frac{n^- - N^-(1 - F)}{\sqrt{N^-F(1 - F)}}\right)$$

$$\phi'(x) \cdot \Phi[Z(n^+, n^-)] \, dx \qquad (25)$$

This can be simplified further, for large N_a, by replacing the sums by integrals, with appropriate limits, which yields

$$P(R_x) = \int_{x = -\infty}^{\infty} \int_{y = -\sqrt{\frac{N^+}{L}}}^{\sqrt{N^+}L} \int_{z = -\sqrt{\frac{N^-}{L}}}^{\sqrt{N^-}L} \phi'(x) \, \phi'(y) \, \phi'(z)$$

$$\Phi[\psi(x, y, z)] \, dx \, dy \, dz \qquad (26)$$

where

$$L = \sqrt{\frac{1 - F}{F}}$$

$$\psi(x, y, z) = Z\left[\sqrt{N^+F(1 - F)}\left(y + \frac{\sqrt{N^+}}{L}\right),\right.$$

$$\left. \sqrt{N^-F(1 - F)}\left(z + \frac{\sqrt{N^-}}{L}\right)\right]$$

$$= Z(n^+, n^-)$$

This last form is the one which has actually been used for numerical computation.

Before going on to a consideration of numerical results, it is interesting to examine the asymptomatic behavior of $P(R_x)$, as well as several information-theoretic conclusions which follow directly from these equations.

It can easily be seen from Eq. (26) that as N_a gets large the integrand will be effectively equal to zero everywhere except in the neighborhood of the expected values of x, y, and z. Equivalently, in the form shown in Eq. (25), this means that the only terms in the summation which carry any weight are those in the neighborhood of the expected values of n^+ and n^-. Consequently, in the limit, as $N_a \to \infty$, $Z(n^+, n^-)$ can be replaced by $Z[E(n^+), E(n^-)]$, which no longer depends on n^+ and n^-. Thus the probability terms derived from the binomials in Eq. (23) can now be summed to unity, yielding

$$P(R_x) \xrightarrow[Na \to \infty]{} \int_{-\infty}^{\infty} 1 \cdot \phi'(x) \cdot \Phi[Z(En^+ \; En^-)] \, dx$$

$$= \int_{-\infty}^{\infty} \Phi \left[\frac{\dfrac{FN^+}{Q_a} - \dfrac{(1 - F) \, N^-}{1 - Q_a}}{\sqrt{[FN^+ + (1 - F) \, N^-]\dfrac{N_a}{Q_a}}} \cdot \frac{E(u_x)}{\sigma(u_x)} \right] \phi'(x) \, dx$$

Substituting $N^+ = Q_a N_a$ and $N^- = (1 - Q_a) \, N_a$, this yields

$$P(R_x) \to \int_{-\infty}^{\infty} \Phi \left[(2F - 1) \cdot \frac{E(u_x)}{\sigma(u_x)} \right] \phi'(x) \, dx \tag{27}$$

where

$$F = \Phi \left(\frac{x\sqrt{\rho} + h}{\sqrt{1 - \rho}} \right)$$

Now, taking a second limit as $E(u_x)/\sigma(u_x) \to \infty$ (corresponding to a perfectly learned response to S_x), note that the argument of Φ will be $+\infty$ with $\dfrac{x\sqrt{\rho} + h}{\sqrt{1 - \rho}} > 0$, and $-\infty$ otherwise.

But

$$\frac{x\sqrt{\rho} + h}{\sqrt{1 - \rho}} = 0 \text{ for } x = -h/\sqrt{\rho}.$$

Therefore, in Eq. (27), $\phi'(x)$ is weighted by 1 for $x > -h/\sqrt{\rho}$, and by 0 for $x < -h/\sqrt{\rho}$. Consequently, we obtain the limiting performance for a perfectly trained perceptron with infinite N_a,

$$\lim_{\substack{N_a \to \infty \\ \frac{Eu_x}{\sigma u_x} \to \infty}} P(R_x) = \int_{-h/\sqrt{\rho}}^{\infty} \phi'(x)\, dx = \Phi\left(\frac{h}{\sqrt{\rho}}\right)$$

This asymptotic formula suggests that the limiting performance may be quite poor if ρ is close to unity. While this is true in principle, note that in practice, large values of N_a will almost certainly be accompanied by large values of N_c. As N_c goes up, the value of h increases, so that the limit, Eq. (28), can become arbitrarily close to perfect performance regardless of ρ. Nonetheless, this formula suggests an explanation for the poor performance which is obtained in the recall of stereotyped sequences of symbols with low diversity, such as strings of binary digits. Suppose, for example, that the environment consists of only two stimuli, a square in a particular location, and a circle in a particular location, and that the perceptron is asked to record a long sequence of these squares and circles in random order. Under these conditions, for the symmetric model, q_{ij} will tend to be either 1 or 0, since there are only two meaningful A-unit sets, and any pair of A-units will either be in the same set or in opposite sets. This yields a maximum value for ρ, and correspondingly poor performance. In the asymmetric model, it may appear that this effect will not occur, but this is deceptive; ϱ_a now takes the place of q as the source of difficulty. For the highly correlated environment, those A-units which respond at all are likely to respond a large fraction of the time, resulting in large values of ϱ_a, hence low values of h and correspondingly poor performance. Thus performance will always be best in a very heterogeneous environment, with a great diversity of stimuli, and it will be poorest in a stereotyped environment, containing only a few patterns or symbols which may occur.

By substituting h and ρ in Eq. (28), it is easy to find the conditions for which the limiting performance of the symmetric model and asymmetric model are identical. This will occur when Q_a for the asymmetric model is equal to $(2q - 1)/4$ for the symmetric model. For example, a symmetric model with $q = 0.52$ (which requires Q_a close to 0.5) would have the same limiting performance as an asymmetric model with $\varrho_a = 0.01$. For sufficiently diverse stimuli the value of ϱ_a can be taken equal to Q_a, the probability that an A-unit responds to any given stimulus.

So far, we have considered only the limits for large values of N_a. As N_c becomes large, other parameters remaining constant, it is clear that the limiting performance will always become perfect (or as nearly so as the that the two are nearly identical for the condition Q_a (in asymmetric model) $= (2q - 1)/4$. In the limit, as was shown in the last section, the performances of the two models are identical when this condition is satisfied. In the four cases completed, q was taken as 0.50, 0.55, 0.60, and 0.75, respectively (corresponding to Q_a of 0, 0.025, 0.05, and 0.125 for the asymmetric case). The results are shown in Table 1. The probabilities should be good to five places, although there is a possibility of a slight error in the fifth place.

These results seem striking enough so that they can really speak for themselves. It appears that if q can be kept sufficiently close to 0.5 (or Q_a, in the asymmetric model, kept small enough) then the probability of correctly identifying a well-learned binary characteristic in retrospect, after having seen and recorded 10^{11} different stimuli, is about 0.994, for a network of 10^9 C-units and an equal number of A-units. This result, in itself, was sufficiently unexpected so that the writer was obliged to reconsider entirely his previous assessment of the Penfield hypothesis of complete storage of experience, and related hypotheses proposed by other investigators. Such a level of performance would permit an individual to record fifteen independent events per second (about the flicker-fusion rate) for over two centuries before the probability of correct binary identification fell below 0.99.

Table 1. Values of $P(R_x)$ for Symmetric Model

$$MN_c = 1,000, E(u_x)/\sigma(u_x) = \infty, Q_c = 0$$

Case 1: q = 0.50

$N_a,$ N_c	\multicolumn{9}{c}{t = length of stored sequence}								
	10^3	10^4	10^5	10^6	10^7	10^8	10^9	10^{10}	10^{11}
10^3	1.0	1.0	0.99425	0.78755	0.59960	0.53179	0.51006	0.50318	0.50101
10^4	1.0	1.0	1.0	0.99419	0.78753	0.59959	0.53180	0.51006	0.50318
10^5	1.0	1.0	1.0	1.0	0.99418	0.78751	0.59960	0.53180	0.51007
10^6	1.0	1.0	1.0	1.0	1.0	0.99418	0.78754	0.59961	0.53181
10^7	1.0	1.0	1.0	1.0	1.0	1.0	0.99418	0.78754	0.59964
10^8	1.0	1.0	1.0	1.0	1.0	1.0	1.0	0.99419	0.78762
10^9	1.0	1.0	1.0	1.0	1.0	1.0	1.0	1.0	0.99420

Case 2: q = 0.55

$N_a,$ N_c	\multicolumn{9}{c}{$t=$ length of stored sequence}
	10^3	10^4	10^5	10^6	10^7	10^8	10^9	10^{10}	10^{11}
10^3	0.99915	0.83962	0.62322	0.53953	0.51252	0.50395	0.50124	0.50039	0.50012
10^4	1.0	0.99915	0.83947	0.62315	0.53949	0.51251	0.50396	0.50125	0.50038
10^5	1.0	1.0	0.99915	0.83944	0.62315	0.53951	0.51251	0.50395	0.50125
10^6	1.0	1.0	1.0	0.99915	0.83946	0.62314	0.53952	0.51251	0.50396
10^7	1.0	1.0	1.0	1.0	0.99915	0.83944	0.62316	0.53952	0.51251
10^8	1.0	1.0	1.0	1.0	1.0	0.99915	0.83947	0.62316	0.53953
10^9	1.0	1.0	1.0	1.0	1.0	1.0	0.99915	0.83946	0.62319

Case 3: q = 0.60

$N_a,$ N_c	\multicolumn{9}{c}{$t=$ length of stored sequence}
	10^3	10^4	10^5	10^6	10^7	10^8	10^9	10^{10}	10^{11}
10^3	0.98664	0.75956	0.58794	0.52778	0.50863	0.50272	0.50086	0.50027	0.50008
10^4	1.0	0.98703	0.75941	0.58801	0.52792	0.50876	0.50275	0.50086	0.50026
10^5	1.0	1.0	0.98703	0.75937	0.58802	0.52792	0.50877	0.50275	0.50086
10^6	1.0	1.0	1.0	0.98702	0.75939	0.58801	0.52793	0.50877	0.50275
10^7	1.0	1.0	1.0	1.0	0.98703	0.75937	0.58802	0.52793	0.50877
10^8	1.0	1.0	1.0	1.0	1.0	0.98702	0.75940	0.58802	0.52794
10^9	1.0	1.0	1.0	1.0	1.0	1.0	0.98703	0.75939	0.58805

Case 4: q = 0.75

$N_a,$ N_c	\multicolumn{9}{c}{$t=$ length of stored sequence}
	10^3	10^4	10^5	10^6	10^7	10^8	10^9	10^{10}	10^{11}
10^3	0.89240	0.66569	0.55871	0.51302	0.50336	0.50039	0.50000	0.50000	0.50000
10^4	0.99999	0.92084	0.67066	0.55802	0.51590	0.50481	0.50151	0.50048	0.50015
10^5	1.0	0.99999	0.92085	0.67075	0.55789	0.51602	0.40486	0.50153	0.50048
10^6	1.0	1.0	0.99999	0.92084	0.67077	0.55787	0.51603	0.50487	0.50153
10^7	1.0	1.0	1.0	0.99999	0.92085	0.67076	0.55788	0.51603	0.50487
10^8	1.0	1.0	1.0	1.0	0.99999	0.92084	0.67078	0.55788	0.51604
10^9	1.0	1.0	1.0	1.0	1.0	0.99999	0.92086	0.67077	0.55790

These probabilities are obviously attenuated considerably for more realistic values of q (or q_a). Nevertheless, the probabilities shown for Case 2, where the parameters should be readily achievable, are still most impressive.

Note that as N_a, N_c, and t all get large simultaneously, $P(R_x)$ approaches a constant for a given ratio of t/N_a. This means that in a large system, to maintain a fixed level of performance, it is necessary to add a fixed number of connections for each new stimulus which the memory must accommodate. This result can also be seen from an examination of the equations in the last section. For example, if a probability of 0.999 is required, with $q = 0.55$ (or $q_a = 0.025$), then one additional C-unit with 1,000 connections must be added to the network for each additional stimulus.

Such probabilities as 0.999, however, are probably too high to expect of a biological system. A complex memory is rarely defined by a single binary characteristic, occurring over a $\frac{1}{15}$-sec period. Redundant information is almost always present, as well as the possibility of many successive "looks" at the same event, so that a relatively low probability, say about 0.6, would probably be sufficient to match human performance. Under these conditions, more than 10 new stimuli could be stored for each additional C-unit.

SELECTIVE RECALL AND PROGRAM-LEARNING PERCEPTRONS

In the memory model as it stands up to this point, the recall of a sequence occurs as a result of setting the system back to its initial state and cutting off all sensory inputs. It was suggested that the resetting might be accomplished by training the perceptron to activate an R-unit which, by virtue of strong connections to the C-system, could override its present activity state and force it into some particular starting state. Actually there might be a considerable number of such R-units, each setting up a different, independent, initial state, so that any one of a number of named sequences might be evoked on command. Thus, if the response R_h was associated to the word "Hamlet," and this was followed by a recitation of *Hamlet*, the repetition of the name "Hamlet" would tend, thereafter, to cause the perceptron to review the subsequent recitation. On the other hand, the word "Faust," associated to a different R-unit R_f, could evoke a sequence in which the dialogue of *Faust* was recorded.

Such a method of recall, while entertaining to contemplate, has several features which make it decidedly unrealistic. Perhaps the most important of these is illustrated by the fact that the word "Hamlet" occurs repeatedly within the text of the play; nonetheless no actor, having memorized the text of *Hamlet*, is likely to be "reset" to the beginning of the play whenever

Hamlet's name is mentioned. This could, it is true, be ameliorated by making the response R_h contingent upon a more complex command, such as the sentence "Begin reciting *Hamlet* from the start of Act I," but this still seems to be a contrived solution.

A second difficulty comes from the fact that recall may be triggered by many events other than a specific command or response which initiated the recalled sequence. The phenomena of free association are too well known to require elaboration here, and an acceptable model should be able to account for them.

A model which seems likely to be able to deal with both of these difficulties in a convincing way is illustrated in Fig. 4. This contains all of the component parts of the perceptron shown in Fig. 2, with several additions. The "set control network" is a set of units which may be triggered by adaptive connections from the A-units, provided their threshold is low enough to allow them to respond. Their threshold is itself under the control of one of the R-units, which can thus make it easy or difficult to set up a new state in the set-control network. The set-control units themselves are assumed to be long-persisting "On" units, possibly of the same type as are found in the C-system. When any of these set-control units becomes active, a strong "on" burst is transmitted to the C-system (possibly relayed by means of an intervening layer of short-persistence on-units, so that a continued bombardment of the C-system does not occur, even though the set-control network continues to hold its state). This burst of impulses arriving at the C-system will tend to force at least some of the C-units to a particular initial state determined by the transmitting set.

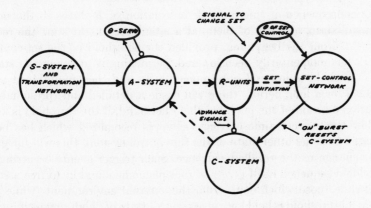

Figure 4

To be explicit, assume that the set-control network is initially silent, with none of its units active. Meanwhile, the R-system assumes some state, corresponding to whatever event is taking place in the perceptron's sensory system or association system. At some point, a state of the association system occurs which signals an important event, or the start of a new situation, which might call for an appropriate memory consultation. Such situations, either due to intrinsic or learned connections, are assumed to activate the R-unit which lowers the threshold of the set-control network (e.g., by delivering an on-burst of excitatory impulses to all of its neurons). As soon as this takes place, the set-control network is forced to assume some state which depends on the particular set of R-units currently active, and which have acquired the strongest connections to it. Let us say this occurs in the auditorium of a theater, at the start of the play *Hamlet*. Then the combination of R-units which serve to identify this situation will determine the state of the set-control network, which, in turn, forces the C-system to assume a corresponding initial state. The subsequent events are then recorded in the C-to-A network just as before, as long as the set-control network does not change its state. But, since the activity of the active set-control neurons is assumed to persist during this time, even though their threshold has been restored to its normally high level, the following succession of R-unit states is presumed to become associated to the presently active set-control state, by precisely the same sort of memory mechanism which causes the C-unit states to form strong connections to active A-unit states. Thus a large number of alternative responses occurring during the play (such as the names "Polonius," "Denmark," etc.) become associated to the same set-control state.

As a consequence of this multiple association of R-states to the same set-control state, any one of them, at a later time, might start the recall of *Hamlet*, from the beginning, provided the threshold of the set-control network has momentarily been lowered, permitting it to change its state. If the threshold is lowered only momentarily and then maintained at a high level for a long period, there will ensue a detailed and (presumably) accurate repetition of the play. On the other hand, if the threshold is kept at a low level, every time a trigger-event is recognized which has been associated to some other state of the set-control system, this will force an abrupt change in the recalled sequence. Such trigger events occurring in the recalled sequence itself give rise to a phenomenon akin to free association, while those which come from the external environment (while the set-control threshold is held low) give rise to a state of "high suggestibility," or "distractability."

All of this is, of course, quite speculative and unproven at the present time, but it seems likely that a model akin to that outlined here will prove to have the necessary flexibility of associative control to permit either exact recall of a sequence or free-associative recall. It seems likely, in fact, that the learning which must take place in order to repeat a long and complicated sequence correctly has little to do with the recording of experience in the C-to-A network itself, but is rather an indication of the difficulty of learning to set up and maintain the necessary set-control states without interference or distraction. This may be part of the answer to points (7) and (8) in the list which was given in the introduction.

It is rather easy to elaborate, in this heuristic manner, on possible sophistications of the basic memory model. We will indulge in only one other such speculation, however, which seems to hold promise of particularly interesting performances in the future. This is the possibility of employing one or more C-systems for the recording of experience, in the above manner, while simultaneously employing another C-system (or systems) to go through a control program, or sequence of instructions. Such a system is shown in Fig. 5.

It has been known for some time that a bias may be introduced into the association system of a perceptron by feedback from an R-unit, which leads to conditional responses to incoming stimuli (cf. Ref. 44, Chaps. 21 and 22). In the system of Fig. 5, the same principle is employed, except that instead of being determined by feedback from a currently active R-unit, the bias-condition of the association system is determined by the state of the $C^{(1)}$ network. The asynchronous operation of the C-networks

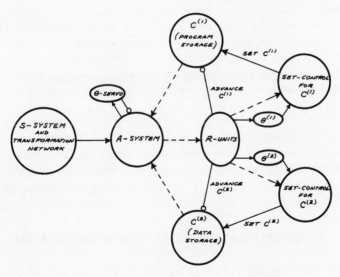

Figure 5

makes it possible to advance either $C^{(1)}$ or $C^{(2)}$ independently of the other. Thus with the control network in one state, a whole sequence of remembered events might be fed out of $C^{(2)}$ until an event is remembered which the $C^{(1)}$ state is concerned with. For example, with $C^{(1)}$ in one "command state," the perceptron might be required to review the first act of *Hamlet* and signal (on a particular R-unit) for each occurrence of the word "king," while with $C^{(1)}$ in a different state, the perceptron might go through the identical memory-sequence, but this time count the references to soldiers, or indicate every entrance and exit of a character. Such program "instructions" can be recorded in precisely the same way that experiential events are recorded, namely, by forcing the association system to the desired bias state (by means of an external stimulus) and recording this state of the A-system in the $C^{(1)}$ memory. For this purpose, it is convenient to be able to "turn on" or "turn off" the memory-recording process, both for $C^{(1)}$ and for $C^{(2)}$, so that only the desired states will be recorded. This memory control might be carried out by additional R-units, with the special function of turning on or turning off the recording process. Thus, a whole sequence of bias states could be "read in" to the association system and stored in $C^{(1)}$, constituting a sequential program which could later be used to modify the perceptron's responses to data or events stored in $C^{(2)}$.

Without further quantitative work, it seems wasteful to speculate at greater length about these possibilities. Nonetheless, it may be worth mentioning that the writer has succeeded in "programming" such a perceptron (on paper) to perform such tasks as forming the logical product of two stored strings of binary digits, and learning an algorithm for counting in binary, which has long been a stumbling block for earlier perceptron models. Perceptual as well as logical operations can be programmed; for example, a perceptron with a movable visual system, or a tactile feeler which it can watch as it moves, can be taught to trace the outline of an object or pattern to determine whether or not it is a closed curve, or it can be taught to search for a particular object in the environment. It seems likely that the most interesting applications of such systems will be in the processing of speech and language, since many of the operations and heuristic methods which were previously applicable only in stored-program digital computers now seem to be almost within reach of our neural networks.

A POSSIBLE BIOCHEMICAL TRACE MECHANISM

In all of the foregoing it has been assumed that the modification of neural connection weights according to a γ-system equation is a tenable postulate. The choice of this particular form of "reinforcement rule" having now been supported, in part, by showing that it leads to psychological behavior of a rather anthropomorphic form, in networks with simple organizational principles, it remains to be seen whether such a choice appears plausible at the neurophysiological level.

During the past year the beginnings of a biochemical model for a gamma-system mechanism, using ordinary enzymological types of reactions, have been constructed. Most of this work will be discussed in more detail in subsequent publications, but a brief outline is presented here in order to indicate the direction of our thinking on the subject.

Since all of our proposed memory mechanisms (alpha system as well as gamma system) involve a change in "synaptic weights," let us begin by reviewing briefly what is known about the mechanism of synaptic excitation and inhibition. The reader who is unacquainted with this subject can find most of the necessary background material in Eccles,[11,12] while selected papers in the collections edited by Florey[18] and Elliott, Page, and Quastel[15] are likely to be helpful in providing missing details.

In a resting neuron, the concentration of potassium is much greater inside the cell than outside, while the concentration of sodium and chloride is much greater outside than inside. These concentration differences, which are maintained by metabolic mechanisms which are only partially understood, result in a Donnan equilibrium across the cell membrane, whereby the outside is normally about 70 to 100 millivolts positive relative to the inside. An excitatory impulse acts by partially depolarizing the cell membrane in the neighborhood of the cell body. If the membrane is sufficiently depolarized, a self-propagating spike impulse is initiated. On the other hand, if the membrane is hyperpolarized the threshold of the cell is effectively raised and excitatory impulses are less effective. It is now generally accepted that excitatory effects at the synapse are mediated by an *excitatory transmitter substance*, such as acetylcholine, which is released by the presynaptic terminal (endbulb) and which binds to a *receptor protein* in the postsynaptic membrane. This induces a change in membrane structure which appears to greatly increase the local permeability of the membrane to all species of ions, thereby causing an electrical "short circuit" which tends to depolarize the cell membrane and initiate a spike discharge. Inhibitory action at synapses is usually assumed to be mediated by an *inhibitory transmitter substance*. It seems increasingly likely that GABA is such an inhibitory transmitter,[36] although there is also accumulating evidence for the belief that some transmitters, such as ACH, may sometimes act as excitatory transmitters and at other times as inhibitory transmitters, depending on the nature of the subsynaptic membrane.[60] In any event, when an inhibitory impulse arrives at a cell, it is established that the membrane becomes hyperpolarized due to a selective increase in the permeability of the membrane to chloride and to potassium, but not to sodium. Recent evidence by Araki, Ito, and Oscarsson,[1] and by Ito, Kostyuk, and Oshima[29] strongly bears out the hypothesis that the inhibitory transmitter substance acts by causing small pores to open in the postsynaptic membrane, large enough to admit the small hydrated potassium and chloride ions, but too small to admit the larger hydrated sodium ions. For an excitatory impulse, on the other hand, it is believed that larger pores are opened which freely admit all of the ions in question. It is readily demonstrated that such a mechanism would, in fact, account for the main empirical facts of both excitatory and inhibitory transmission.

This pore hypothesis, it must be emphasized, is specific to *synaptic* transmission. Outside the region of the synapse, it is likely that rather different mechanisms control the permeability of the membrane, such as those suggested by Shanes.[52,53] These other mechanisms (which cause an increase in permeability of the depolarized membrane) are responsible for the propagation of the nerve impulse over the membrane.

We shall accept the membrane-pore hypothesis as the starting point for developing a hypothetical memory-trace mechanism. Clearly any change which permanently blocks one of the small inhibitory pores at a synapse, or which removes a previous block from a potential excitatory pore, or which widens an inhibitory pore (making it into an excitatory pore) will tend to increase the excitatory effect (or, what is often equivalent, reduce the inhibitory effect) of a synapse.

Because the asymmetric model of the proposed memory mechanism seems to operate under much more plausible biological conditions than the symmetric model (and also because the symmetric model is much more difficult to find a convincing mechanism for) we shall concentrate on defining a possible mode of operation of the asymmetric γ-system. This system requires that the following basic conditions be satisfied:

1. No reinforcement shall occur unless the post-synaptic neuron is active.
2. Assuming the post-synaptic cell is active, then an increment should accrue to the excitatory weight of each active synapse, but not at inactive synapses.
3. The sum of the synaptic weights of all connections to a given neuron must remain constant; if one synapse gains in excitatory weight, at least one other must lose a compensating amount.

Two basic mechanisms have been considered by which these conditions might be realized:

A. Active inhibitory pores to the active cell might be plugged or the active sites of the inhibitory transmitter at these pores might be blocked.

At the same time, an equal number of previously blocked inhibitory pores elsewhere in the same cell would have to be released, to satisfy condition (3).

B. Active excitatory pores in the active cell might be unblocked, or facilitated. At the same time, an equal number of previously "clear" excitatory pores elsewhere in the same cell would have to be blocked.

From the three basic conditions (stated above) which must be satisfied for the γ-system, it is possible to make some inferences about the trace mechanism:

1. The condition that the postsynaptic neuron must be active for a memory change to occur implies either

   (a) A critical chemical component or catalyst for the recording process mu stpass through the active cell membrane (during its period of heightened permeability), or else

   (b) A critical component or catalyst must be manufactured or released by the postsynaptic cell as part of the metabolic activity which follows excitation.

2. The limitation of the weight-gain to *active* synapses suggests that the mechanism of synaptic action must either unmask or create an active site for the trace mechanism to operate.

3. The conservation rule for the γ-system requires that the trace must be maintained by a substance or structure capable of metabolic normalization for the cell as a whole.

An additional condition, not directly imposed by the γ-system rules, is that the trace mechanism should be subject to disruption by the conditions which are conducive to amnesia, and should be capable of recovery in a manner consistent with empirical data.

Of the various models which have been considered which appear to satisfy these conditions, the following seems to be among the most plausible:

The memory trace depends upon four kinds of molecules which bind successively to the postsynaptic membrane. These are a *transmitter substance*, a *marker substance*, a *recorder substance*, and a *stabilizer substance*. The relationship of these molecules to one another and to the membrane structures is illustrated in a highly schematic form in Fig. 6. The diagram shows (obviously not to scale) a single inhibitory pore in a patch of sub-synaptic membrane. Related diagrams can be constructed for excitatory pore mechanisms. Normally, of course, we would expect a great number of such pores to exist at every synaptic junction, so that a change in a single pore, as shown here, constitutes only a slight quantized increment to the weight of a synapse. This figure, which makes use of inhibitory pore blocking as the memory effect, corresponds to one form of mechanism (A) above. There are at least two possible synaptic arrangements under which this mechanism might be used:

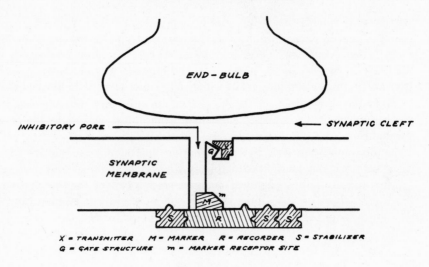

X = TRANSMITTER   M = MARKER   R = RECORDER   S = STABILIZER
Q = GATE STRUCTURE   m = MARKER RECEPTOR SITE

Figure 6

1. The input connections (from the C-network) may include both specific excitatory connections and specific inhibitory connections. Reducing the inhibitory signal component from a given C-state to a particular A-unit would be equivalent to increasing the excitatory signal component, as prescribed in the γ-system equation [Eq. (1)].
2. The connections from the C-units to the A-units may be undifferentiated, releasing a single transmitter substance which acts indiscriminately to open both excitatory and inhibitory pores. If a mixture of both types of pores exists at each synapse, then the synapse will be excitatory in effect if the excitatory pores outnumber the inhibitory pores, and it will be inhibitory if the inhibitory pores outnumber the excitatory pores to a sufficient degree. Thus, by blocking inhibitory pores or removing the blocks from them, a single synapse of this type can be transformed from an inhibitory to an excitatory synapse, or vice versa.

The origin, function, and important properties of each of the four postulated substances can now be described.

1. *Transmitter substance.* Released by the presynaptic endbulb. The transmitter has the function of opening the synaptic pore, and thus unmasking an active site for the marker substance, which must enter from outside the cell. Its reaction time is very fast, and it is quickly hydrolyzed by an antitransmitter substance, which restores the pore to its resting condition. In the diagram it is suggested that the transmitter opens the pore by a steric interaction with the receptor protein which causes a change

in the tertiary structure of the pore, causing a "gate" (G) to be displaced from the pore opening. Such a mechanism has also been suggested by Eccles,[14] but the reader should not be misled by the diagrammatic representation into thinking that gross physical deformation is the only possible blocking and unblocking mechanism; changes in the electrical distribution around the pore, possibly by means of charge transfer complexes (cf. Szent-Györgyi[56]) are in many ways a more attractive possibility.

2. *Marker substance.* Extracellular in origin, possibly released by glial cells. Enters open pores and occupies a receptor site (m in the diagram) near the intracellular end of the pore. Its required reaction rate is fast, requiring a high concentration in the neighborhood of the synapse. It must probably be removed by an *antimarker substance* within several seconds (or by a spontaneous decay process) to prevent it from saturating all available pores, and to prevent it from acting as a functional mimetic of the recorder substance, which would prevent the proper metabolic control of the γ-system normalization. The functions of the marker are: (*a*) to bridge the time gap between the fast transmitter substance reaction and the much slower recorder substance reactions; (*b*) to satisfy condition (2), above, since, by virtue of its mode of entry, it limits the subsequent process to active synapses; (*c*) to create an active site for the recorder molecule on the intracellular membrane; (*d*) although not essential, the marker itself may block the pore prior to the arrival of the recorder molecule, thus forming a temporary memory trace, with a duration of several seconds.

3. *Recorder substance.* Intracellular in origin, with the total concentration in the cell held constant under metabolic control. Free concentration is very low. It is possible to control the concentration of bound recorder by means of a production inhibitor, which is formed on the bound R molecule as a template, and tends to prevent the formation of more recorder substance by the cell. An equilibrium will be established, with the inhibitor acting as a negative feedback mechanism, tending to hold the number of bound recorder molecules (and thus the number of altered synaptic pores) constant for the entire cell. The bound recorder is assumed to be fairly stable (with a time constant of many minutes or hours) in a resting cell, but is dissociated from the membrane relatively easily during or after activity. This might be a direct consequence of the membrane changes during activity, or might be due to the production or admission through the active membrane of an *antirecorder substance*. As soon as recorder is thus removed from some of its occupied sites, during or following a period of activity, the metabolic control mechanism will tend to increase its recorder production, and the new molecules will bind to whatever sites are available, until the number of molecules bound is restored to its normal level. But only those sites marked by a marker molecule (or possibly an

unoccupied bed of stabilizer molecules) are able to bind the recorder. Consequently, the net effect of the transaction will be a shift of recorder from previously occupied synapses (each of which will lose a few molecules) to newly marked sites at the recently active synapses. Thus the functions of the recorder are (a) to maintain the memory trace, either by direct modification of the pore structure, or by protecting the previously bound marker substance from the action of anti-marker, or by interacting with the transmitter substance receptor protein, thus blocking a transmitter site; (b) to satisfy condition (1), since the redistribution can occur only after a period of activity which causes accelerated dissociation of marker from previously occupied sites; (c) to satisfy condition (3), by means of the metabolic conservation mechanism.

4. *Stabilizer substance.* Intracellular in origin. This is assumed to be a large molecule (possibly a protein) which binds to the combination of active sites provided by a recorder molecule and the synaptic membrane, or else by another stabilizer molecule and the synaptic membrane. Thus, at any occupied pore, a "bed" of stabilizer molecules will be built up, which tends to pyramid until all available sites are occupied. As a consequence of this pyramiding effect (particularly if there are more than two active sites on each recorder or stabilizer molecule) old sites, which already have a stabilizer bed established, will tend to preempt the available supply of stabilizer in preference to new sites. This would lead to a heightened stability of the earliest memory traces, and ultimately to an inability to stabilize new traces (as in senility). The free concentration of stabilizer is assumed to be at a very low level, and its reaction rate is very slow. Its functions are to protect the recorder molecules from dissociation, and to provide a "bed" in the neighborhood of the occupied pore, so that if a recorder molecule is dissociated (say as a result of convulsive activity in the nervous system), the prepared bed is more likely to recapture free recorder molecules in the future, thus permitting a gradual recovery from amnesia effects. Note that since the best prepared beds will be the oldest ones, recovery from amnesia should occur in the original temporal order, without regard to the importance of the remembered events, which checks well with the empirical data.

While obviously lacking in any sort of direct experimental confirmation at this time, we see that the above theory does, in fact, satisfy the conditions which were originally required for the asymmetric γ-system, without postulating any radical innovations in biochemistry. It is gratifying to find that such additional phenomena as the amnesia effects and stability of early memory follow directly from this model, even though they were not present in the purely logical form of the γ-system, discussed in the preceding sections. It is also tempting to consider the possibility that the hippocampus may play a role as a source of one of the extracellular components in this process, such as the marker substance, or a catalyst required for the fabrication of new marker substance. If this were the case, then the removal of the hippocampus would lead to precisely the effects observed by Milner and Penfield, which were cited in Item 22 of the list in the Introduction.

Psychogenic amnesias would, of course, involve a different mechanism, presumably an inability to reestablish the cognitive set which initializes the appropriate memory sequence in the system shown in Fig. 4. If such a set could be reestablished (which might occur by free association with any of the responses which were formerly associated to it, even if the normal trigger response had been suppressed) then recovery of the "missing memories" would be immediate and complete, unlike recovery from the physiological amnesias resulting from seizures or convulsions in the above model. The similarity of this effect to actual psychoanalytic observations is most striking.

Some of the Penfield observations on memory sequences induced by temporal lobe stimulation may also find an explanation in terms of Fig. 4. If the temporal-lobe stimulation activates a previous state of the set-control mechanism (which will be likely to occur if the states of the set-control system are mutually exclusive, so that the probability of inducing a meaningless mixture of states is reduced) then as long as the electrical stimulus is maintained, the C-system will be forced to recapitulate the corresponding stored sequence, without any possibility of being diverted by free association or changes in the cognitive set. Such an explanation is clearly tenuous at this point, but it serves to support the conclusion that most of the phenomena listed in the introduction, even if they are not clearly predicted by the present model, are at least not inconsistent with it.

Some of these remaining points will be considered in more detail in later reports. It is particularly important to examine the proposed biochemical mechanism from a mathematical point of view, to see the exact form of the γ-system equation which results (since this is complicated by such previously disregarded variables as decay rates, stability of old traces, etc.), and to try to obtain a more exact description of the biochemical reactions and molecular characteristics which this implies. At the same time, an empirical program has now been initiated at Cornell University to study transmitter substances and the mechanism of their action. This program, together with the work being done at many other such laboratories throughout the world, may eventually come up with evidence which will be sufficient to confirm or refute the hypotheses proposed here.

REFERENCES

1. Araki, T., M. Ito, and O. Oscarsson, "Anion Permeability of the Synaptic and Non-synaptic Motoneurone Membrane," *J. Physiol.*, 159, 1961, pp. 410–435.
2. Bartlett, F., *Remembering*, Cambridge U. P., 1954.
3. Beurle, R. L., "Properties of a Mass of Cells Capable of Regenerating Pulses," *Phil. Trans. Royal Soc. London*, B240, No. 669, 55.
4. Block, H. D., "The Perceptron: A Model for Brain Function," *Rev. Mod. Phys.*, 34, 1962, pp. 123–135.
5. Block, H. D., B. W. Knight, and F. Rosenblatt, "Analysis of a Four-Layer, Series-Coupled Perceptron," *Rev. Mod. Phys.*, 34, 1962, pp. 135–142.
6. Briggs, M. H., and G. B. Kitto, "The Molecular Basis of Memory and Learning," *Psych. Rev.* 69, 1962, pp. 537–541.
7. Brown, J., "Information, Redundancy, and Decay of the Memory Trace," in *Proceedings of Symposium on the Mechanization of Thought Processes*, H. M. Stationery Office, London, 1958.
8. Burns, B. D., *The Mammalian Cerebral Cortex*, Arnold, London, 1958.
9. Culbertson, J. T., *Consciousness and Behavior*, Brown, Dubuque, Iowa, 1950.
10. Curnow, R. N., and C. W. Dunnett, "The Numerical Evaluation of Certain Multivariate Normal Integrals," *Annals of Math. Stat.* 33, 1962, pp. 571–579.
11. Eccles, J. C., *The Neurophysiological Basis of Mind*, Clarendon, Oxford, 1953.
12. Eccles, J. C., *The Physiology of Nerve Cells*, Johns Hopkins, Baltimore, 1957.
13. Eccles, J. C., "The Effects of Use and Disuse on Synaptic Function.," in Fessard, Gerard, and Konorski (eds.), *Brain Mechanisms and Learning*, Blackwell, Oxford, 1961.
14. Eccles, J. C., "The Synaptic Mechanism for Postsynaptic Inhibition," in Florey (ed.), *Nervous Inhibition*, Pergamon, New York, 1961.
15. Elliott, K. A. C., I. H. Page, and J. H. Quastel, *Neurochemistry*, Thomas, Springfield, Ill., 1962.
16. Farley, B., and W. Clark, "Activity in Networks of Neuron-like Elements," in Cherry (ed.), *Information Theory*, Butterworths, Washington, 1961.
17. Fessard, A., R. W. Gerard, and J. Konorski, *Brain Mechanisms and Learning*, Blackwell, Oxford, 1961.
18. Florey, E., *Nervous Inhibition*, Pergamon, New York, 1961.
19. Florey, E., "Excitation, Inhibition, and the Concept of the Stimulus," in Florey (ed.), *Nervous Inhibition*, Pergamon, New York, 1961.
20. Gaito, J., "A Biochemical Approach to Learning and Memory", *Psych. Rev.*, 68, 1961, pp. 288–292.
21. Gerard, R. W., "What is Memory?" *Sci. Am.*, 189, 1953, pp. 118–126.
22. Gerard, R. W., "The Fixation of Experience," in Fessard, Gerard, and Konorski (eds.), *Brain Mechanisms and Learning*, Blackwell, Oxford, 1961.
23. Gerard, R. W., T. J. Chamberlain, and G. H. Rothschild, "RNA in Learning and Memory," *Science*, 140, 1963, p. 381.
24. Hebb, D. O., *The Organization of Behavior*, Wiley, New York, 1949.
25. Hebb, D. O., "Distinctive Features of Learning in the Higher Animal," in Fessard, Gerard, and Konorski (eds.), *Brain Mechanisms and Learning*, Blackwell, Oxford, 1961.
26. Hebb, D. O., "The Semi-autonomous Process: Its Nature and Nurture," *Amer. Psychol.* 18, 1963, pp. 16–27.

27. Hubel, D. H., and T. N. Wiesel, "Receptive Fields, Binocular Interaction, and Functional Architecture in the Cat's Visual Cortex," *J. Physiol.*, 160, 1962, pp. 106–154.

28. Hydén, H., "A Molecular Basis of Neuron-Glia Interaction," in Schmidt, F. O. *Macromolecular Specificity and Biological Memory*, MIT Press, Cambridge, Mass., 1962.

29. Ito, M., P. G. Kostyuk, and T. Oshima, "Further Study on Anion Permeability of Inhibitory Post-synaptic Membrane of Cat Motoneurones," *J. Physiol.*, 164, 1962, pp. 150–156.

30. Jacobsen, A. L., "Learning in Flatworms and Annelids," *Psych. Bull.* 60, 1963, pp. 74–94.

31. John, E. R. "Some Speculations on the Psychophysiology of the Mind," in J. Scher, (ed.), *Theories of the Mind*, Free Press, New York, 1962.

32. Joseph, R. D., "On Predicting Perceptron Performance," *Record of IRE National Convention*, Part 2, New York, 1960.

33. Jung, R., "Neuronal Integration in the Visual Cortex," in Rosenblith (ed.), *Sensory Communication*, MIT Press, Cambridge, Mass, 1961.

34. Konorski, J., "The Physiological Approach to the Problem of Recent Memory," in Fessard, Gerard, and Konorski (eds.), *Brain Mechanisms and Learning*, Blackwell, Oxford, 1961.

35. Lashley, K. S., "In Search of the Engram," in Beach, Hebb, Morgan, and Nissen (eds.), *The Neuropsychology of Lashley*, McGraw-Hill, New York, 1960.

36. McLennan, H., "Inhibitory Transmitters—A Review," in Florey (ed.), *Nervous Inhibition*, Pergamon, N.Y., 1961.

37. Miller, G. A., "The Magical Number Seven, Plus or Minus Two: Some Limits on Our Capacity for Processing Information," *Psych. Rev.* 63, 1956, pp. 81–97.

38. Milner, B., and W. Penfield, "The Effect of Hippocampal Lesions on Recent Memory," *Trans. Am. Neurol. Assn.*, 1955, pp. 42–48.

39. Milner, P. M., "A Neural Mechanism for the Immediate Recall of Sequences," *Kybernetik*, No. 1, Berlin, July, 1961.

40. Morrell, F., "Electrophysiological Contributions to the Neural Basis of Learning," *Physiol. Rev.*, 41, 1961, pp. 443–494.

41. Morrell, F., "Information Storage in Nerve Cells," in Fields and Abbott (eds.), *Information Storage and Neural Control*, Thomas, Springfield, 1963.

42. Penfield, W., and T. Rasmussen, *The Cerebral Cortex of Man*, Macmillan, New York, 1950.

43. Penfield, W., and L. Roberts, *Speech and Brain Mechanisms*, Princeton U. P., Princeton, N.J., 1959.

44. Rosenblatt, F., *Principles of Neurodynamics: Perceptrons and the Theory of Brain Mechanisms*, Spartan, Washington, 1962.

45. Rosenblatt, F., "A Comparison of Several Perceptron Models," in Yovits, Jacobi, and Goldstein (eds.), *Self-Organizing Systems-1962*, Spartan, Washington, 1962.

46. Rosenblatt, F., *A Theory of Biological Memory* (Cognitive Systems Research Program Report, Cornell University; in preparation.)

47. Roy, A., "On a Method of Storing Information," *Bull. Math. Biophysics*, 22, 1960, pp. 139–168.

48. Sandel, T. T., and N. Y. S. Kiang, "Off Responses from the Auditory Cortex of Anesthetized Cats: Effects of Stimulus Parameters," *Arch. Ital. de Biol.*, 99, 1961 pp. 105–120.

49. Schaefer, E., "Das Menschliche Gedächtnis als Informationsspeicher," *Elektronische Rundschau*, Telefunken, vol. 14, no. 3, 1959, pp. 79–84.
50. Schmidt, F. O., *Macromolecular Specificity and Biological Memory*, MIT Press, Cambridge, Mass., 1962.
51. Scoville, W. B., and B. Milner, "Loss of Recent Memory After Bilateral Hippocampal Lesions," *J. Neurol. Neurosurg. Psychiat.*, 20, 1957, pp. 11–20.
52. Shanes, A. M., "Quantitative Molecular Approach to the Permeability Changes of Excitation," *Science*, 140, 1963, pp. 51–53.
53. Shanes, A. M., "Membrane Permeability: Monolayer Relationships," *Science*, 140, 1963, pp. 824–825.
54. Shannon, C. E., and W. Weaver, *The Mathematical Theory of Communication*, Univ. of Illinois Press; Urbana, 1959.
55. Smith, C. E., "Is Memory a Matter of Enzyme Induction?" *Science*, 138, 1962, pp. 889–890.
56. Szent-Györgyi, A., *Introduction to a Sub-Molecular Biology*, Academic, New York, 1960.
57. Von Foerster, H., *Das Gedächtnis: Eine Quantenmechanische Untersuchung*, F. Deuticke, Vienna, 1948.
58. Wechsler, D., "Engrams, Memory Storage, and Mnemonic Coding," *Amer. Psychol.* 18, 1963, pp. 149–153.
59. Widrow, B., "Generalization and Information Storage in Networks of Adaline 'Neurons.' In Yovits, Jacobi, and Goldstein (eds.), *Self-Organizing Systems—1962*, Spartan, Washington, 1962.
60. Wiersma, C. A. G., "Inhibitory Neurons: A survey of the History of their Discovery and of their Occurrence," in Florey (ed.), *Nervous Inhibition*, Pergamon, New York, 1961.

SOME FUNDAMENTAL THEOREMS
OF PERCEPTRON THEORY
AND THEIR GEOMETRY*

A. CHARNES

Director, Systems Research Group
Professor of Mathematics, Economics, Engineering Sciences,
Northwestern University

INTRODUCTION

The concept of the perceptron, due to F. Rosenblatt,[1] and various of its attributes, developments and literature are reviewed in a particularly cogent manner in the paper[2] by his co-worker, H. D. Block. A still more recent coverage of literature is to be found in the 1962 Proceedings of the ONR Symposium on Self-Organizing Systems. Although the fundamental theorems on the convergence of learning procedures for a simple perceptron are developed in[2] in a highly ingenious manner (a distillation of a succession of proofs by Rosenblatt, Joseph, Kesten, and Block), it is not clear from their "hard analysis" what lies behind this convergence, in any intuitive manner, and thereby what general classes of procedures may be expected to converge or diverge, or when indeed any "learning" can make the differentiations required.

For instance, it should be expressly noted that the perceptron convergence theorems are *false* if more general cases of a system of linear inequalities are considered. The iterative procedures involved are particular types of relaxation or cyclic projection methods which one knows[3] converge

* Research underlying this paper was partly undertaken for the project *Temporal Planning and Management Decision under Risk and Uncertainty* at Northwestern University, under contract with the U.S. Office of Naval Research, contract Nonr-1228(10), project NR 047-021.

then at best in an infinite number of steps and are also subject to well-known difficulties of numerical entrapment, etc. Further, since more elaborate perceptrons[4] involve more elaborate (and less complete) hard analytic arguments, what kinds of extensions are likely to work and how these may be characterized is not at all evident, or intuitive, mathematically.

The results which follow were developed shortly after a lecture visit by H. D. Block last September. I present the problems in a completely geometric setting and develop an intuitive proof of convergence (restricting myself here to the case of a simple perceptron and the error-correction procedure) whose essential argument requires only two-dimensional visualization, although it encompasses the general case of variable correction step magnitudes. Also the question of existence of a solution, i.e., of *in principle* possibility of learning, hardly touched on in Ref. 2, but elsewhere designated as the "linear separability" problem, (see Ref. 5—this work became available to me only months after my results, which overlap little if at all, were accomplished) is placed in a geometric linear programming framework developed earlier by the writer and others.[3,6,7] *En passant*, a computational solution is suggested.

GEOMETRIC FRAMEWORK

Employing a matrix paraphrase of Block's notation in Ref. 2, pp. 128–130, the possibility or linear separability question is, does there or does there not exist a solution to

$$y^T B > \theta e^T \qquad (1)$$

In case the set Y of points y satisfying Eq. (1) is not vacuous, it forms a very special type of open convex body, e.g., a truncated polyhedral cone, of which an arbitrary two-dimensional section which contains the line through the origin and a point d of Y has the typical form shown.

To see this note that the point d is at a nonzero distance from each of the finite number of bounding hyperplanes to the open half-spaces designated by the system of inequalities of Eq. (1). There is thus a least distance from d to the boundary of Y and therefore any sphere of radius ρ less than this minimum is completely contained within Y. Thus Y is a convex body, since trivially it is also convex. It is polyhedral since its boundary is composed of portions of hyperplanes. It is truncated because the origin is cut off from Y because θ is strictly greater than zero. Clearly, then, any two-dimensional slice through the origin in d must be of the form indicated in Fig. 1.

For later use we note also that if S_ρ designates the solid sphere (really hypersphere) of center d and radius ρ, as before, then the sphere of radius

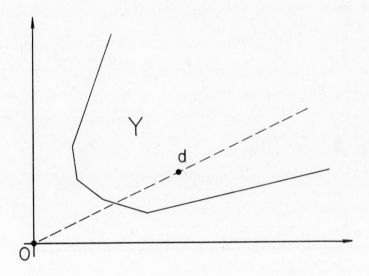

Figure 1

$\mu\rho$ about the point μd is contained in Y for all $\mu \geq 1$. Thus the minimum distance from the point μd to the boundary of Y tends to infinity with μ. As we shall see later, this is a special characteristic of the set Y which will make any procedure involving successive steps the size of whose sum becomes large enough and which remains within a fixed finite cylinder about the line through d and the origin, to become a finitely convergent process. Graphically, the situation is as in Fig. 2.

Since the cylinder becomes swallowed up in Y a finite distance out from the origin, so, a fortiori, must any point which describes a path lying within the cylinder and traveling out toward infinity in the direction Od. This is the basis for my geometric proof of convergence which will be taken up in detail after first providing a geometric characterization and computational note for the possibility or linear separability question.

It may be noted additionally that my proof applies a fortiori to any system of decision boundaries in which a polyhedral set like Y may be inserted and for which the correction steps based on these boundaries projects into valid steps for Y. In particular, the proof holds for decision boundaries which contain convex bodies "radially" increasing to infinity.

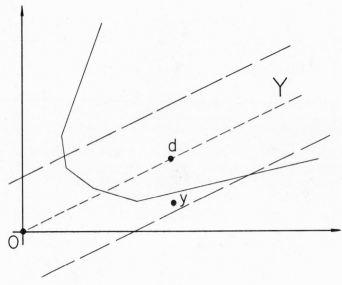

Figure 2

"IN PRINCIPLE" LEARNING

To make contact with the mainstream of linear programming theory we must change the question of existence of solutions to Eq. (1), which involves an "open" system of linear inequalities to a question of existence for a "closed" system of inequalities. Evidently the system of Eq. (1) has a solution if and only if the system

$$y^T B \geq \theta' \tag{1.1}$$

has a solution where $0 < \theta < \theta'$.

Now then we have, see theorem (2), page 211 of the Charnes-Cooper monograph:[7]

THEOREM

There exists no y satisfying Eq. (1.1) if and only if there exists $x \geq 0$, $\theta' e^T x > 0$, such that $Bx = 0$.

An obvious equivalent form is the following:

THEOREM

There exists y such that $y^T B \geq \theta' > 0$ if and only if for all $x \geq 0$ with $e^T x = 1$, the condition $Bx \neq 0$ must hold.

NOTE:

The condition $e^T x = 1$ means merely that $x \neq 0$, since $x \geq 0$ and the theorem statements involving x and B are positive homogeneous in x.

As an immediate corollary we have the preliminary lemma (on page 129 of Ref. 2) in Block's convergence proof that

$$0 < \inf \frac{|Bx|}{|x|}, \qquad x \geq 0, \qquad x \neq 0 \tag{2}$$

since

$$\sum_i |(Bx)_i|/e^T x \leq K \frac{|Bx|}{|x|} = K|Bz|, \qquad z = x/|x| \tag{2.1}$$

and the minimum of the left number is taken on for some x. Here the absolute value signs mean Euclidean norm (= Euclidean length) when a vector is contained within them.

Incidentally, this argument does not require topological considerations as in Ref. 2, since the linear programming theory utilized holds for finite dimensional vector spaces over arbitrary ordered fields. (See Ref. 7.)

An immediate consequence of the above is the possibility of computing whether or not a y exists satisfying Eq. (1) since the linear programming problem

$$\begin{aligned}
\min \ & e^T(z^+ + z^-) \\
& z^+ - z^- - Bx = 0 \\
& e^T x = 1 \\
& z^+, z^-, x \geq 0
\end{aligned} \tag{3}$$

will have minimum value greater than zero if and only if such a y exists.

Another geometric characterization of the possibility theorem can be obtained by reference to the opposite sign theorem of Charnes and Cooper.[6] This proposition is so fundamental that it can be employed (see Ref. 7) to develop all of the major theorems of the theory of linear inequalities and convex polyhedral sets without reference to topology or to constructs such as the separating hyperplane. The opposite-sign theorem may be stated as follows:

OPPOSITE-SIGN THEOREM

The set

$$\Lambda = \left\{ \lambda : \sum_{j=1}^n P_j \lambda_j = P_0, \qquad \lambda_j \geq 0 \right\}$$

is spanned by its extreme points (hence bounded) if and only if whenever $\alpha = (\alpha_1, \ldots, \alpha_n) \neq 0$ and $\Sigma_j P_j \alpha_j = 0$ some α_r and α_s must be of opposite sign.

Hence it follows that

THEOREM

There exists y satisfying Eq. (1) if and only if the set X of all x such that $Bx = b$ and $x \geq 0$ is a bounded polyhedron for $b \neq 0$.

This equivalence yields another linear-programming computational test. The linear programming problem

$$\max e^T x$$
$$Bx = \frac{1}{n} Be \qquad (4)$$
$$x \geq 0$$

has a finite maximum if and only if there exists y satisfying Eq. (1).

It should be noted that in computing this problem by the simplex method or its variants, the presence of an infinite maximum may be automatically signaled in the course of the computation by a specific property of the vector seeking to come in, or, if preliminary "regularization" (see Ref. 7) is employed, by obtaining an optimum solution involving an artificial bound.

CONVERGENCE PROOF

Returning now to the geometric framework, the error correction procedure (see Block, Ref. 2, pp. 128–129) consists at each stage in making a step in the direction of the inward normal to the bounding (decision) hyperplane corresponding to the stimulus for which the incorrect response has just been elicited. Geometrically, recall that the point y (see Fig. 2, for example) will give an incorrect response to a stimulus whenever it is on the wrong side of the corresponding decision hyperplane.

Now, the inward normals to all of the decision hyperplanes make angles of less than 90° with the line from the origin through the (previously mentioned) interior point d. To verify this requires, evidently, only a two-dimensional slice passing through the line Od and On where On has the same direction as the normal to the decision hyperplane.

Thus each error correction step moves the point y in the direction Od by an amount proportional to the size of the step. Therefore any succession of error correction steps, the sum of whose sizes tends to infinity, will have a projection in the direction of Od tending to infinity at the same rate. If

Δ_n is the size of the nth step, we shall require that $\Sigma_n \Delta_n \to \infty$. If we require

further that $\Delta_n / \sum_{j=1}^{n} \Delta_j$ tends to zero with n (as will be seen, it would be

sufficient merely to require that $\Delta_n / \sum_{j=1}^{n} \Delta_j$ become and remain less than

some small fraction of ρ) then after a certain number of steps, the size of the succeeding steps will be small compared to the distance of the point to the line Od. This is of course on the assumption that the point y has not yet moved into Y, for if it has we have already achieved the objective in a finite number of steps.

At the current juncture suppose an incorrect response has just been elicited and a step is to be made in the direction of the inward normal to a decision hyperplane. Let $y + \Delta$ be the position after making this step. This situation is depicted in Fig. 3 which is a three-dimensional slice containing the plane through y, $y + \Delta$ and μd, the point nearest to y on the line Od (in scalar product notation $\mu = (y,d)/(d,d)$), and also containing Od.

Since the direction of the line between y and $y + \Delta$ is perpendicular to the trace of the hyperplane, which must also cut in between y and μd, and since the step size is small compared to the length of $(y)(\mu d)$, the side $(\mu d)(y + \Delta)$ of the triangle y, $y + \Delta$, μd is smaller than the side $(y)(\mu d)$. *A fortiori*, $y + \Delta$ must be closer to Od than y. Thus the subsequent points

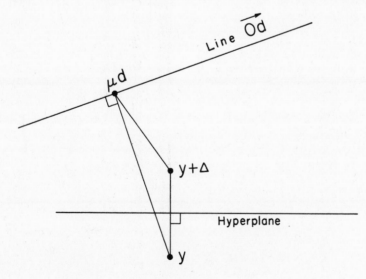

Figure 3

attained by correction remain within a hypercylinder of fixed radius about the line Od, and therefore must enter Y in a finite number of steps. This concludes the proof.

ADDITIONAL REMARKS

1. It should be noted that specific numerical bounds for the maximum number of steps necessary can be obtained in terms of the minimum cosine of the angle between a decision hyperplane and the line Od (this measures the minimum rate of progress along the direction of Od), and the minimum distance between d and the decision hyperplanes which form the part of the boundary of Y extending to infinity in the direction of Od. These constructs can be combined into a geometric interpretation of the scalar products involved in analytic convergence proofs as in of Refs. 2 and 5.

2. It should be repeated that extensions to a wide class of nonpolyhedral decision boundaries immediately reduce to the preceding arguments by use of polyhedral inscription or polyhedral approximation in obvious ways.

3. Reduction of convergence proofs for other learning methods to the above constructs will be indicated elsewhere.

REFERENCES

1. Rosenblatt, F., *Principles of Neurodynamics*, Spartan, Washington, D.C., 1962.
2. Block, H. D., "The Perceptron: A Model for Brain Functioning, I," *Rev. Mod. Phys.*, vol. 34, no. 1, January 1962, pp. 123–135.
3. Charnes, A., W. W. Cooper, and A. Henderson, *An Introduction to Linear Programming*, Wiley, New York, 1953.
4. Block, H. D., B. W. Knight, Jr., and F. Rosenblatt, "*Analysis of a Four*-Layer Series-Coupled Perceptron. II," *Rev. Mod. Phys.*, v. 34, no. 1, January 1962, pp. 135–142.
5. Singleton,. R. C., "A Test for Linear Separability as Applied to Self-Organizing Machines," in M. C. Yovits, G. T. Jacobi, and G. D. Goldstein, (eds.), *Self-Organizing Systems-1962*, Spartan, 1962.
6. Charnes A., and W. W. Cooper, "The Strong Minkowski-Farkas-Wehl Theorem For Vector Spaces Over Ordered Fields," *Proc. Nat. Acad. Sci.*, v. 44, no. 9, September 1958.
7. Charnes, A., and W. W. Cooper, *Management Models and Industrial Applications of Linear Programming*, vols. I and II, Wiley, New York, 1961.

3

DETERMINATION AND DETECTION OF FEATURES IN PATTERNS*

H. D. BLOCK,** N. J. NILSSON,† and R. O. DUDA†

INTRODUCTION

TWO-LAYER LEARNING MACHINES

A typical perceptron-type learning machine consists of layers of *associators* or threshold elements.[1] The inputs to the learning machine are connected, through weights, to the associators in the first layer. The outputs of the first-layer associators are connected, through weights, to the associators in the second layer.

In a two-layer learning machine, the outputs of the associators in the second layer are taken to be the outputs of the machine. Such a two-layer machine is illustrated in Fig. 1.

The ensemble of inputs to the machine at a given instant is called a *pattern*; the ensemble of outputs is called a *response*. A central problem is to find a set of weight values in the first and second layers such that the machine responds to a list of patterns in accordance with some prescribed set of responses. Generally, the task of specifying these weight values as the result of a direct calculation is impractical, and one looks for algorithms by which the weight values can be iteratively modified while the machine is being exposed to a set of representative patterns from the list. The employment of such an algorithm *designs* the machine by a process commonly called *training*.

* The research reported in this paper was supported in part by the Office of Naval Research (Contract Nonr-3438(00), in part by the U.S. Public Health Service (Contract PHT 1-77B-62), in part by the U.S. Air Force (RADC) [Contract AF 30(602)-2943 FSC-A082], and in part by Stanford Research Institute.

** Cornell University, Ithaca, N. Y.

† Stanford Research Institute, Menlo Park, Calif.

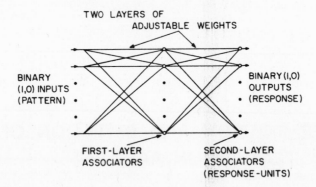

Figure 1

Algorithms have been proposed that specify how to adjust the values of the weights in one of the layers if those in the other layer remain fixed. Training procedures for the α-perceptron[1] (to adjust the weights in the second layer) and for the Madaline[2] (to adjust the weights in the first layer) are examples. No universally successful methods, however, are known for adjusting the weights in both layers simultaneously.

This paper presents a procedure for adjusting the weights in the first layer that can be performed without regard to the way in which the second layer is trained. The weights in the first layer are adjusted during training until the first-layer associators *detect* significant *features* in the patterns. (Precisely what constitutes a feature will be described later.) The weights in the second layer can then be adjusted to obtain the prescribed responses. Thus, the problem of adjusting the weights in the first layer is viewed as a problem of *feature determination*.

REPRESENTATION OF PATTERNS AND WEIGHT SETS

For ease of explanation, suppose that the inputs to the learning machine are arranged in a rectangular array or *retina*, so that every possible binary pattern can be represented by a mosaic of black and white cells. Each of these mosaics will be called an *image*. The image illustrated in Fig. 2 represents a pattern on a 5 × 5 retina. This image can also be represented by the binary 25-tuple

$$(1,1,1,1,1,0,0,1,0,0,0,0,1,0,0,0,0,1,0,0,0,0,1,0,0)$$

where a "1" corresponds to a black cell and a "0" corresponds to a white cell. The correspondence between each cell in the retina and each component of the 25-tuple is defined according to the scanning convention indicated by Fig. 3.

Figure 2

1	2	3	4	5
6	7	8	9	10
11	12	13	14	15
16	17	18	19	20
21	22	23	24	25

Figure 3

We shall restrict the weights in the first layer to the values *one* and *zero*. An image will also be used to represent the values of a set of binary weights incident on each first-layer associator. A black cell will be used to represent a weight value equal to *one*, and a white cell will be used to represent a weight value equal to *zero*. If there are K first-layer associators, then K images completely describe the wiring between the learning-machine input terminals and the first layer of associators. If the word *associator* is taken to include the set of weights as well as the usual summing and threshold devices, then each possible binary-weight associator can be represented by an image together with a threshold value.

An associator will be said to be *matched* to a pattern if its image representation is identical with the image representation of that pattern. Such an associator plays the role of a *template*.

FEATURE DETERMINATION AS A MEANS TO ORGANIZE THE FIRST LAYER OF WEIGHTS

Consider the problem of selecting the values of the first-layer weights in an α-perceptron. One well-known solution is to choose these weights randomly.[1] An alternative is to provide a first-layer associator matched to each pattern (see Fig. 4). Indeed, matching or template techniques are quite usefully employed in pattern recognition when the patterns tend to "cluster" around prototypes. For more diffuse sets of patterns, however, the number of different templates needed becomes prohibitively large.

If it is reasonable to assume that each pattern is composed of simpler patterns or *features*, then a matching scheme can still be used. The features are then building blocks of the complete patterns, and *subtemplates* matched to features can be used (see Fig. 5). The number of features is usually much smaller than the number of patterns that can be composed from them, and, therefore, a subtemplate matching scheme could be an economical solution to the problem of specifying the first layer of weights.

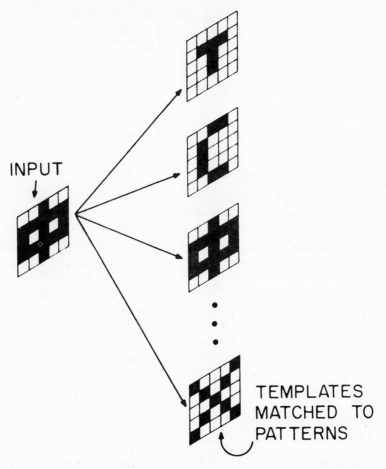

Figure 4

The problem of organizing the first layer of weights will be viewed as one of determining such features. Some important aspects of this problem can be illustrated by a simple example in which we construct patterns out of the six features shown in Fig. 6. The patterns will be formed, let us say, by combining any two distinct features from this set of six features. Thus, for example, the pattern of Fig. 2 is formed by the superposition of features F_1 and F_5 of Fig. 6. If we use all of the combinations of two features out of the six, we get $\binom{6}{2} = 15$ patterns. These are shown in Fig. 7.

We now ask the reader to forget, for a moment, the preceding discussion, and to suppose that the patterns of Fig. 7 were presented to him in some

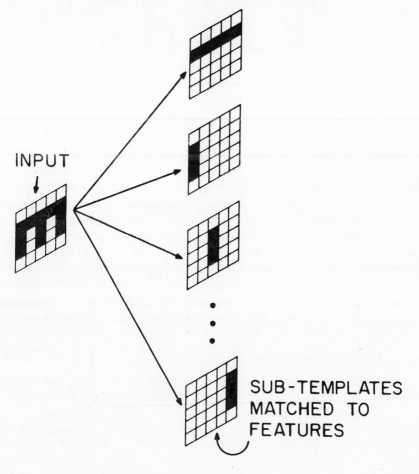

Figure 5

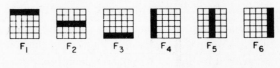

Figure 6

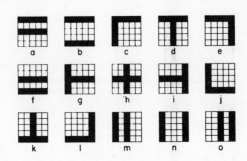

Figure 7

sequence, possibly with repetitions allowed. It would not be very long before he would discover that these fifteen patterns were, in fact, constructed out of the six features of Fig. 6. This discovery would enable him to organize a learning machine with six associators in the first layer, one matched to each feature, rather than fifteen associators, one matched to each pattern. Furthermore, these features would also be suitable for other patterns of similar structure, and thus would provide much greater flexibility than that provided by simple template matching. In general, if the environment of presented patterns is actually structured, in the sense that there are a few basic features out of which all the presented patterns are composed, then it is likely that substantial advantages can be realized by making use of this fact in the processing performed by the first layer of associators. The striking economies that can be obtained by appropriate organization are demonstrated in Appendix A.

While the advantages of determining features are clear, the general problem of finding them is not easily solved. Consider again the set of patterns formed by superposing precisely two of the six features shown in Fig. 6, namely, the set of patterns shown in Fig. 7. Let us remember the retinal cells by permuting the numbers $(1, 2, \ldots, 25)$, and then again represent all images according to the scheme of Fig. 3, but with the new numbers assigned to the retinal cells of the image. To be specific, we take (at random) the following permutation:

Old retinal cell number	1	2	3	4	5	6	7	8	9	10	11	12	13	14	15	16	17	18	19	20	21	22	23	24	25
New retinal cell number	8	15	24	25	14	17	9	1	16	21	2	11	20	22	10	13	6	3	12	7	4	19	23	5	18

Under this permutation the 15 patterns shown in Fig. 7 go over into the 15 patterns shown in Fig. 8. The order of the patterns is (intentionally) not the same in Fig. 8 as in Fig. 7. The actual correspondence is as follows:

Fig. 7	a	b	c	d	e	f	g	h	i	j	k	l	m	n	o
Fig. 8	a	d	j	l	h	m	e	i	o	b	n	f	g	k	c

Since the permutation of the retinal cells is a one-to-one transformation, it is clear that the organizational structure of the 15 patterns of Fig. 8 is the same as that of Fig. 7, namely, there are six basic features and each of the 15 patterns is made up by superposing precisely two of these features.

Now we ask the reader to forget, for a moment, the preceding discussion and to suppose that the patterns of Fig. 8 were presented to him in some sequence, possibly with repetitions allowed. We invite him to try to determine the number of basic features involved and their composition, working under this assumed ignorance. We believe, that he will find, as we did, that the solution is not quite so trivial.* Of course the reader might take the position that each retinal cell is a feature, since each pattern can be constituted by superposing a subset of these. This, however, would require 25 features, whereas we know that 6 suffice. Alternatively, he might take each of the 15 patterns to be a feature. This is open to the same objection. What is desired is a minimal set of features sufficient to account for all the given patterns.

Since the abstract mathematical structures represented by Fig. 7 and Fig. 8 are isomorphic, it is clear that our ease in solving the problem of Fig. 7 as compared to the difficulty of Fig. 8 reflects a psychological or physiological phenomenon, rather than a mathematical distinction between the problems. If the environment actually consists of "bars" as in Fig. 7,

---

* This problem can, however, be solved by a simple algorithm, as has been pointed out to us by W. R. Lynn. For a slightly more challenging problem, use as the features all 5 horizontal and all 5 vertical bars. Form the patterns by taking any vertical plus any horizontal bar. The 25 patterns thus obtained are rearranged on the retina as before.

COMPUTER AND INFORMATION SCIENCES

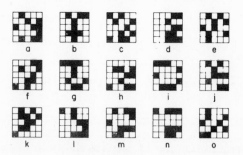

Figure 8

and if we know this in advance, then it is clearly advantageous to build "bar detectors" into a recognition system for this environment of patterns. However, if we know nothing about the structure of the patterns in advance, then any algorithm or adaptive process that is to lead to the determination of the features will have to be equally effective when applied to the patterns of Fig. 8 as it is to Fig. 7. Although "bars" may be likely to occur in everyday visual patterns, there are also situations in which nothing may be known in advance about the structure of the patterns. Suppose, for example, that each "retinal cell" represents not a cell of a two-dimensional visual image but the presence of a certain feature already abstracted at a previous stage of the process. Thus, for example, the first retinal cell might represent the presence of a horizontal bar, the second might represent a moving spot in the center of the field, the third a shrill sound coming into the system, and so on. In this case there may be no obvious a priori features, although the features, or "syndromes," may exist, and we may find it very helpful indeed to know them.

As another example of a situation in which "bars" may not be the natural features, consider the qualitative analysis, say, of the chemical pollutants in a river. On the first day an examination of a sample of the water might reveal the presence of pollutant chemicals A, B, C in excess of a normal threshold. On the second day there may be excessive quantities of C, D, E, F. On the third day A, B, C, G, H, I, and so on. These findings for 15 days might be represented by data such as shown in Fig. 9. Here again we have 25 "retinal cells" and 15 patterns. Now, if it turns out that the occurrence or nonoccurrence of the various chemicals is not really independent, but in fact that daily pollution patterns can be described in terms of a few features, or syndromes, then one would suspect that there is a reason for this and investigate the cause. For example, if a certain combination of chemicals occurs repeatedly, and if a particular upstream factory is known to have these chemicals as waste products, then one may be led to investigate whether this factory is giving sufficient treatment to its effluent.

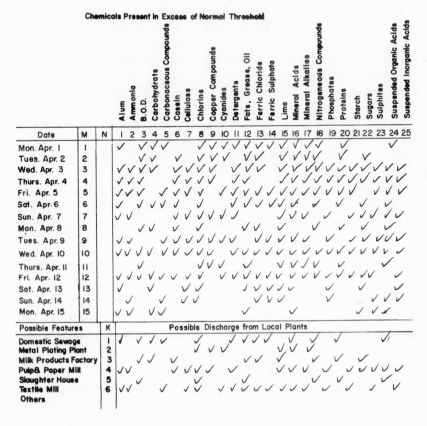

Figure 9

STATEMENT OF THE PROBLEM

Suppose that matched to each feature occurring in the set of patterns there is an associator in the first layer. By observing the responses of the associators in the first layer, we could *reconstitute* the pattern being presented. This reconstitution would be performed by combining all features whose presence is detected.*

* The ability to reconstitute patterns from features suggests a means to transmit a set of high-resolution photographs over a low-bandwidth channel. Rather than transmit the black or white information about each cell in the retina (high bandwidth), we transmit only the information regarding which features are present and which are absent for any particular image. At the receiver, the high-resolution image is reconstituted by combining the features that were present. If the total number of features for any set of patterns is less than the total number of retinal cells, then the feature-detection technique can be a means for achieving bandwidth reduction in an image-transmission system.

In learning machine pattern-classification tasks, it is not necessary to reconstitute the pattern. One desires only to know to which of a relatively small number of categories each pattern belongs. If the first layer of associators is to be trained to detect features, the features can be limited to those that are most helpful in establishing the category of the input pattern. The number of features needed for pattern classification might be substantially smaller than the number needed for pattern reconstitution. Nevertheless, in this paper we shall confine ourselves to the following question: What algorithms can be used to direct the training of a layer of associators such that they eventually become matched to a set of features sufficient to *reconstitute* all of the patterns presented?

We shall begin by presenting a mathematical formulation that includes the following more general problem: Given a set of patterns, determine a set of features, minimal in number, such that each pattern can be formed by the superposition of a subset of these features. Unfortunately, we have not yet been able to find a reasonably brief algorithm to solve the problem in this degree of generality. However, we shall present two useful algorithms for the case in which the features are large compared to their mutual overlap. Results of experiments by digital-computer simulation will be used to show that these algorithms can lead to valuable results, even when this restriction is not met.

MATHEMATICAL FORMULATION

THE GENERAL PROBLEM

The problem of feature determination introduced above can be formulated in set-theoretical terms as follows:

Let S be a given set of points $\{s_n\}$ $(n = 1, \ldots, N)$. (This represents a retina of N retinal cells.) Any subset of S is called an *image*. Let P_m $(m = 1, \ldots, M)$ be given images. These are called the *patterns*. This collection of M patterns is denoted by $\mathcal{P} = \{P_m\}$ $(m = 1, \ldots, M)$. A collection of K images $\mathcal{F} = \{F_k\}$ $(k = 1, \ldots, K)$ is called *a set of features for* $\mathcal{P}$ if each P_m is the union of some subcollection of the F_k, i.e., if for each m there exists a subset $\sigma(m)$ of the integers $(1, \ldots, K)$ such that

$$P_m = \bigcup_{k \in \sigma(m)} F_k \qquad (m = 1, \ldots, M) \tag{1}$$

Given $\mathcal{P}$, the general problem is to find a set of features $\{F_k\}$ $(k = 1, \ldots, K)$ for $\mathcal{P}$ such that K is minimal.

Equation (1) will have no solution if K is too small. On the other hand, if $K \geq \min(N, M)$ a solution will clearly exist: if $M \leq N$, take $K = M$

and $F_k = P_k$ for $k = 1, \ldots, M$; if $N < M$, take $K = N$ and $F_k = s_k$ for $k = 1, \ldots, N$.

Even if a solution to Eq. (1) exists, it may not be unique, i.e., the features F_k and/or the selection $\sigma(m)$ may not be unique. For example, consider the set of patterns of Fig. 7, with patterns (a), (b), (c), and (d) deleted. If we let $\mathcal{P}$ be the remaining set of eleven patterns, then the top horizontal bar occurs only in the presence of the right vertical bar. Instead of using the top horizontal bar as a feature, we could take the top horizontal bar plus any subset of the right vertical bar. We shall find it convenient to *normalize* to the "maximal size feature" possible. Thus, in this instance we would choose the pattern of Fig. 7(e) rather than the top horizontal bar as our first feature. In general, given a set of features $\mathcal{F} = \{F_k\}$ ($k = 1, \ldots, K$), we can find a new set of features $\bar{\mathcal{F}} = \{\bar{F}_k\}$ ($k = 1, \ldots, K$) by taking $\bar{F}_k$ as the intersection of all of the patterns containing F_k. That is,

$$\bar{F}_k = \bigcap_{m \ni P_m \supseteq F_k} P_m \qquad (k = 1, \ldots, K)$$

Clearly, $\bar{F}_k \supseteq F_k$ and $\bar{\mathcal{F}}$ is a set of features for $\mathcal{P}$. Furthermore, the $\bar{F}_k$ satisfy the equation

$$\bar{F}_k = \bigcap_{m \ni P_m \supseteq \bar{F}_k} P_m \qquad (k = 1, \ldots, K) \tag{2}$$

Thus, we may replace any set of features by their "hulls," which satisfy Eq. (2).

Even with this normalization of the features, however, the selection $\sigma(m)$ may not be unique. For example, in the case just considered, the pattern of Fig. 7e can be represented either as the pattern consisting of the feature of Fig. 7e alone or of the feature of Fig. 7e plus the right vertical bar. Again, we shall find it convenient to *normalize* to the "maximal set." That is, in this instance we would include both features in the right hand side of Eq. (1). In general we shall include in the right-hand side of Eq. (1) all features contained in the pattern. With this convention, Eq. (1) takes the form

$$P_m = \bigcup_{k \ni F_k \subseteq P_m} F_k \qquad (m = 1, \ldots, M) \tag{3}$$

and, if the features F_k have been normalized, then

$$F_k = \bigcap_{m \ni P_m \supseteq F_k} P_m \qquad (k = 1, \ldots, K) \tag{4}$$

A GENERAL SOLUTION

Equation (3) by itself provides a logically complete algorithm for testing whether a given set of features satisfies Eq. (1). Consequently, one obvious (but impractical) algorithm for solving the general problem of Eq. (1) with minimal K would be to start with $K = 1$, ($K = 0$ for mathematicians) and examine the possibility of a solution of Eq. (3) for all possible choices of the single feature F_1. There are 2^N such cases. If no solution exists for $K = 1$, take $K = 2$ and examine whether a solution exists for all possible choices of the pair of distinct features F_1, F_2. There are $2^N_2 = 2^{N-1}(2^N - 1)$ such cases. If there is no solution for $K = 2$, we try $K = 3$, and so on. A solution will be found for $K \leq \min(N, M)$, and the first such solution will clearly have K minimal. Although the number of cases at each step can be substantially reduced by considering only those choices for F_k ($k = 1, \ldots, K$) that satisfy Eq. (4), this verification itself will take some computing, and we can hardly claim that this is a practical algorithm.

ALGORITHMS

THE THRESHOLD CONDITION

The general problem we have posed is that of determining a set of features $\{F_k\}$ ($k = 1, \ldots, K$), minimal in number, such that

$$P_m = \bigcup_{k \ni F_k \subseteq P_m} F_k \qquad (m = 1, \ldots, M) \qquad (3)$$

where

$$F_k = \bigcap_{m \ni P_m \supseteq F_k} P_m \qquad (k = 1, \ldots, K) \qquad (4)$$

In words, Eq. (4) states that the intersection of all patterns sharing a common feature *is* that feature. A basic problem, then, is that of determining whether or not all the patterns in a given group of patterns share a common feature.

Consider the simpler problem of determining whether or not two given patterns share a common feature. If they do, that feature is included in their intersection; if they do not, their intersection contains merely intersections of distinct features (i.e., overlaps of features). This is illustrated in Fig. 10, where the pertinent features are assumed to be horizontal and vertical bars. Note that in this example the *size* of the intersection, i.e., the number of retinal points it contains, is large when the patterns share a common feature, and is small when they do not. Henceforth we shall restrict our attention to such situations. More precisely, we shall assume that there exists a *threshold*, θ, such that any two patterns share a common feature if and only if the size of their intersection equals or exceeds this threshold.

An associator can be used to compare the size of the intersection of two patterns with the value of the threshold. Consider the patterns P_1 and P_2, and the associator shown in Fig. 11. The associator has been matched to P_1 by setting the values of the weights to points in P_1 equal to one, and setting the values of the weights to points not in P_1 equal to zero. If P_2 is presented to the retina, then the sum S gives the size of the intersection $P_2 \cap P_1$. If the threshold of the associator is equal to the threshold θ, then the associator is active if and only if P_1 and P_2 share a common feature.

TRAINING ONE ASSOCIATOR

When such a threshold, θ, exists, a simple algorithm can be used to train an associator so that it eventually becomes matched to a feature. Consider

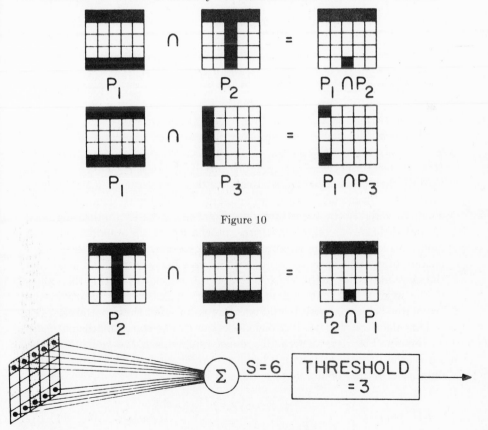

Figure 10

Figure 11

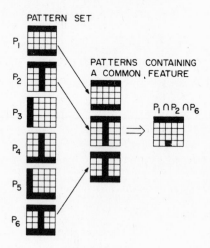

Figure 12

the set of patterns shown in Fig. 12. Suppose that patterns P_1, P_2, and P_6, and only those patterns, share a common feature, so that the feature is given by their intersection $P_1 \cap P_2 \cap P_6$. The associator can form this joint intersection by forming successive pairs of intersections, *viz.*, $P_6 \cap [P_2 \cap P_1]$.

This result is achieved in the following way. The associator is matched to the first pattern, P_1 (see Fig. 11). The second pattern, P_2 is presented. If the associator becomes active, indicating that P_1 and P_2 share a common feature, then the associator is matched to the intersection $P_2 \cap P_1$; this is easily done by merely setting the value of the weights to points not in P_2 equal to zero. If the associator does not become active, indicating that P_1 and P_2 have no common features, no changes in the weight values are made. This process is now repeated with the other patterns. Whenever a pattern presented shares a feature with all previous patterns that activated the associator, that pattern also activates the associator; setting the values of the weights to points not in that pattern equal to zero results in the associator being matched to the intersection of all of these patterns.

This algorithm for training one associator can be stated mathematically as follows. Let $A(i)$ denote the image representing the weights of the associator after the ith pattern has been presented, and let $\|I\|$ denote the number of retinal points in any image I. Then

$$A(i+1) = \begin{cases} A(i) \cap P_{i+1} \text{ if } \|A(i) \cap P_{i+1}\| \geqq \theta \\ \\ A(i) \qquad \text{otherwise} \end{cases} \qquad (i = 0, \ldots, M-1) \quad (5)$$

where

$$A(0) = \bigcup_{i=1}^{N} s_i \tag{6}$$

It is shown in Appendix B that after the Mth pattern has been presented, $A(M)$ is one of the features if the following conditions are satisfied:

$$(1) \quad P_m = \bigcup_{k \epsilon F_k \subseteqq P_m} F_k \quad (m = 1, \ldots, M) \tag{3}$$

$$(2) \quad F_k = \bigcap_{m \epsilon P_m \supseteqq F_k} P_m \quad (k = 1, \ldots, K) \tag{4}$$

and

$$(3) \quad \frac{1}{2} K(K-1) N_{\max} < \theta \leqq N_{\min} - (K-1) N_{\max} \tag{7}$$

where

$$N_{\min} = \min_{i} ||F_i|| \tag{8}$$

and

$$N_{\max} = \max_{\substack{i,j \\ i \neq j}} ||F_i \cap F_j|| \tag{9}$$

The first two conditions are merely statements of the basic relations between patterns and normalized features. The third condition, *the threshold condition*, is a more precise statement of the fact that we are concerned with pattern sets for which the size of the intersection of any two patterns indicates whether or not they share a common feature. It is sufficient (although not necessary) to guarantee that the associator will be activated by a pattern if and only if it shares a feature with all previous patterns that activated the associator.*

A SEQUENTIAL ALGORITHM

The algorithm just described gives a way of determining one of the features. The remaining features could, in principle, be determined in the same way by permuting the order in which the patterns are presented. [In view of Eq. (4) such an ordering is always possible.] This scheme suffers from the difficulty that the number of permutations of the patterns necessary to guarantee the determination of every feature ($M!$) will usually be prohibitively large. If random permutations are used, it will usually result in several associators being matched to each feature. It seems

---

* The threshold condition has been stated in a form that will be convenient later. If only one associator is to be trained, this condition can be relaxed by replacing the right side of Eq. (7) with $N_{\min}$.

desirable, in the interest of economy, to prevent more than one associator from becoming matched to the same feature. This can be done by raising the threshold of the associator being trained whenever the pattern presented contains features already determined. The amount that the threshold is raised depends upon the relation of these features to the image of the associator being trained. To be more specific, the threshold is increased by the size of the union of those features of the pattern that (a) have been detected by other associators, and (b) are contained in the image of the associator being trained.

One way to incorporate this mechanism for preventing the multiple determination of features is to begin by training the first associator as before. After one iteration of the patterns, the first associator has been matched to, say, the first feature. Then the second associator is trained, using this threshold-raising mechanism to prevent it from also becoming matched to the first feature. After the second iteration of the patterns, the second associator has been matched to, say, the second feature. This procedure is continued, a new associator being trained after each iteration of the patterns, until, after K iterations, all of the features have been found. This algorithm is referred to as the *sequential algorithm* because features are determined in sequence.

This algorithm can be stated mathematically as follows. Let $A_1(M), \ldots, A_j(M)$ denote the images representing the weights of the first j associators after j iterations of the patterns. (These, of course, are supposed to be j different features.) Let $A_{j+1}(i)$ denote the image representing the weights of the $(j + 1)$-th associator after the presentation of the ith pattern on the $(j + 1)$-th iteration. Let K_{ij} be the set of integers $k(0 < k < j)$ defined by

$$K_{ij} = \{k; 0 < k < j, \quad \|A_k(M) \cap P_i\| \geqq \theta, \quad A_k(M) \subseteq A_j(i)\} \quad (10)$$

Then

$$A_{j+1}(i + 1) = \begin{cases} A_{j+1}(i) \cap P_{i+1} \text{ if } \|A_{j+1}(i) \cap P_{i+1}\| \geqq \theta \\ \qquad\qquad + \|\bigcup_{k \epsilon K_{i+1,j+1}} A_k(M)\| \quad (11) \\ A_{j+1}(i) \qquad \text{otherwise} \end{cases}$$

$$(i = 0, \ldots, M - 1$$
$$j = 0, \ldots, K - 1)$$

where
$$A_{j+1}(0) = \bigcup_{i=1}^{N} s_i \quad (12)$$

It is shown in Appendix B that the conditions given by Eqs. (3), (4), and (7) are sufficient to guarantee that after K iterations of the patterns, the images $A_1(M), \ldots, A_K(M)$ will be the K features $F_1, \ldots, F_K$.

It should be emphasized that of these conditions, it is the threshold condition,

$$\frac{1}{2} K(K - 1) N_{\max} < \theta \leqq N_{\min} - (K - 1) N_{\max} \tag{7}$$

that limits the generality of the results. It should also be noted that this condition was obtained by a "worst-case" analysis; in many situations the algorithm can be used to find useful features even though this condition is not met.

A PARALLEL ALGORITHM

Instead of training the associators one after another, we can obtain the features more rapidly by training several of the associators at once. One algorithm for such a training procedure starts with a single associator as before, and introduces new associators whenever they are needed for *reconstitution*. After a pattern has been presented and the weight changes have been made, a test is made to see if the union of the images of the active associators reproduces that pattern. If it does, the next pattern is presented. If it does not, a new associator matched to that pattern is introduced, and then the next pattern is presented.

This procedure for training several associators, which is referred to as the *parallel algorithm*, begins by matching the first associator to the first pattern. Suppose that, at the ith step, j associators are being trained. (At the second step, one associator is being trained.) Let $A_1(i), \ldots, A_j(i)$ denote the corresponding images. When pattern P_{i+1} is presented, the new images are determined as follows:

1. A_1 is active if and only if $\|A_1(i) \cap P_{i+1}\| \geqq \theta$. If A_1 is active, $A_1(i + 1) = A_1(i) \cap P_{i+1}$; if A_1 is inactive, $A_1(i + 1) = A_1(i)$.

2. A_2 is active if and only if $\|A_2(i) \cap P_{i+1}\| \geqq \theta + \theta_2$. Here, $\theta_2 = \|A_1(i + 1)\|$ if (a) A_1 is active, and (b) $A_1(i + 1) \subseteq A_2(i)$; otherwise, $\theta_2 = 0$. If A_2 is active, $A_2(i + 1) = A_2(i) \cap P_{i+1}$; if A_2 is inactive, $A_2(i + 1) = A_2(i)$.

3. In general, A_l is active if and only if $\|A_l(i) \cap P_{i+1}\| \geqq \theta + \theta_l$. Here, $\theta_l = \| \cup A_k(i + 1)\|$, where $k \epsilon K_l$ if and only if (a) A_k is active $(k < l)$ and (b) $A_k(i + 1) = A_l(i)$. If A_l is active, $A_l(i + 1) = A_l(i) \cap P_{i+1}$; if A_l is inactive, $A_l(i + 1) = A_l(i)$.

After the j new images have been found, the union of the images of the active associators is formed. If this union yields pattern P_{i+1}, then the next pattern is presented. If it does not, a new associator matched to this pattern is introduced, and then the next pattern is presented. This pro-

cedure is continued for as many iterations of the pattern set as is needed
to obtain the features.

The example given in Fig. 13 illustrates the operation of this algorithm.
Except for numbering, the six patterns involved are the same as those
shown in Fig. 12. The threshold θ is taken to be three. The procedure begins
by matching A_1 to P_1. Next, P_2 is presented, and since $\|A_1(1) \cap P_2\| =
10 \geqq 3$, A_1 is active, and $A_1(2) = A_1(1) \cap P_2$. Since P_2 can be reconstituted
by A_1, P_3 is presented. P_3 also activates A_1, and $A_1(3) = A_1(2) \cap P_3$.
Now, however, P_3 can not be reconstituted by A_1 alone, and a new associator A_2 matched to P_3 is introduced. The presentation of P_4 activates A_1,
and its image, $A_1(4)$, is reduced to the lower horizontal bar. Since A_1 is
active and $A_1(4) \subseteq A_2(3)$, the threshold for A_2 is raised to $3 + \|A_1(4)\| =
8$; this prevents A_2 from becoming active, and thus prevents its image
from being reduced to the same lower horizontal bar. The pattern P_4 can
not be reconstituted, and a new associator A_3 matched to P_4 is introduced.
The remaining steps are performed similarly, and the four features are
found in less than two iterations of the pattern set.

The parallel algorithm often yields a set of features in fewer than the
K iterations of the patterns required by the sequential algorithm. This
speed is gained by training new associators before old associators have
determined a feature. This complicates the action of the threshold-raising
mechanism, however, and frequently leads to the determination of more
features than are needed for reconstitution.

SELECTION OF THE THRESHOLD

In order to use either the sequential or the parallel algorithm, we must
know the value of the threshold, θ. If the features were known, a threshold
for the sequential algorithm could be obtained from the bounds given by
Eq. (7). However, the determination of the features is our goal; furthermore, even if Eq. (7) can not be satisfied by any value of θ, there may well
exist a threshold for which the algorithm will disclose a set of useful
features. An efficient, generally applicable method of determining such a
threshold has not yet been found. However, it is often practical to repeat
the procedure for several values of θ, and to select that value that gave the
best results.

For example, consider the 24 patterns shown in Fig. 14. These patterns
were constructed from 7 features—horizontal, vertical, and diagonal bars.
(For these features, incidentally, Eq. (7) can not be satisfied by any value
of θ.) The results of using the parallel algorithm with a threshold of *one*
are shown in Fig. 15. Of the 15 features found, the seven largest features
are sufficient to reconstitute all of the patterns. Similar results were
obtained with a threshold of *two* (see Fig. 16). Higher thresholds led to

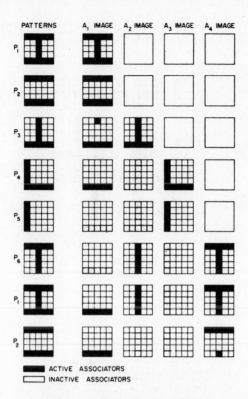

Figure 13

Figure 14

features with excessive overlap, and poorer results; however, the features obtained using the lower thresholds are clearly useful.

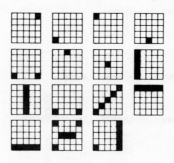

Figure 15

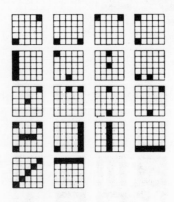

Figure 16

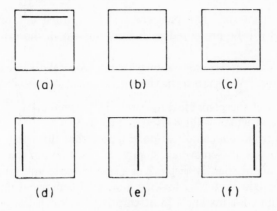

Figure A1

CONCLUDING COMMENTS

In this paper we have investigated feature determination as a method of training the first layer of weights in a two-layer learning machine. The problem was viewed as one of examining a set of patterns and determining a set of simpler patterns, or features, so that each of the original patterns can be formed by superposing the features. While the general problem of finding a minimal set of features was not solved, two algorithms were given that solve the problem for restricted pattern sets.

These results suggest several other problems worth further study. On the one hand, one can seek useful algorithms that apply to less restricted or even unrestricted pattern sets. On the other hand, one can seek useful algorithms for pattern sets containing topological constraints characteristic of special patterns, such as visual patterns. In either case, the effects of noise and small distortions must be investigated to ensure the practicability of this approach. Finally, attention should be given to the problem of determining those features most valuable for pattern classification. A good solution to this problem would be a major contribution to the theory of self-organizing systems.

APPENDIX A

FEATURE DETECTION AND EFFICIENT MACHINE ORGANIZATION

The purpose of this appendix is to show how the utilization of features may result in a much more efficient use of associators. We shall compare three different organizations of associators which can correctly categorize some simple patterns. The patterns will be formed out of straight-line features, and will be presented to a retina for which the gridwork is very fine.

Consider first the six lines shown in Fig. A-1. We shall call these the "ideal features." We shall form the set of "ideal patterns" by combining any three out of these six ideal features. Thus there are $\binom{6}{3}$ = 20 ideal patterns, one of which is illustrated in Fig. A-2.

Now we introduce a complication. Suppose that the artist who is sketching the patterns is somewhat sloppy in positioning the features. For example, he might slightly displace or slightly rotate any given feature. In addition, he might sketch by making more than one try at drawing a given ideal line. Thus, for instance, in attempting to sketch the pattern of Fig. A-2 he might start by sketching the upper horizontal line of Fig. A-1a. Figure A-3 shows five lines, any one of which might be the outcome of his effort to draw the top horizontal line. Let us call these five lines "equivalent representations" of the ideal line of Fig. A-1a. Similarly, suppose that each of the six ideal lines of Fig. A-1 has, say, five equivalent representations. Thus a given ideal pattern, such as Fig. A-2, might be represented by any one of $(2^5 - 1)^3$ actual patterns, one of which is shown in Fig. A-4.

Figure A2

Figure A3

Figure A4

We shall also be interested in the case in which the artist is restricted to draw only a single line in his attempt to denote any ideal feature of Fig. A-1 ("drawing" rather than "sketching"). In this case, in attempting to draw Fig. A-1a, he could use only one of the five lines in Fig. A-3. Then a given ideal pattern, such as Fig. A-2, can be represented by any one of 5^3 actual patterns. For brevity, let us call this *Case* (b), and the case considered above, in which the artist can use any one or more lines, *Case* (a). Thus, although there are only $\begin{pmatrix} 6 \\ 3 \end{pmatrix}$ = 20 ideal patterns, there are actually $20(2^5 - 1)^3 \cong 6 \cdot 10^5$ distinct patterns that might be presented to the retina in *Case* (a), and $20 \cdot 5^3 = 2500$ distinct patterns in *Case* (b).

Suppose that we have available associators having an arbitrary number r of inputs, each with weight $+1$, and a threshold, θ. If $\theta = r$, the associator responds if and only if *all* of its inputs are active; if $\theta = 1$, it responds if and only if *at least one* of its inputs is active.

We now consider a system having for its input a retina on which the patterns will be projected, and having for its output 20 associators of the type described, corresponding to the 20 ideal patterns. It is desired that when any representative of an ideal pattern is shown to the retina, the corresponding associator should become active; otherwise it should remain inactive. The problem is to form a network of associators to accomplish this task. We shall examine three solutions and compare them as to the number of associators and the number of connections used.

For the purpose of computing the number of connections, we assume for simplicity that the number of retinal points in each ideal feature is a constant, p, and that this is also the number of retinal points in each equivalent representation of any ideal feature. Let $\|P_i\|$ denote the number of retinal points in the ith pattern. Then, in *Case* (a), $3p \leqq \|P_i\| \leqq 15p$, and in *Case* (b), $\|P_i\| \cong 3p$.

For *Case* (a), one such solution (Solution I) is shown in Fig. A-5, where the ith "internal" associator has a threshold of $\|P_i\|$ and has connections with unit weights to all of the retinal points of the ith pattern. Thus, each of these associators is activated by a particular pattern on the retina. Each output associator has a threshold equal to one, and connections of unit weights to those internal associators which represent the same ideal pattern. Thus each output associator is active in response to its "equivalence class" of patterns, as required.

This arrangement requires $20(2^5 - 1)^3$ associators (we shall not count the 20 "response" associators, since they must be present in any system, and we are interested in comparing systems). The number of connections is $6 \cdot 5 \cdot \begin{pmatrix} 5 \\ 2 \end{pmatrix} p(2^5 - 1)^2 \cdot 2^4 \cong 4.6p \cdot 10^6$ in the first layer, and $20(2^5 - 1)^3$

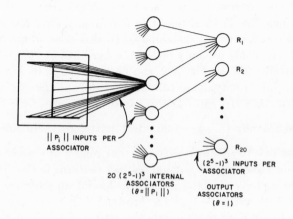

Figure A5

in the second layer of connections. If we let N_A denote the number of associators used (not counting response units), and N_C the number of connections, we have for this arrangement

$$N_A = 20(2^5 - 1)^3 \cong 6 \cdot 10^5 \tag{A-1a}$$

$$N_C = 6 \cdot 5 \cdot \binom{5}{2} p(2^5 - 1)^2 \cdot 2^4 + 20(2^5 - 1)^3 \cong 4.6p \cdot 10^6 \tag{A-1b}$$

An economy can be effected by considering the *Case* (b) and using a similar arrangement, where now there are only $\binom{6}{3}$ 5^3 patterns to be considered. Here

$$N_A = \binom{6}{3} 5^3 = 2500 \tag{A-2a}$$

and

$$N_C = 2500(3p + 1) \tag{A-2b}$$

It is easy to see that this arrangement also solves *Case* (a), and we call it Solution II.

A much more economical solution (Solution III) may be obtained by having each associator of the first layer respond to a particular realization of a line feature (see Fig. A-6). Each associator of the second layer represents the presence of a particular ideal feature, and the associators of the third layer (the responses) are activated by any representative of the

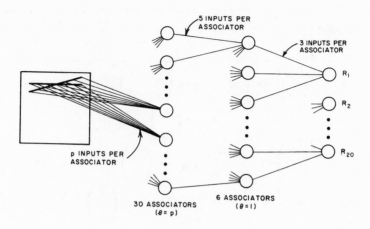

Figure A6

corresponding ideal pattern.* The threshold in the first layer is p, the number of retinal points in a feature. There are $6 \cdot 5 = 30$ associators in the first layer and six in the second. Hence

$$N_A = 36 \qquad\qquad\qquad\qquad (A\text{-}3a)$$

The number of connections in the first set is $30p$, in the second $6 \cdot 5 = 30$, and in the third $3 \cdot 20 = 60$. Hence

$$N_C = 30p + 90 \qquad\qquad\qquad\qquad (A\text{-}3b)$$

A comparison of Eqs. (A-1a) and (A-1b) with Eqs. (A-2a) and (A-2b), and (A-3a) and (A-3b) shows the enormous savings that may be realized as a result of appropriate organization. The principle of "early generalization" to effect such economies has been pointed out by Rosenblatt.[3]

To compare these three types of organization in the general case, let the number of ideal features be F, and let the ideal pattern be composed by the superposition of precisely f ideal features. Let E denote the number of equivalent representations of each feature. Then for the three types of organization discussed above, the results are as follows:†

* In the particular problem being discussed, the first layer of associators could be eliminated by connecting each associator of the second layer to that part of the retina covering a feature and its "perturbation." If the features were less disjoint, however, this method might fail. We shall not discuss it further here.

† Note that N_A does not include the number of response units, since these must be used in any case. N_C, however, does include the connections to the response units.

Organization type	N_A	N_C
I	$\binom{F}{f}(2^E - 1)^f$	$pEF\binom{F-1}{f-1}2^{E-1}(2^E - 1)^{f-1} +$ $\binom{F}{f}(2^E - 1)^f$
II	$\binom{F}{f}E^f$	$(fp + 1)\binom{F}{f}E^f$
III	$F(E + 1)$	$EF(p + 1) + f\binom{F}{f}$

Even more impressive economies are possible if the structural organization of the patterns is hierarchial. To illustrate this, let us elaborate the previous problem. Suppose that the patterns described above represent "letters" in an alphabet of 20 letters. Suppose the retina is extended to four times its original width, so that four-letter words of this alphabet can be placed on it (see Fig. A-7).

Suppose further that each letter can be positioned in each box in, say, seven ways. Although there are now $20^4 = 160{,}000$ ideal four-letter words, there are actually $20^4 \cdot 7^4 \cdot (2^5 - 1)^{12} \cong 3 \cdot 10^{26}$ distinct patterns that are possible on the enlarged retina in *Case* (a), and $20^4 \cdot 7^4 \cdot 5^{12} \cong 9 \cdot 10^{16}$ in *Case* (b). We suppose that we have as response units associators corresponding to each ideal four-letter word on the retina. It is desired to construct a system of associators such that when any particular representation of an ideal word is placed on the retina, the response unit that corresponds to that ideal word becomes active and all others remain inactive. Again we consider three types of solution, analogous to the previous example.

For Solution I we use an internal associator for each distinct pattern and then combine them into words, as shown in Fig. A-8. Here the number of associators used is

$$N_A = 20^4 \cdot 7^4 \cdot (2^5 - 1)^{12} \cong 3 \cdot 10^{26} \qquad (\text{A-}4a)$$

and the number of connections is

$$N_C = p \cdot 4 \cdot 5 \cdot 6 \cdot 7 \cdot \binom{5}{2}(2^5 - 1)^2 2^4 \left[7\binom{6}{3}(2^5 - 1)^3 \right]^3 + N_A$$

$$\cong (31p + 1)N_A \cong p \cdot 10^{28} \qquad (\text{A-}4b)$$

where, as before, p represents the number of retinal points in an ideal line feature of Fig. A-1. The number of inputs to a first-layer associator is $\|P_i\|$, where $\|P_i\|$ is now the number of points in the ith four-letter word. Clearly, in *Case* (a) $12p \leq \|P_i\| \leq 60p$; in *Case* (b), $\|P_i\| \cong 12p$.

For Solution II we use a similar arrangement, but start instead with *Case* (b). It is easy to see that this arrangement will also solve *Case* (a), but now only $20^4 \cdot 7^4 \cdot 5^{12}$ internal associators are required in the middle layer. There will be $12p \cdot 20^4 \cdot 7^4 \cdot 5^{12}$ connections in the first set, and $20^4 \cdot 7^4 \cdot 5^{12}$ connections in the second. Hence we have in this case

$$N_A = 20^4 \cdot 7^4 \cdot 5^{12} \cong 10^{17} \qquad (A\text{-}5a)$$

and

$$N_C = (12p + 1)\, N_A \cong p \cdot 10^{18} \qquad (A\text{-}5b)$$

A much greater saving can be achieved if we organize the system so as to reflect the organization of this particular environment of patterns. This is illustrated in Fig. A-9. Here the first layer consists of associators that

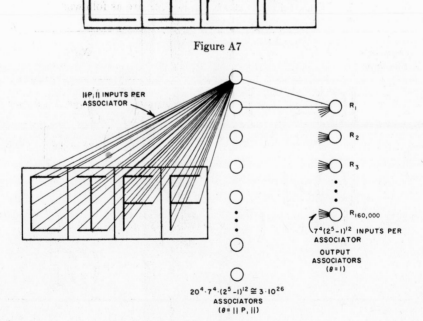

Figure A7

Figure A8

respond to a particular representation of a given line feature in a given box in a given position in the box. Thus there are $4 \cdot 6 \cdot 5 \cdot 7 = 840$ such associators. In the second layer, the five equivalent representations of a given line feature in a given box in a given position are combined to represent the ideal line in a given box in a given position in the box. The third combines the ideal lines into ideal letters in a given box in a given position in the box. The fourth layer combines the seven possible positions of a given ideal letter in a given box. The fifth layer is the response units. The number of internal associators used in this system is therefore

$$N_A = 4 \cdot 6 \cdot 5 \cdot 7 + 4 \cdot 6 \cdot 7 + 4 \cdot 20 \cdot 7 + 4 \cdot 20 = 1648 \qquad \text{(A-6a)}$$

and the number of connections is

$$N_C = 840p + 5 \cdot 168 + 3 \cdot 560 + 7 \cdot 80 + 4 \cdot 20^4$$
$$= 840p + 643,080 \qquad \text{(A-6b)}$$

The enormous saving is evident. To compare the three types of organization in general, let L denote the number of letters in a word and P the number of ways in which a given letter can be positioned in a given box. With $F, f,$ and E as defined earlier, the results are as follows:

Organization type	N_A	N_C
I	$\left[\binom{F}{f} P(2^E - 1)^f \right]^L$	$pEFPL \binom{F-1}{f-1} (2^E - 1)^{f-1} 2^{E-1} \left[P \binom{F}{f} (2^E - 1)^f \right]^{L-1} + N_A$
II	$\left[\binom{F}{f} PE^f \right]^L$	$(fLp + 1)N_A$
III	$L \left[FP(E + 1) + \binom{F}{f} (P + 1) \right]$	$L \left[FPE(p + 1) + P \binom{F}{f} (f + 1) + \binom{F}{f}^L \right]$

Another advantage to the organization of Solution III is that the number of inputs to a given associator is reduced. (*Cf.* Fig. A-5 with Fig. A-6, and Fig. A-8 with Fig. A-9.) If we think of the model as representing

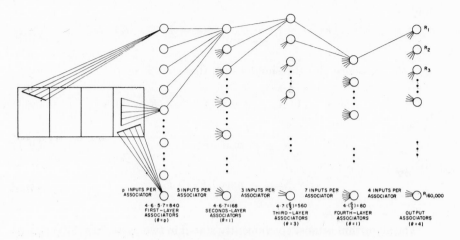

Figure A9

an industrial organization, with associators representing decision-making individuals, then, in view of the natural limitations of human capacity for handling information, such a reduction of input data may be essential for the individual's mental health.

In order to achieve the advantage of matching the organizational structure of the system with that present in the environment of the patterns, it appears that one must be able either to determine the structure of the environment and design the system accordingly, or else formulate reinforcement rules by means of which the system will adapt its structure to that present in the environment. Since the patterns of active units at any given layer themselves represent input patterns to the subsequent layer, the algorithms developed can be used to find the features of the "patterns" in any given layer.

APPENDIX B

CONVERGENCE PROOF FOR THE SEQUENTIAL ALGORITHM

This appendix contains the convergence proof for the sequential algorithm. As before, we let $S = \{s_n\}$ $(n = 1, \ldots, N)$ denote the set of retinal points and $\mathcal{P} = \{P_m\}$ $(m = 1, \ldots, M)$ denote the set of patterns. We assume the existence of a set of features $\mathcal{F} = \{F_k\}$ $(k = 1, \ldots, K)$ such that

$$P_m = \bigcup_{k \ni F_k \subseteq P_m} F_k \qquad (m = 1, \ldots, M) \qquad \text{(B-1)}$$

and

$$F_k = \bigcap_{m \epsilon P_m \supseteq F_k} P_m \qquad (k = 1, \ldots, K) \tag{B-2}$$

and the existence of a threshold θ such that

$$\frac{1}{2} K(K-1) N_{\max} < \theta \leqq N_{\min} - (K-1) N_{\max} \tag{B-3}$$

where

$$N_{\min} = \min_i ||F_i|| \tag{B-4}$$

and

$$N_{\max} = \max_{\substack{i,j \\ i \neq j}} ||F_i \cap F_j|| \tag{B-5}$$

The algorithm is most conveniently stated in two parts. Let $A_1(i)$ denote the image representing the weights of the first associator after the ith pattern has been presented. Then the algorithm for changing the weights of the first associator is

$$A_1(i+1) = \begin{cases} A_1(i) \cap P_{i+1} \text{ if } ||A_1(i) \cap P_{i+1}|| \geqq \theta \\ A_1(i) \qquad \text{otherwise} \end{cases} \quad (i = 0, \ldots, M-1) \tag{B-6}$$

where

$$A_1(0) = \bigcup_{n=1}^{N} s_n \tag{B-7}$$

The presentation of all of the M patterns is called an *iteration* of the patterns. Let $A_1(M), \ldots, A_j(M)$ denote the images representing the weights of the first j associators after j iterations of the patterns. Let $A_{j+1}(i)$ denote the image representing the weights of the $(j+1)$-th associator after the presentation of the ith pattern on the $(j+1)$-th iteration. Let K_{ij} be the set of integers $k(0 < k < j)$ defined by

$$K_{ij} = \{k; 0 < k < j, ||A_k(M) \cap P_i|| \geqq \theta, A_k(M) \subseteq A_j^{(i-1)} \tag{B-8}$$

Then the algorithm for changing the weights of the $(j+1)$-th associator is

$$A_{j+1}(i+1) = \begin{cases} A_{j+1}(i) \cap P_{i+1} \text{ if } ||A_{j+1}(i) \cap P_{i+1}|| \geqq \theta \\ \qquad\qquad\qquad + ||\bigcup_{k \epsilon K_{i+1,j+1}} A_k(M)|| \\ A_{j+1}(i) \qquad \text{otherwise} \quad (i = 0, \ldots, M-1) \\ \qquad\qquad\qquad\qquad\qquad (j = 1, \ldots, K-1) \end{cases} \tag{B-9}$$

where

$$A_{j+1}(0) = \bigcup_{n=1}^{N} s_n \qquad (B\text{-}10)$$

We shall show that if conditions (B-1), (B-2), and (B-3) are satisfied, then, after K iterations, the images $A_1(M), \ldots, A_k(M)$ are the features $F_1, \ldots, F_k$. We shall first show that after one iteration $A_1(M)$ is a feature, and we shall then show that, after $j + 1$ iterations, $A_{j+1}(M)$ is a feature other than $A_1(M), \ldots, A_j(M)$.

PART 1. CONVERGENCE OF A_1

We begin by repeating the algorithm for A_1.

$$A_1(i+1) = \begin{cases} A_1(i) \cap P_{i+1} \text{ if } ||A_1(i) \cap P_{i+1}|| \geqq \theta \\ \qquad\qquad\qquad\qquad\qquad (i = 0, \ldots, M-1) \\ A_1(i) \qquad \text{otherwise} \end{cases} \qquad (B\text{-}6)$$

where

$$A_1(0) = \bigcup_{n=1}^{N} s_n \qquad (B\text{-}7)$$

From Eq. (B-3),

$$||A_1(0) \cap P_1|| = ||P_1|| \geqq N_{\min} \geqq \theta$$

so that

$$A_1(i) = P_1 \qquad (B\text{-}11)$$

If at the $(i + 1)$-th step $||A_1(i) \cap P_{i+1}|| \geqq \theta$, we shall say that P_{i+1} *activates* A_1. Thus, at the first step P_1 activates A_1. Let the first n patterns that activate A_1 be denoted by $P_{i_1}, \ldots, P_{i_n}$. Then after step i_n

$$A_1(i_n) = \bigcap_{j=1}^{n} P_{i_j} \qquad (B\text{-}12)$$

Define $i_{n+1} = i_n + 1$, so that at the next step, pattern $P_{i_{n+1}}$ is encountered. One of two cases can arise:

Case (a): $P_{i_1}, \ldots, P_{i_{n+1}}$ have at least one common feature.
Case (b): $P_{i_1}, \ldots, P_{i_{n+1}}$ have no common features.

CASE (a)

Let F_1 be a feature common to $P_{i_1}, \ldots, P_{i_{n+1}}$. Then

$$F_1 \subseteq \bigcap_{j=1}^{n+1} P_{i_j} \qquad (B\text{-}13)$$

and, from Eqs. (B-4) and (B-9),

$$||A_1(i_n) \cap P_{i_{n+1}}|| \geqq ||F_1|| \geqq N_{\min} \geqq \theta \tag{B-14}$$

Thus, in *Case (a)*, $P_{i_{n+1}}$ activates A_1.

CASE (b)

LEMMA 1: Let I_j be a subset of the set of integers $\{i\}$ $(i = 1, \ldots, K)$, and let the collection of sets $\{I_j\}$ $(j = 1, \ldots, m)$ have the property that no integer is in every set of integers. Let $\mathfrak{F} = \{F_k\}$ $(k = 1, \ldots, K)$ be a collection of point sets. Then

$$S' = \bigcup_{j=1}^{m} \left(\bigcup_{i \in I_j} F_i \right) \subseteq \bigcup_{i=1}^{K-1} \bigcup_{j > i}^{K} F_i \cap F_j \tag{B-15}$$

Proof: Let $s \in S'$. Then s cannot be a member of one and only one of the sets of $\mathfrak{F}$, for, were it so, there would be an I_j such that $s \in F_i \bigcup_{i \in I_j}$ and hence $s \notin S'$. Thus $\exists (i,j)$, $i \neq j$, $\ni s \in F_i$ and $s \in F_j$. Thus $s \in F_i \cap F_j$, and, since all possible pairs of intersections appear in the right side of Eq. (B-15), the lemma is proved.

Now suppose that $P_{i_1}, \ldots, P_{i_{n+1}}$ have no common features. Then, from Eqs. (B-12) and (B-1) and the lemma,

$$A_1(i_n) \cap P_{i_{n+1}} = \bigcap_{j=1}^{n+1} P_{ij} = \bigcap_{j=1}^{n+1} \left(\bigcup_{i \ni F_i \subseteq P_{ij}} F_i \right) \subseteq \bigcup_{i=1}^{K-1} \bigcup_{j > i}^{K} F_i \cap F_j \tag{B-16}$$

and

$$||A_1(i_n) \cap P_{i_{n+1}}|| \leq \left\Vert \bigcup_{i=1}^{K-1} \bigcup_{j > i}^{K} F_i \cap F_j \right\Vert$$

$$\leqq \sum_{i=1}^{K-1} \sum_{j > i}^{K} ||F_i \cap F_j||$$

$$\leqq \sum_{i=1}^{K-1} \sum_{j > i}^{K} N_{\max}$$

$$\leqq \frac{1}{2} K(K - 1) N_{\max}$$

$$< \theta \tag{B-17}$$

Thus, in *Case (b)*, $P_{i_{n+1}}$ does not activate A_1.

It follows that $P_{i_{n+1}}$ activates A_1 if and only if the patterns $\{P_{i_1}, \ldots, P_{i_{n+1}}\}$ have at least one feature in common. After M steps, let

$\{P_{i_1}, \ldots, P_{i_{n_0}}\}$ be the set of patterns that activated A_1, and let F_1 be one feature they share. Then

$$A_1(M) = \bigcap_{j=1}^{n_0} P_{i_j} \tag{B-18}$$

But $F_1 \subseteq P_{i_j}[(j = 1, \ldots, n_0)$, and F_1 is not contained in any other pattern. Thus by Eq. (B-2),

$$A_1(M) = F_1 \tag{B-19}$$

PART 2.   CONVERGENCE OF A_{j+1}

We begin by repeating the algorithm for A_{j+1}.

$$A_{j+1}(i+1) = \begin{cases} A_{j+1}(i) \cap P_{i+1} & \text{if } ||A_{j+1}(i) \cap P_{i+1}|| \geqq \theta \\ & + \left|\left| \bigcup_{k \in K_{i+1,j+1}} A_k(M) \right|\right| \\ A_{j+1}(i) & \text{otherwise} \end{cases} \tag{B-9}$$

$$(i = 0, \ldots, M - 1)$$
$$(j = 0, \ldots, K - 1)$$

where

$$A_{j+1}(0) = \bigcup_{n=1}^{N} s_n \tag{B-10}$$

and

$$K_{ij} = \{k; 0 < k < j, ||A_k(M) \cap P_i|| \geq \theta, A_k(M) \subseteq A_j^{(i-1)}\} \tag{B-8}$$

Suppose that the algorithm has operated successfully for $A_1, \ldots, A_j$ and we are starting the $(j + 1)$-th iteration. Then $A_1(M), \ldots, A_j(M)$ are j distinct features; for convenience we number them so that

$$A_i(M) = F_i \qquad (i = 1, \ldots, j) \tag{B-20}$$

If at the $(i + 1)$-th step

$$||A_{j+1}(i) \cap P_{i+1}|| \geqq \theta + \left|\left| \bigcup_{k \in K_{i+1,j+1}} A_k(M) \right|\right|$$

we shall say that P_{i+1} activates A_{j+1}. Let the first n patterns that activate A_{j+1} be denoted by $P_{i_1}, \ldots, P_{i_n}$.* Then after step i_n

$$A_{j+1}(i_n) = \bigcap_{l=1}^{n} P_{i_l} \tag{B-21}$$

Define $i_{n+1} = i_n + 1$, so that at the next step pattern $P_{i_{n+1}}$ is encountered. One of two cases can arise:

* By adopting the convention $P_{i_1} = \bigcup_{n=1}^{N} s_n$ we can avoid the need for a separate proof that some pattern will activate A_{j+1}.

CASE (a):

$P_{i_1}, \ldots, P_{i_{n+1}}$ have at least one common feature, besides perhaps some or all of $F_1, \ldots, F_j$.

CASE (b):

$P_{i_1}, \ldots, P_{i_{n+1}}$ have no common features, besides perhaps some or all of $F_1, \ldots, F_j$.

Before considering these cases in detail, we shall establish some useful facts.

LEMMA 2: $\|F_i \cap P_j\| \geq \theta$ if and only if $F_i \subseteq P_j$.

Sufficiency: If $F_i \subseteq P_j$, then $F_i \cap P_j = F_i$, and

$$\|F_i \cap P_j\| = \|F_i\| \geq N_{\min} \geq \theta$$

Necessity: If $F_i \nsubseteq P_j$, then $F_i \cap P_j \subseteq F_i \cap (\bigcup_{j \neq i} F_j)$, and

$$\|F_i \cap P_j\| \leq \| \bigcup_{i \neq j} F_i \cap F_j\| \leq \sum_{i \neq j} \|F_i \cap F_j\| \leq (K-1) N_{\max}$$

If $K = 1$, $\|F_i \cap P_j\| = 0 < \theta$. If $K \geq 2$, $\frac{1}{2} K \geq 1$, and

$$\|F_i \cap P_j\| \leq \frac{1}{2} K(K-1) N_{\max} < \theta \qquad \text{Q.E.D.}$$

Consider now the set of integers $K_{i_{n+1}, j+1}$,

$$K_{i_{n+1}, j+1} = \{k; 0 < k < j+1, \|A_k(M) \cap P_{i_{n+1}}\| \geq \theta,$$
$$A_k(M) \subseteq A_{j+1}(i_{n+1})\}$$

From Eqs. (B-20) and (B-21), and Lemma 2, we can write this as

$$K_{i_{n+1}, j+1} = \{k; 0 < k < j+1, F_k \subseteq P_{i_{n+1}}, F_k \subseteq \bigcap_{l=1}^{n} P_{i_l}\} \qquad \text{(B-22)}$$

Let F^c denote the union of all of the features from $F_1, \ldots, F_j$ that are *common* to $P_{i_1}, \ldots, P_{i_{n+1}}$. Clearly

$$K_{i_{n+1}, j+1} = \{k; F_k \subseteq F^c\} \qquad \text{(B-23)}$$

and

$$\bigcup_{k \in K_{i_{n+1}, j+1}} A_k(M) = F^c \qquad \text{(B-24)}$$

CASE (a)

In *Case* (a), $P_{i_1}, \ldots, P_{i_{n+1}}$ have at least one common feature, besides perhaps some or all of $F_1, \ldots, F_j$, which we number as F_{j+1}. Then

$$P_{i_l} = F^c \cup F_{j+1} \cup F^{il} \qquad (l = 1, \ldots, n+1) \qquad \text{(B-25)}$$

where F^{il} is the union of those features in P_{i_l} and not in $F^c \cup F_{j+1}$. Then at step i_{n+1}, it follows from Eqs. (B-21), (B-25), (B-24), and (B-20) that

$$||A_{j+1}(i_n) \cap P_{i_{n+1}}|| = ||\bigcap_{l=1}^{n+1} P_{i_l}|| = ||(F^c \cup F_{j+1}) \cup \bigcap_{l=1}^{n+1} F^{il}||$$

$$\geq ||F^c \cup F_{j+1}|| = ||F^c|| + ||F_{j+1}|| - ||F^c \cap F_{j+1}||$$

$$\geq ||F^c|| + N_{\min} - ||\bigcup_{k \in K_{i_{n+1}, j+1}} F_k \cap F_{j+1}||$$

$$\geq ||F^c|| + N_{\min} - (K-1) N_{\min} \qquad \text{(B-26)}$$

and thus, from Eqs. (B-3) and (B-24), that

$$||A_{j+1}(i_n) \cap P_{i_{n+1}}|| \geq \theta + ||\bigcup_{k \in K_{i_{n+1}, j+1}} A_k(M)|| \qquad \text{(B-27)}$$

Thus, in *Case* (a), $P_{i_{n+1}}$ activates A_{j+1}.

CASE (b)

In *Case* (b), $P_{i_1}, \ldots, P_{i_{n+1}}$ have no common features, besides perhaps some or all of $F_1, \ldots, F_j$. Then

$$P_{i_l} = F^c \cup F^{il} \qquad (l = 1, \ldots, n+1) \qquad \text{(B-28)}$$

where F^{il} is the union of features in P_{i_l} and not in F^c. In particular, the F^{il} have no common features. Then at step i_{n+1}, it follows from Eqs. (B-21) and (B-28), and Lemma 1 that

$$||A_{j+1}(i_n) \cap P_{i_{n+1}}|| = ||\bigcap_{l=1}^{n+1} P_{i_l}||$$

$$= ||F^c \cup \bigcap_{l=1}^{n+1} F^{il}||$$

$$\leq ||F^c|| + ||\bigcap_{l=1}^{n+1} F^{il}||$$

$$\leq ||F^c|| + ||\bigcup_{i=1}^{K-1} \bigcup_{j>i}^{K} F_i \cap F_j||$$

$$\leq ||F^c|| + \sum_{i=1}^{K-1} \sum_{j>i}^{K} ||F_i \cap F_j||$$

$$\leq ||F^c|| + \frac{1}{2} K(K-1) N_{\max}$$

and thus, from Eqs. (B-3) and (B-24), that

$$||A_{j+1}(i_n) \cap P_{i_{n+}}|| < \theta + ||\bigcup_{k \in K_{i_{n+1}, j+1}} A_k(M)|| \qquad \text{(B-29)}$$

Thus, in *Case* (b), $P_{i_{n+1}}$ does not activate A_{j+1}.

It follows that $P_{i_{n+1}}$ activates A_{j+1} if and only if the set of patterns $\{P_{i_1}, \ldots, P_{i_{n+1}}\}$ have at least one feature in common, not counting the features that have already been detected by $A_1, \ldots, A_j$. After M steps, let $\{P_{i_1}, \ldots, P_{i_{l_0}}\}$ be the set of patterns that activated A_{j+1}, and let F_{j+1} be one feature besides $F_1, \ldots, F_j$ that they share. Then

$$A_{j+1}(M) = \bigcap_{l=1}^{l_0} P_{i_l} \qquad \text{(B-30)}$$

But $F_{j+1} \subseteq P_{i_l}$ $(l = 1, \ldots, l_0)$, and F_{j+1} is not contained in any other pattern. Thus by Eq. (B-2),

$$A_{j+1}(M) = F_{j+1} \qquad \text{(B-31)}$$

REFERENCES

1. Rosenblatt, F., *Principles of Neurodynamics: Perceptrons and the Theory of Brain Mechanisms*, Spartan, Washington, D.C., 1961.
2. Widrow, B., "Generalization and Information Storage in Networks of Adaline 'Neurons'" in M. C. Yovits, G. I. Jacoby, and G. D. Goldstein (eds.), *Self-Organizing Systems—1962*, Spartan, Washington, D.C., 1962, pp. 435–461.
3. Rosenblatt, F., "A Comparison of Several Perceptron Models," in M. C. Yovits, G. I. Jacoby, and G. D. Goldstein (eds.), *Self-Organizing Systems—1962*, Spartan, Washington, D.C., 1962, pp. 463–484.

4

HYPERPLANES, HYPERSPHERES, AND HYPERQUADRICS AS DECISION BOUNDARIES

PAUL W. COOPER

Applied Research Laboratory
Sylvania Electronic Systems
Waltham, Mass.

SUMMARY

Viewing pattern recognition as a problem in statistical classification wherein an n-dimensional space is partitioned into category regions with decision boundaries, this paper focusses attention on certain boundary forms which are tractable, yet general. Of particular interest are the hyperplane, the hypersphere, and the hyperquadric, which are implemented, respectively, as a correlation, a Euclidean distance determination, and an evaluation of a quadratic form. This paper turns the usual classification problem around and shows that these selected boundary forms are in fact fully optimum for a wide range of probability distributions which could arise in real problems. Classes of distributions for which this is true are prescribed, techniques are given for determining the actual decision boundary from known samples and for efficiently reducing the dimensionality, and measures of merit are included.

INTRODUCTION

The classical formulation of the classification problem within the broad framework of statistical inference strives for optimal partitioning of the sample space, subject to the constraints and criteria imposed.[3,17,27,28,30] Any real pattern recognition problem in which the data can be adequately described in a particular n-space can be treated with this statistical model, wherein the coordinate directions correspond to n measured or derived attributes.[1,5,6,7,12,15,18]. These attributes could correspond to discrete properties or to samples[25] of a time function associated with a category member.

The statistical approach is predicated upon the existence of probability distributions describing the distribution in n-space of members of each category. The distribution of points associated with each category may arise because the members of a category inherently differ among themselves, as, for example, do the different samples of a particular spoken word as said by different people; or because the ideal category member has been corrupted in some fashion, as in the case of a fixed signal in the presence of additive stochastic noise.

Usual statistical approaches make use of techniques of hypothesis testing for decision making and of parameter estimation for "learning" the distribution parameters (having assumed a functional form for the distribution) from sets of known samples of the categories. Methods of nonparametric statistics are introduced when little or nothing is known a priori about the functional forms of the distributions.[14] But in general, the "would-be" pattern recognizer is plagued with the following simple facts. Nonparametric solutions, although fully general, can be far inferior to the true solution which would prevail if one knew the distribution forms, particularly for small sample sets. Parametric solutions essentially are predicated upon assumption of a functional form for the distributions involved, and the usual assumption of normality certainly is not representative of most real distributions. And finally, even though one can, in the straightforward hypothesis-testing problem, describe the optimum boundary mathematically, it may often be extremely complicated to implement, either by computer program or with a special purpose device.

SEMIPARAMETRIC APPROACH

The approach taken in this paper begins with the fundamental observation that classification is an information-destroying process, and that any decision boundary is fully optimum for discrimination between many pairs of distributions. And with this in mind, we have directed attention toward particular boundary forms which are simple to implement, are fully optimum for broad classes of distribution pairs, and are excellent approximations for even broader classes of distributions arising in real problems.

Various tests and procedures which we use in this connection may be termed *robust*, in that they are to some extent insensitive to departures from the assumptions which underlie them. The procedures, suitable for normal distributions, are shown to be applicable for larger classes. We term the overall approach, *semiparametric*. It is to be noted that the hyperplane[2,4,8,16,29] has experienced wide use as a linear discriminant function in statistics studies and as a matched filter (or correlation detector) in communications studies. This paper shows that it is optimum for a wider range of real problems than is usually treated.[8] The hyperquadric is the boundary surface arising when the distributions are multivariate normal. This paper shows that this quadratic decision procedure is optimal under much wider assumptions than normality.[10] Central to this discussion are distributions which are multivariate developments of univariate Pearson Type II and Type VII distributions. The procedures of this paper apply to these distributions, as well as to the normal.

This paper is based largely upon three previous publications by the author, one treating each of the three basic boundary forms.[8,9,10] Although specific reference to these publications is made only infrequently in this present paper, it might be noted that they delve into a number of the topics in considerably greater detail than here considered.

Unless otherwise stated, the fundamental criterion of optimality used throughout this work is that that partition be employed which achieves the minimal total probability of misclassification under the assumption that all categories have equal *a priori* probability. This corresponds to a minimal total conditional error probability, or to a Bayes criterion for equal costs of misclassification and equal costs of correct classification, as well as equal prior probabilities. As described at the end of the paper in the remarks section, the techniques can be easily modified to accommodate more general decision criteria.

Throughout most of the paper, except where stated to the contrary, the discussion examines partitioning between two categories. Because of the optimal nature of the partitioning, however, the techniques extend to the multiple-category case as well.

BOUNDARIES

The hyperplane[8] is the optimal partitioning boundary between two unimodal distributions differing only in location and having probability density functions which are ellipsoidally symmetric and monotonically decreasing away from the mean. For each distribution so described, the location parameters, the median, mode, and mean are all the same, although in some cases of interest the mean exists only in a restricted sense. As can be readily appreciated the number of forms of probability density functions having these characteristics is quite large. The hyperplane boundary bisects the line connecting the distribution means and has an orientation dependent upon the means and the common covariance matrix (or scaling matrix). When the distributions are spherically symmetric, the boundary is simply the perpendicular bisector of the line of the means. Many other classes of distributions give rise to a hyperplane boundary, but this paper is confined to the ones described above.

The hypersphere[9] partitioning boundary is optimal when the two distributions are spherically symmetric normal, with different variances. But it is also optimal for spherically symmetric multivariate extensions of the Pearson Type II and Type VII distributions, when the two category distributions differ only in location and scale. The interior region of the sphere is associated with the tighter distribution, and the exterior with the other. A spherical boundary can also arise for these distribution types when the two category distributions are each ellipsoidally symmetric and have different scaling matrices, but where these matrices have principal axes which are identically oriented and where a certain relationship exists between these matrices. When the distribution means are the same, any spherically symmetric distributions give rise to a partitioning by a multiplicity of hyperspheres centered at the common mean. Under certain loose conditions, this latter case leads to a single sphere as its boundary.

When the two category distributions are multivariate normal with different means and covariance matrices the decision procedure, involving a comparison of quadratic forms, is equivalent to a partitioning of the sample space with a hyperquadric. But the hyperquadric also optimally partitions the space when the distributions are multivariate Pearson Type II or VII, differing in location and in scaling matrix.[10] The hyperquadric[26] in n-space can have the form of a hyperellipsoid or a hyperhyperboloid of number of sheets varying from 1 to $(n - 1)$. The central region of the hyperquadric is associated with the tighter distribution, i.e., with the one whose scaling matrix $\mathbf{W}$ has the larger determinant, and whose covariance matrix, where it exists, has the smaller determinant.

The relationships between the two scaling matrices determine the actual form of the hyperquadric. An interesting case occurs when the matrices differ only in that they are scalar multiples of one another. The boundary hyperquadric is then a hyperellipsoid having the same shape and orientation as the ellipsoids defining the scaling matrices. Of course the hyperplane and hypersphere are special cases of the hyperquadric, and the general quadric solution will reduce to these special ones where the appropriate parameter relationships are present. Under special conditions the quadric reduces to two parallel hyperplanes, or to two intersecting hyperplanes. The latter arises, for example, when the two scaling matrices differ only in that they are reflections of one another about some hyperplane passing between them. The remainder of this paper will consider use of the hyperplane for the ellipsoidally symmetric and spherically symmetric distributions having common scaling matrix, the hypersphere for spherically symmetric distributions, and the hyperquadric for all remaining cases. All

of the remaining special cases are therefore included in the general hyperquadric solution. We might point out that in a comprehensive implementation of these techniques, one might take note of the specific form of
the quadric and consider using the more specialized and often simplified
steps appropriate to it.

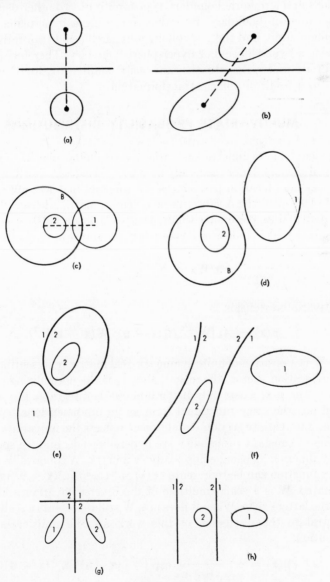

Figure 1

Figure 1 illustrates in terms of a 2-space model the various cases cited. Each illustration shows a constant probability contour (elliptical or circular) representing each of the two density functions; and the corresponding partitioning boundary is portrayed.

Of course, under a linear transformation of the space, two density functions and a quadric boundary transform into two other densities with another quadric boundary. Situations involving a hyperplane retain the hyperplane form, and those involving a hyperellipsoid transform into ones involving a hyperellipsoid or hypersphere boundary. Therefore any results appropriate under one situation are easily adapted to situations differing simply as a result of a linear transformation.

MULTIVARIATE PROBABILITY DISTRIBUTIONS

We denote a symmetric univariate probability density function by $p(x) = A_1 f(x)$, and more generally by $p(x) = A_1 \omega f[\omega(x - u)]$, where ω and u are scale and location parameters. Vectors and matrices are represented by bold-face symbols. A subscript on a vector, matrix, density function, or other distribution parameter will index the category, unless it is clear from the context that it indicates a coordinate. In terms of a quadratic form

$$\mathbf{x}'\mathbf{W}\mathbf{x} = \sum_{i=1}^{n} \sum_{j=1}^{n} w_{ij} x_i x_j$$

a multivariate extension is

$$p(\mathbf{x}) = A_n |\mathbf{W}|^{1/2} f([(\mathbf{x} - \mathbf{u})' \mathbf{W} (\mathbf{x} - \mathbf{u})]^{1/2}) \tag{1}$$

where $\mathbf{W}$ is a positive-definite symmetric real matrix representing a scaling, $\mathbf{u}$ is the location vector (the mean), and A_n is the normalizing constant in n-space. The $p(\mathbf{x})$ exists only if the function is integrable in n-space, and it then has the same functional form as its unidimensional counterpart. That is, a univariate section (conditional) reflects the univariate form. The contours of constant probability are hyperellipsoids, and we speak of this density function as being ellipsoidally symmetric. A spherically symmetric density function can be represented $p(\mathbf{x}) = A_n \omega^n f([\omega^2(\mathbf{x} - \mathbf{u})'(\mathbf{x} - \mathbf{u})]^{1/2})$. The matrix $\mathbf{W}$ is a scalar multiple of the inverse covariance matrix $\mathbf{\Sigma}^{-1}$, when the latter exists. When it does not, $\mathbf{W}$ still represents a scaling matrix.

Central to the discussion of this work are the multivariate normal distribution,

$$p(\mathbf{x}) = \frac{1}{(2\pi)^{n/2} |\mathbf{\Sigma}|^{1/2}} \exp \left[-\tfrac{1}{2} (\mathbf{x} - \mathbf{u})' \mathbf{\Sigma}^{-1} (\mathbf{x} - \mathbf{u}) \right] \tag{2}$$

where $\mathbf{W} = \mathbf{\Sigma}^{-1}$, and multivariate extensions[9,10] of the Pearson Type II and Type VII distributions.[22,23]

The univariate Pearson Type II distribution is

$$p(x) = \frac{\omega}{B(\frac{1}{2}, m + 1)} [1 - \omega^2(x - u)^2]^m \qquad |x - u| \leq \frac{1}{\omega} \qquad (3)$$

A multivariate extension of this distribution is defined in terms of a function

$$h(\mathbf{x}) = \frac{\Gamma(m + n/2 + 1)}{\pi^{n/2}\,\Gamma(m + 1)}\,|\mathbf{W}|^{1/2}[1 - (\mathbf{x} - \mathbf{u})'\,\mathbf{W}(\mathbf{x} - \mathbf{u})]^m \qquad (4)$$

The density function is

$$p(\mathbf{x}) = \begin{cases} h(\mathbf{x}) & \text{over region } T \\ 0 & \text{elsewhere} \end{cases} \qquad (5)$$

where T is the interior of the hyperellipsoid $(\mathbf{x} - \mathbf{u})'\,\mathbf{W}(\mathbf{x} - \mathbf{u}) = 1$. We are not interested in this paper in U-shaped distributions, and our discussion of Type II distributions will assume that $m \geq 0$. The scaling is

$$\mathbf{W} = \frac{1}{(2m + n + 2)}\,\mathbf{\Sigma}^{-1}$$

The univariate Type VII distribution is

$$p(x) = \frac{\omega}{B(\frac{1}{2}, m - \frac{1}{2})} [1 + \omega^2(x - u)^2]^{-m} \qquad 2m > 1 \qquad (6)$$

The multivariate extension is

$$p(\mathbf{x}) = \frac{\Gamma(m)}{\pi^{n/2}\,\Gamma(m - n/2)}\,|\mathbf{W}|^{1/2}\,[1 + (\mathbf{x} - \mathbf{u})'\,\mathbf{W}(\mathbf{x} - \mathbf{u})]^{-m} \qquad 2m > n \qquad (7)$$

If $2m > n + q$, the qth moment exists. In particular, if $2m > n + 2$, the covariance matrix exists and

$$\mathbf{W} = \frac{1}{(2m - n - 2)}\,\mathbf{\Sigma}^{-1}$$

For both Pearson Types, the limiting distribution as m increases to infinity is the multivariate normal. Figure 2 illustrates some of these distributions in their univariate form, where of course the functions are symmetric and extend over the negative real line also. They have been normalized to have the same peak value, for comparison purposes. We observe that the Type II is uniform for $m = 0$, is parabolic for $m = 1$, changing in shape to normal for large m. This type is nonzero only over a finite region. By confining its peak amplitudes in the illustration, the scale parameter is forced to decrease with m, and the region of definition increases to infinity. The Type VII, including the normal as its limiting form, includes the t-distribution for half-integer values of m, and for appropriate scale parameter. For $m = 1$, the univariate form is the Cauchy distribution. We show the $m = 0.55$ curve as an example of one approaching the lower limit on m. The parameter m is a continuous one.

One of the many interesting properties of the multivariate normal distribution is that its marginal distributions are also normal. The Pearson Types also have an interesting property in this respect, as in many others. The marginals of the Types II and VII remain of the same Type, changing only in parameter by an amount of $\frac{1}{2}$ for each dimension change, increasing for Type II and decreasing for Type VII when the dimension is decreased. Therefore one of these distributions having parameter $m = m'$ in n-space has a marginal in a k-subspace having parameter

$$m = m' + (n - k)/2 \qquad \text{if it is Type II}$$

or $\hspace{9cm}$ (8)

$$m = m' - (n - k)/2 \qquad \text{if it is Type VII}$$

In going to a marginal in a k-subspace, the portion of the original n-space covariance matrix corresponding to the k-subspace is preserved. The same is true of the inverse scaling matrix, i.e., of $\mathbf{W}^{-1}$. It is interesting to note

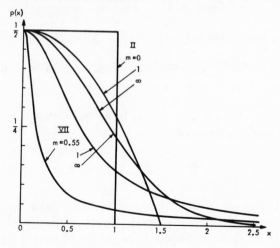

Figure 2

that for spaces of high dimension the unidimensional marginal for Type II approaches the normal distribution. The marginals of Type VII, however, diverge away from the normal distribution.

DECISION PROCEDURES

As is well known, Bayes, Minimax, and Neyman-Pearson decision criteria are satisfied by the decision rule:

$$\text{If} \quad \frac{p_2(\mathbf{x})}{p_1(\mathbf{x})} \geq L \qquad \begin{array}{l} \text{decide on category 2} \\ \text{otherwise, category 1} \end{array} \tag{9}$$

Taking the above as an equality, the boundary is defined. Since this paper considers only the distribution types described in the previous section, the general boundary so defined is a quadric. Setting $L = 1$ is equivalent to employing the minimal error probability criterion, wherein the boundary corresponds to that contour on which the two density functions are identical.

THE HYPERPLANE[8]

Taking $\mathbf{b}$ as a vector perpendicular to the hyperplane boundary, and ρ as a threshold, the decision procedure then consists in performing a correlation of $\mathbf{b}$ with the unknown $\mathbf{x}$:

$$\text{If } \mathbf{b}'\mathbf{x} - \rho \geq 0 \qquad \begin{array}{l} \text{decide on category 2} \\ \text{otherwise, category 1} \end{array} \tag{10}$$

Then $\mathbf{b}$ and ρ are expressed in terms of the means and the common scaling matrix:

$$\begin{aligned} \mathbf{b} &= \mathbf{W}(\mathbf{u}_2 - \mathbf{u}_1) \\ \rho &= \frac{1}{2}(\mathbf{u}_2 - \mathbf{u}_1)' \mathbf{W}(\mathbf{u}_2 + \mathbf{u}_1) \end{aligned} \tag{11}$$

When the covariance matrix $\boldsymbol{\Sigma}$ exists, $\mathbf{W}$ in Eq. (11) may be replaced with $\boldsymbol{\Sigma}^{-1}$. When the distributions are spherically symmetric, Eq. (11) reduces to

$$\mathbf{b} = (\mathbf{u}_2 - \mathbf{u}_1) \qquad \rho = \frac{1}{2}(\mathbf{u}_2'\mathbf{u}_2 - \mathbf{u}_1'\mathbf{u}_1) \tag{12}$$

Equations (11) and (12) are completely independent of the distribution form from within the entire class of distribution pairs which are ellipsoidally symmetric, monotonically decreasing, and have equal scaling matrices.

Within this large class this decision procedure may be termed robust, since it is independent of the form of the underlying distributions.

THE HYPERSPHERE[9]

Associating the index 2 with the more compact distribution, the decision rule is

$$\text{If } \sum_{i=1}^{n} (x_i - c_i)^2 \leq R_n^2 \qquad \begin{array}{l} \text{decide on category 2} \\ \text{otherwise, category 1} \end{array} \tag{13}$$

where $\mathbf{c} = (c_1, c_2, \ldots, c_n)$ is the sphere center, and R_n is its radius in n-space. The hypersphere is optimal when both category distributions are of the same type and have the same parameter m. It has been shown that the boundary hypersphere parameters, expressed in terms of the scaling ω or the standard deviation σ, are:

For the normal:

$$\mathbf{c} = \frac{\sigma_1^2 \sigma_2^2}{\sigma_1^2 - \sigma_2^2} \left[\frac{\mathbf{u}_2}{\sigma_2^2} - \frac{\mathbf{u}_1}{\sigma_1^2} \right]$$

$$\tag{14}$$

$$R_n^2 = 2n \frac{\sigma_1^2 \sigma_2^2}{\sigma_1^2 - \sigma_2^2} \log \left(\frac{\sigma_1}{\sigma_2} \right) + \frac{\sigma_1^2 \sigma_2^2}{(\sigma_1^2 - \sigma_2^2)^2} (\mathbf{u}_2 - \mathbf{u}_1)' (\mathbf{u}_2 - \mathbf{u}_1)$$

For Type II:

$$\mathbf{c} = \frac{\mathbf{u}_2 \omega_2^{(n/m)+2} - \mathbf{u}_1 \omega_1^{(n/m)+2}}{\omega_2^{(n/m)+2} - \omega_1^{(n/m)+2}}$$

$$R_n^2 = \frac{\omega_2^{n/m} - \omega_1^{n/m}}{\omega_2^{(n/m)+2} - \omega_1^{(n/m)+2}} + \frac{(\omega_1 \omega_2)^{(n/m)+2}}{(\omega_2^{(n/m)+2} - \omega_1^{(n/m)+2})^2} (\mathbf{u}_2 - \mathbf{u}_1)' (\mathbf{u}_2 - \mathbf{u}_1) \tag{15}$$

For Type VII:

$$\mathbf{c} = \frac{\mathbf{u}_2 \omega_2^{2-(n/m)} - \mathbf{u}_1 \omega_1^{2-(n/m)}}{\omega_2^{2-(n/m)} - \omega_1^{2-(n/m)}}$$

$$\tag{16}$$

$$R_n^2 = \frac{\omega_1^{-n/m} - \omega_2^{-n/m}}{\omega_2^{2-(n/m)} - \omega_1^{2-(n/m)}} + \frac{(\omega_1 \omega_2)^{2-(n/m)}}{(\omega_2^{2-(n/m)} - \omega_1^{2-(n/m)})^2} (\mathbf{u}_2 - \mathbf{u}_1)' (\mathbf{u}_2 - \mathbf{u}_1)$$

THE HYPERQUADRIC[10]

Letting $F_j(\mathbf{x})$ represent for the jth category an appropriate quadratic form plus a constant, the decision rule is:

$$\text{If } F_1(\mathbf{x}) - F_2(\mathbf{x}) \geq 0 \qquad \text{decide on category 2} \qquad (17)$$
$$\text{otherwise, category 1}$$

Both category distributions are assumed to be of the same type and to have the same parameter m.

For normal distributions:

$$F_j(\mathbf{x}) = (\mathbf{x} - \mathbf{u}_j)' \, \Sigma_j^{-1}(\mathbf{x} - \mathbf{u}_j) + \log |\Sigma_j| \qquad (18)$$

For Type II:

$$F_j(\mathbf{x}) = |\mathbf{W}_j|^{1/2m} \, [(\mathbf{x} - \mathbf{u}_j)' \, \mathbf{W}_j(\mathbf{x} - \mathbf{u}_j) - 1] \qquad (19)$$

For Type VII:

$$F_j(\mathbf{x}) = |\mathbf{W}_j|^{-1/2m} \, [(\mathbf{x} - \mathbf{u}_j)' \, \mathbf{W}_j(\mathbf{x} - \mathbf{u}_j) + 1] \qquad (20)$$

The equality condition in Eq. (17) defines the boundary quadric. It might be noted that for Type II distributions, the decision rules associate the portion of the sample space complementary both to regions T_1 and T_2 to one or the other of the categories. This is of no consequence, and in fact this complementary region can be partitioned arbitrarily since an unknown could occur there only with probability zero anyway. When regions T_1 and T_2 are themselves disjoint, then the solutions as already prescribed can be used, or almost any type of partitioning boundary could be used, since one would then have two disjoint convex sets. A hyperplane could be used, or a hypersphere, or T_2 itself could be the boundary.

ERROR PROBABILITIES

Although the parameters of the optimal hyperplane boundary are independent of the actual functional form of the distributions, the perform-ance *is* dependent upon the form. The probability of misclassification is dependent upon the uni-dimensional marginal distribution in the direction perpendicular to the boundary plane. For a particular form of distribution the error probability, P_e, can be expressed in terms of a normalized separation measure which essentially is proportional to the perpendicular distance of a distribution mean from the boundary plane expressed in units of standard deviation in this direction. Letting $\sqrt{\alpha}$ represent such a distance measure,

$$P_e = \int_{\frac{1}{2}\sqrt{\alpha}}^{\infty} P_m(x)\, dx \tag{21}$$

where $\alpha = (\mathbf{u}_2 - \mathbf{u}_1)'\, \Sigma^{-1}(\mathbf{u}_2 - \mathbf{u}_1)$

and $P_m(x)$ is the marginal density function with unit variance. Particularly when the second moments do not exist, we use a normalized distance measure expressed in terms of units of inverse scaling. Letting $\sqrt{\beta}$ represent such a distance measure,

$$P_e = \int_{\frac{1}{2}\sqrt{\beta}}^{\infty} P_m(x)\, dx \tag{22}$$

where $\beta = (\mathbf{u}_2 - \mathbf{u}_1)'\, \mathbf{W}(\mathbf{u}_2 - \mathbf{u}_1)$

and here $P_m(x)$ is the marginal density function having unit scaling, i.e., $\omega = 1$. We then have

For normal distributions:

$$P_e = \frac{1}{\sqrt{2\pi}} \int_{\frac{1}{2}\sqrt{\alpha}}^{\infty} e^{-(1/2)x^2}\, dx = \frac{1}{2}\left[1 - \phi(\tfrac{1}{2}\sqrt{\alpha})\right] \tag{23}$$

where [19] $\phi(x) = \dfrac{1}{\sqrt{2\pi}} \displaystyle\int_{-x}^{x} e^{-(1/2)\,t^2}\, dt$

For Type II:

$$P_e = \begin{cases} \dfrac{1}{2}\left[1 - \dfrac{B_x(\tfrac{1}{2}, m+1)}{B(\tfrac{1}{2}, m+1)}\right] & \text{for } x \leq 1 \\ 0 & \text{for } x > 1 \end{cases} \tag{24}$$

where $x = \alpha/4(2m+3)$, m is the marginal m for $k = 1$ as defined in Eq. (8) for a distribution having parameter m' in n-space, and $B_x(a,b)$ is the Incomplete Beta Function [21]

$$B_x(a,b) = \int_0^x y^{a-1}(1-y)^{b-1}\, dy \qquad x \leq 1$$

For Type VII:

$$P_e = \frac{1}{\sqrt{2m-3}\, B(\tfrac{1}{2}, m-\tfrac{1}{2})} \int_{\frac{1}{2}\sqrt{\alpha}}^{\infty} [1 + x^2/(2m-3)]^{-m}\, dx \tag{25}$$

$$\text{or } \quad P_e = \frac{1}{B\left(\frac{1}{2}, m - \frac{1}{2}\right)} \int_{\frac{1}{4}\sqrt{\beta}}^{\infty} [1 + x^2]^{-m} \, dx$$

In terms of the cumulative t-distribution,[20]

$$P(t; v) = \frac{1}{\sqrt{v}\, B\left(\frac{1}{2}, v/2\right)} \int_{-\infty}^{t} \frac{du}{(1 + u^2/v)^{(v+1)/2}}$$

these are expressed as

$$P_e = 1 - P\left(\tfrac{1}{2}\sqrt{\alpha}\sqrt{\frac{2m - 1}{2m - 3}} \; ; \; 2m - 1\right) \tag{26}$$

$$\text{or } \quad P_e = 1 - P\left(\tfrac{1}{2}\sqrt{\beta}\,\sqrt{2m - 1} \; ; \; 2m - 1\right)$$

where the first form is used only if $2m > 3$.

Figure 3 portrays probability of misclassification as a function of $\sqrt{\alpha}$ for some of the probability distributions, and m is the value of the parameter belonging to the unidimensional marginal. We observe that for small values of α all of the Type II curves are above the normal, but come increasingly close to it for larger values of the parameter m. As a result of the behavior of the marginals, which was presented in an earlier section, a normal and a Type II distribution having the same means and covariance matrices in n-space will have marginals which, when n is large, are essentially both the same and normal. Therefore, when the hyperplane boundary is optimum, Type II distributions in a space of large dimension have error probabilities which tend to be the same as for the normal. For small α the Type VII curves lie below the normal, but come closer to it with increased m. The marginals here diverge from the normal, and Type VII distributions in a space of high dimension have a tendency to perform differently from the normal. For $m < 1.5$, the error performance for Type VII cannot be shown on an α plot but rather must be shown on a β scale. For univariate distributions $\sqrt{\alpha}$ is simply $|u_2 - u_1|/\sigma$.

To gain some feeling for the improvement in performance of the optimal hyperquadric boundary for different distribution types over the assumption of normality, let us consider partitioning for two categories having distributions (uniform) of Type II, $m = 0$, with different covariance matrices and separated so that regions T_1 and T_2 are disjoint but tangent to each other. The true partitioning leads to perfect classification. But if we were to assume the distributions to be multivariate normal, with covariances and means as above, the error incurred using this normal boundary when the underlying distributions are in fact uniform, is readily seen to be nonzero. As a simple example consider the distributions to be univariate

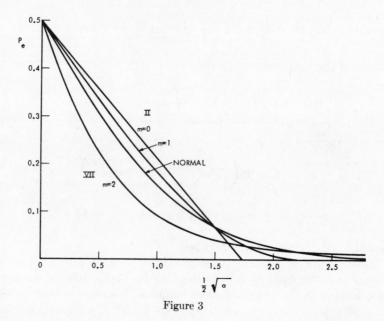

Figure 3

Type II, $m = 0$, with $\sigma_1 = 2\sigma_2$, and $(u_2 - u_1) = 5.2\sigma_2$, whereby they are disjoint but tangent. The error probability is zero. Under the assumption of normality, the actual error probability then incurred is 1.7 percent. The improvement in the true solution over the one obtained under the assumption of normality, is 100 percent in this case. It might be of interest to note that if the distributions were truly normal, the error probability would then be 3.8 percent. As another univariate case, when the underlying distributions are again Type II, $m = 0$, with $\sigma_1 = 2\sigma_2$, but having the same means, the error probability is 25 percent with the true solution, and 30.4 percent, using a partitioning obtained under an assumption of normality.

Specific expressions for error probability for the hypersphere boundary are given elsewhere.[9]

MULTIPLE-CATEGORY

Discrimination among J categories all of which pairwise satisfy the boundary conditions outlined above can be achieved with boundaries between each pair of categories, and these boundaries can each be determined as in the 2-category classification problem. Such a procedure requires $(1/2) J(J - 1)$ boundaries. An unknown can be assigned by making only $(J - 1)$ pairwise comparisons, each time rejecting the less likely category.

Assignment can also be made by comparing the likelihood functions of the J categories, and selecting the largest. When hyperquadrics are appropriate, this all-at-once comparison involves a selection of that category for which $F_j(\mathbf{x})$ is least, where $j = 1, 2, \ldots, J$, and where $F_j(\mathbf{x})$ is given by Eq. (18), (19), or (20). When hyperspheres are appropriate, Euclidean distance is measured from the unknown to the various category means, and assignment is again based upon selection of that category for which $F_j(\mathbf{x})$ is least, where now a simplified form is used:

Normal:
$$F_j(\mathbf{x}) = \sigma_j^{-2}(\mathbf{x} - \mathbf{u}_j)'(\mathbf{x} - \mathbf{u}_j) + 2n \log \sigma_j \tag{27}$$

Type II:
$$F_j(\mathbf{x}) = \omega_j^{n/m}[\omega_j^2(\mathbf{x} - \mathbf{u}_j)'(\mathbf{x} - \mathbf{u}_j) - 1] \tag{28}$$

Type VII:
$$F_j(\mathbf{x}) = \omega_j^{-n/m}[\omega_j^2(\mathbf{x} - \mathbf{u}_j)'(\mathbf{x} - \mathbf{u}_j) + 1] \tag{29}$$

When hyperplanes are appropriate, assignment simply depends upon comparison of J correlation measurements and is achieved by selection of that category for which $D_j(\mathbf{x})$ is largest, where

$$D_j(\mathbf{x}) = \mathbf{d}_j'\mathbf{x} - \rho_j \tag{30}$$

and where

$$\mathbf{d}_j = \mathbf{W}\mathbf{u}_j \quad \text{and} \quad \rho_j = (1/2)\,\mathbf{u}_j'\,\mathbf{W}\mathbf{u}_j$$

When the covariance matrix exists, $\mathbf{W}$ may be replaced with $\mathbf{\Sigma}^{-1}$

There appear in the literature suggestions that in multicategory classification problems, pairwise partitioning of the sample space does not lead to unique partitioning, but that there are regions of ambiguity. For example, hyperplane partitioning of 3 categories in 2-space is shown to generate a triangular uncertainty region[16] which is not associated with any one category, but for which each category is rejected by one of the planes. Such is not the case in the procedures of this paper, however, and our partitioning *is* unique, and there are *no* regions of ambiguity. That this is true can be readily appreciated from consideration of the fact that the techniques of this paper deal with optimal partitioning and that this corresponds to assigning any unknown $\mathbf{x}$ on the basis of selecting that likelihood function which is largest; a procedure which is unique.*

* Of course there may be regions in sample space where two or more likelihood functions have the same value, in which regions assignment is unique, but could be considered arbitrary. For the distributions treated in this paper, this could occur only over regions in which the unknown could fall with probability zero, unless the distributions are uniform, nondisjoint, and have the same scaling determinants, in which case the intersecting regions could be assigned arbitrarily. This also applies to the two-category case.

Figure 4 portrays hyperplane partitioning in 2-space for spherically symmetric distributions centered in the small circles. For the 3-category case, the unique partitioning results in intersection of the planes in a single nodal point. For the four-category case, partitioning is of course also unique, although there is then more than one node. It is of interest to note that in a space of n dimensions $(n + 1)$ categories, having means whose difference vectors (with respect to one of the means) are linearly independent, have partitioning hyperplanes which all intersect in a single nodal point.

Even if we were to treat distributions for which the true optimal partitioning appropriate for the underlying distributions did not involve hyperplanes, a partitioning obtained under the assumption of optimal hyperplane partitioning *would* be unique. In such a case, a common scaling matrix would be estimated and used just as if all the scaling matrices were really equal. However, the resultant partitioning would of course be inferior to the best one which could be applied, and even the pairwise partitioning would in general be inferior to the best hyperplane partitioning which could be obtained for two categories with unequal scaling matrices.

This discussion carries over directly to partitioning with hyperspheres and hyperquadrics. Assignment is unique here too, and each category region is bounded with segments of hyperquadrics or of hyperspheres, rather than with planar segments.

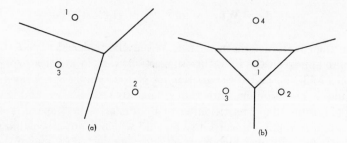

Figure 4

SIGNIFICANT DIRECTIONS

A facet of the classification problem of much interest is the ordering of the coordinate directions in importance so that, where desired, the dimensionality can be most efficiently reduced. An important motive for such a reduction is of course to reduce the computational complexity of both the learning and the recognition phases of the problem. The hypersphere and the perpendicular hyperplane solutions are sufficiently easy to implement, however, that once it has been determined that one of these boundary forms is applicable, the above motive loses its urgency. With skew plane boundaries the recognition phase is also simple, but the learning phase involves determination of and inversion of the scaling matrix, and here the potential saving in complexity is important. Another motive exists, however, even for the simpler decision procedures. This is that a reduction in dimensionality results in a corresponding reduction in the number of data sensors required to supply the inputs.

The philosophy here underlying an evaluation of the relative significance of coordinate directions is that importance is determined according to the extent to which measurements in a particular direction contribute toward satisfying the decision criterion. There has been much discussion in the literature of ordering techniques based upon methods of principal components whereby coordinate directions are said to be important in describing a category inversely according to the variances in each direction without regard to the characteristics of the other categories. However, in contrast to the principal components viewpoint, the real significance of coordinate directions in a discrimination problem arises in the extent to which the various categories differ from one another in the various directions.[8] Therefore, for a 2-category classification problem, we are interested in determining those coordinate directions which are most decisive in distinguishing the two distributions. (Discriminant analysis approaches the problem within this framework.)

Considering now a 2-category problem, and in particular the hyperplane, it is the direction perpendicular to the plane, i.e., the direction of the vector **b** in Eqs. (11) or (12), which contains *all* of the discriminatory capability. If measurements can be made in this direction, the problem could, in principle, be reduced to a univariate one, and no additional information would be obtained from measurements in other directions.

Suppose, however, we were constrained to a particular set of coordinate directions defined by the orthonormal set $\{\mathbf{e}_i\}$, $i = 1, 2, \ldots, n$. For the perpendicular bisecting plane boundary, these orthonormal vectors are ordered in decreasing importance according as $\mathbf{e}_i{}'(\mathbf{u}_2 - \mathbf{u}_1)$ is ordered in decreasing value. For the ellipsoidal distributions, leading to a skew plane boundary, the ordering procedure is more involved. To find the best k-subspace we choose the largest of

$$\beta_k = (\mathbf{u}_2 - \mathbf{u}_1)_k{}' \, \mathbf{W}_k (\mathbf{u}_2 - \mathbf{u}_1)_k \qquad (31)$$

for all possible subspaces of dimension k. The mean vectors and the scaling matrix used in this equation are expressed in terms of the basis for each k-subspace. Here too, where the covariance matrix exists Eq. (31) can be replaced with α_k expressed in terms of Σ_k^{-1}. Referring to Eq. (21) and (22) it is at once clear that α_k and β_k are performance measures, and that the larger they are, the smaller is the probability of error. Of course, the actual error incurred for any of these subspaces can be readily determined from substitution of α_k into the appropriate error-probability equation, or from Fig. 3. The number of possible subspaces of dimension k is given by the combinatorial coefficient C_k^n. Within each subspace, the vector perpendicular to the optimum plane boundary is $\mathbf{W}_k(\mathbf{u}_2 - \mathbf{u}_1)_k$.

Taken singly, the orthonormal vectors could be ordered with Eq. (31), where k is taken to be 1, or a related form can be used. For this other form, the orthonormal vectors are ordered in decreasing importance as Q_{1i} is ordered in decreasing magnitude, where

$$Q_{1i} = \frac{|\mathbf{e}_i'(\mathbf{u}_2 - \mathbf{u}_1)|}{(\mathbf{e}_i'\Sigma\mathbf{e}_i)^{1/2}} \qquad i = 1, 2, \ldots, n \qquad (32)$$

In relations like Eqs. (31) and (32) we show $\mathbf{W}$ in one case and Σ^{-1} in another just to further indicate their equivalence for these hyperplane solutions, and either may be used so long as the covariance matrix does exist, and if not it is $\mathbf{W}$ which should then of course be used. These orderings are independent of the form of the underlying distributions, and could be termed robust.

Figure 5 indicates the plane boundary and the corresponding significant directions for a number of cases. Figures 5a and b show ellipsoids of constant probability which are intended to be extremely narrow. Under these circumstances the significant direction is vertical, as indicated in Fig. 5a, for all relative locations of the means, except when the line of means is horizontal. In this latter case, Fig. 5b, all of the discriminatory information is in the horizontal direction. Figure 5d portrays the general skew plane case, in which we observe that the significant direction is oriented between the line of means and the direction of minimum variance.

For the hypersphere partition for two spherically symmetric distributions, the one most important direction is the one joining the distribution means, and all other directions are equally important, but less so than the principal one. In terms of a prescribed orthonormal basis $\{\mathbf{e}_i\}$, the directions defined by these basis vectors are ordered in decreasing importance according as $|\mathbf{e}_i'(\mathbf{u}_2 - \mathbf{u}_1)|$ is ordered in decreasing value.

For the multiple-category case where there are J categories having means for which the $(J - 1)$ difference vectors (between one of the means and each of the remaining ones) are linearly independent, there is a $(J - 1)$-dimensional subspace which assumes special importance. When the optimal partitioning is made with hyperplanes for spherically sym-

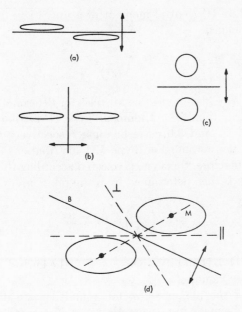

Figure 5

metric distributions, *all* of the discriminatory information is contained in the $(J - 1)$-subspace determined by the J means. This space is spanned by the $(J - 1)$ vectors, $\{(\mathbf{u}_j - \mathbf{u}_i)\}$, for $j = 1, 2, \ldots, J$, but $j \neq i$. For skew hyperplane boundaries, the $(J - 1)$-subspace containing all of the discriminatory information is spanned by the $(J - 1)$ vectors $\{(\mathbf{d}_j - \mathbf{d}_i)\}$, $j = 1, 2, \ldots, J$, but $j \neq i$, and where $\mathbf{d}_j = \mathbf{Wu}_j$. An orthogonal basis within this subspace can be obtained with a Gram-Schmidt orthogonalization.

For the multiple-category case where spherically symmetric distributions lead to partitioning with hyperspheres, the best subspace of $(J - 1)$ dimensions is the one spanned by the vectors $\{(\mathbf{u}_j - \mathbf{u}_i)\}$, $j = 1, 2, \ldots, J$, but $j \neq i$. For $(J - 1) < K < n$, any space of dimension K containing the aforementioned $(J - 1)$-subspace is as good as any other.

ESTIMATION

If the actual distributions are not known, we would then like to make a best fit of one of the Pearson curves to the data available for describing a particular category distribution. We need to determine the distribution type, the parameter m, and the location and scale parameters. Letting $\overline{x^q}$

denote the absolute qth central moment of a univariate distribution, the kurtosis can be defined,

$$\beta_2 = \frac{\overline{x^4}}{\left(\overline{x^2}\right)^2} \tag{33}$$

K. Pearson and W. Elderton use the kurtosis for determining the form for a univariate distribution.[13,22,23] Unimodal Type II distributions have a β_2 ranging between 1.8 and 3.0 corresponding respectively to the uniform distribution and the normal. For Type VII distributions, β_2 ranges from 3.0 to infinity. Therefore, the Type is selected according to the value of β_2. The parameter m is then determined from the relation,

$$m = \left(\frac{1}{2}\right)\frac{(5\beta_2 - 9)}{|3 - \beta_2|} \tag{34}$$

Since for Type VII β_2 is infinity when $m \leq 5/2$, the kurtosis cannot be used to determine these values of m.

In determining the parameter m for a multivariate distribution, the evaluation could be made in n-space. However, it is usually easier to work in 1-space, and Eqs. (33) and (34) can be used for determining m for the marginals. In practice we would determine β_2 for the marginal in each coordinate direction, and an arithmetic average of these would be used for determining the marginal m. Then making use of an inversion of Eq. (8), the value of m for the corresponding multivariate distribution is obtained.

When the distribution parameters must be determined from a set of M known samples, the problem of suitable estimators arises. Sample moments are effective in a wide range of situations, and in terms of a set of M known samples $\{z^{(v)}\}$, $v = 1, 2, \ldots, M$, these are:

$$\hat{u} = \frac{1}{M}\sum_{v=1}^{M} z^{(v)}$$

$$\hat{\Sigma} = \frac{1}{M-1}\sum_{v=1}^{M}(z^{(v)} - \hat{u})(z^{(v)} - \hat{u})' \tag{35}$$

$$\hat{\overline{x^q}} = \frac{1}{M-1}\sum_{v=1}^{M}|z^{(v)} - \hat{u}|^q$$

Where a common covariance matrix is desired for J categories, it is estimated as

$$\hat{\Sigma} = \left[\sum_{j=1}^{J}(M_j - 1)\right]^{-1}\left[\sum_{j=1}^{J}(M_j - 1)\hat{\Sigma}_j\right] \tag{36}$$

Estimation with sample moments has serious limitations with Type VII distributions, because of the fact that lower moments do not exist. In n-space, the qth moment exists only if $2m > (n + q)$. And the qth sample moment doesn't converge unless $2m > (n + 2q)$. Maximum-likelihood estimators do not offer a practical way out for sample sets which are not very small, because of the algebraic complexity involved.

Two estimation procedures which have merit are ones making use of order statistics and ones using fractional moments. We describe the estimation of parameters with order statistics for a univariate problem, whereby the set of M known samples is ordered in increasing value. We express the location, scale, and type parameters in terms of selected percentile points and take the corresponding order statistic to make our estimate. Best linear estimates make use of a weighted linear combination of all the order statistics. We will confine our present attention, however, to procedures making use of a single-order statistic. The location is estimated with the sample median. The scale parameter ω is determined in terms of the difference of two particular order statistics, and the parameter m in terms of the ratio of two differences.

Before proceeding, let us remark that we are using estimation with order statistics for the Type VII distributions, with low value of m. We set up a procedure involving good order statistics, but not necessarily the best. The best order statistic to be used in a particular estimation would depend upon the particular distribution form, and to some extent on the sample size. The estimates are assumed to be based upon a large sample set, and they converge for any value of m.

We denote with $z_{(t)}$ the ordered sample which is closest to the tth percentage point, where we take $t < \frac{1}{2}$, and where this corresponds to the (tM)th ordered sample.* The scale parameter is estimated as

$$\hat{\omega} = G_t(m)[z_{(1-t)} - z_{(t)}]^{-1} \tag{37}$$

where $G_t(m)$ is a function of the particular value for t selected and of m, or an estimate of m. A reasonable value for t is 0.15. The parameter m may be determined from

$$\hat{H}_{s,t}(m) = \frac{[z_{(1-t)} - z_{(t)}]}{[z_{(1-s)} - z_{(s)}]} \tag{38}$$

A reasonable value for t is 0.15, and for s is 0.35. $H_{s,t}(m)$, for these values of s and t, is denoted simply as $H(m)$ and is plotted as a function of m in Fig. 6. Substituting the indicated order statistics into (38) gives an estimate for $H(m)$, and the corresponding m is read off the abscissa in Fig. 6. This

* Or the closest one to it, or an inbetween point between the two adjacent samples.

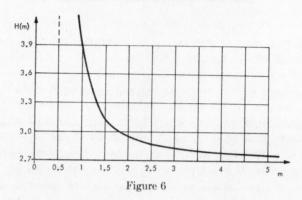

Figure 6

curve was determined from a tabulation of the percentage points for the t-distribution.

For multivariate distributions, m is determined by first determining the marginal value with Eq. (38), which then determines the multivariate parameter. The median is determined by taking the sample median for each coordinate direction. The marginal scale parameters can be obtained as discussed earlier, and the scaling matrix can be obtained from these and from an estimate of the correlation matrix. A method for estimating the correlation matrix is described by J. Ogawa.[24]

The method of fractional moments draws upon absolute central moments of low fractional order. We again consider Type VII distributions and treat the univariate case, and denote the qth moment with $\overline{x^q}$, where $q > 0$, and where q is a continuous parameter. No matter how small m is, so long as $m > \frac{1}{2}$, there are fractional moments which exist and for which the sample moments converge. The moments and scale parameter are related as

$$\omega^q \overline{x^q} = \frac{\Gamma[(1+q)/2]\ \Gamma[m-(1+q)/2]}{\Gamma(\frac{1}{2})\ \Gamma(m-\frac{1}{2})} \tag{39}$$

We can select two values for q, say $\frac{1}{8}$ and $\frac{1}{4}$. In terms of these two moments, we can define a shape parameter analagous to the kurtosis. Denoting this parameter Δ,

$$\Delta = \frac{\overline{x^{1/4}}}{\left(\overline{x^{1/8}}\right)^2} \tag{40}$$

where Δ is a function of m, and exists for $m > \frac{5}{8}$ and where the above sample (fractional) moments converge for $m > \frac{3}{4}$. The functional relation between Δ and m is defined by Eqs. (39) and (40), but since it is in terms of gamma functions it does not allow for solution for m in simple form. However, a Δ versus m curve can be drawn, and the sample moments can then be used to estimate Δ, whence m is read off the abscissa. The scale parameter can be obtained from Eq. (39) and $\overline{x^{1/8}}$.

The fractional moments involve equations requiring graphic solution rather than the simple algebraic relations associated with the even-ordered integer moments. But fractional moments, of low enough order, do exist, and their sample moments will converge.

One of the features of sample moments, integer or fractional, is that in an adaptive problem all of the necessary information is contained in the latest estimate. A moment estimate from $(M + 1)$ samples can be obtained simply from the latest sample and the estimate based on the other M samples. Estimation with order statistics, however, requires that the entire sample be retained for updating.

IMPLEMENTATION

In making use of the hierarchy of decision boundaries for an actual classification problem, a number of tests are performed on the input data for determining the simplest boundary form applicable.

Figure 7 portrays a possible testing procedure, where, for purposes of illustration, we treat a 2-category problem in which the covariance matrices are assumed to exist. An actual problem might make use of a computer or a special purpose device capable of operating with any of the boundary forms and capable of performing the tests indicated in the illustration. Or, perhaps, an actual problem might make use of a simple form of decision rule directly, where the selection from within the hierarchy may have been made during an earlier evaluation. Therefore, let us view Fig. 7 as a concept diagram, which indicates the essence of the underlying evaluation procedure, but which might not be necessary in a specific problem.

Having estimated the covariance matrices from the known samples, each matrix is subject to several tests. To determine whether a hyperplane is the appropriate boundary, the matrices are examined for equality. To check spherical symmetry, each matrix is examined to see whether it is essentially diagonal with equal elements. Each network gives an output when its condition is satisfied, and the boundary form is chosen by selecting the first output, viewed from the right, giving an indication.

Practical considerations would suggest that, although the limiting boundary forms are contained within the general quadric model, it is better to first determine that a limiting form is applicable, and go directly to its simpler solution. Also, in some cases, when limiting forms are applicable, the more general solution can behave anomalously. For example, a spherical boundary becomes a plane in the limit as the variances become the same.

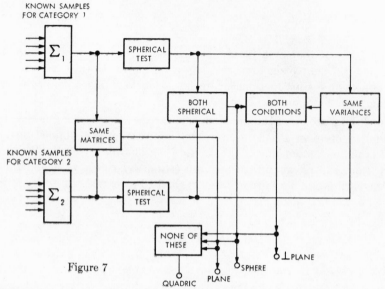

Figure 7

Under this limiting condition the hypersphere then becomes unreliable, and we would then prefer to use a hyperplane solution directly.*

REMARKS

Although the decision boundaries described have been obtained for the minimal error probability criterion, simple modification[9,10] can account for a wider range of criteria wherein the likelihood ratio is compared with a threshold L as shown in Eq. (9). Depending upon the particular criterion and specifications chosen, L can have any nonnegative value, and is not confined to unity. For different values of L, general hyperquadric boundary forms are retained, but the boundary parameters are altered. Hyperspheres remain hyperspheres, but hyperplanes (for the Pearson Types) will become hyperspheres or hyperellipsoids. An important exception to the latter occurs for multivariate normal distributions, for which hyperplanes remain hyperplanes, but where the actual hyperplane boundary experiences a parallel shift dependent upon L. In examining the behavior of a spherical boundary as L is increased from unity, we note that in general the boundary sphere shrinks until it disappears, and for greater values of L the entire sample space is then associated with category 1.

However, when the distributions of the two categories are Type II and when region T_2 is not fully contained in T_1, the behavior is somewhat

---

* Or comparisons of weighted distance measurements, which is equivalent to the sphere solution.

different. As L is increased the sphere increases in size until a critical value at which it becomes a hyperplane. As L is further increased the sphere flips over and the interior is then associated with category 1. As L increases toward infinity, the spherical boundary approaches the boundary of T_1. Behavior for L less than unity is similarly described.

For multiple-category classification the minimal error-probability criterion used corresponds to a Bayes (minimum cost) criterion for which all costs of misclassification are assumed to be the same as are costs of correct classification. Solutions for the case involving a general costs matrix involves partitioning which is considerably more complicated than the methods of this paper. However, a costs matrix having only a partial symmetry lends itself to the simple procedures of this paper, and yet allows consideration of cases for which a different cost is associated with mis-classification of samples from each category.[10,11]

The discussion of this paper has centered on situations where the techniques described are fully optimal. It is of course apparent that when the actual distributions are not much different from the ones described, these techniques can serve as good approximations to the actual optimum ones. When using these techniques as approximative procedures, a best fit is made with the Pearson Types to the true underlying distributions in the problem of concern.

Even when the functional forms of the distributions may not be very close to the Pearson Types, many situations are well approximated with the quadric boundary forms. Two distributions of essentially similar functional form and essentially unimodal and spherically symmetric can be fairly well separated with a hypersphere boundary. And when the two distributions differ primarily in location, the partitioning can often be achieved fairly well with a hyperplane. When distributions are tightly clustered and widely separated, almost any boundary form is good, particularly the simple ones. When one distribution is tightly clustered with respect to the other, the hypersphere boundary has merit.

The Pearson curves cover a wide range of forms, as can be seen in Fig. 2. We have shown that with these we can fit real world classification problems with a class of distributions, rather than only with the normal, and yet we can make use of tractable techniques similar to those used for the normal. Many kinds of categories could be distributed as Pearson functions. Pearson points out, for example, that Type VII distributions are not infrequent in biological statistics. In our techniques, the distributions involved in a particular problem are assumed to be of the same form, i.e., have the same parameter m. Two distributions so related could perhaps arise from the same type of process, whereby they differ only in location, scaling, and orientation.

There are myriad reasons why category distributions could have the relative shapes described in this paper. Several are here suggested. Two distributions having equal covariance matrices, eliciting a hyperplane boundary, could represent two categories described by the same process, but differing in location. Or they could arise from two deterministic signals corrupted by the same additive monotone ellipsoidal noise, or from two stochastic signals whose distributions differ in location and to which is added the monotone noise.

Two spherically symmetric distributions, differing in location and scale parameter, could represent similar processes undergoing growth, but each at different stages (because of differences in starting time, or of basic rate of growth). Spherical distributions could arise also where, for example, additive spherical normal noise corrupts the determination of whether or not a signal is present, where the signal is stochastic and also spherical normal. In this case, representing the noise distribution with $N(u_n, \sigma_n{}^2)$, and the signal with $N(u_s, \sigma_s{}^2)$, where these signify normal distributions with the means and variances indicated, the following two distributions arise:

No signal: $N(u_n, \sigma_n^2)$

With signal: $N(u_n + u_s, \sigma_n^2 + \sigma_s^2)$

Two ellipsoidal distributions having scaling matrices which are scalar multiples of one another could arise from the same type of growth process, at different stages of development. Two distributions with different scaling matrices could of course arise merely in describing two different categories. And two stochastic signals, each described by a normal distribution, corrupted with additive normal noise generate two signal sets which differ and are normally distributed.

As can be seen, the solutions described in this paper are applicable to a wide range of signal detection problems, including both deterministic and stochastic signals corrupted by additive noise, and also cases where the channel itself is random with impulse response distributed according to the distributions we have considered.

Various aspects and refinements of the research described in this paper are still under study by the author, and it is anticipated that further results will be reported upon in the near future.

ACKNOWLEDGMENT

I am indebted to David B. Cooper of Columbia University for his many informative suggestions and comments throughout the course of this research. I am grateful also to Donald B. Brick of the Sylvania Applied Research Laboratory for his interest and support. To Robert Stout, for his helpful comments, and to Mrs. Mary Rodimon, for her excellent typing of the manuscript, I wish also to express my appreciation. This research was initiated by the author while a Staff Consultant at the Melpar Applied Science Division, and it has been continued at Sylvania.

REFERENCES

1. Abramson, N., and D. Braverman, "Learning to Recognize Patterns in a Random Environment," *IRE Trans. Inform. Theory*, vol. IT-8, no. 5, September 1962, pp. 558–563.
2. Albert, A., "A Mathematical Theory of Pattern Recognition," *Ann. Math. Stat.*, vol. 34, no. 1, March 1963, pp. 284–299.
3. Anderson, T. W., *An Introduction to Multivariate Statistical Analysis*, Wiley, New York, 1958.
4. Anderson, T. W., and R. R. Bahadur, *"Classification into Two Multivariate* Normal Distributions with Different Covariance Matrices," *Ann. of Math. Stat.*, vol. 33, no. 2, June 1962, pp. 420–431.
5. Brick, D., "A Mathematical Approach to Pattern Recognition and Self Organization," Sylvania Applied Research Memorandum No. 296, Sylvania Applied Research Laboratory, June 1962.
6. Brick, D., and G. Zames, "Bayes Optimum Filters Derived Using Wiener Canonical Forms," *IRE Trans. Inform. Theory*, vol. IT-8, no. 5, September 1962, pp. 535–546.
7. Chow, C. K., "An Optimum Character Recognition System Using Decision Functions," *IRE Trans. Electron. Computers*, vol. EC-6, no. 4, December 1957, pp. 247–254.
8. Cooper, P. W., "The Hyperplane in Pattern Recognition," *Cybernetica*, vol. 5, no. 4, 1962.
9. ———, "The Hypersphere in Pattern Recognition," *Information and Control*, vol. 5, no. 4, December 1962, pp. 324–346.
10. ———, "Statistical Classification with Quadratic Forms," *Biometrika*, vol. 50, December 1963.
11. ———, "The Multiple-Category Bayes Decision Procedure," *IEEE Trans. Electron. Computers*, vol. EC-12, no. 1., February 1963, p. 18.
12. ———, "Classification by Statistical Methods—Pattern Recognition," *Melpar Technical Note 61/2*, Melpar Applied Science Division, April 1961.
13. Elderton, Sir W. P., *Frequency Curves and Correlation*, Harren, New York, 1953.
14. Fraser, D., *Nonparametric Methods in Statistics*, Wiley, New York, 1957.
15. Fu, K. S., "A Statistical Approach to the Design of Intelligent Machines—Pattern Recognition and Learning," *Cybernetica*, vol. 5, no. 2, 1962.
16. Highleyman, W. H., "Linear Decision Functions, with Application to Pattern Recognition," *Proc. IRE*, vol. 50, no. 6, June 1962, pp. 1501–1514.
17. Kendall, M. G., and A. Stuart, *The Advanced Theory of Statistics*, vol. 1 and 2, Griffin, London, 1958, 1961.
18. Marill, T., and D. Green, "Statistical Recognition Functions and the Design of Pattern Recognizers," *IRE Trans. on Electronic Computers*, vol. EC-9, no. 4, December 1960, pp. 472–477.

19. National Bureau of Standards, *Tables of Normal Probability Functions*, Applied Mathematics Series 23, U.S. Government Printing Office, Washington, D.C , 1953.
20. Pearson, E. S , and H. O. Hartley (eds.), *Biometrika Tables for Statisticians*, vol. 1, Cambridge, London, 1958.
21. Pearson, K. (ed.), *Tables of the Incomplete Beta Function*, Cambridge, London, 1934.
22. ———, "Contributions to the Mathematical Theory of Evolution: II, Skew Variation in Homogeneous Material," *Phil. Trans. Royal Soc. London*, series A, vol. 186, 1895, pp. 343–414.
23. ———, "Mathematical Contributions to the Theory of Evolution. XIX. Second Supplement to a Memoir on Skew Variation," *Phil. Trans. Royal Soc. London*, series A, vol. 216, 1916, pp. 429–457.
24. Sarhan, A. and B. Greenberg (eds.), *Contributions to Order Statistics*, Wiley, New York, 1962.
25. Shannon, C., "Communication in the Presence of Noise," *Proc. IRE*, vol. 37, January 1949, pp. 10–21.
26. Sommerville, D. M. Y., *An Introduction to the Geometry of N Dimensions*, Dover, New York, 1958.
27. Van Meter, D., and D. Middleton, "Detection and Extraction of Signals in Noise from the Point of View of Statistical Decision Theory," parts I and II, *J. Soc. Indust. Appl. Math.*, vol. 3, December 1955, pp. 192–253, and vol. 4, June 1956, pp. 86–119.
28. Wald, A., *Statistical Decision Functions*, Wiley, New York, 1950.
29. Welch, P. D., and R. S. Wimpress, "Two Multivarite Statistical Computer Programs and Their Applications to the Vowel Recognition Problem," *Acoust. Soc. Am.*, vol. 33, April 1961, pp. 426–434.
30. Wilks, S. S., *Mathematical Statistics*, Wiley, New York, 1962.

5

A MATHEMATICAL APPROACH TO PATTERN RECOGNITION AND SELF-ORGANIZATION

Donald B. Brick and Joel Owen

Applied Research Laboratory
Sylvania Electronic Systems
Waltham, Mass.

INTRODUCTION

It is difficult to proceed very far in a study of pattern recognition without becoming aware of its relationship to the more general field of artificial intelligence. Consequently, we are not surprised to find most papers on either subject discussing the other. Certainly intelligence includes a larger class of problems than pattern recognition; however, all pattern-recognition techniques can be included as a subclass of the class of intelligent (or stupid) machines. In addition to pattern recognition, the other major elements of intelligence are search, learning, planning, and induction.[1] It is not uncommon, though, to find pattern recognition being used, as it is here, as the entrée to artificial intelligence.

A conceptual model for an adaptive pattern recognition system is presented here which, as will become obvious, has implications to other aspects of artificial intelligence. However, specific claims for the model are limited presently to self-organization for pattern-recognition purposes. Furthermore, the model *per se* does not provide a solution to the problem but does, in fact, lead to a procedure and series of questions which provide guidelines and goals for a program of research which is presently being pursued.

In the following, the concept of an "intelligent" pattern recognizer is treated as a learning and classification problem in multidimensional characteristic, feature, or measurement space. Learning from past experience is treated in terms of probability measures. Individual samples of patterns, if considered in measurement space, represent points in that space. Pattern classes consist of sets of sample points. Set membership is based upon teleological criteria (which in turn are defined via the goal-seeking or selection criteria evaluated in terms of utility or risk). Overlying the space as a measure of the frequency of occurrence of particular members are a set of characterizing measures; estimates, obtained from previous experience or past samples, of the actual characterizing probability measures. They converge to the true probabilities as the numbers of learning samples become infinite, i.e., the system reaches a terminal state in its learning procedure.

The above discussion identifies one type of learning as the computation of estimates of the probability measures from sample data during a conditioning phase.* This concept is not new. However, the approach, to be introduced, of using distribution-free or nonparametric probability estimation techniques *especially designed for Bayes risk analysis*[2] *is to our knowledge, unique.*

As has been implied, it is proposed to embed the classification or selection problem within the framework of decision theory; minimum risk being used as a heuristic. If a sequential decision procedure is utilized, additional "learning" is included by virtue of the "history" of sample values. A further type of learning can be included if the aforementioned estimates of the probability measures are updated after the initial conditioning or supervised learning phase has been concluded. This is unsupervised learning. Caution must be exercised here to assure that the procedure used has more virtue than potential harm.

Finally, provision is made for supplementary "intuitive" adjustment of the system parameters based on seeking unique, orthogonal, or invariant pattern characteristics, features, or universals, e.g., searching for methods of simplifying or reducing the dimensionality of the required coordinate system as an aid towards (a) ease of computation and (b) reduction of the tendency towards exponential growth of such systems.[1] The procedures investigated are reinforcement, reward and extinction, and coordinate transformations aimed at simplifying, directly, the estimated probability distributions, such as covariance diagonalization procedures.

It is believed that the approach described here may hold ultimate promise of satisfying many of the requirements of a conceptual and structurally-realizable model of a finite intelligent automaton,[1,3,4,5,6,7] as discussed later in the paper.

---

* During a conditioning or supervised learning phase, the system is fed samples of each particular stimulus class and asked to respond to (or learn) this class and/or is fed samples from all classes at random with the proper *a priori* probabilities and is corrected or graded by a trainer on its responses.

STATEMENT OF THE PATTERN-RECOGNITION PROBLEM

Pattern recognition implies the assignment of a name* or representation (be it simple or complex) to a class (or group of classes) of stimuli whose members have something in common in the way of values, goals, or problem-solving abilities. They are "similar" in a useful sense. If they arise from identical stimuli (with any variation, distortion, or noise being that added by the environment or representation) they form an important subclass of patterns—the so-called "prototype-derived" patterns.[1] Mechanically, then, pattern recognition can be thought of as grouping certain sets into common categories which are given common descriptions. It is logical to expect (or hope) that these descriptions will be simpler than the original sets. Minsky[1] has defined a pattern, "teleologically, to mean a set of objects which can in some (useful) way be treated alike." He also states that "We should not be surprised, then, to find ourselves using inverse or teleological expressions to define the classes." One of the major practical factors in the design of a pattern recognizer is the generation of a sufficiently descriptive ensemble of properties or characteristics.[1,8] By this we mean that they provide a representation of each pattern class which is sufficiently insensitive to individual variations among class members to encompass the class and, at the same time, are sufficiently sensitive to other deviations to provide a description of the class which is sufficiently unique to allow discriminating its members from those of other classes. Furthermore, the choice and effectiveness of these are constrained by the adequacy of (i) the sensing and testing procedures, (ii) the teleological descriptions arrived at or imposed, and (iii) practical considerations of economy.

To put these intuitive concepts into a mathematical model, consider a multisensor system (or multiproperty filter system) with sensors (or property filters), $S_1, S_2, \ldots, S_i, \ldots, S_I$, (denoted by S_i)each of which provides a measure of a characteristic or property of a stimulus or pattern. In a geometrical pattern-measuring system, the sensors may be retinal sensing elements while for waveform patterns they could be samples of the waveforms or, if time varying, of their spectra or combinations thereof, etc. However, the model is capable of including as patterns much more generalized abstract groups of objects, responses, or concepts. Therefore, the most general notion of "sensor or property filter" is intended here. We are interested in utilizing the joint response of the sensors to assign the stimulus to one of J classes (which may include a rejection class). The sensors must, of necessity, monitor different characteristics of the stimuli. In other words, they should be at least partially nonredundant or nondegenerate ($s_i{}^{\delta m}$ and

---

* The name or symbol need not be given explicitly; the class may be generated by the pattern recognizer as a recognition of an unnamed association, concept, or the selection of a course for possible action.

$s_k^{\delta_n}$ should be at least partially uncorrelated for some $i \neq k$ and/or some $m \neq n$, where δ_m is the mth stimulus or pattern class and $s_i^{\delta_m}$ is the response of the ith sensor S_i to the class δ_m.*). As implied above, one of the major problems in pattern recognition is the determination of a set of represent-ative** characteristics which (*a*) *exploit differences between pattern stimulus classes,* (*b*) *are of minimal sensitivity to variations among members of the same class, i.e., they are most characteristic of the class as a whole, and* (*c*) *satisfy* (*a*) *and* (*b*) *with maximum efficiency as measured over the ensemble of J pattern classes to be handled.* In other words for (*c*) we desire that set of (sufficient**) characteristics whose size I is minimum. These goals are expanded upon below:

In most cases, a stimulus class δ_m does not provide a unique set $\{s_i^{\delta_m}\}$ of sensor (or property-filter) response values.† More often members of each class $\{s_i^{\delta_m}\}$ form aggregates of response values representing all members of the ensemble of patterns included in the stimulus class δ_m. These J aggre-gates of arrays $\{s_i^{\delta_m}\}$ may be viewed as defining J sets of points in I-dimensional space. This space may be either a real number space, a function space, or a combination of both; depending upon the character of the s_i's. The density and closure properties†† of the sets depend upon those of the pattern classes and upon the characteristics of the operations S_i. In any case the J sets in the I-dimensional s-space define regions (intervals) whose interior points (and boundaries, if the regions are closed) represent a mapping of the J-classes, δ_m, $(m = 1, \ldots, J)$, into I-dimensional s-space.

With this discussion of an initial mapping process as a background, the problem of choosing property characteristics may now be described as follows:

The filters (or mappings) should be such as to provide [for requirement (*a*), above] regions in s-space with maximum separation properties (mini-mum redundancy); they should be adjusted to maximize the probability of discriminating a member of one set from that of any other.§ Therefore, if possible, the mappings should provide discrete regions with maximum

---

* Normally if there is no rejection class included in J, $1 \leq m \leq J$, for consistency, or if we include a rejection class for lumping together "other" or unrecognizable patterns $1 \leq m \leq J - 1$.

** By representative we imply that the set is at least of sufficient size and variety to "describe" the pattern classes and their differentiating properties to the accuracy desired.

† In other words, we are, in most cases of interest, not fortunate enough to (*i*) be able to obtain a set of characteristics with zero sensitivity to variations among stimuli of a class or (*ii*) have a set of stimulus classes with zero internal variation.

†† For example, if the set is perfect (closed and dense in itself) it forms an interval in the I-dimensional space, otherwise it consists of discrete points of subintervals.

§ Note that we have used the notation "any other" rather than lumping "all others" together into one alternate hypothesis as is sometimes done.

average separation. (In the case of pattern representations with random or nondeterministic properties, it is usually impossible to obtain complete separation of the regions. One therefore searches for characteristics providing minimum overlap, in some sense, in probability space. Lewis[9a] proposed the use of average information about the pattern contained in each characteristic as a measure of goodness. This corresponds to using, as a guide, the equivocation loss function in decision theory. Marrill and Green[9b] propose the use of pairwise differences between expected values of the logarithms of the likelihood ratios for pairs of classes. They show this to be equivalent to minimizing the probability of error for likelihood ratio tests on pairs of normal distributions. In any case, when the problem is to be treated by decision-theory techniques, the loss function associated with the problem can be used as a guide for the choice of characteristics.)

In order to satisfy (b) above, the mapped regions should be as compact as possible without violating (a). If the spread of a region in a particular dimension s_i, is large, causing overlap with other regions, thought should be given to reducing the weight given this property or discarding it completely since it is too sensitive to internal variation within the class without compensating for this sensitivity by enhancing discrimination capability. Such a procedure is illustrated in Fig. 1 for a two-dimensional region, where after a coordinate rotation, it is seen that one of the coordinates may be discarded. (It must be emphasized that if the statistical behavior of the problem were known precisely, then, in theory, the decision rules derived by risk theory as described later, are self-contained. They are not aided by such nonsingular affine transformations in so far as minimizing risk is concerned.* However, in practice such procedures may be useful in compensating for lack of knowledge of the relevant probability distributions, simplifying their estimation, and as a means of reducing the inherent noise for improving the accuracy of the actual decision circuitry. The ultimate goal here would be, if possible, the determination of a transformed and reduced s-space with the property that the individual pattern classes would be characterized by nonoverlapping subspaces, each corresponding to a set of unique features.

Finally, condition (c) states that, as a goal, the members of a set of ideal characteristics should be *maximally efficient*. Efficiency here refers to the size of the sensor set; maximum efficiency implying a set of minimum size, with respect to the ensemble of expected pattern classes, which in turn implies economy in that there is a minimum of repetitive or redundant information between responses of the members of the sensor set. This suggests the search for a set of characteristics which are orthogonal, in

---

* This can be proved for absolute scale invariant decision functions in a manner similar to the way in which Highleyman[10] has proven it for a linear decision function.

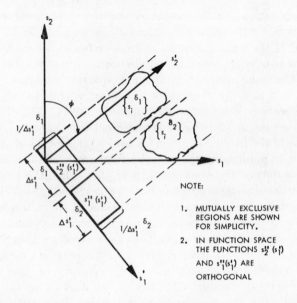

Figure 1

either a vector or function sense (with respect to the range of variations included in the J pattern classes), and matched to the patterns in the sense that they best satisfy (a) and (b) with minimum number of "dimensions." The minimum dimensionality achievable is J, the number of patterns.* Ideally, then, the goal of requirement (c) is to determine the lowest dimensional orthogonal set of characteristics, satisfying (a) and (b). The condition $I = J$ defines a "most efficient" set of sensors or characteristics. $J/I = e_s$ is a measure of efficiency of the s_i's.

If, in fact, the most ideal characteristics according to (b) and satisfying conditions (a) and (c), could be found, we could end up with a J-dimensional real number and/or function space, where each pattern class is most

---

* Some question may be raised about the possibility of obtaining dimensionality lower than J. The example cited might be that the pattern classes may be described by distinct regions in an s-space of dimensionality I less than J. Since our goal is to identify each pattern uniquely with an orthogonal coordinate, this I-space really represents a Euclidean space of J dimensions where the additional $(J - I)$ dimensions result from identifying each distinct pattern region as an orthogonal function of the I-dimensional space; orthogonal because of nonoverlap of regions (c.f. Fig. 1). As an example, consider the case where the patterns are initially one-dimensional; each pattern class being represented by an interval along the axis. Then each of the J nonoverlapping intervals represents an orthogonal function of the one dimension, e.g., a square function of nonzero value inside the interval and zero value outside the interval and therefore the ensemble is a J-dimensional function space.

characteristically represented by a set of points lying along its own co-ordinate axis, which represents a unique feature of the respective pattern class. In other words, we would have as an ideal, $s_i{}^{\delta m} \propto \delta_{im}$, where δ_{im} is the Kronecker delta ($= 1$ for $i = m$ or 0 for $i \neq m$).

Two simplified situations that may occur are illustrated for two-dimensional s-space situations in Figs. 1 and 2. In both situations illustrated, the two regions are nonoverlapping for initial simplicity. (In all cases where such clear-cut separation between classes is obtained, 100 percent efficiency can also be obtained.)

In Fig. 1 it is seen that a simple transformation (rotation) of the coordinates provides a new coordinate s_1', along which the regions are separable. s_2', in this case, does not contribute to the discrimination capability. In fact, s_2' may confuse the issue and may be discarded according to (b). In other cases, a coordinate may be completely redundant with another coordinate and hence discarded for the sake of compactness (b) and efficiency (c) requirements. The two new characteristics, the square functions, s_1'' and s_2'' are orthogonal *functions* of s_1', normalized for convenience. They are 100 percent efficient characteristics of their repective classes. Hence this is a simple example where we have been able to determine (via a coordinate rotation and definition of a simple function space) a most efficient set of functional characteristics s_1'' and s_2'' satisfying the "ideal" relationship, $s_i{}''^{\delta m} \propto \delta_{im}$.

The situation in Fig. 2 is much more complicated. An affine transformation will provide no additional simplification. Since the regions are mutually exclusive, a 100 percent efficient set *can* be defined; however, a simple analytic definition cannot be made as for Fig. 1. The two orthogonal functions which define the function space are $\{s_i{}^{\delta_1}\}$ and $\{s_i{}^{\delta_2}\}$ themselves. A more "natural" set of characteristics or sensors to arrive at the type of situation that was observed in Fig. 1 should be considered in cases such as this.

Condition (a), maximum separation of the regions, has not been discussed with respect to Figs. 1 and 2. With regard to Fig. 1, such a requirement would dictate metric distortion of the s_1' axis. It is not clear how to apply it to Fig. 2. Normally, the requirement of maximum separation is impossible to apply in a meaningful way unless some constraint, such as preservation of total area, energy, etc., as exemplified by Sebestyen,[11] is applied. Furthermore, in idealized situations where the regions are not as sharply defined nor as clearly separated as those in the figures, the need for maximizing the separation is not immediately obvious, nor is it obvious in cases where overlap exists and is defined by a known probability measure. The nomenclature "ideal" has been carefully included in the previous paragraphs, however, for the following reasons:

ASSUMING MUTUALLY EXCLUSIVE
COMPLEX REGIONS

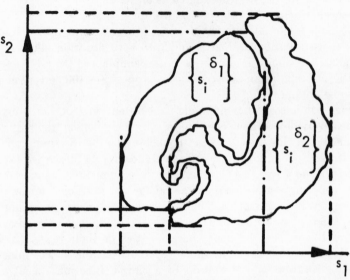

Figure 2

In practically all real situations, if the measurements are sufficiently sensitive, the pattern classes will be found to have a degree of randomness associated with them. Furthermore, thermodynamic considerations indicate that the sensors or property filters will add additional randomness. Hence the boundaries of the $s_i^{\delta m}$ regions are not clearly defined.* Indeed, this lack of definition is usually sufficient, as indicated previously, to cause overlap. Even in the absence of randomness, the complexities of most representative actual, real, or abstract pattern-class spaces are such as to dictate the type of interwoven topology, shown in Fig. 2; and thus clear-cut, completely disjunctive area separations in the aforementioned orthogonal unique-feature sense are difficult to discover or even define, in practice. Therefore, the possibility of finding characteristics which express even subtle differences between stimulus classes—i.e., those which highlight separations in s-space—is not one to be overlooked.

Previously, the relationships of the individual members of the sets composing the pattern classes to the classes themselves were not specified, although a probabilistic behavior was mentioned. For the purposes of this study, they will be assumed to be related by an overlying probability

* Normally the boundaries, even if originally well-defined, are distorted by the sensitivity and randomness (noise) introduced by the subsequent measuring apparatus.

distribution.* In other words, given the occurrence of the class, there is a probability of occurrence of each member of the class, or a probability density on the Borel set of measurements of members of the class. Most real situations of interest fall into this category. However, unless we have had sufficient prior experience with the pattern classes, or, can accurately describe the physical model into which these patterns fall so that we can describe their behavior, the probability distributions are not initially known to us.

In many cases, guesses are made as to the probability distributions or they are just arbitrarily assumed.[11,12,13] In other cases,[14,15] a knowledgeably wrong distribution is chosen under the assumption that it is not radically wrong and later corrections (during a supervised-learning or conditioning phase) will improve upon the choice. Others choose a distribution (e.g., Gaussian)[14,15] but leave parameters of that distribution for later "learning-period" determination (the well-known T-test approach of statistics). Finally, Braverman,[16] Highleyman,[10] Tou and Fu[17] and ourselves,[2,14] operate under the assumption that at the outset (i.e., prior to the learning phase) there is negligible knowledge of the parametric form of the distribution functions. All knowledge is to be acquired via the learning samples. The estimates of the distribution functions are then to be used to determine the actual probability distributions for decision making. Baran and Estrin[18] have implemented a simple version of the last approach on a computer using 48 samples of the numbers 0 through 9. At Sylvania we have been using at least 100 samples per character of all members of many type faces. Thus, these approaches to the pattern recognition problem imply the procedures of (a) "learning" the distribution function and (b) operating in a most efficient manner (in the light of the initial ignorance) so as to make optimum use of the data obtained during the statistical "learning" phase. These procedures result in a single-stage or nonsequential, discrimination or decision problem. The last approach is a so-called "nonparametric" one. Later the sequential manner of operating will be described where the estimated probability measures may be continually updated during actual operation of the system after the initial learning or conditioning stage and where the system categorizes according to updated sequential decision rules.

Finally, there is another approach or way of looking at the problem which is essentially similar to the nonparametric discrimination problem.

---

* Statistical methods may, in some cases, serve only as a convenient or simplifying tool or algorithm for describing the behavior of large numbers of members of the individual pattern sets. Consequently true or complete randomness is not required; statistical tools being introduced primarily from the point of view of convenience or unification in large number theory.

This is the "Pandemonium" or ordered nets model of Selfridge and Minsky.[6,19,20] Here the property filters or sensors are looked at as data demons which shriek in response to a stimulus. Decisions are made on the basis of the loudest-shrieking demons. Initially, Selfridge[19] discussed a simple model of Pandemonium, essentially a three-level device. (Data demons feeding cognitive demons, from which a decision demon derives its data). This model is equivalent to a machine which has perfect *a priori* knowledge of its statistics so that no learning phase is involved. Incidentally, this model is also equivalent to one in which the first mapping process, previously discussed, is 100 percent efficient and where the requirements on the characteristics have been as closely met as possible. Then, Selfridge adds a host of computational or subdemons whose functions are to provide adaptation via adaptable weighting of each data demon's signal transmitted to each cognitive demon. In Selfridges' work, adaptation is accomplished via a "hill-climbing" procedure. If adaptation is accomplished by a reinforcement procedure, Minsky indicates how this procedure is equivalent to the process of statistical learning in a simple Bayes' net model.[1] In effect, the initial first mapping is assumed to be inefficient, redundant, overly sensitive to internal class variations, etc. Adaptation is designed to reduce these towards the optimum.

Because of the practical difficulties involved in predetermining an optimum set of characteristics and the weights to be attached to each, it is believed in certain quarters that the best way to attack the pattern recognition problem is with an initial choice of a large random set of properties arbitrarily weighted (providing, hopefully, at least a sufficient set) with adjustment provided by a supervised learning phase.[6,19,20] No initial effort is devoted to efficiency although completeness (or sufficiency) is important. In fact, some workers have gone even further; utilizing, in addition, nets which are randomly connected.[21-23]

Now that the concept of statistical behavior has been introduced, let us examine its effect on the first mapping. Assuming that the *a priori* probability distributions are known, the s-space can be considered to be an $I + 1$-dimensional space. (The $I + 1$th dimension is the probability distribution—a function of the other I variables $\{s_i\}$.) No clear-cut boundaries are in general definable. The best one can hope for in the way of approaching the previously described orthogonal real-number function space is to find orthogonal coordinates coincident with, e.g., "major axes" of the respective pattern classes. However, in fact in many cases, there is even great difficulty in determining if one has found sets that are even sufficient, no less orthogonal and of maximum efficiency. Since the ultimate decision process is to be made as a choice or estimate from among J possible choices, in cases where $I > J$ (efficiency, $e_s < 1$), a second mapping or dimensional-reduction operation is made or implied by the decision rule itself following the first mapping. Optimization of the efficiency of the first mapping process to the limit $e_s = 1$ or $I = J$ is so formidable that it is rarely attempted—sufficiency being the major goal. (As stated previously, there is a school of thought that believes any attempt at initial optimization of the characteristics to be valueless. In any case because of the practical difficulties involved, it will be assumed from now on that unity efficiency in the first mapping cannot be obtained.)

THE FUNDAMENTAL MECHANICS OF PATTERN RECOGNITION FROM A DECISION THEORY POINT OF VIEW

Because pattern recognition can be treated as a decision problem, decision theory[24,25] provides a mathematically tractable way of handling the problem involved plus a yardstick for measuring performance. It is therefore used as a basis for this model.[17]

KNOWN PROBABILITY DISTRIBUTIONS, NONSEQUENTIAL DECISION PROCEDURE

The desired transformations for pattern recognition take I-dimensional descriptions, the sets $\{s_i{}^\delta\}$ *, into J regions, $\{D_j\}$, $j = 1, 2, \ldots, J$. If the patterns were initially deterministic and uncorrupted as, for example, by noise when sensed by the system, the transformations would be uniquely defined. Otherwise, they are found to depend upon conditional probabilities; however, the final transformations still are deterministic, i.e., nonrandomized decision rules. As discussed earlier, it is convenient to introduce probability measures as a tool for analyzing the problem with the understanding that these specialize, in the normal manner,[25] for deterministic parameters.

If the relevant probability measures were known, the problem could be cast into the standard format of decision theory.[24,25] The following notation is introduced:

$$\left. \begin{array}{l} P(\delta_m) \\ \\ P(D_j) \end{array} \right\} = a\ priori\ \text{probability of} \left\{ \begin{array}{l} \text{class } \delta_m \\ \\ \text{decision } D_j \end{array} \right.$$

$\sigma(\delta)\quad\ \ = a\ priori$ probability density of stimulus value δ

$P(X \,|\, Y) = $ conditional probability of X given Y

$W(X \,|\, Y) = $ conditional probability density of X given Y

---

* The notation indicates a set or vector consisting of $s_1{}^\delta$, $s_1{}^\delta$, $\ldots$, $s_i{}^\delta$, $\ldots$, $s_I{}^\delta$, not a set of values of one $s_i{}^\delta$. When subscript m is added to δ, then the notation $s_1{}^\delta m$ refers to the class of vectors corresponding to all stimuli in class δ_m.

Then, in terms of decision theory, the optimum classification problem is stated generally as follows:

(a) Minimize the average risk[24,25], R, (assuming, for unity in format, that d is continuous over decision space, D)

$$R(\sigma,F) = \int_\Delta d\delta \int_S d\{s_i\} \int_D dd\, W(\{s_i\},\delta)\, L(\delta,d)\, F(d|\{s_i\})$$

if the *a priori* density distribution $\sigma(\delta)$ is known, where $\sigma(\delta)\, W(\{s_i\}|\delta) = W(\{s_i\}, \delta)$, and

$$\Delta = \sum_{m=1}^{j} \delta_m, \text{ or, if } \sigma(\delta) \text{ is unknown,}$$

(b) minimize the conditional risk, r,

$$r(\delta,F) = \int_S d\{s_i\} \int_D dd|\, W(\{s_i\}|\delta)\, L(\delta,d)\, F(d|\{s_i\})$$

(or as another sometimes more sensible alternative, a minimax rule may be applied). An optimum or Bayes decision rule, $F(d|\{s_i\})^*$; is obtained by minimizing (minimaxing) R or r. In most practical cases F is deterministic,[24] the so-called nonrandomized decision rule. $L(\delta, d)$ is the "loss function." This function is a (subjective) weighting placed on the decision d as a function of δ.

If the decision space D consists of discrete hypotheses d_j each one corresponding to a class δ_m, then this is a problem in hypothesis testing and the decision rules are of a generalized maximum likelihood class.** A model of such a pattern recognition system, similar to those of Minsky,[1] Chow,[13] and Fu and Tou[17] is shown in Fig. 3.

It is important to note here that one of the shortcomings of some earlier pattern recognition efforts was the attempt to bypass the difficult computational aspects of the multiple hypothesis problem by treating m separate signal-plus-noise versus noise-alone problems—one to test the presence or

---

* I.e., given s, a decision d is made about δ as determined by the decision rule F.
** The general decision formula for discrete d_j and δ_m is:

$$\min_{j} \Sigma_{m} L(\delta_m, d_j)\, P(\delta_m)\, W(\{s_i\}|\delta_m) \qquad \text{all } j$$

For special assignments of loss function, this reduces to comparisons (possibly weighted) between, and/or threshold operations on, the individual $P(\delta_j)\, W(\{s_i\}|\delta_j)$, the likelihood functions.

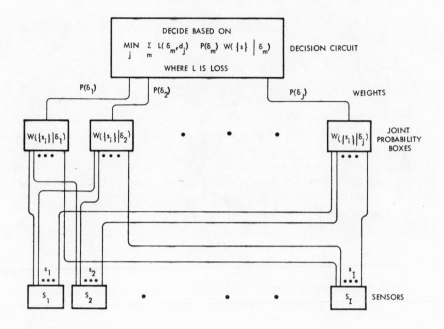

Figure 3

absence of each pattern class separately (a null test). Because of the finite probabilities of error that may be involved in the null tests and the absence of any cross referencing between individual classes in this shortcut method, this method is not optimum. The multiple hypothesis problem should be treated directly. However, the (multiple hypothesis) problem may be simplified considerably for particular assignments of loss function (e.g., equal losses for all errors except rejection).[13,15,25,26,27]*

KNOWN PROBABILITY DISTRIBUTIONS, SEQUENTIAL DECISION PROCEDURE

Earlier discussion has treated the decision problem as a single decision to be made on an ensemble of available data (or a series of single decisions to be made on a corresponding series of ensembles) obeying known probabilistic behavior. In most cases, a more accurate decision can be made if additional observations are available. Sequential decision theory[24,28] optimizes the use of these additional observations. In some cases it specifies the use of all or most of the observations, while in other cases, if early decisions can be made with sufficiently low probability of error a data ensemble of smaller size is used, especially, if there is a cost advantage to be gained from this reduction. For example, sometimes the reception of data is spread over a period of time and it is desirable to make a decision as soon as possible.

The problem is then stated in the following form: For average risk, minimize $R(\sigma, F) = R_1(\sigma, F) + R_2(\sigma, F)$ or, for conditional risk, minimize $r(\delta, F) = r_1(\delta, F) + r_2(\delta, F)$, where R_1 and r_1 are modified versions of the previous average and conditional risks, respectively, arising from the imposition of a loss for errors, and R_2 and r_2 are average and conditional risks caused by performing q experiments prior to making a terminal decision on the $q + $ 1st experiment (i.e., an average cost of experiment). Consequently, on the basis of minimizing average costs, one sets up a sequence of decision rules for utilizing the sequence of data,* as follows

$$R_1(\sigma,F) = \sum_{q=0}^{\infty} \sum_{d_1^e, \ldots, d_q^e} \int_\Delta d\delta \int_{(S_{q+1})} d\{s_i\}_{q+1} \int_{\bar{D}^t} dd^t$$
$$L(\delta, d^t) \, F(d^t | \{s_i\}_{q+1}, d_1^e, \ldots, d_q^e) \, W(\{s_i\}_{q+1}, \delta)$$

and

$$R_2(\sigma,F) = \sum_{q=1}^{\infty} \sum_{d_1^e, \ldots, d_q^e} \int_\Delta d\delta \int_{(Sq)} d\{s_i\}_q \, P(d_1^e, \ldots, d_q^e, d^t | \{s_i\}_q)$$
$$C(\{s_i\}_q; d_1^e, \ldots, d_q^e) \, W(\{s_i\}_q, \delta)$$

where q is the number of stages of experiment performed prior to making a decision on the $q + $ 1st stage.

d_i^e is an element of decision space, D_i^e, for the outcome of the ith decision which is not a terminal decision (superscript e $=>$ experiment); each sum over d_i^e above is over the respective space D_i^e. $\bar{D}^t$, with elements d^t, is the subset of D space for which terminal decisions are allowed (superscript t). $\{s_i\}_q$ indicates a sequence of q sets or vectors, $\{s_i\}$ (S_q) is the space of $\{s_i\}_q$. $F(d^t | \{s_i\}_{q+1}, d_i^e, \ldots, d_q^e)$ is the sequential decision function for q experimental stages and a terminal stage decision D^t.

$P(d_1^e, \ldots, d^t | \{s_i\}_q)$ is the probability of experimental outcomes d_1^e through d_q^e followed by d^t for sequence $\{s_i\}_q =$

$$F(d^t | \{s_i^{\delta_m}\}_q, d_1^e, \ldots, d_q^e) \prod_{k=1}^{q} F(d_k^e | \{s_i^{\delta_m}\}_k; d_1^e, \ldots, d_{k-1}^e).$$

$C(\{s_i\}_q; d_1^e, d_2^e, \ldots, d_q^e)$ is the cost for performing q experiments on a sequence of q samples of $\{s_i\}$ prior to making a decision. r_1 and r_2 are obtained by removing the first integral from R_1 and R_2 and making W conditional on the sequence of $q - \delta$'s.

---

* Note that the formalism allows the conditional probabilities $W(\{s_i\} | \delta)$ to vary from stage to stage (as q changes), consequently adaptational adjustment is possible within this framework.

Computationally the problem is amenable to solution by those techniques used in solving stochastic programming problems.[29]

IMMEDIATE IMPLICATIONS TO LEARNING THEORY

The previous concepts provide a framework for a self-adapting (or learning) system. The sequential approach whose introduction, in the last section, was justified for reasons of economy will provide, in addition, the possibility for self-adaptation by virtue of its ability to utilize its past history to effect its future operation (or configuration). Furthermore, situations can be accommodated for which, in addition, the statistical behaviors are not defined *a priori*. Consequently, the system can be given the capability to determine these during an initial learning phase to the best of its ability. Then, its decision rules are determined via sequential theory and in addition, it can continue to improve its knowledge of the characteristics of its environment based on its operation. The degree of initial ignorance and amount of data that can be collected and collated during the conditioning stage is crucial and determines the difficulty of the problem and the amount of continued updating or reorganization that is required.

Previously, it was shown that the terminal* solution of the single-stage pattern-recognition problem should result in a transformation as determined by decision theory and illustrated in Fig. 3. The transformation for nonsequential operations is of the form of an $I \times J$ matrix transformation on the I dimensional inputs, $\{s_i\}$, to yield the J-dimensional decision space D followed by a $J \times 1$ transformation matrix which is the embodiment of the decision rule. The elements of the first transformation matrix are the conditional probabilities $W(\{s_i\} \mid \delta_m)$, in some cases weighted by the *a priori* probabilities $P(\delta_m)$ and the appropriate components of the loss function. This is the optimum configuration of a thoroughly adapted system designed to make a decision on a single experiment and whose value judgments fit within the framework of Wald's risk model.

In certain cases (where for example degraded decisions are acceptable at reduced cost, or where only a parameter of a process with known distribution is to be estimated) it was argued that the final solution may be most economically reached in sequential stages of experiments.

This has been identified with a step in the process of learning. The situation can be analyzed in terms of the aforementioned matrix transformation (see Fig. 3) with the following added: (1) a $J + 1$st level to

---

* This implies that the optimum form of the processor when we are given complete information about the statistical behaviors of the stimuli classes will be of the decision theory form described (assuming that the system's goal-seeking value judgments or heuristics and logic are such as to fit within the framework of decision theory).

transform the matrix to an $I \times (J + 1)$ matrix in order to provide for the decision to call for an additional experiment via the added nonterminal decision, D^e; (2) feedback; and (3) *repeated* tests of $\{\delta\}$ via repeated measurements of $\{s_i\}$. The feedback is applied at the end of each stage from the $(J + 1) \times 1$ decision box, if activated by the D^e box, to the other D boxes and also to itself. This feedback provides to the system what may be called an adaptive memory and gives it a nonstationary Markov characteristic. In either the sequential or nonsequential case, the configuration arrived at is optimum from the point of view of minimum risk provided we know the relevant governing statistical distributions exactly.[24,28] In other cases much less knowledge is available prior to the time a decision is called for; in fact, in many cases complete knowledge is never available. Considerable learning is required to proceed from complete initial ignorance to some state of semblance of order.

Different degrees of initial machine ignorance can be postulated. For example, the system may be given the law of distribution of the stimulus processes, δ_m (e.g., Gaussian) and may be asked to decide upon the mean and variance or we may have enough knowledge of the physical bases of the process to give its distribution law. This type of problem is a straightforward one (parameter estimation, etc.) amenable to the aforementioned statistical and sequential treatment. Unfortunately, many of the problems faced in practice are not of this straightforward type, i.e., only limited numbers of samples of the stimuli are available and the physical principles governing their statistical behavior are unknown or only vaguely known. Furthermore, such systems may be required to make decisions which are optimum at each stage of their lives. In other words, a system optimally designed at the start for its initial state of ignorance is desired as discussed above; but the system should be capable of upgrading itself, as knowledge is acquired. Such a system falls into the category of a self-adaptive or intelligent pattern-recognition device discussed in more detail in a later section.

A DISTRIBUTION FREE METHOD FOR PATTERN RECOGNITION

INTRODUCTION

The problem of pattern recognition, when all the required statistics are known, can be effectively solved by decision theory as indicated earlier. This is not so for the case of nonparametric (unknown statistical behavior) discrimination. The difficulty arises when an attempt is made to use Wald's minimum-risk criterion. Since this requires distributional knowledge, no general conclusion from this type of analysis can be reached. To bypass this problem, further assumptions have been made. For example, although he started out more generally, Braverman[16] has assumed the existence of enough characteristics to apply the Central Limit Theorem, reducing the problem to the parametric (Gaussian) case. Jacobs[30] has generalized this argument and has suggested an alternative optimality condition based on least-mean-square arguments. Most of the previous writers, including Highleyman,[10] refer to "linear" discriminators.

It has been shown in the parametric case that discrimination should be accomplished by using the likelihood criterion. If done so, the probability of misclassification is minimized. Because of the reduced information in the nonparametric case, we cannot hope to do as well as the aforementioned criterion. It is then proposed to consider procedures which approach this criterion in the limit with large sample size. Heuristically, one might justify this by stating that if enough samples of a given distribution are available, the distribution is "almost" known.

GENERAL REMARKS

The areas of Hypothesis Testing and Estimation together make up a large part of classical statistics. Although they are different in the types of problems they solve, occasionally they are used together in the same problem. As an example, consider the discrimination of two Gaussian populations with the same covariance matrices. This requires a linear discriminator as dictated by the likelihood ratio. However, when the means and covariances are unknown, sample estimates of the parameters are placed into the linear model. This combination of techniques is justified by showing, for large samples, that the "linear discriminant" gets arbitrarily close to the true linear form. Thus the notion of replacing unknown quantities by their estimates seems to be a plausible approach to hypothesis testing when convergence can be demonstrated.

This suggests that the decision theoretic foundations may be reformulated so as to include the notion of adaptation. Let us consider the standard theory.[31] Typically, in a pattern recognition situation, we must associate a particular sample of a quantity into one of J categories. It is necessary that the space be partitioned with J regions so that when a particular point appears in a given region, the corresponding decision is made. To each category is assigned a distribution function, and to each distribution function, corresponds a possible decision. The parameter space is then of the same dimension as the decision space. The notation of the previous section will be altered for convenience. Since, in the following context, the parameter space and the decision space are in one to one correspondence to their indices, they will be identified as such (i.e., the decision d_j is replaced by j) with no ambiguity. Therefore, define

$W(s|j)$ = probability density of observed points given that they come from the jth category

$P(j)$ = *a priori* probability of drawing a member of the jth category

$L(j, i)$ = loss in deciding on the ith category given that it was a member of the jth category.

$$\tau_s(i) = \frac{\sum\limits_{j=1}^{J} L(j,i)\, W(s|j)\, P(j)}{\sum\limits_{j=1}^{J} W(s|j)\, P(j)} = a \textit{ posteriori } \text{risk}$$

$\varphi(i, s)$ = probability of deciding on i given that s was observed. The decision function which minimizes the risk function, is then given by

$$\varphi(i|s) = \begin{cases} 1 & \text{if} \quad \tau_s(i) = \min\,[\tau_s(1), \ldots, \tau_s(J)] \\ 0 & j \neq i \end{cases}$$

The function $L(j, i)$ is usually determined by the experimentor's evaluation of the system. The function $P(j)$ must be determined prior to the experiment. What is left to consider is the function $W(s|j)$. In general this function is not known. It is at this point that assumptions are made. That is, in order to have an "optimum" discriminator, distributional assumptions are either explicitly (assuming a specific distribution) or implicitly (functional form of τ_s assumed) made. However, the optimality of the resulting discriminator now depends directly on these assumptions. Under such circumstances no true adaptation can exist, i.e., the sequential procedure of pattern recognition is conforming to the assumptions rather than adapting to the environment.

In the pattern-recognizing system that is envisioned, we have at our disposal a learning process. In this period, samples are generated in a way that the observer knows the true classification of each. This can be accomplished by a completely supervised learning phase or a corrective punishment reward technique. That is, we have the sample points

$$\{s_i^j\} \begin{array}{l} j = 1, \ldots, J \\ i = 1, \ldots, n_j \end{array}$$

where s_i^j represents the ith sample known to have come from the jth distribution or category. Since this data contains information about the true distributions, the proper implementation of these statistics will yield an adaptive approach without misleading assumptions.

If we think of the set of J distributions, $W(s|j)$, as a point in an J-dimensional function space, then we can imbed this point in a space say, S. A typical point in this space will consist of a vector of J distributions of a certain class. A norm may then be introduced between points in this space to measure the closeness of points. If we now construct the set of estimates of $W(s|j)$, which are denoted by $W_n(s|j)$, through the data

$$\{s_i^j\}_{i=1,\ldots,n_j}^{j=1,\ldots,J}$$

we are in a position to define the notion of adaptation. Since the functions $W_n(s|j)$ are not dependent on the distributions $W(sj,)$, we can define the sample risk functions as

$$\{\tau_{s,n}(i)\} \; i = 1, \ldots, J$$

which is a function of the $W_n(s|i)$. Finally define

$$\varphi_n(i|s) = \begin{cases} 1 & \text{if } \tau_{s,n}(i) = \min\,[\tau_{s,n}(1), \ldots, \tau_{s,n}(J)] \\ 0 & j \neq i \end{cases}$$

We shall call the procedure for pattern recognition an adaptive procedure if $\varphi_n(i|s) \to \varphi(i|s)$ in the topology of S.

A PARTICULAR CONFIGURATION

The purpose of this section is to show that it is possible to construct the sequence $\varphi_n(i|s)$ in a practical situation, which does not depend on the true distribution, but which does converge to the optimum decision function.

Consider a two-decision problem with a simple loss function, i.e.,

$$L(i,j) = \begin{cases} 1 & i \neq j \\ 0 & i = j \end{cases}$$

Assume that the a priori probabilities are equal. It can then simply be shown that the optimum decision function is of the form

$$\varphi(1|s) = \begin{cases} 1 \text{ if } s \, \epsilon \, \left\{ x\colon \dfrac{W(x|1)}{W(x|2)} \geq 1 \right\} \\ 0 \text{ if } s \, \epsilon \, \left\{ x\colon \dfrac{W(x|1)}{W(x|2)} < 1 \right\} \end{cases}$$

and

$$\varphi(2|s) = \begin{cases} 1 \text{ if } s \in \left\{x : \dfrac{W(x|1)}{W(x|2)} \leq 1\right\} \\[2em] 0 \text{ if } s \in \left\{x : \dfrac{W(x|1)}{W(x|2)} > 1\right\} \end{cases}$$

If the functions $W(x|i)$ are continuous, then the optimum decision function is determined by the intervals where one density function is larger than the other. These intervals, in turn, are determined by their endpoints. The problem of finding a sequence of functions which converge to $\varphi(i|s)$ reduces here to the problem of finding a sequence of estimates which converge to the solutions of the equation

$$\frac{W(x|1)}{W(x|2)} = 1$$

The notion of convergence must be defined. This will coincide, in this illustration, to the statistical notion of consistency. Recall that a parameter $\hat{\theta}_n$ is called consistent if

$$\hat{\theta}_n \underset{p}{\to} \theta$$

which is the notation for

$$P_r\{\,|\,\hat{\theta}_n - \theta\,| > \epsilon\} \underset{n \to \infty}{\longrightarrow} 0$$

That is, the type of convergence to be considered is convergence in probability. So that, if the set of intervals or equivalently the set of endpoints converge in probability to those given by the risk condition, the adaptation criterion will have been established.

In this situation there is a heuristic argument which leads to a properly convergent sequence. The equation to solve is

$$\frac{W(x|1)}{W(x|2)} = 1$$

which can be rewritten as $W(x|1) - W(x|2) = 0$. Let

$$F(s|i) = \int_{-\infty}^{s} W(x|i)\, dx$$

Then the solutions we seek occur at the locations of the extrema of the function

$$F(s|1) - F(s|2)$$

The following theorem has been proven by Owen:[32]

THEOREM. Let $F_n(x|i)$ be a function of the observations. Let

$$F_n(x|1) \xrightarrow[p]{U} F(x|1)$$

and

$$F_n(x|2) \xrightarrow[p]{U} F(x|2)$$

(the convergence implied is uniform convergence in probability). Let L_{in} be the locations of the extrema of the sample function

$$F_n(x|1) - F_n(x|2)$$

Let L_i be the locations of the extrema of the function

$$F(x|1) - F(x|2)$$

Then

$$L_{in} \xrightarrow[p]{} L_i$$

With this theorem we can construct the intervals upon which the appropriate decision must be made and thereby construct the

$$\varphi_n(i|s)$$

Therefore as a corollary to the theorem we have

COROLLARY 1. $\varphi_n(i|s) \xrightarrow[p]{} \varphi(i|s)$

The condition that the *a priori* probabilities be the same may be relaxed. In this case we are interested in the solutions of

$$W(s|1) - \lambda_{12} W(s|2) = 0$$

where

$$\lambda_{12} = \frac{P(2)}{P(1)}$$

Then as a second corolary to the theorem becomes
COROLLARY 2.

Under the same conditions, the location of the extrema of

$$F_n(x\,|\,1) \;-\; \lambda_{12}\,F_n(x\,|\,2)$$

converge in probability to the location of the extrema of

$$F(x\,|\,1) \;-\; \lambda_{12}\,F(x\,|\,2)$$

THE J-DECISION PROBLEM

Under the assumption of a simple loss function the J-decision criterion is a sequence of inequalities involving only two of the distributions at a time. Therefore for each i, construct the regions of testing the ith category against the remaining $J-1$ categories. We may then proceed in the usual fashion using estimates rather than the true values. That is, if the point s is observed we look at the decision function of say the first and second categories. If the second category is chosen we then test the second category against the remaining ones until we find that the decision function changes our choice. We conclude when we reach the "most probable" category.

It is of some interest to point out that the specific loss function used in this and the preceding section's results, in the deterministic case, has the following interpretation. Under this condition, the minimum risk corresponds to minimizing the probability of error. Therefore the adaptive procedure suggested, is approaching the state of minimum error.

THE MULTIVARIATE PROBLEM

Suppose s is now considered as a vector whose components comprise the several characteristics of a given sample. The distributions $W(s\,|\,i)$ now become multivariate distributions. If, as one might hope, the characteristics are independent of each other, then the multivariate problem becomes similar to the univariate problem in the sense that each coordinate will undergo the treatment of the previous sections. If, on the other hand, there is a dependence between characteristics then the situation becomes more complicated. There is however a transformation which still reduces the problem to a much simpler one.

Consider the learning phase which is characterized by

$$\{\, \vec{s_i}^{\,j} \,\} \quad \begin{aligned} j &= 1, \ldots, J \\ i &= 1, \ldots, n_j \end{aligned}$$

where the $\vec{s_i}^{\,j}$ are now vectors in the Euclidean space of say k dimensions.

Introduce the metric $D(\vec{x}, \vec{y})$ into this Euclidean space. Choose a reference point in this space and call it the zero point. Compute the distances of vector data points from the reference point. This will result in the set

$$\{D_i^j\} \begin{array}{l} j = 1, \ldots, J \\ i = 1, \ldots, n_j \end{array}$$

where D_{ji} are now scalar quantities. (Reflection upon the transformation will show that in practice this is similar to what is usually done. But rather than stop at assuming the form of the metric D this proceeds to approximate the distribution of the distances when thought of as random variables.) We may then proceed with the previous mentioned techniques to establish a decision criterion. However, this transformation, when used, will not satisfy the adaptive conditions defined earlier. This follows because of the loss of information incurred through the transformation.

STOCHASTIC MODELS FOR LEARNING VIA AN AUGMENTED SEQUENTIAL RISK PROCEDURE

Analogies can be made between the problem of learning or adaptation by an "intelligent machine" having available to it only at most nonparametric estimates of the laws of behavior of its stimulus environment, and the problem of environmental adaptation and/or learning by an organism.[13, 33,34,35] Present and previous efforts to tackle the problem have been along many lines.

The approach we favor combines several techniques. It includes stage-by-stage (nonparametric) estimates of the probability measures required for and provided by the decision formulation, and either biologically justified or intuitive tactics aimed at improving the interim nonparametric conditional probability estimates and convergence rate, (as discussed in the Appendix) wherever these appear to be advantageous. The stage-by-stage estimates refer to an initial set of (nonparametric) estimates made during the conditioning phase plus updating at the end of each subsequent unsupervised stage based upon the techniques discussed in the last section and by Cooper.[26] The nonstatistical measures take the form of adjustments of the conditional probabilities, based not on purely statistical estimation procedures but on such heuristic techniques as reinforcement, reward and extinction, and feature or property extraction. These can be considered as transformations of the $\{s_i\}$ space, and add to the previous estimation techniques, an attempt at an optimum mapping, as described earlier, aimed at obtaining a more efficient representation of the pattern characteristics.

Since, with the sequential-decision, minimum-risk approach, a measure of stage-by-stage goodness or goal attainment is provided, and since minimization techniques are an inherent part of the risk methodology proposed here, then a heuristic algorithm is provided which is both optimum and measurable to the extent of the accuracy of our nonparametric estimates, our computational ability, and the degree to which the decision theory formulation is capable of fitting the goals and logic of the desired machine. It thus gives promise of providing a guided and, hopefully, rapidly-converging hill-climbing procedure. It is at least mathematically satisfying; algorithmic via stochastic programming techniques; and, via the adjustment measures outlined in the Appendix, amenable to physical and intuitive "doctoring."

Consider the following more-detailed train of thought: From an initial configuration, a system (or organism) adapts to its environment in a step-by-step procedure as it obtains more and more information. The learning phase can be of two types: supervised or unsupervised. The system itself learns by adjusting its decision (or associative and threshold) and weighting parameters. *This can be considered to manifest itself as a change in the system decision rules or decision regions and conditional probabilities, respectively.* The latter, in fact, implies a spatial transformation in sensor or characteristic space as discussed previously. The criterion for adaptation is either one of trial and error evaluation of responses with respect to goal-seeking measures (heuristics), one of punishment (extinction) or reward (loss or utility), or one of neural-like reinforcement (e.g., used paths are reinforced). It should be noted again at this point that the decision theory approach has implicitly built into it the reward and punishment, and trial and error heuristic procedures (based on probabilistic extrapolations) but has explicitly, *in past work*, limited adaptation to control of the decision and threshold parameters. However, other approaches (e.g., the reinforcement, reward and extinction procedures of Bush and Mosteller[5] and Minsky[1] and Selfridge[6] and, implicitly, the random net approaches) have treated the adjustment of the weighting parameters, although not always in terms of adjustment of the conditional probabilities. Furthermore, these methods have at least in practice been limited to the conditioning phase. The system conditional probabilities can be viewed as a compilation of previous experience and knowledge. Therefore, to truly simulate the complete process of continuous learning, provision for updating these during the postconditioning phase must be made. Thus, the sequential procedure should be extended to include postconditioning adjustment of the conditional probabilities as well as of the decision rules, (corresponding to adjusting the sizes and shapes of the decision regions D). This, thereby, formalizes what is already built into the sequential decision theory formulation.

The approach is in theory, analogous to that outlined by Bellman.* It operates as follows:

1. The system is given an initial supervised learning period. This learning period provides numerical data in the form of histograms of frequency of occurrence of various phenomena, etc. These are the initial sample statistics.

2. On the basis of these sample statistics, nonparametric measures are established, an initial configuration, and a set of decision rules (based upon minimum risk) are established. Nonstatistical measures are also used where advantageous, as outlined in the Appendix to transform the coordinate system to a preferred one.

3. As additional (unknown) samples are received, the system is updated in three ways: First, the previously arrived at sequential decision rules are applied to make a decision. Then, as a result of the latest decisions the probability measures are updated. Second, advantage is taken of the new data in updating the decision rules (to minimize risk). Third, additional adjustment of the probabilities, according to intuitive techniques outlined in the Appendix may be applied when appropriate. These constitute the postconditioning learning procedure.

4. This process may continue for the life of the system or, on the basis of certain considerations, it may be desired to terminate adaptation at some earlier stage.

With regard to step (4), above, our initial impulse would be to decide without doubt to continue postconditioning adaptation ad infinitum. Two factors may dictate against this and consequently force a compromise: (1) There may be a cost for continuing to adapt, a variant of the cost for experimentation, and (2) there is a finite probability that elements will be misclassified which could lead to false enlargements or drifts of the decision regions. The danger here is the possibility of drifts towards larger and larger error probabilities. Consequently, great care must be taken in avoiding this during unsupervised learning. In fact, it is possible that unsupervised learning may, in some cases, be harmful. Block[21] and Rosenblatt[22] have discussed the useful case where the transition probabilities of samples of the classes of stimuli are known or controlled in some manner.

---

* Bellman[33] points out the analogy between the stochastic learning model and a Markov process. He also outlines the stochastic programming approach in which the governing probability distributions are transformed at each stage, analogous to our model. Memory is, in addition to that inherently contained in the probability measures, included as a cross-coupling factor from stage to stage. Thus, all of the elements of our augmented sequential risk model can be accommodated in Bellman's algorithmic outline (his Stochastic Model II).

APPENDIX

A learning process must involve adjusting or organizing the sets of data used for decisions and the decision functions to convert the system from an initially high-entropy to a lower-entropy state. This can be accomplished in several ways, for example, (a) varying the weights (conditional probabilities) alloted to each sensor output in the connections to the decision circuits, (b) varying the decision functions (decision rules and decision regions) and, (c) application of a transformation to the set of s_i's between the sensor outputs and the decision circuits. Mechanically, procedure (c) can be identical to (a) in that they both involve varying the weights or conditional probabilities alloted to each sensor connection. Philosophically, they differ though, in that (a) implies individual adjustment via a counting-type updating operation and (c) implies looking for and transforming to features or characteristics obtained by looking at the ensemble of sensor responses. Such a procedure is implied by Minsky[1] and Minsky and Selfridge[6] when they refer to the sensors as property filters implying that some selection appropriate to the patterns has been made. However, their assumption of statistical independence, is highly specialized* since it is a simplifying assumption, perhaps it should be one goal of the transformations (a) and (c).

In the following, adjustment of the decision functions, (b) above, will be left to the operation of minimizing risk already discussed. Attempts will be made to reconcile (a) and (c), above, with self-organization based upon biological learning concepts (particularly reinforcement and reward and extinction) and feature or property extraction. We call these intuitive approaches. The goal will be to indicate how such approaches might provide guidelines for more efficient procedures of organization or hill climbing.

Recalling that once the underlying probability functions are known, the problem is one of decision theory with specified error probabilities, etc., what then can "intuitive" adjustment of the conditional probabilities add to the continually updated nonparametric estimation procedure? First, it could conceivably improve the efficiency of classification of an unknown, prior to the accession of complete knowledge of the statistics, i.e., it could improve the efficiency of the nonparametric tests. Second, it could ease the computational burden since the formulation of the minimum risk problem is, in many cases, a far cry from obtaining usable decision processes or numerical results. Third, biological principles (e.g., reinforcement) tempt

---

* A system which computes from samples the first-order conditional probabilities and the joint statistics when independence is not a necessary assumption has been treated by Uttley[4], but, as noted by Minsky[1], Uttley does not show how to avoid exponential growth. This would be one objective of using other than straightforward untransformed estimates of the parameters.

us to consider such techniques. It has been theorized, that based on the experience with neural net systems[21–23] (and, of course, biological systems[34]) additional adjustment or weighting via reinforcement or coordinate transformation procedures, e.g., property filtering might be profitable, not insofar as improving operation in the terminal state but for enhancing the efficiency of intermediate-state decisions and for simplifying the actual decision processing. These would tend to hasten or supervise the convergence and learning procedures in a heuristic manner. Also, the goal of attempting to obtain statistically independent characteristics or features is a desirable one.

Three attractive procedures have been proposed, each of which, in the present model, takes the form of an additional adaptive weighting or transformation layer imposed in cascade along the connections between the sensors and decision boxes; yielding a four-layer system rather than the three-layer net of Fig. 3. The first method is that of direct reinforcement via past experience[6], the second is reinforcement via reward and extinction[5], and the third is the method of applying a coordinate transformation on the sensor outputs, $\{s_i\}$, for the purpose of obtaining a new coordinate-system representation of the patterns which is more efficient with regard to the dimensional reduction involved in pattern recognition or classification[11]. This implies looking for (although not necessarily attaining) statistically independent or separated characteristics*.

The first method of direct reinforcement via past experience is the philosophy most commonly attributed to biological learning and self-organization. A method of implementing it in the Bayes's-net model has been described by Selfridge and Minsky[6] and Minsky[2]. They propose to modify the initial estimates of the conditional probabilities by changing them from $W(\{s\}|\delta_m)$ to $[W(\{s\}|\delta_m) + 1]\,\theta$, for a successful decision, or to $W(\{s\}|\delta_m)\,\theta$, for an unsuccessful one, during the learning phase. θ is a factor slightly less than unity.

The second method[5], that of reinforcement via reward and extinction, operates formally in an identical manner to the previous method, except that reward or extinction is imposed by an external trainer, who, in turn, applies a value judgment to the correctness of the outcomes.

The fundamental difference between these two appears to be primarily philosophical but also, in practice, one of consistency. With a machine applying the reinforcement, the success or failure judgment criteria used are either predictable or predictably unpredictable; not so with an external trainer, especially if a human.

---

* Note that this does not differ from the goal established by Rosenblatt's Theory of Statistical Separability for the Perception[22].

The advantages of the first and second methods, above, over those of direct nonparametric estimation are questionable in view of the fact that they apply only during a supervised learning or conditioning phase. Perhaps their advantage lies only in their simplicity vis-à-vis, the complications that may arise in nonparametric estimation, (the latter however is capable of being continued into an unsupervised learning phase). Minsky and Selfridge[6] and Bush and Mosteller[5] have shown their procedures to converge, in fact, to the correct values of the conditional probabilities—i.e., they are unbiased estimates. The question is, are they most efficient? Certainly, if they are less efficient than the nonparametric estimates we are using already in the procedure, they add nothing to the problem. If they are more efficient or much simpler algorithmically, they will be used in the nonparametric estimates.

The final method is exemplified by the type of affine transformations utilized by Sebestyen[11]. However, it is unfortunate that Sebestyen's very attractive concepts are marred by three shortcomings: (a) Each pattern class is transformed (or clustered) based on criteria established for that class alone without reference to discrimination between classes, (b) Each pattern class is transformed into its own characteristic space thereby making it difficult to apply optimum decision techniques for selecting a "best" match when the patterns are "close" to more than one class, (c) Disregarding the above restrictions, optimum decision processing is attempted only for the special assumed class of normal distributions.

Sebestyen's concepts are, however, attractive in that the new sensor outputs (considering each new coordinate as a sensor output) are either geometrically orthogonal[11b] or with zero cross-correlation (i.e., characterized by a diagonal, sample covariance matrix) as measured over sample space.[11a] Thus, this layer of the 4-matrix Bayes'-net machine provides transformation filter outputs (which may be termed property filter outputs) that are linearly independent over learning sample space—approximating one of our aforementioned goals. They are also extendable into the unsupervised learning phase—but here the possible drift effect of continued cascaded coordinate transformations must be considered.

Thus we are led to consider techniques similar to Sebestyen's, hopefully, without the aforementioned shortcomings, as an intuitive technique.

Other methods of intuitive adjustment can be readily conceived. We are investigating the generation and choice of such procedures with the objective of optimizing and simplifying the overall learning process.

REFERENCES

1. Minsky, M., "Steps Toward Artificial Intelligence," *Proc. IRE*, vol. 9, no. 1, January 1961, pp. 8–30.

2. *a.* Owen, J., *An Approach to Non-Parametric Discrimination*, Note No. 333 Applied Research Laboratory, Sylvania Electronic Systems, June 1, 1962.

   b. Cooper, P. W., *Classification by Statistical Methods (Pattern Recognition)*, Melpar Technical Note 61/2, April 1961.

3. McKay, D. M., "The Epistemological Problem for Automata," in Shannon and McCarthy (eds.), *Automata Studies*, Princeton, 1951, pp. 235–250.

4. Uttley, A. M., "Conditional Probability Machines and Conditional Reflexes," and "Temporal and Spatial Patterns in a Conditional Probability Machine," in Shannon and McCarthy (eds.), *Automata Studies*, Princeton, 1956, pp. 253–285.

5. Bush and Mosteller, *Stochastic Models for Learning*, Wiley, New York, 1955.

6. Minsky, M. L., and O. G. Selfridge, "Learning in Random Nets," in C. Cherry (ed.), *Fourth London Symposium on Information Theory*, Butterworth, 1961.

7. Minsky, M. L., "Some Universal Elements for Finite Automata," in Shannon and McCarthy (eds.), *Automata Studies*, Princeton 1956, pp. 117–128.

8. Selfridge, O. G., discussion of the generation of properties in "Pattern Recognition and Modern Computers," *Proc. WJCC*, March 1955.

9. *a.* Lewis, P. M., II, "The Characteristic Selection Problem in Pattern Recognition," *IRE Trans. Inform. Theory*, vol. IT–8, no. 2, February, 1962, p. 171.

   b. Marril, T. and D. M. Green, "On the Effectiveness of Receptors In Recognition Systems." *IRE Trans. Inform. Theory*, vol. 1 no. IT–9, January, 1963, pp. 11–17.

10. Highleyman, W. H., *Linear Decision Functions, With Application to Pattern Recognition*, Ph.D. Thesis, Polytechnic Institute of Brooklyn, June 1961.

11. *a.* Sebestyen, G. S., Recognition of Membership in Classes, *IRE Trans. Information Theory* vol. IT–7, no. 1, January 1961, pp. 48–50.

    b. Sebestyen, G. S., *On Pattern Recognition With Application to Silhouettes*, Sc. D. Thesis, 1959, E.E. Dept., MIT.

    c. ———, *Classification Decisions in Pattern Recognition*, MIT, R.L E. Tech. Report No. 301 April 1960.

    d. ———, Pattern Recognition by an Adaptive Process of Sample Set Construction, *IRE Trans. Information Theory*, vol. IT–8, no. 5, September 1962, pp. S–82–S–91.

12. Laemmel, A., *Linear Statistical Classification*, MIT, Lincoln Lab. Report No. 54 G–0021, May 16, 1960.

13. Chow, C. K., "An Optimum Character Recognition System Using Decision Functions," *IRE Trans. Electron. Computers*, vol. EC–6, no. 4, December 1957, pp. 247–254.

14. *a.* Cooper P. W., "The Hyperplane in Pattern Recognition," *Cybernetica* vol. V, no. 4, 1962.

    b. Cooper, P. W., "The Hypersphere in Pattern Recognition," *J. Inf. & Cont.*, vol. 5, no. 4, December 1962.

    c. ———, *Statistical Pattern Recognition with Quadratic Forms*, Melpar Technical Note 62/4, June 1962.

15. Marril, T. and D. M. Green, "Statistical Recognition Functions and the Design of Pattern Recognizers," *IRE Trans. Electron. Computers*, vol. EC–9, no. 4, December 1960, pp. 472–477.

16. Braverman, D. J. Although the theory presented is general, illustrative examples in the following are restricted to the normal case.

    a. ———, *Machine Learning and Automatic Pattern Recognition*, Stanford Electronics Laboratory, Tech. Report No. 2003–1, Feb. 17, 1961.

    b. ———, "A Decision Theoretic Approach to Machine Learning and Pattern Recognition," Report 3813, WESCON 1961.

    c. ——, "Learning Filters for Optimum Pattern Recognition," submitted to *IRE Trans. Information Theory.*

17. *a.* Tou, J. T. and K. J. Fu, "Digital Control Concepts for Nervous System Synthesis and Simulation," Third International Congress on Cybernetics, Namur Belgium, September 11–15, 1961.

    b. Fu, K. S., "A Statistical Approach to the Design of Intelligent Machines-Pattern Recognition and Learning," *Cybernetica*, vol. V, no. 2, 1962 pp. 88–102.

    c. ——, "A Learning System Using Statistical Decision Functions" AIEE Winter General Meeting, 1962.

    d. Fu, K. S., "A Sequential Decision Model for Optimum Recognition" in, E. E. Bernard, and M. R. Kare, (eds.), *Biological Prototypes and Synthetic Systems*, Plenum, New York, 1962, p. 270.

18. Baran, P. and G. Estrin, "An Adaptive Character Reader," Rand Report, Aug. 10, 1960.

19. Selfridge, O. G., "Pandemonium: A Paradigm for Learning," *Proc. Symp. on Mechanization of Thought Processes*, Her Majesty's Stationery Office, London, 1959.

20. ——, and U. Neisser, "Pattern Recognition by Machine," *Sci. Amer.*, vol. 203, no. 2, August 1960, pp. 60–68.

21. Block, H. D., "Analysis of Perceptrons," *Proc. WJCC*, May 1961, pp. 281–289.

22. Rosenblatt, F., *Principles of Neurodynamics: Perceptrons and the Theory of Brain Mechanisms*, Spartan, Baltimore, 1962.

23. Farley, B. C., and W. A. Clark, "Generalization of Pattern Recognition in a Self-Organizing System," *Proc. WJCC*, 1955, and "Simulation of Self-Organizing Systems by Digital Computer," *IRE Trans. Inform. Theory*, vol. IT–4, September 1954, pp. 76–84.

24. Wald, A., *Statistical Decision Functions*, Wiley, New York, 1950.

25. Middleton, D., *An Introduction to Statistical Communication Theory*, McGraw-Hill, New York, 1960.

26. Cooper, P. W., "A Note on the Multiple-Category Bayes Decision Procedure" *IEE Trans. Electron. Computers*, February 1963, vol. EC–12, no. 1.

27. Brick, D. B., *On the Design of Linear Weighting Functions for Character Recognition*, Memorandum No. 289, Applied Research Laboratory, Sylvania Electronic Systems, Waltham, Mass. April 2, 1962.

28. Wald, A., *Sequential Analysis*, Wiley, New York, 1947.

29. Bellman, R., Dynamic Programming, Princeton U. P., Princeton, N.J., 1957.

30. Jacobs, I. M., *Classification of Noisy Patterns Following a Finite Learning Period* Memorandum No. 239, Applied Research Laboratory, Sylvania Electronic Systems, Waltham, Mass., March 1961.

31. Blackwell, D. and M. A. Girshick, *Theory of Games and Statistical Decisions*, Wiley, New York, 1954.

32. Owen J., *Consistency of a Non-Parametric Decision Procedure*, Engineering Note. No. 334, Applied Research Laboratory, Sylvania Electronic Systems, Waltham, Mass., June 1962.

33. Bellman, R., *Adaptive Control Processes, A Guided Tour*, Princeton U. P., Princeton, N.J., 1961.

34. McCulloch, W. S. and W. Pitts, "A Logical Calculus of the Ideas Imminent in Nervous Activity," *Bull. Math. Biophys.*, vol. 5, 1943, pp. 115–133.

6

A PATTERN-IDENTIFICATION DEVICE USING LINEAR DECISION FUNCTIONS

J. S. Griffin Jr., J. H. King, Jr., and C. J. Tunis

International Business Machines, Endicott, New York

INTRODUCTION

Every pattern-identification system consists of two fundamental parts: a *transducer*, which senses the patterns to be identified and converts the information acquired into electrical signals, and a *processor*, which accepts these signals and by some means interprets them so as to achieve the required identification. There may, of course, be other parts to the system, such as a paper transport or other device for presenting the patterns to the transducer, or a device which utilizes the information provided the processor, and a set of gates which direct documents into bins according to the particular pattern identified, but we shall not be concerned with such peripheral apparatus.

The patterns to be identified could consist, for instance, of a family of characters printed on paper or a vocabulary of spoken words. In the former case the transducer might consist of a lens system and a means of measuring the darkness of various parts of the resulting image; or the characters might be printed in magnetic ink, and the transducer could then consist of one or another of the various kinds of magnetic reading heads that have been used or proposed. In the case of speech signals, the transducer would be simply a microphone.

The processor has the function of accepting the signals that are produced by the transducer when a pattern is present and from them extracting enough information to (with a high degree of probability) correctly identify the pattern. In the case of printed characters, the first step might be to periodically sample the output from the transducer and to quantize the result into two levels in such a way as to produce a binary matrix which is a direct electrical image of the character; the result could be interpreted in many ways, including those based on correlation techniques, searching for the presence or absence of certain critical features, or by the linear method reported blow. But there are many other ways to construct a processor for printed characters. In the case of speech signals, the processor often consists of a filter bank which determines the energy present at various frequencies, and then some means of analyzing the resulting pattern.

An early example of such a system was described by Eldredge, Kamphoefner, and Wendt[1-3] and publicized under the acronym ERMA. In this instance the patterns to be identified were the ten digits and four special symbols of a specially designed font. These were printed with an ink containing iron ferrite particles, so that upon being magnetized each character acquired a field which was peculiar to the class to which it belonged. The transducer was a suitably designed magnetic reading head; a magnetized character, upon being passed under this reading head, caused the production of an electrical signal which went to the processor for interpretation. The processor operated essentially as follows. The signal from the read head was sampled at several successive points in time, the resulting values being say $x_1, x_2, \ldots x_n$; let these numbers be the components of the vector X. Let the values which would be produced by a perfect pattern from the ith class be $w_1^{(i)}, w_2^{(i)}, \ldots, w_n^{(i)}$, and let these be the components of the vector $W^{(i)}$; here i will evidently run from 1 to 14. The processor identified the pattern as belonging to the ith class provided

$$\theta\, W^{(i)} \cdot X > W^{(j)} \cdot X \qquad \text{for all } j \neq i \tag{1}$$

where θ was a fixed value lying between 0 and 1; otherwise the processor responded that identification was not possible.

Upon recalling the relation between the dot product of two vectors and the cosine of their included angle, one realizes that the inequalities (1) described a region of n-dimensional space roughly in the shape of a cone, or more nearly a prism, with vertex at the origin. Included in this region were the standard vector $W^{(i)}$ associated with the ith pattern, together with almost all of the vectors which arose from patterns belonging to the ith class. The regions associated with the various classes were, of course, nonoverlapping, and in fact did not exhaust the whole space; patterns which produced signals whose vectors did not lie inside any of these regions were of course not identified. Note that by decreasing θ these regions could be diminished, the likelihood of announcing an incorrect identification being thereby decreased, but at the expense of increasing the regions corresponding to nonidentification, which in turn would cause an increase in the rejection rate.

Soon after the appearance of the Eldredge, Kamphoefner, and Wendt papers, C. K. Chow[4] observed that the task of the processor could be stated as a problem in statistical decision theory. Chow's analysis may be summarized as follows. He noted that the signals which arise from the presentation of patterns to the transducer could, after certain preliminary transformations in the processor, be regarded as points of a *measurement space*. The identification problem became to determine which pattern was presented to the transducer, given that it had generated a certain point in measurement space; hence the operation of the processor could be represented by a decision rule—i.e., by an assignment to each point of the measurement space either one of the classes of patterns, or else the statement "no identification is possible." Chow postulated that with each class of patterns there was associated a probability distribution on the measurement space, this distribution being a description of the likelihood of occurrence of a given point in measurement space upon presentation to the transducer of a member of its corresponding class of patterns. For example, in the system described above, the preliminary transformation consists in sampling the waveform from the transducer at n points, and the measurement space is an n-dimensional vector space. The decision rule has already been stated, namely for each i it assigns the ith class to each point of the region defined by the inequalities (1) and the statement "no identification is possible" to all other points. Whatever its exact nature, the probability distribution associated with the ith class of patterns is evidently concentrated within this same region, for otherwise this decision rule would not be effective. Chow also postulated that the result of each possible decision (correct identification, erroneous identification, and failure to make any identification) could be evaluated on a unit cost basis. Specifically, suppose we let there be m classes to be identified, say $S_1 S_2, \ldots, S_m$, and let us assign the cost c_{ij} to the decision "a member of S_i is identified as belonging to S_j"; then c_{ii} is the cost (perhaps negative) of correctly identifying a member of S_i, whereas if $i \neq j$ then c_{ij} is the cost of misidentifying a member of S_i as a member of S_j. Let c_{io} be the cost of a failure to make any identification when the pattern presented belonged to S_i. In general of course if $i \neq j$ and $i \neq 0$ then

$$c_{ij} > c_{io} > c_{ii}$$

This corresponds to the usual notion of utility in statistical decision theory.

For purposes of calculation any particular decision rule can be represented as follows. If $1 \leq i \leq m$ and X is any point of measurement space, let

$$\delta_i(X) = \begin{cases} 1 \text{ if the } i\text{th class is assigned to } X \\ \\ \text{otherwise} \end{cases}$$

and similarly set $\delta_0(X)$ take the value 1 if there is assigned to X the statement "no identification is possible" and the value 0 elsewhere. Finally we let p_i be the probability of occurrence of the ith pattern, i.e., the relative frequency with which members of S_i are presented to the transducer. Using this convention, Chow calculated the expected unit cost of operation of this system due to identifying the ith character as the jth to be

$$a_{ij} = \int_M \beta_i(X)\, c_{ij}\delta_j(X)\, dX$$

where M is the measurement space and β_i is the probability distribution on M associated with the ith pattern; the value $j = 0$ is of course to be interpreted as the average cost of failure to make any identification when the ith character appears. It follows that the total average cost of operation of the system will be

$$A = \sum_{j=0}^{m} \sum_{i=1}^{m} p_i a_{ij}$$

Now

$$A = A_0 + A_1$$

where

$$A_0 = \sum_{i=1}^{m} p_i c_{io}$$

and

$$A_1 = {}_M \cdot \sum_{j=0}^{m} Z_j(X)\, \delta_j(X)\, dX$$

where

$$Z_0(X) = 0$$

and

$$Z_j(X) = \sum_{i=1}^{m} (c_{ij} - c_{io})\, p_i\, \beta_i(X)$$

for $1 \leq j \leq m$. The quantities $Z_j(X)$ may be interpreted as measuring the excess of the cost of identifying a pattern which gives rise to the point X of measurement space as belonging to S_j over the cost of failure to make any identification. Chow observed that the total average cost A may be minimized by associating with X the class S_j for which $Z_j(X)$ is least: he let $\delta_j(X) = 1$ if $Z_j(X) \leq Z_i(X)$ for all $i \neq j$ (ties are decided arbitrarily).

It may be noted that the particular decision function which Chow obtained may be described as *optimum*, in the sense that it minimizes the cost of operation for a fixed relation between the patterns and the measurement space; and the processor, in as far as it implements this decision function, may also be called optimum. However, this adjective cannot be applied to the transducer or to that part of the processor whose function it is to convert the signals from the transducer into points of the measurement space: it is mainly a matter of experimentation to select adequate transducers and to properly extract information from their output signals. Other limitations of Chow's analysis include the fact that the unit cost assumption is not always tenable; and there may be dependences among the successive patterns of a sequence, as when a self-checking account number or a fixed format for control characters is used. And finally, as Chow himself remarked, even if the probabilities of occurrence of the various patterns and the distributions which they generate are accurately known, it may still be very difficult to implement the optimum decision functions given by this algorithm.

Some kinds of decision function happen to be quite convenient to implement, and it has proved expedient to use certain of these even when they bear little relation to the optimum decision functions in Chow's sense. Acceptable performance generally has to be achieved by incurring costs elsewhere in the system, e.g., by using better transducers and preliminary processing, or in some cases by controlling the input patterns; but this kind of trade-off is familiar in engineering design.

The work to be reported here centers around the so-called *linear decision function*, a broad discussion of which has been given by Highleyman[5,6]. In simplest terms, the measurement space is taken to be a vector space, say of dimension n, and a linear decision function is any partitioning of the space by one or more hyperplanes (each of dimension $n - 1$). The question, in which region of the partition does a given vector lie, evidently can be reduced to the question, on which side of each hyperplane does this vector lie. The utility of this notion is based first on the ease with which a mechanism for answering this latter question can be constructed. Indeed, a typical implementation is by means of a current summing network, as follows. Suppose that n measurements are made on the signal from the transducer, and let these measurements result in voltages on n lines; let these voltages have the values $v_1, v_2, \ldots, v_n$, and let these numbers be the components of the vector V. If the lines are connected through resistors to a current measuring device, then the current I which is observed to flow will be $g_1 v_1 + g_2 v_2 + \ldots + g_n v_n$, where g_i is the conductance (reciprocal of the resistance) of the ith resistor. One may then determine whether the vector V lies on one or the other side of the hyperplane with equation

$$g_1 v_1 + g_2 v_2 + \cdots + g_n v_n - t = 0$$

by noting whether the current I exceeds or is less than t. Negative conductances may be implemented by inverting the corresponding input voltages. Thus there will be required one such network as this for each hyperplane involved in the linear decision function. Obviously the effectiveness of a linear decision function in identifying a given family of patterns is contingent upon the possibility of specifying an adequate linear decision function in terms of an economically reasonable number of hyperplanes. We have found it feasible, for example, to use one hyperplane to separate the signals arising from patterns of any one category from the signals arising from patterns from all other categories; thus altogether there would be as many hyperplanes as there were classes of patterns.

A second important attribute of linear decision functions is the ease with which suitable hyperplanes can often be found. The particular method we have used is a variant of the adaptive training or programmed error correction technique used by Frank Rosenblatt in his Perceptron experiments[7,8] and is explained in detail below.

Using an IBM 7090 computer, we have applied this method to the determination of a decision function for the identification of the characters from the E13-B font for magnetic ink character recognition; some of the details of this experiment are described below. We have implemented some of the resulting hyperplanes using networks similar to those mentioned above; this device is also described later in the paper. Since commercially available resistors are not specified exactly but only to lie within certain narrow limits, any particular hyperplane in such a device will differ slightly from the ideal one obtained from the computer simulation ;this necessitated a tolerance analysis, which appears below.

CONSTRUCTION OF A SUITABLE LINEAR DECISION FUNCTION

Suppose then that one has a family of patterns to be identified and that a transducer together with the preliminary processing has been decided upon, so that the presentation of a pattern to the transducer will produce a known vector in measurement space. In the following sections, we address ourselves to the problem of how to construct an appropriate linear decision function. We first give an explicit description of the algorithm or training procedure for the simplest possible case, namely when there are only two classes of patterns to be identified and the separating hyperplane may be presumed to pass through the origin of measurement space. Next it is shown how to modify this procedure so as to give two parallel hyperplanes placed symmetrically about the origin; this allows for a zone of indecision—i.e., a rejection region, and may incidentally shorten the length of the training procedure required. Following this, a further modification which frees these planes from their special relation to the origin is described. Finally, these techniques are extended to provide for the indentification of more than two classes of patterns.

The effectiveness of these procedures will depend primarily on the distribution of the images of the various patterns in measurement space. Generally speaking, if the vectors produced by patterns from S_1 are concentrated in a region R_1, and those produced by S_2 are concentrated in a region R_2, and if there is a hyperplane which lies between R_1 and R_2, then this training procedure may be expected to produce a satisfactory decision rule. Thus, the transducer and the preliminary part of the processor must be so designed that this condition is met; failure to obtain a satisfactory decision rule after a reasonably lengthy training procedure would suggest that the design of these parts should be reconsidered. Theoretical arguments have been adduced to justify this position, but our view is mainly heuristic: it has turned out to be practical to design experimental pattern identification systems using this approach.

Suppose initially that there are just two classes of patterns to be identified, say S_1 and S_2. We go about looking for a linear decision function which will suffice to distinguish members of these two classes in the following way. We seek a vector W such that if a vector X is produced by the presentation of a pattern from the class S_1 then (with a high degree of probability)

$$X \cdot W > 0 \tag{2}$$

whereas if X is produced by a member of S_2 then

$$X \cdot W < 0 \tag{3}$$

If such a vector can be found, then an unknown pattern will be identified as belonging to S_1 or S_2 according to the following decision rule: if the vector X produced in measurement space by the pattern satisfies Eq. (2) then the pattern is identified as belonging to S_1; if X satisfies Eq. (3) then the pattern is identified as belonging to S_2; if neither of these conditions is satisfied, i.e., if $X \cdot W = 0$, then no decision is rendered (or, as we say, the pattern is *rejected*). Speaking geometrically, we will have a hyperplane passing through the origin, with almost all of the vectors produced by members of S_1 lying on one side of it, and with almost all of those produced by S_2 lying on the other.

We attempt to find W by a trial-and-error technique. Let $p_1, p_2, \ldots, p_k$ be a sequence of patterns, some from S_1 and the remainder from S_2; let $X_1, X_2, \ldots, X_k$ be the sequence of corresponding vectors arising in measurement space from the presentation of these patterns to the transducer. Let

T_1 be any vector; typically T_1 is taken to be the zero vector. We define a sequence of vectors T_2, T_3, . . . , T_{k+1} iteratively, as follows:

(a) if p_i is from S_1 and $T_i \cdot X_i > 0$, then $T_{i+1} = T_i$
(b) if p_i is from S_1 but $T_i \cdot X_i \leq 0$, then $T_{i+1} = T_i + X_i$
(c) if p_i is from S_2 and $T_i \cdot X_i < 0$, then $T_{i+1} = T_i$
(d) if p_i is from S_2 but $T_i \cdot X_i \geq 0$, then $T_{i+1} = T_i - X_i$

In other words, if the vector T_i behaves as desired with regard to the ith pattern, then it is left unchanged [statements (a) and (c)]; but if not then it is corrected [statements (b) and (d)]. That statements (b) and (d) do in fact represent corrections is clear: if for example p_i is from S_1 but $T_i \cdot X_i \leq 0$ then

$$T_{i+1} \cdot X_i = T_i \cdot X_i + X_i \cdot X_i > T_i \cdot X_i$$

so that T_{i+1} is an improvement, at least as far as the ith pattern is concerned. The last pattern in this sequence, namely T_{k+1}, is a tentative choice for W. Such procedures as this are frequently described in anthropomorphic terms: we speak of the procedure as a *training routine*, of the statements $a - d$ as *training rules*, and of the processor as being *trained* by the application of these rules.

There is no *a priori* reason to believe that the choice $W = T_{k+1}$ is acceptable, i.e., to believe that the above decision rule with T_{k+1} substituted for W will represent a processor with satisfactory performance. The next step, therefore, is to estimate the frequency with which errors and rejections will occur if the choice $W = T_{k+1}$ is made. (By *error* we understand a *substitution*, i.e., the identification of a pattern as belonging to one class when in fact it belonged to another.) If the choice $W = T_{k+1}$ does not prove to be acceptable, then one may augment the sequence of patterns and continue the training procedure; or perhaps one will decide to abandon the search for this particular W.

Once a satisfactory hyperplane is found, it can be implemented using a circuit of the type described above. The output of this circuit can be quantized to two levels, say 0 and 1, so that, e.g., a 0 will be interpreted as indicating that a member of S_1 is present whereas a 1 will indicate a member of S_2.

A simple but significant improvement results from choosing a positive number d and then replacing the training rules $a - d$ with these:

(a) if p_i is from S_1 and $T_i \cdot X_i > d$, then $T_{i+1} = T_i$
(b) if p_i is from S_1 but $T_i \cdot X_i \leq d$, then $T_{i+1} = T_i + X_i$
(c) if p_i is from S_2 and $T_i \cdot X_i < - d$, then $T_{i+1} = T_i$
(d) if p_i is from S_2 but $T_i \cdot X_i \geq - d$, then $T_{i+1} = T_i - X_i$

Correspondingly one might modify the decision rule to read: if the vector X produced by a pattern satisfies the condition

$$W \cdot X > d \tag{4}$$

then the pattern is identified as belonging to S_1; if the vector produced satisfies the condition

$$W \cdot X < -d \tag{5}$$

then the pattern is identified as belonging to S_2, and if neither of these conditions is satisfied then the pattern is rejected.

This decision rule can be visualized in terms of a pair of hyperplanes placed symmetrically about the origin; between them lies the rejection region, and of the other two regions, one is identified with S_1 and the other with S_2. A moment's reflection will show that the training rules may be understood similarly: they represent an attempt to place a pair of parallel hyperplanes between the regions in which the images of patterns from the two classes are concentrated, with the proviso that as the training routine progresses, the vectors T_i tend to get longer, so that in effect the two hyperplanes drift toward the origin. Thus there is a relation between the choice of d and a suitable length of the training routine. But the main point here is that by using two hyperplanes one may expect to get a better fit.

Finally, we note that the decision rule may be further modified: one could replace the inequalities, Eqs. (4) and (5), by

$$W \cdot X > \theta d \tag{6}$$

and

$$W \cdot X < -\theta d \tag{7}$$

respectively, where generally θ is chosen between 0 and 1. Note that the effect of increasing θ would be to decrease substitution errors but at the expense of increasing the number of rejections.

It is also easy and worthwhile to free these hyperplanes from their peculiar relation to the origin; that is, we can find and use a single hyperplane which need not pass through the origin, or a pair of parallel hyperplanes which are not necessarily symmetrically placed about the origin. The simplest way to accomplish this is to append a fictitious component to the vectors produced by the presentation of patterns to the transducer, and to always take this component to have the value 1. The training procedures previously described and may be used to produce a vector, the last component of which may be taken to be the constant term in the equation of the desired hyperplane.

To be more explicit, suppose that we are looking for a single hyperplane as before, and that we have the sequence $X_1, X_2, \ldots, X_k$ of vectors in measurement space, as there. Let the dimension of measurement space be n, and let the sequence $X_1', X_2', \ldots, X_k'$ of $(n + 1)$-dimensional vectors be defined as follows: for each index i, the first n components of X_i' are the components of X_i, and the $(n + 1)$st component of X_i' is 1. We now define a sequence of X_i, and the $(n + 1)$st component of X_i' is 1. We now define a sequence $T_1, T_2, \ldots, T_k$ by the training rules stated above, but with X_i' replacing X_i. There results finally the vector T_k; we define W to be the n-dimensional vector whose components are the first n components of T_k, and we let t be the $(n + 1)$st component of T_k. We now use the following decision rule: if the vector X results from the presentation of a pattern to the transducer, then X is identified as having belonged to S_2, or is rejected, according as $W \cdot X + t$ is positive, negative, or zero.

The treatment of a pair of parallel hyperplanes may be similarly modified.

Ordinarily in pattern-identification work one must deal with several distinct classes of patterns rather than just two classes. If there are m classes, then one may dichotomize the family of classes p times, where p is the least integer which is as large as $\log_2 m$; the identification of a pattern could then consist in the determination of which half of each of these dichotomies the class containing the relevant pattern belonged to (in other words, only p bits of information are required to specify one object out of m). Interpreting this remark in terms of measurement space, we see that in principle it is possible to use just p hyperplanes to identify a pattern as having come from one of m classes, subject of course to the requirement that the regions in which the images of various classes are concentrated be well spread out in measurement space. It has not proved to be practical to implement so economical a scheme as this, however, because we do not know of a simple way to recognize which dichotomies of a family of classes of patterns can be implemented with a hyperplane in measurement space.

This has been called the coding assignment problem; the essential difficulty is illustrated in Fig. 1, which is intended to suggest the regions of concentration of the measurements in a two-dimensional measurement space arising from each of four classes of patterns, say S_1, S_2, S_3, and S_4. It is evident that if we lump S_1 and S_4 together into one class and S_2 and S_3 together into another, then we may expect the training procedure to yield the hyperplane (line) A and we would obtain therefrom an assignment, say, of 0 to members of S_1 and S_4 and of 1 to members of S_2 and S_3. If next we take S_2 and S_4 to form one class and S_1 and S_3 to form the other then we should arrive at the hyperplane B, and the assignment of 0 to members of

S_2 and S_4 and 1 to members of S_1 and S_3. On taking these two together, we would identify patterns according to the following scheme:

00	S_4	10	S_2
01	S_1	11	S_3

But if we had the misfortune to put S_1 and S_2 together into one class and S_3 and S_4 into the other, we could not expect to find a suitable hyperplane.

Another scheme which one would certainly expect to be quite effective consists in the use of a hyperplane (or a pair of parallel hyperplanes) to distinguish between members of each pair of classes; thus $m(m - 1)/2$ hyperplanes (or pairs of hyperplanes) are required. Each such hyperplane (or pair of hyperplanes) can of course be found by using the methods given earlier. The decision rule must take into account the fact that if a hyperplane is suitably located to differentiate between two particular classes, then the location with respect to this hyperplane of any vector arising from a pattern from any third class will contain no information. This method has been called *class pair separation*; the three hyperplanes which would separate S_1 from S_2, S_3, and S_4 are indicated in Fig. 2. The disadvantage of this method is the comparatively large number of hyperplanes required; if there were 14 characters in the font, then 91 hyperplanes would be needed, and if there were 26 characters then 325 hyperplanes would be necessary.

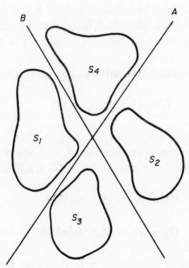

Figure 1

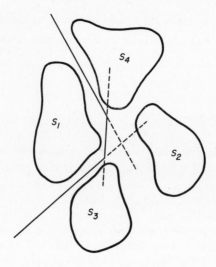

Figure 2

We have had some success with a scheme intermediate between these two, namely the use of one hyperplane to separate the vectors arising from the presentation of patterns from one class from those arising from the presentation of members of all other classes taken together. Thus to distinguish among the members of m different classes of patterns there are required m hyperplanes. To write this out a little more formally, suppose we let $S_1, S_2, \ldots, S_m$ be the m classes of patterns to be identified. For each value of i between 1 and m, let W^i and t_i be chosen (using the method described above) so that the hyperplane with equation

$$W^i \cdot X + t_i = 0$$

distinguishes the vectors arising from the presentation of members of S_i from those arising from the presentation of members of all other classes. An appropriate decision rule is: if a pattern produces the vector X in measurement space, then this pattern is identified as belonging to S_i provided

$$W^i \cdot X + t_i > r$$

and for all $j \neq i$

$$W^j \cdot X + t_j < -r$$

for some suitably chosen value of r; if these conditions are not satisfied for any value of i, then the pattern is rejected.

Another decision rule which may be implemented using these same vectors W^1, W^2, ..., W^m and constants t_1, t_2, ..., t_m is the following: if a pattern produces the vector X in measurement space, then it is identified as having come from S_i provided

$$W^i \cdot X + t_i > W^j \cdot X + t_j + \epsilon \qquad (8)$$

for all values of j different from i, where ϵ is a positive number chosen in advance; if this condition is not satisfied for any value of i, then the pattern is rejected. It is evident that this rule can be useful only if the vectors W^1, W^2, ..., W^m bear a suitable relation to one another, as for example might be true if they were all unit vectors, so that the linear forms $W^i \cdot X + t_i$ would represent signed distances of the vector X from the corresponding hyperplanes. Our experience indicates that the performance of a processor using this rule is about an order of magnitude better than that of a processor using the rule given in the last paragraph. This is the decision rule on which we have concentrated our attention; we have referred to it as the *ramp method* because of the circuitry used in its implementation.

Geometrically, this ramp method amounts to class-pair separation. In fact, this becomes quite clear if the inequality of Eq. (8) is rewritten

$$(W^i - W^j) \cdot X + (t_i - t_j) > \epsilon \qquad \text{for all } j \neq i$$

and we note further that there is no restriction on the values of the quantities

$$(W^k - W^j) \cdot X + (t_k - t_j)$$

when both k and j are different from i.

EXPERIMENTAL RESULTS

Because of its relative simplicity and familiarity, we chose to base our experimental work on the fourteen patterns of the magnetic ink character recognition font now in use in the banking industry. This font is shown in Fig. 3.

The pattern identification system we had in mind operated as follows. The characters were printed in magnetic ink, as described in an earlier paragraph. Before presentation to the transducer, they were to be magnetized with an alternating field. The transducer was a row of ten reading heads, arranged so as to scan the character along ten equally spaced horizontal paths, the taller characters being nominally covered by seven or

Figure 3

eight of these paths. The alternating field was to permit the detection of the presence of ink rather than edges of inked regions. The processor may most conveniently be thought of as divided into two parts. Its initial part sampled the output of each of the ten channels at seven equally spaced times and quantized the result into two levels in such a way that as a character was scanned there was produced a 70-bit binary pattern which resembled the original printed characters. The remainder of the processor accepted these 70-bit patterns and performed the required identifications; we will refer to this part as the *categorizer*. Functionally this system is identical with the pattern identification system used in the IBM 1210 Reader-Sorter, which is now in commercial use; however, in the 1210 the categorizer is based on Boolean logic, whereas we have worked with linear decision functions as described above.

We have not actually constructed such a pattern recognition system in its entirety. Instead we have used the transducer and the initial part of the processor of the 1210 to record the 70-bit patterns on magnetic tape; the training and testing of the categorizer was then simulated using the IBM 7090 computer. The simulation program was exactly an implementation of the scheme described earlier (Figs. 1 and 2); for training we used one pair of parallel hyperplanes to separate each class from all other classes, and for recognition we used the ramp method. Some indication of the results obtained with this program are described below. In order to relate to reality these simulation results, a hardware implementation of a limited version of such a categorizer was constructed. This machine accepted 70-bit patterns set manually with switches and identified a pattern as a 0, 1, 2, or 3; this machine was not an adaptive network, but was constructed using the results of the simulation program. Its successful performance demonstrated that the simulation results did in fact have the meaning they purported to have. This machine and one of the problems arising in its construction are described below.

The main source of data for our experimental work was a magnetic tape upon which was recorded the result of presenting slightly over one million characters to the IBM 1210. Mint documents with nominally perfect printing were used. Our tape contained about 27,000 distinct binary patterns; to save handling time, it was edited so as to list each pattern only once, but to indicate with each pattern its frequency of occurrence. Thus in effect we worked with a typical distribution of patterns produced by mint documents; all recognition results refer to this distribution. For training purposes, we extracted about 5,000 of these patterns and recorded them on a separate tape.

The result of a training routine would be a set of fourteen vectors in 70-dimensional space, or *masks* as we have called them. Three such masks are shown in Figs. 4, 5, and 6. The upper parts of these figures are the ideal

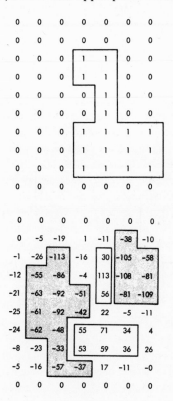

Figure 4

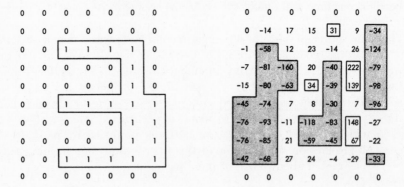

Figure 5

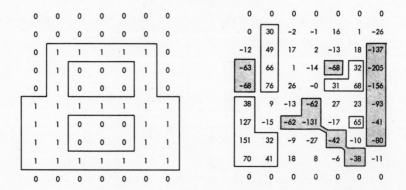

Figure 6

or nominally perfect patterns as seen by the categorizer, while the lower parts are the masks themselves. One can well think of these in terms of contour maps of surfaces; in this instance we have encircled the higher parts of the ridges and shaded the deeper parts of the valleys. In general, the peaks will be contributed by the character itself, whereas the valleys will be due to other characters which overlap the character in question in a significant way.

We refer to the entries in the masks as *weights*. The variation of these quantities over the entire family of masks is of some interest, for it provides an indication of the range of values required of a variable weight in order that it be useful in an adaptive device. For this particular system and this particular font, the weights ranged in increments of 1 from 1 up to about 200. But this is not meant to imply that accuracy to within ½ of 1 percent is required or even useful: actually we have not yet ascertained how the performance of the system deteriorates as the weights are rounded off or otherwise perturbed.

Figure 7 illustrates the performance typical of the simulated system. In this particular instance, d was chosen to be 200 (here d has the same mean-

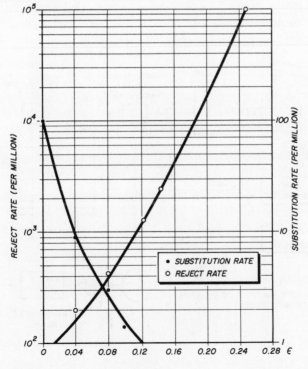

Figure 7

ing as in the training rules on page 176. As suggested above, in order to use the ramp method some normalization of the masks (vectors) is required; in this instance we merely divided each weight in a particular mask by the sum of the absolute values of the weights which originally appeared in that mask. Thus the output of any one mask ranges over some interval of length 1. As before, ϵ represents the minimum permissible difference between the maximum signal and the next largest one. Note that as ϵ is decreased, the rejection rate is decreased, but at the expense of permitting substitution errors.

The categorizer which was actually constructed in hardware is illustrated in Fig. 8. Provision was made for entering 70-bit patterns manually by setting switches. Four circuits representing masks with weights determined by the simulation program described above were constructed, one of these circuits being for each of the characters 0, 1, 2, and 3; for our purposes there seemed to be very little need to build all fourteen. For a given input pattern X, the output of each of these circuits was proportional to the corresponding quantity $W^i \cdot X + t_i$. This output could have been either a current or a voltage; we elected to use voltage. Provision was made to determine which circuit had the largest output, and whether this output exceeded the next largest output by a predetermined amount which we will call η; the various possible outcomes were indicated by means of lights.

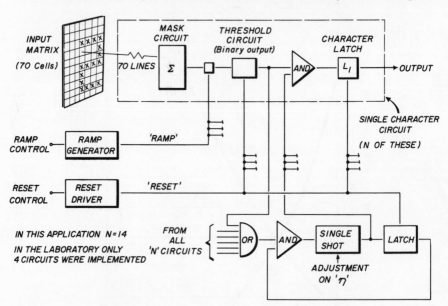

Figure 8

A convenient method of comparing the outputs of the several circuits is as follows. As indicated in Fig. 8, a "ramp control" is added to the threshold circuits which follow each of the mask circuits, there being but a single ramp generator for the entire system. Initially, the input from the ramp generator is sufficiently great to cause all threshold circuits to be off, no matter how large the output of the mask circuits. Then, at some time during the character cycle, the ramp voltage decreases linearly. When the first threshold circuit comes on, it sets its latch and a single shot fires, the width of the single shot pulse being proportional to η. If any other threshold circuit comes on while the single shot is on, it also sets its latch, but those coming on after the single shot goes off do not set their latches. At the end of the ramp cycle, if just one latch is on then the pattern is identified as the corresponding character, but if more than one is on then the pattern is rejected.

TOLERANCE CONSIDERATIONS

One of the problems which we considered in the construction of a physical implementation of the categorizer was to take into account the deviations from their nominal values of commercially available components. We made the appropriate analyses for both the case of a voltage output and a current output; because it is somewhat more transparent, we give here the current case, although for circuit reasons we actually built mask circuits with voltage outputs.

A schematic representation of a mask circuit with current output is shown in Fig. 9. The output signal is to be proportional to

$$S = w_1 x_1 + w_2 x_2 + \cdots + w_n x_n + \bar{t}$$

where $x_1, x_2, \ldots, x_n$ are binary variables—i.e., take the values 0 and 1, and the numbers $w_1, w_2, \ldots, w_n$ are arbitrary subject to the condition that

$$|w_1| + |w_2| + \cdots + |w_n| = 1$$

A suitable physical analog is the current summing network of Fig. 10. The output current I is given by

$$I = g_1 v_1 + g_2 v_2 + g_3 v_3 + \cdots + g_n v_n + \bar{t}$$

where the numbers $g_1, g_2, \ldots, g_n$ are conductances chosen to be proportional respectively to $|w_1|, |w_2|, \ldots, |w_n|$ and each v_i takes on the values 0 and V respectively as $x_i = 0$ or $x_i = 1$ if $w_i \geq 0$ and the values 0 and $-V$ respectively as $x_i = 0$ or $x_i = 1$ if $w_i < 0$. The current I flowing in the network will thus be proportional to the output signal S for any binary pattern. However, the three voltages present, namely V, 0, and $-V$, are an inconvenience to the circuit designer, and therefore it is worthwhile to

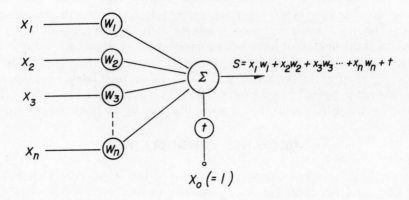

Figure 9

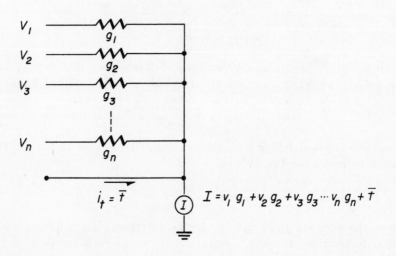

Figure 10

make the following alteration, which is familiar in the field of Boolean threshold logic: the variables $v_1, v_2, \ldots, v_n$ are replaced by $v_1', v_2', \ldots, v_n'$, where

$$v_i' = v_i \qquad \text{if } w_i \geq 0$$

$$v_i' = v_i + V \qquad \text{if } w_i < 0$$

so that

$$I = g_1 v_1' + g_2 v_2' + \cdots + g_n v_n' + \bar{i}'$$

where

$$t' = t - V \cdot \mathbf{\Sigma} \, g_i$$

the sum ranging over those i for which $w_1 < 0$. And now v_i' takes the value 0 or V according as x_i is 0 or 1 if $w_i \geq 0$, but if $w_i < 0$ then v_i' takes the values V and 0 as x_i takes the values 0 and 1 respectively. Geometrically this amounts to moving the configuration consisting of a cube V units on its edge and a hyperplane passing through it parallel to itself until the cube lies in the "first 2^n-ant," i.e., until that cube coincides with the cube whose edges are the n vectors $(V, 0, 0, \ldots, 0), (0, V, 0, \ldots, 0), \ldots, (0, 0, 0, \ldots, V)$. Note that this same translation scheme could be used more generally to cause the circuit to operate between any two voltages V_1 and V_2. Thus at any rate we see that there can be constructed a current summing network which is analogous to any given mask and which uses as inputs only the two voltages 0 and V.

Let us suppose, then that a mask is to be implemented using this circuit. The conductances $g_1, g_2, \ldots, g_n$ are to be implemented using resistors which may deviate from their nominal values by as much as a certain fixed percentage, so that the actual conductances used will also deviate from their nominal values by as much as essentially the same percentage, at any rate for sufficiently precise resistors; thus there is a certain number p such that for each i the value of the ith conductance lies between $(1 - p) \, g_i$ and $(1 + p) \, g_i$. Similarly the voltages nominally equal to V and 0 may lie between $V - \delta$ and $V + \delta$ and between $-\delta$ and δ respectively, where δ is a constant. The number $\bar{t}$ can be determined rather more accurately than $g_1, g_2, \ldots, g_n$ and its deviations from nominal will be ignored. Suppose we let c be the sum of the conductances:

$$c = g_1 + g_2 + \cdots + g_n$$

Now when a pattern is presented, some of the input lines will receive a nominal voltage of V; the remainder will nominally receive 0 volts. Let the sum of the conductances associated with the first of these sets of lines be

c_1, and the sum of the other conductances be c_2. Then the nominal value of the current will be

$$I_{nom} = c_1 V + \bar{i}$$

the largest possible value will be

$$I_{max} = (1 + p) c_1(V + \delta) + (1 + p) c_2\delta$$

and similarly the smallest possible value will be

$$I_{min} = (1 - p) c_1(V - \delta) + (1 - p) c_2(-\delta)$$

We find then that

$$I_{max} - I_{nom} = c\delta + pc_1 V + cp\delta$$

and since $c_1 \leq c$ we conclude that

$$I_{max} - I_{nom} \leq c(\delta + pV - cp\delta)$$

A similar calculation may be made for I_{min}-, and therefore we conclude that the actual current will differ from the nominal by at most $cV\ (p + q + pq)$ where we have set

$$q = \frac{\delta}{V}$$

Evidently the maximum current which can flow through any mask circuit is cV, so that the measurements of the output of any mask circuit can be uncertain by as much as

$$\frac{cV(p + q + pq)}{cV} \approx p + q$$

as a fraction of the maximum current, since $pq \ll 1$. In other words, the tolerance on the output of the mask circuit is $100\ (p + q)$ percent; this shows explicitly the relation of the voltage and conductance tolerances to the tolerance of the mask circuits. The deviations of the threshold detector and the ramp generator from nominal are ignored, for they can be controlled quite precisely.

Now suppose that there are to be k such mask circuits, and for X a binary pattern and $i = 1, 2, \ldots, k$ let

$$f_i(X) = W^i \cdot X + t_i$$

and let $\phi_t(X)$ be the (actual) output of the ith mask circuit. Evidently the nominal output of the ith mask circuit is $cVf_i(X)$, and therefore the above conclusion is that

$$|\phi_i(X) - cVf_i(X)| \leq (p + q)cV \qquad (9)$$

Suppose that it has been decided to use a certain discrimination level ϵ, i.e., that we want to use the decision rule: the binary pattern X is identified as having come from the ith character provided

$$f_i(X) > f_j(X) + \epsilon \qquad \text{for all } j \neq i \qquad (10)$$

This inequality is equivalent to

$$cV f_i(X) > cVf_j(X) + \epsilon cV \qquad \text{for all } j \neq i$$

In virtue of Eq. (9), in order to insure Eq. (10) it is sufficient to require

$$\phi_i(X) > \phi_j(X) + \epsilon cV + 2(p + q) cV$$

i.e., to choose the parameter η to be

$$\eta = cV(\epsilon + 2p + 2q) \qquad (11)$$

Thus if η is so chosen, we can infer from the coming on of the ith light that the set of inequalities of Eq. (10) holds. Of course, in any specific device the deviations of the actual values from the nominal values may well be such that the choice of η given by Eq. (11) imposes rather more stringent requirements than those given by Eq. (10). For instance, if the device at hand happened to give actual values in exact agreement with the nominal values, and η were given by Eq. (11) then the inequalities of Eq. (10) could be replaced by

$$f_i(X) > f_j(X) + \epsilon + 2p + 2q \qquad (12)$$

In the particular case of the model we built, we used 1 percent resistors, so that $p = 0.01$; V was 12 volts and δ was 0.78 volts, so that $q = 0.065$. For example, if one wanted to guarantee (for this sample) no errors at all, then one might choose $\epsilon = 0.12$, and η would be $3.24\,c$. Or one might choose $\epsilon = 0$ and $\eta = 1.8\,c$, in which case one would be sure (again for this sample) that there would be no more than 100 substitution errors per million characters.

For a number of patterns we measured the outputs of the mask circuits and compared them with the corresponding (properly scaled) quantities in the simulated categorizer; agreement was found to be within 1 percent. This agreement was well within the limits set by the pessimistic design philosophy upon which the above analysis was based, and there is a strong suggestion that pessimistic criteria are too severe. Thus it appears that in the case of our model ϵ is very nearly proportional to η, i.e., that our model uses the decision rule: the binary pattern X is identified as having come from the ith character provided

$$f_i(X) > f_j(X) + \frac{\eta}{cV} \qquad \text{for all } j \neq i$$

Since the input to this categorizer was manual, it was not economically feasible to test it with a large sample of patterns, and therefore we have no extensive experimental curves corresponding to those shown in Fig. 7. However, the response of this categorizer to each of 100 patterns presented to it was identical to the response of the simulated categorizer to the same patterns. Thus we feel able to conclude that the simulated categorizer can be designed to operate substantially as predicted, and in particular that the curves shown in Fig. 7 very nearly describe our categorizer.

SUMMARY

The categorizer simulated, designed, and tested in the present work represents the most straightforward application of linear decision functions to a pattern recognition task, inasmuch as the categorizer inputs were simple measurements representing individual spots of ink in the input pattern. One intention was to determine the capability of such a simple network when realistic devices and component tolerances are taken into account. A second purpose was to test the utility of adaptive learning techniques in handling realistic patterns.

More complex networks capable of improved performance immediately suggest themselves; indeed some of these have already been simulated. Some of the modifications that may be made include: the addition of a layer of Boolean logic operating on the raw measurements (for instance to accomplish feature detection), the use of additional class-pair planes to resolve particular class-pair conflicts remaining in the existing categorizer, and the use of several layers of threshold circuits wherein the early layers are trained according to codes indicating the presence of particular features.

REFERENCES

1. Eldredge, K. R., F. J. Kamphoefner, and P. H. Wendt, "Teaching Machines to Read," *SRI J.*, First quarter, 1957; pp. 18–23.
2. ——————, "Automatic Input for Business Data Processing Systems," *Proc. EJCC*, Dec. 10–12, 1956, pp. 69–73.

3. Booth, W. T., G. M. Miller, and O. A. Schleich, "Design Considerations for Stylized Font Character Readers," in Fischer et al. (eds.), *Optical Character Recognition*, Spartan, Washington, 1962, pp. 115–128.
4. Chow, C. K., "An Optimum Character Recognition System using Decision Functions," *IRE Trans. Electron. Computers*, vol. EC–6, no. 4, December 1957, pp. 247–254.
5. Highleyman, W. H., "Linear Decision Functions, with Application to Pattern Recognition," *Proc. IRE*, vol. 50, no. 6, June 1962, pp. 1501–1514.
6. ———, "Linear Decision Functions, with Application to Pattern Recognition," Ph.D. Thesis, Polytechnic Institute of Brooklyn, N.Y., June 1961, available from University Microfilms, Ann Arbor, Mich.
7. Block, H. D., "The Perceptron: A Model for Brain Functioning, I" *Rev. Mod. Phys.*, vol. 34, no. 1, January 1962, pp. 123–135.
8. ———, B. W. Knight, Jr., and F. Rosenblatt, "Analysis of a Four-Layer Series-Coupled Perceptron, II," *Rev. Mod. Phys.*, vol. 34, no. 1, January 1962, pp.135–142.

7

A THEORETICAL AND EXPERIMENTAL STUDY OF A MODEL FOR PATTERN RECOGNITION

L. A. KAMENTSKY and C. N. LIU

International Business Machines Corporation
Yorktown Heights, N. Y.

INTRODUCTION

A pattern recognition system has been considered as performing two functions:

1. To measure certain attributes of the patterns to be recognized and
2. To classify the patterns—that is to decide into which classes the patterns belong on the basis of the results of these measurements.

The basis for choosing the measurements in a recognition system may be through intuition,[1] by random selection,[2,3] or by machine generation and selection.[4] The number of measurements used in recognition systems has varied from one per pattern class to many thousands. There has been a considerable literature[5,6] on the subject of classifiers describing their optimum form, why this form can not be realized, and describing subsequent approximations to the optimum classifier. The present paper is an attempt to relate each of these two aspects of the recognition problem by deriving equations for the performance of a recognition system as a function of the number and power of the measurements and the type of classifier used in the system.

Until recently there has been little work reported in methods of quantitatively describing the best properties of measurements to be used. The performance of any recognition system must be a function of the power of the measurements used and this should be reflected in theories describing the performance of recognition systems. We have used two quantities to quantitatively describe measurements and have incorporated them in a computer program[4] to select good recognition measurements. An information measure I was used to describe the discrimination and stability of individual measurements; a distance measure D was used to describe the redundancy of a set of measurements. The performance of a recognition system will be related to the quantities I, D, and the number of measurements N.

The major work in recognition has been in the application of binary measurements whereupon the points in the N dimensional space of measurement states are restricted to an N dimensional hypercube. The model described in this paper is based on this fact and will not use normal approximations to the value of each measurement.

The classification procedures to be modeled are related to our experiments. The first is, a Bayes decision with the assumption of independent measurements. This decision procedure will, with stationary distributions of the measurement states, produce the minimum error rate when the measurements are statistically independent. The derived performance is, therefore, a lower bound on the error rate of any decision procedure when the measurements are described in terms of the parameters, I, D, and N. The second decision procedure to be modeled is based on computing a binary distance between each unknown pattern and a set of reference patterns. This decision procedure may be considered to be related to the Bayes decision procedure with probabilities quantized into zeros and ones.

A computer program described in an earlier paper[4] had been written to design character recognition logics by processing data samples to select measurements based on the I and D values of the measurement sets. Several different logics have been designed to read single and miltifont sets of printed characters. This program will be described briefly and the empirical distributions of the decision statistics and the empirical error rates will be compared with theory.

THE CLASSIFICATION PARAMETERS

DECISION MODEL

Measurements are performed on the unknown pattern S_l to yield N different parameter values x_j, $j = 1, 2, \ldots, N$. All of these N values are presented to the classifier at the same time and will be considered here as a point $\overline{X}$ in an N-dimension space. The classifier, using all of the parameter values, produces one of m possible codes C_i, $i = 1, 2, \ldots, m$. In the simplest case, to be considered here, each code represents one pattern class to be recognized, and classification is made in one stage.

Classification may be considered as a statistical decision problem, and proper costs assigned to each of the possible misrecognitions of each pattern class or to the rejection of the input. For purposes of simplification, we will consider only a recognition system structured to achieve minimum error, that is, to produce the smallest total number of misclassifications of patterns. Given an observation $\overline{X}$, the probability of misclassifications is minimized if we assign this state of the parameters to the pattern class having the largest a posterior probability $P\{C_i|\overline{X}\}$ [5].

That, in practical problems, the probabilities $P\{C_i|\overline{X}\}$ can rarely be estimated, or stored if estimated, is the core of the problem of pattern recognition, since the number of states of $\overline{X}$ is usually extremely high. Thus, $P\{C_i|\overline{X}\}$ must be approximated with a number of parameters that are tractable to estimate and store. One such approximation, in which only $N \times m$ quantities need be estimated and stored, is to assume that the parameter values x_j are statistically independent, thus,

$$P\{\overline{X}|C_i\} = \prod_{j=1}^{N} P\{x_j|C_i\} \qquad \text{for all } i \tag{1}$$

where $P\{\overline{X}|C_i\}$ is the likelihood, or conditional probability of the parameter state $\overline{X}$ given the pattern C_i, and $P\{x_j|C_i\}$ the likelihood of a state of x_j given C_i. Each x_j corresponds to the state of one measurement for the particular unknown input pattern. It will be assumed that the a priori probability of each pattern class is known at the time when classification is made. If this probability is $P\{C_i\}$ then by Bayes rule,

$$P\{C_i|\overline{X}\} = \frac{P\{C_i\}\ P\{\overline{X}|C_i\}}{P\{\overline{X}\}} \tag{2}$$

If the parameter values are statistically independent,

$$P\{C_i|\overline{X}\} = \frac{P\{C_i\}}{P\{\overline{X}\}} \prod_{j=1}^{N} P\{x_j|C_i\} \tag{3}$$

The minimum-error rule is to choose the pattern C_i for which

$$G_i = P\{C_i\} \prod_{j=1}^{N} P\{x_j|C_i\} \tag{4}$$

is a maximum, since $P\{\overline{X}\}$ is not a function of C_i. It is more convenient to consider the quantity $W_i = \log G_i$ which is also a maximum when G_i is a maximum.

The problem of finding the error rate of a pattern recognition system given N measurements and a decision criterion using the independence assumptions will be considered. If the measurements are not statistically independent, the error rate derived will be a lower bound. We further confine our consideration to measurements that can be represented by binary parameters. This restriction corresponds to most of the work in pattern recognition and to our experimental work. The decision criterion for binary measurements is linear since

$$W_i = \log P\{C_i\} + \sum_{j=1}^{N} \log P\{x_j|C_i\}, \qquad x_j = 0, 1 \qquad (5)$$

Then:

$$W_i = a_0 + \sum_{j=1}^{N} a_{ij}x_j \qquad (6)$$

where:

$$a_0 = \log P\{C_i\} + \sum_{j=1}^{N} \log P\{x_j = 0|C_i\}$$

and

$$a_{ij} = \log P\{x_j = 1|C_i\} - \log P\{x_j = 0|C_i\}$$

Thus the decision $W_i > W_k$ is equivalent to finding the C_i for which the input pattern class is always on the positive side of the N-dimensional hyperplanes $W_i - W_k = 0, k \neq i$

The quantities $\log P\{x_j|C_i\}$ must be stored in some form to realize a decision system. Of importance is the precision of their specification. A simplified decision criterion in which the terms $\log P\{x_j|C_i\}$ are quantized into the values 0 and 1 will form the basis for a second decision model to be studied.

MEASURES OF THE POWER OF MEASUREMENTS

In general, any measurement can be applied to a set of patterns and rated in terms of its discriminating power. A binary measurement, for example, will be optimum if it can separate equal *a priori* probability pattern classes perfectly into two parts. In this case: the likelihoods computed in various instances of each of m pattern classes will have

$$P\{x_j = 1|C_i\} = 1 \quad \text{for} \quad i = 1, 2, \ldots, \frac{m}{2}$$

and $\quad P\{x_j = 0|C_i\} = 1 \quad \text{for} \quad i = \frac{m}{2} + 1, \frac{m}{2} + 2, \ldots, m$

Conversely, a measurement for which

$$P\{x_j = 0|C_i\} = K \quad \text{or} \quad P\{x_j = 1|C_i\} = K$$
$$\text{for} \quad i = 1, 2, \ldots, m, 0 \leq K \leq 1$$

has no discriminating power. All measurements will fall between these extremes. Fig. 1a shows a typical distribution of $P\{x_j = 1|C_i\}$ as a function of C_i taken from a problem in which the patterns are the 52 alphanumeric symbols and x_j represents a "good" measurement. Figure 1b shows a distribution for a "poor" measurement.

Shannon's information has been used as a measure of the information provided by an experiment[7,8]. We have applied it to evaluating recognition logics[4] and will show its utility. The information value used in our previous study[4]

$$ I = \sum_{x_j=0,1} P\{x_j\} \sum_{i=1}^{m} P\{C_i|x_j\} \log_2 P\{C_i|x_j\} - P\{C_i\} \log_2 P\{C_i\} $$

(7)

will be used in the present study as a quantitive measure of the worth of each parameter j. The error rate of a recognition system will be related to the average information $<I>$ of the set of measurements. I ranges in value between 0 and 1; the particular values of I for the distributions shown in Fig. 1 are $I_a = 0.721$ and $I_b = 0.226$.

In applying the information measure I to a set of m pattern classes in which $m > 2$, there is no assurance that each measurement will not divide the pattern classes into the same two parts. We therefore define a distance D_{ik} to be applied to all of the $m(m - 1)/2$ pairs of pattern classes. If a given measurement j separates a pair of pattern classes C_i and C_k, we say that the measurement adds a distance of one to that particular pair of pattern classes ($D_{ik,j} = 1$). D_{ik} then is the number of measurements of the N measurements that separate the pair of pattern classes C_i and $C_k(D_{ik} = \sum_{j=1}^{N} D_{ik,j})$. There are a number of criteria to use for defining separation.

Two criteria are nearly equivalent and are used interchangeably:

1. An information value $I_{ik,j}$ can be computed for x_j only over the pair of patterns C_i and C_k. $D_{ik,j} = 1$ if $I_{ik,j} \geq \theta$ where θ is a threshold value.

2. $D_{ik,j} = 1$ if $P\{x_j = 1|C_i\} \geq \theta_1$ and $P\{x_j = 1|C_k\} \leq \theta_2$ where $\theta_1 > \theta_2$. We have used the particular values $\theta_1 = 0.8$, $\theta_2 = 0.2$.

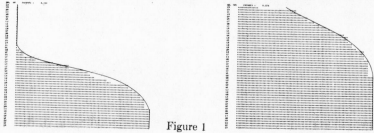

Figure 1

THE BAYES DECISION STATISTIC

Let $P\{x_j|C_i\}, j = 1, 2, \ldots, N$, be the likelihoods for the pattern class C_l corresponding to the true identity of an unknown pattern and define $P_{lj} = P\{x_j = 1|C_i\}$ for $C_i = C_l$. Let Y_j be a random variable with the two states one and zero and the corresponding probabilities P_{lj} and $1 - P_{lj}$. The random variable

$$X_{ij} = Y_j \log P\{x_j|C_i\} + (1 - Y_j) \log (1 - P\{x_j|C_i\}) \qquad (8)$$

will be called the Bayes decision statistic for the pattern class C_i and the measurement j, and the quantity

$$\chi_i = \sum_{j=1}^{N} \chi_{ij} \qquad (9)$$

the Bayes decision statistic of a recognition system with N measurements. If the quantities $P\{x_j|C_i\}$ have been estimated for each measurement and pattern class and these distributions are stationary, and furthermore, if the *a priori* probabilities $P\{C_i\}$ are assumed to be equal for each pattern, then:

1. χ_l is a random variable corresponding to the sum of the Bayes weight of Eq. 5 when the unknown pattern belongs to class C_l. This sum will be called the "null" channel.
2. $\chi_i, i \neq l$ is a random variable corresponding to the sum of the Bayes weights when the unknown pattern does not belong to the class C_i. These sums will be called the "alternative" channels.

In the remainder of this section, we will derive the distributions of the quantities χ_l and $\xi = \chi_l - \chi_i, i \neq l$, the gain in likelihood of the null channel over a single alternative channel.

THE NULL AND ALTERNATIVE CHANNEL CHARACTERISTIC FUNCTIONS

The random variable Y_j is Bernoulli and has the characteristic function:

$$C_Y(z, P_{lj}) = P_{lj}e^{iz} + (1 - P_{lj}) \qquad (10)$$

The characteristic function for χ_{lj} may be determined by noting that Eq. 8 has the linear form

$$\chi_{1j} = [\log P_{lj} - \log (1 - P_{lj})] Y_j + \log (1 - P_{lj}) \qquad (11)$$

since $C_i = C_l$ for the null channel. Thus,

$$C_\chi(z,P_{lj}) = P_{lj}{}^{iz+1} + (1 - P_{lj})^{iz+1} \tag{12}$$

The characteristic function for N independent channels is

$$C_\chi(z,P_i) = \prod_{j=1}^{N} P_{lj}{}^{iz+1} + (1 - P_{lj})^{iz+1} \tag{13}$$

$$\text{Let} \quad P_{ij} = P\{x_j = 1 | C_i\} \quad \text{for} \quad C_i \neq C_l$$

The Bayes statistic for an alternative channel is

$$\chi_{ij} = Y_j \log P_{ij} + (1 - Y_j) \log (1 - P_{ij}) \quad i \neq 1 \tag{14}$$

and the Bayes statistic for the gain per measurement of the null channel over an alternative C_i is

$$\xi_j = Y_j \log P_{lj} + (1 - Y_j) \log (1 - P_{lj})$$
$$-[Y_j \log P_{ij} + (1 - Y_j) \log (1 - P_{ij})] \tag{15}$$

The characteristic function for ξ_j can be obtained by noting that ξ_j is a linear function of Y_j:

$$C_\xi(z,P_{lj},P_{ij}) = \frac{P_{lj}{}^{iz+1}}{P_{ij}{}^{iz}} + \frac{(1 - P_{lj})^{iz+1}}{(1 - P_{ij})^{iz}} \tag{16}$$

The characteristic function for ξ is then

$$C_\xi(z,P_l,P_i) = \prod_{j=1}^{N} \frac{P_{lj}{}^{iz+1}}{P_{ij}{}^{iz}} + \frac{(1 - P_{lj})^{iz+1}}{(1 - P_{ij})^{iz}} \tag{17}$$

THE DISTRIBUTION OF THE LIKELIHOODS

The distributions of the statistics χ_l and ξ may be estimated if the distributions of the likelihoods P_{lj} and P_{ij} are known. In this section we will postulate a model for these distributions, relating them to the parameters I and D.

The likelihoods P_{ij} can be considered to be numbers distributed on the interval zero to one. If the measurements have high discrimination the values of P_{ij} are near one for $i = 1, 2, \ldots, m/2$ and near zero for $i = m/2$

$+ 1, m/2 + 2, \ldots, m$. The beta variate which is distributed on the interval zero to one is a function of two parameters α and β and given by:

$$\phi(P) = \frac{1}{B(\alpha,\beta)} P^{\alpha-1}(1 - P)^{\beta-1} \qquad \begin{array}{l} 0 \leq P \leq 1 \\ 0 < \alpha, 0 < \beta \end{array} \qquad (18)$$

where $B(\alpha, \beta)$ is the Beta function of α and β. The parameters α and β can be related to I by using Eq. 7 or by an equation to be derived later. Figure 2a shows the beta density function for $\alpha = \beta$ for various values of I. Figure 2b shows the beta cumulative distribution and the cumulative distribution of the likelihoods of a set of 31 recognition measurements to be described later in this paper. It is assumed that the likelihoods P_{ij} have the Beta distribution $\phi(P_{ij})$ for $i = 1, 2, \ldots, m, j = 1, 2, \ldots, N$.

Setting $\alpha = \beta$ in the model implies that the frequency of each of the two states are equal over the ensemble of measurements. This was found to be

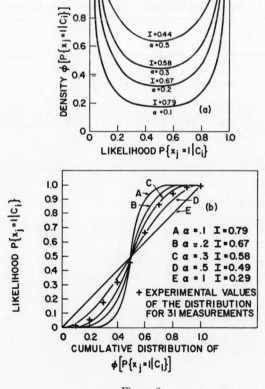

Figure 2

the case for our experiments. This assumption simplifies the solution of the decision statistics and will be used in the present paper.

Two different models are postulated to relate P_{lj} and P_{ij}. In the first model P_{lj} and P_{ij} are considered to be independent. In the second model the likelihoods of the null and alternative channels are correlated so that:

$$P_{ij} = P_{lj} \text{ for } j = 1, 2, \ldots, N - D$$

$$P_{ij} = 1 - P_{lj} \text{ for } j = N - D + 1, N - D + 2, \ldots, N$$

Thus, of the N measurements, the null and alternative channels have $N - D$ measurements which are positively correlated and D measurements which are correlated so as to add distance between the channels.

THE DISTRIBUTION OF THE NULL CHANNEL

Assuming a beta density for the frequency of each of the independent likelihoods P_{lj}, the characteristic function for the null channel is

$$C_x(z) = \prod_{j=1}^{N} \int_0^1 \phi(P_{lj})[P_{lj}{}^{iz+1} + (1 - P_{lj})^{iz+1}] \, dP_{lj} \tag{19}$$

Since the measurements have the same density,

$$C_x(z) = \left[\frac{1}{B(\alpha,\beta)} \int_0^1 P_{lj}{}^{iz+\alpha}(1 - P_{lj})^{\beta-1} + P_{lj}{}^{\alpha-1}(1 - P_{lj})^{iz+\beta} \, dP_{lj} \right]^N \tag{20}$$

Integrating we have

$$C_x(z) = \left[\frac{1}{B(\alpha,\beta)} [B\{iz + 1 + \alpha,\beta\} + B\{\alpha,iz + 1 + \beta\}] \right]^N \tag{21}$$

The beta function may be related to the gamma function by

$$B\{\alpha,\beta\} = \frac{\Gamma(\alpha)\,\Gamma(\beta)}{\Gamma(\alpha + \beta)} \tag{22}$$

Setting $\alpha = \beta$, the characteristic function is

$$C_x(z) = \left[\frac{2\Gamma(2\alpha)}{\Gamma(\alpha)} \frac{\Gamma(iz + \alpha + 1)}{\Gamma(iz + 2\alpha + 1)} \right]^N \tag{23}$$

Let

$$\rho_1 = \alpha + 1 - \lambda$$

$$\rho_2 = 2\alpha + 1 - \lambda \tag{24}$$

where

$$\lambda = \left[\frac{2\Gamma(2\alpha)}{\Gamma(\alpha)} \right]^{1/\alpha} \tag{25}$$

Then

$$\Gamma(iz + \alpha + 1) = \Gamma(iz + \lambda + \rho_1)$$

$$\Gamma(iz + 2\alpha + 1) = \Gamma(iz + \lambda + \rho_2) \tag{26}$$

Using the assymptotic expression[9]

$$\frac{\Gamma(iz + \lambda + \rho_1)}{\Gamma(iz + \lambda + \rho_2)} = (iz + \lambda)^{\rho_1 - \rho_2} \left[1 + \frac{1}{2(iz + \lambda)} (\rho_1 - \rho_2)(\rho_1 + \rho_2 - 1) \right.$$

$$\left. + \text{ Terms of Order } \left(\frac{\rho_1 - \rho_2}{iz + \lambda} \right)^2 \right] \tag{27}$$

$$C_\chi(z) = \left[\left(\frac{1}{\lambda} \right)^\alpha \left[iz + \lambda \right]^\alpha \left[1 + \frac{\alpha(3\alpha + 1 - 2\lambda)}{2(iz + \lambda)} + O\left(\frac{\alpha}{iz + \lambda} \right)^2 \right] \right]^{-N} \tag{28}$$

The following approximation to $C_\chi(z)$ can be made by neglecting terms which are of the order of 0.01 compared to unity:

$$C_\chi(z) = \left[1 + \frac{iz}{\lambda} \right]^{-\alpha N} \tag{29}$$

This is the characteristic function of the Gamma Distribution:

$$\psi(-\chi) = \frac{\lambda^{\alpha N}}{\Gamma(\alpha N)} \chi^{\alpha N - 1} e^{-\lambda \chi} \tag{30}$$

The mean of the gamma null channel statistic is:

$$\mu_\chi = -\frac{\alpha N}{\lambda} = -\alpha N \left[\frac{\Gamma(\alpha)}{2\Gamma(2\alpha)} \right]^{1/\alpha} \tag{31}$$

The mean μ_χ may be related directly to the average information $< I >$ of the set of measurements giving a simple relationship between the distribution parameters and the average information. The mean value of Eq. 9 is:

$$\mu_\chi = < \chi > = N < Y_j \log P_{1j} + (1 - Y_j) \log (1 - Y_j) > \tag{32}$$

But $< Y_j > = P_{lj}$. Then,

$$\mu_x = N(P_{lj} \log P_{lj} + (1 - P_{lj}) \log (1 - P_{lj})) \tag{33}$$

Using Bayes rule and equal *a priori* probabilities, $P(C_i) = 1/m$, Eq. 7 has the form

$$I = \sum_{x_j=0,1} P\{x_j\} \log_2 P\{x_j\} + \frac{1}{m} \sum_{i=1}^{m} P_{lj} \log_2 P_{lj} \tag{34}$$

Assuming equal probability states of x_j, the expected value of the information of N identically distributed measurements is

$$<I> = 1 + P_{lj} \log_2 P_{lj} + (1 - P_{lj}) \log_2 (1 - P_{lj}) \tag{35}$$

Thus,

$$\mu_x = N(<I> - 1) \text{ where the base of } \mu_x \text{ is } 2 \tag{36}$$

If the Bayes statistic uses logarithms to some base b other than 2 then,

$$\mu_x = (\log_b 2) N(< I > - 1) \tag{37}$$

μ_x (using the base ϵ) is plotted as a function of I in Fig. 3.

THE DISTRIBUTION OF THE GAIN IN LIKELIHOOD

INDEPENDENT PATTERN CLASSES

If P_{lj} and P_{ij} are independent the characteristic function of the gain in likelihood ξ is:

$$C_\xi(z) = \prod_{j=1}^{N} \int_0^1 \int_0^1 \phi(P_{lj}) \, \phi(P_{ij}) \left[\frac{P_{lj}^{iz+1}}{P_{ij}^{iz}} + \frac{(1 - P_{lj})^{iz+1}}{(1 - P_{ij})^{iz}} \right] dP_{ij} dP_{lj} \tag{38}$$

With identical densities,

$$C_\xi(z) = \left[\frac{1}{B^2(\alpha,\alpha)} \int_0^1 \int_0^1 P_{1j}^{iz+1} P_{ij}^{-iz+\alpha-1}(1 - P_{ij})^{\alpha-1} \right.$$
$$\left. + (1 - P_{lj})^{iz+1} P_{ij}^{\alpha-1}(1 - P_{lj})^{-iz+\alpha-1} \, dP_{ij} dP_{lj} \right]^N \tag{39}$$

Integrating,

$$C_\xi(z) = \left[2 \frac{B\{-iz + \alpha,\alpha\} \, B\{iz + \alpha + 1,\alpha\}}{B^2(\alpha,\alpha)} \right]^N \tag{40}$$

In terms of gamma functions

$$C_\xi(z) = \left[\left[\frac{\Gamma(-iz + \alpha)\ \Gamma(2\alpha)}{\Gamma(-iz + 2\alpha)\ \Gamma(\alpha)} \right] \left[\frac{2\Gamma(iz + \alpha + 1)\ \Gamma(2\alpha)}{\Gamma(-iz + 2\alpha + 1)\ \Gamma(\alpha)} \right] \right]^N \tag{41}$$

The moments of this distribution may be obtained by differentiating the characteristic function. The mean and variance are

$$\mu_\xi = \frac{N}{2\alpha} \tag{42}$$

$$\sigma_\xi^2 = \frac{3N}{4\alpha^2} \left[1 + \frac{8}{3}\alpha^2 \left[\psi'(\alpha + 1) - \psi'(2\alpha + 1) \right] \right] \tag{43}$$

where $\chi(\alpha)$ is the logarithmic derivative of the Gamma Function. The ratio of the mean to mean square deviation is:

$$\left(\frac{\mu_\xi}{\sigma_\xi} \right) = \left[\frac{N}{3} \frac{1}{1 + \frac{8}{3}\alpha^2 [\psi'(\alpha + 1) - \psi'(2\alpha + 1)]} \right]^{1/2} \tag{44}$$

For $0.2 < \alpha < 1, \Psi'(\alpha + 1) - \Psi'(2\alpha + 1) \approx 0.25$

$$\left(\frac{\mu_\xi}{\sigma_\xi} \right) \approx \left(\frac{N}{3} \frac{1}{1 + \frac{2}{3}\alpha^2} \right)^{1/2} \tag{45}$$

If we define,

$$\lambda' = \left[\frac{\Gamma(2\alpha)}{\Gamma(\alpha)} \right]^{1/\alpha} \tag{46}$$

Eq. 27 may be applied to the characteristic function $C_\xi(z)$ to arrive at the form,

$$C_\xi(z) = \left[1 - \frac{iz}{\lambda'} \right]^{-\alpha N} \left[1 + \frac{iz}{\lambda} \right]^{-\alpha N} \tag{47}$$

The distribution of the gain in likelihood $\chi(\xi)$ si the convolution of two gamma distributions, the null channel distribution $\chi(-X)$, and the reversed distribution of

$$\psi'(-\chi) = \frac{\lambda'^{\alpha N}}{\Gamma(\alpha N)} \chi^{\alpha N - 1} e^{-\lambda' \chi} \tag{48}$$

CORRELATED PATTERN CLASSES

We now seek the distribution of ξ when $P_{ij} = P_{lj}$ for $j = 1, 2, \ldots,$

$N - D$ and $P_{ij} = (1 - P_{lj})$ for $j = N - D + 1, N - D + 2, \ldots, N$.

In this case Eq. 17 becomes

$$C_\xi(z, P_l) = \prod_{j=N-D+1}^{N} \frac{P_{lj}^{iz+1}}{(1 - P_{lj})^{iz}} + \frac{(1 - P_{lj})^{iz+1}}{P_{lj}^{iz}} \tag{49}$$

If the measurements are independent and beta,

$$C_\xi(z) = \left[\frac{1}{B(\alpha, \alpha)} \int_0^1 P_{lj}^{iz+\alpha} (1 - P_{lj})^{-iz+\alpha-1} \right.$$

$$\left. + P_{lj}^{-iz+\alpha-1} (1 - P_{lj})^{iz+\alpha} \, dP_{lj} \right]^D$$

$$C_\xi(z) = \left[\frac{2B\{iz + \alpha + 1, - iz + \alpha\}}{B\{\alpha, \alpha\}} \right]^D$$

$$C_\xi(z) = \left[\frac{\Gamma(iz + \alpha + 1) \Gamma(\alpha - iz)}{\alpha \Gamma^2(\alpha)} \right]^D \tag{50}$$

The mean, variance, and ratio of mean to variance of the gain in likelihood are:

$$\mu_\xi = \frac{D}{\alpha} \tag{51}$$

$$\sigma^2 = \frac{D}{\alpha^2} [1 + 2\alpha^2 \psi'(\alpha + 1)] \tag{52}$$

$$\left(\frac{\mu}{\sigma} \right) = \left[\frac{D}{1 + 2\alpha^2 \psi'(\alpha + 1)} \right]^{1/2} \tag{53}$$

We will not attempt to find the exact form of the distribution of Eq. 50. It should be noted that the distance D is present in the mean rather than $N/2$ as in the independent model and the mean to variance ratio is approximately $\sqrt{D}$ rather than $\sqrt{N}/3$. As the value of I approaches 1 the two distributions should converge for the optimum value of $D = N/2$ since P_{ij} can be only zero or one when $I = 1$. μ_ξ is plotted as a function of I in Fig. 3.

THE ERROR RATE

The error rate E for a two-pattern class-recognition system is the probability that $\xi \leq 0$ or

$$E = \int_{-\infty}^{0} \psi(\xi) \, d\xi \tag{54}$$

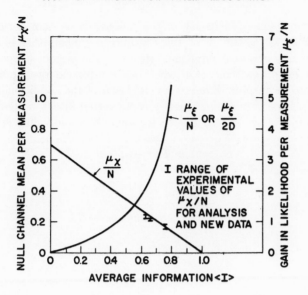

Figure 3

If the recognition system must distinguish m pattern classes where $m > 2$ then the probability of correct recognition $1 - E$ is

$$1 - E = \int_{-\infty}^{0} \psi(\chi_1) \left[\text{Prob } \chi_2 \leq \chi_1 \right]^{m-1} d\chi_1 \qquad (55)$$

where χ_2 has the alternative channel distribution $\psi'(\chi)$, then,

$$E = 1 - \int_{-\infty}^{0} \psi(\chi_1) \left[\int_{-\infty}^{\chi_1} \psi'(\chi_2) \, d\chi_2 \right]^{m-1} d\chi_1 \qquad (56)$$

The error rate has been computed using the independent pattern class model. Curves of E as functions of the parameters N and I are plotted in Figs. 4 and 5. The value of $m = 10$ has been used in these curves so that the theory may be compared with a ten pattern class recognition experiment.

THE MINIMUM DISTANCE DECISION STATISTIC

In the simple Bayes Rule decision, the conditional probabilities, $p\{x_j | C_i\}$, are estimated to an accuracy inversely proportional to the number of samples analyzed. In other words, if ten samples of each pattern class are used, then the conditional probabilities can assume only ten distinct numerical values. The sensitivity of the recognition system performance with respect to the accuracy of the conditional probabilities is of great importance when practical implementations of the system is considered. Let us consider an extreme case where all conditional probabilities are quantized into only three different levels. Each of the conditional probabilities for each pattern C_i and logic j is converted into a representation S_{ij} based on the following assignments for some threshold values θ_1 and θ_2:

$$S_{ij} = 1, \text{ if } P\{x_j|C_i\} \geq \theta_1$$

$$S_{ij} = 0, \text{ if } P\{x_j|C_i\} \leq \theta_2 \tag{57}$$

and $S_{ij} = \phi$ or don't care, if

$$\theta_2 < P\{x_j|C_i\} < \theta_1$$

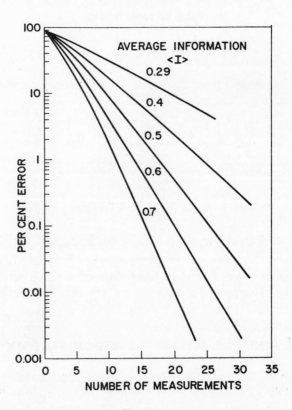

Figure 4

For the state vector $\overline{X}$ of each unknown pattern a distance d_i between this unknown and the representation of the state vector for the class i is computed as follows:

$$d_i = \sum_{j=1}^{N} |S_{ij} - x_j| \qquad \text{for} \quad S_{ij} = 0 \text{ or } 1 \tag{58}$$

The unknown pattern is assigned to the class C_1 for which $d_1 < d_i$ for all $i \neq l$.

The null channel distribution for the minimum distance decision statistic, which is the distribution of d_l when $\overline{X}$ comes from the class C_l, can be obtained by noting that Eq. 58 represents a binominal process. If each of the components of S_{lj} are independent and have the probabilities P_{lj} then the probability that r of n components will not match is

$$\text{Prob } \{d_l = r\} = b\{r, n, (1 - P_{lj})\} \tag{59}$$

$$b\{r, n, (1 - P_{lj})\} = \binom{n}{r} P_{lj}^{n-r} (1 - P_{lj})^r$$

and n is the number of components of $\bar{S}_{lj} = 1$ or 0.

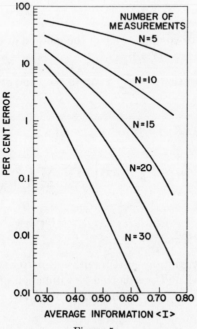

Figure 5

The distribution of P_{lj}, ϕ (P_{lj}) may be related to I, however, we have found it more convenient to specify an average value of P_{lj} when $S_{lj} = 1$ and $1 - P_{lj}$ when $S_{lj} = 0$ which we will call the stability of the measurements. This is valid for θ_1 close to 1 and θ_2 close to 0.

The alternative channel distribution for the minimum distance statistic is the distribution of d_i when $\overline{X}$ does not come from the class C_i. As in the previous section we use the distance D between pattern classes where $N - D$ measurements will have $P_{ij} = P_{lj}$ and D measurements will have $P_{ij} = 1 - P_{lj}$.

The number of components of $\overline{X}$ not matching $\bar{S}_i$ can be considered to come from the sum of components taken from two Bernoulli trials, $b\{r, D, P_{lj}\}$ and $b\{r, n - D, 1 - P_{lj}\}$. This sum is the convolution

$$\text{Prob} \quad \{d_i = r\} = \sum_{s=0}^{r} \binom{n-D}{r-s}\binom{D}{s} q^{r-s} p^{(n-D)-(r-s)} p^s q^{D-s} \tag{60}$$

where the simplified notation, $p = P_{lj}$, $q = 1 - P_{lj}$ has been used and

$$\binom{u}{n} = 0 \text{ for } n > u.$$

The error rate may be computed using the method described previously.

$$\text{Prob \{Correct recognition\}} = \sum_{r=0}^{n-1} \text{Prob } \{d_i = r \text{ and } d_k > r \text{ for all } k \neq i\}$$

$$= \sum_{r=0}^{n-1} \text{Prob } \{d_i = r\} \cdot [\text{Prob } \{d_k > r \text{ for } k \neq i\}]^{m-1} \quad \text{or}$$

$$E = 1 - \sum_{r=0}^{n-1} \binom{n}{r}(1-p)^r p^{n-r} \left[\sum_{t=r+1}^{n} \sum_{s=0}^{t} \binom{n-D}{t-s}\binom{D}{s} p^{t-s} \right.$$

$$\left. q^{(n-D)-(t-s)} q^s p^{D-s} \right]^{m-1} \tag{61}$$

Error rates for a recognition system with ten pattern classes have been computed using Eq. 61 and are plotted as a function of the average stability P and the number of measurements N in Fig. 6

$$\left(\frac{D}{N} = \frac{1}{2}\right) \quad \text{and Fig. 7} \quad \left(\frac{D}{N} = \frac{1}{3}\right).$$

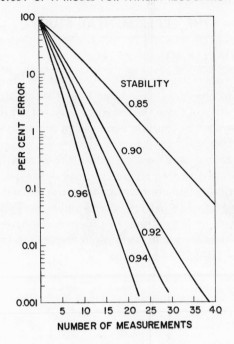

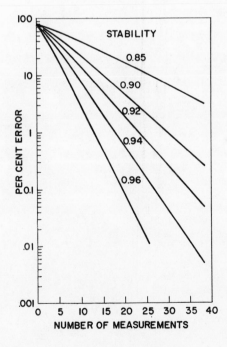

THE EXPERIMENTAL STUDY

A RECOGNITION LOGIC

In a previous paper[4] we described a computer-automated character-recognition design procedure based on a statistical analysis of actual samples representative of those the recognition machine will be called upon to classify. Our present recognition logic design program will be described briefly in this section.

A flying-spot scanner was used to reduce the images of characters on photographs of printed text to records on magnetic tape. Each character was isolated from its neighbors by circuits in the scanner and was represented on magnetic tape as a pattern of ones and zeros. Typical bit patterns are shown in Fig. 8. A large group of different characters was manually identified. The character identities and corresponding bit patterns were then read into the IBM 7090 computer.

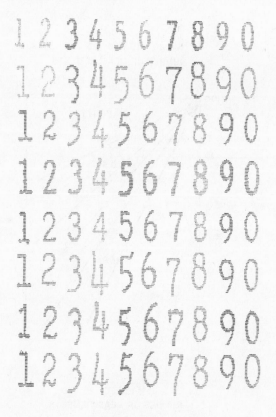

Figure 8

Each pattern was transformed into a state vector $\overline{X}$ consisting of a fixed set of 5 to 96 measurements on every character, these measurements being independent of character registration. A measurement consists of a determination of the occurrence in the scanned character of a set of black and white points satisfying some prescribed spatial relationship. This feature guarantees that recognition will be independent of misregistration inherent on the source document or instabilities and inaccuracies in document handling of optical equipment. A classification is made by using either of the two decision methods described previously on the state vector X.

More specifically, the measurements consist of seven-tuples in a prescribed spatial arrangement and with a prescribed assignment of zero and one states. These seven-tuple logics are shifted with respect to the input pattern so that the logics are tested for a match in all possible positions. If the jth logic matches a pattern in any position, $x_j = 1$ for that logic. A typical logic chosen for high information in discriminating the ten numerals is shown in Fig. 9. Also shown is the distribution of P_{ij} with C_i for the logic.

The logics are generated at random but subject to certain constraints on their spatial arrangement. The logics are evaluated individually using the information measure I on representative samples of all of the pattern classes. It was found to be too time-consuming to compute the information measure I over more than a single measurement at a time. The logics having the largest value of I are selected. These logics are then perturbed by moving each of the seven points, one at a time, to neighboring positions so as to maximize I.

The random generation procedure increases the likelihood that the individual measurements are independent. However, the distance between

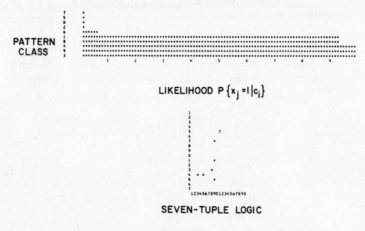

Figure 9

pattern classes was not found to be uniform and a procedure was developed to optimize the measurement set. The distance measure D was used to further evaluate a set of measurements. The distance between all pairs of pattern classes was determined for the set of measurements. Measurements that only increase the distance of pairs of classes which already had a large distance were omitted from the measurement set. Samples of pattern classes with small distances between them were used as the basis for deriving new measurements with a high value of I computed only over these classes. The measurement set was contracted and expanded a number of times using this procedure until a given distance D was achieved between all pattern classes.

COMPARISON OF EXPERIMENTS AND THEORY

Figure 8 shows examples of 324 samples of the ten numbers from eleven different type fonts commonly used in manual and electric typewriters that were scanned and used to design four different logics. These logics differ in the number of measurements N and distance D between classes. This same set of data was used to establish sets of values of P_{ij} and S_{ij} for each of the four sets of measurements. Each of the measurement sets was tested on 360 different instances of data from the same typewriters. The resultant error rates are termed the new data errors. The logics were also tested on the 324 samples of design data. The error rates in this case are termed the analysis errors.

Table I lists the number of measurements, the design distance D, the average information $< I >$, and the Bayes and minimum-distance-decision error rates on new and analysis data for each of the four measure-

Table I.   Design Parameters and Results

Number of measurements, N	Design distance, D	Average information, I	Error rates in Percent			
			Bayes		Minimum Distance	
			Analysis data	New data	Analysis data	New data
5	1	0.76	8.02	11.4	9.6	12.1
17	4	0.66	1.54	2.5	2.48	4.2
31	7	0.63	0	0.84	0.31	1.1
37	8	0.63	0	0.28	0.31	0.28

ment sets. The cumulative distribution of the likelihoods P_{ij} are compared with the beta distribution in Fig. 2. The likelihoods plotted were determined from the 31 measurement set having an average I of 0.63. The quantities μ_x/N, stability and average D are tabulated as a function of N in Table II. The cumulative distribution of the Bayes decision statistic χ was determined for each of two sets of measurements on both the new and analysis data sets. These data are plotted in Fig. 10 along with curves of the distribution,

$$\cdot \frac{1}{\Gamma(\alpha N)} \int_0^{\lambda x} \nu^{\alpha N - 1} e^{-\nu} \, d\nu \tag{62}$$

to confirm the distribution of this decision statistic. This is repeated in Fig. 11, for the minimum distance statistic and the cumulative binomial distribution.

Table II. Design Parameters and Results

Number of measurements, N	Average distance, D	Stability	Null channel mean per measurement μ_x/N	
			Analysis data	New data
5	2	0.94	1.69	1.63
17	7	0.95	1.47	1.44
31	11	0.94	1.39	1.36

CONCLUSIONS

A model has been presented for a pattern recognition system where certain average properties of the set of measurements used in the system are specified and these properties are assumed to be uniform over the set of measurements and pattern classes. Assumptions of equal *a priori* probabilities of the pattern classes and statistical independence of the measurement likelihoods were also made. Two classification procedures covering two extremes of specification of the likelihoods of the measurements were used in deriving quantities relating the performance of a recognition system to the design parameters.

The average properties of information per measurement and average distance between pattern classes were used as the basis for an automatic-recognition logic design procedure. Experiments were performed where the

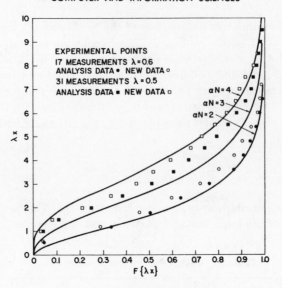

Figure 10

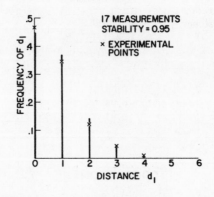

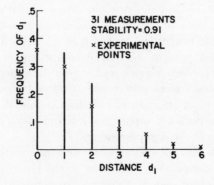

Figure 11

a priori probabilities of pattern classes were equal, variations of the design parameters were minimized, and some randomization was used to achieve independence of the likelihoods. The theoretical prediction of the error rates was good for 5 and 17 measurement-recognition systems. Because of the difficulty of estimating the low error rates for the 31 and 37 measurements-recognition systems, it is misleading to relate this data to the theoretical predictions. However, the independence assumption should fail as the number of measurements increases.

Much of the recognition literature is concerned with approaches using pattern templates or a single complex logic statement per pattern class. It is of interest to note the requirements on stability as a function of distance between classes for systems where the number of measurements is equal to the number of classes. Figure 12 illustrates the predicted error rate of the minimum distance decision procedure with ten pattern classes, ten measurements, and two or three measurements separating each class. The usual design procedures determine a single templete or logic per pattern, thus, yielding a single "one" for each row and column of the S_{ij} matrix and a distance between classes of two. Note that the performance of the recognition system can be increased an order of magnitude by choosing measurements to increase the distance between classes to three. Use of the information measure during design is one way of maximizing the number of distances obtained between pattern classes per measurement.

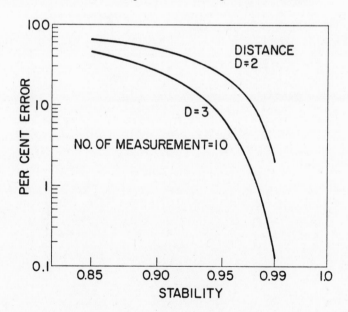

Figure 12

REFERENCES

1. Kamentsky, L. A., "The Simulation of Three Machines which Read Rows of Handwritten Arabic Numbers," *IRE Trans. Electron. Computers*, EC–10, 1961, pp. 489–501.
2. Bledesoe, W. W , and I. Browning, "Pattern Recognition and Reading by Machine," *Proc. EJCC*, 1959, pp. 225–233.
3. Palmieri, G., and R. Sanna, "Automatic Probabilistic Programmer/Analyzer for Pattern Recognition," *Estr. Riv. Meth. 12*, no. 18, 1960.
4. Kamentsky, L. A., and C. N. Liu, "Computer-Automated Design of Multifont Print Recognition Logic, *IBM Journal 7*, 1963, pp. 2–13.
5. Marill, T., and D. M. Green, "Statistical Recognition Functions and the Design of Pattern Recognizers," *IRE Trans. Electron. Computers*, EC–9, 1960, pp. 472–477.
6. Sebestyen, G. S., *Decision Making Processes in Pattern Recognition*, Macmillan, New York, 1962.
7. Lindley, D. V., "On A Measure of the Information Provided by an Experiment," *Ann. Math. Stat. 27*, 1956, pp. 986–1005.
8. Lewis, P. M., "The Characteristic Selection Problem in Recognition Systems," *IRE Trans. Inform. Theory*, vol. IT–8, 1962 pp. 171–178.
9. Bateman, H., *Higher Transcendental Functions*, Vol. 1, McGraw-Hill, New York, 1953, pp. 47.

8

NEW DEVELOPMENTS IN ARTIFICIAL
INTELLIGENCE AND PATTERN RECOGNITION

A. Gamba

Institute of Physics, University of Genoa, Italy

I will report on the work done in the field of artificial intelligence at the Institute of Physics of the University of Genoa, Italy. Most of the work has already been published. A list of references can be found by looking in some of the latest issues of *Supplemento del Nuovó Cimento*, the Italian journal of Physics that is available in any physics library. Therefore, I shall not go into details and I shall limit my talk to a survey of the general ideas involved, for the benefit of those who are unfamiliar with our work, in order to be able to discuss later the future developments in this field as I see them.

My interest in the field of artificial intelligence was prompted some three years ago by reading several papers on Rosenblatt's Perceptron. Since in the words of the organizers of this Symposium "the approaches emphasized (in this Symposium) will be those of the engineering and physical sciences, rather than of biology or psychology *per se,*" it might not be unappropriate for me to say here that at first I could hardly understand the basic ideas of Rosenblatt. As a theoretical physicist I was confused by words such as "reward," "punishment," etc. I began wondering whether a clear-cut definition of intelligence could be given—or, more precisely, whether we could establish a measure for the quantity "intelligence" such that given a set of intelligent machines (artificial or not) we could order them according to their intelligence.

Intelligence must first be defined. The more "intelligent" part of intelligence, according to my point of view, is the ability of making induction. This doesn't mean that other qualities, such as memory, logic, etc., are irrelevant—Einstein, with the same brain, could hardly have been such a great scientist, had he been born deaf and blind. My statement must be understood in the same sense of the sentence "the most important part of the human body is the brain." It means that a man—as distinguished from other animals—is *homo sapiens* mostly because of his brain. It does not mean that you should pay no attention to your liver. Having thus reduced intelligence, so to speak, to a single, most important parameter, we can now search for a general principle for induction.

As a working hypothesis, consider the following definition of induction: from the information obtained through past experience, an inductive machine must correctly guess similar future events. With this definition I don't see what else a machine can do in order to make such guesses, except to use past experiences to establish probability weights to be used for statistical inferences.

An intelligent machine can then be nothing more than an Automatic Programmer and Analyzer of Probabilities (the Italian acronym for it spells PAPA). My statement is that *all* intelligent machines—not only those that we built in our laboratory—are essentially PAPAs, and that on the road towards artificial intelligence there is nothing more to be found than probability calculus. Let us discuss this point a little further. Consider a set of intelligent machines $A, B, C, \ldots, M$, represented by the boxes in Fig. 1. The upper arrow on each box indicates the information flow, and we assume that each intelligent machine gets the same information. This means that the information is really identical, and not only in equal amounts in Shannon's sense. In other words all machines "see" the same things, have the same past experiences. The lower arrow indicates the intelligent output, the "guesses" of each machine.

My statement that intelligence is nothing but probability calculus means then that a perfect mathematician in M will beat all other machines in performance. The mathematician in this context is the analogue of the reversible Carnot machine in the field of converting heat into mechanical work. It sets an upper limit to the performance of any machine.

It seems to me that, if this principle is accepted, the subject of intelligent machines is cleared of much misunderstanding caused by rather vague concepts, thus permitting indeed a more physical approach.

So, you have invented a new intelligent machine? Fine. Let us see how you compute probabilities. If you do it better than I—i.e., if your strategy approximates that of the perfect mathematician better than my strategy, your machine works better than mine. We can now discuss whether it pays off—in term of hardware—to make practical devices your way or my way. (Going back to the example of the thermal engine, you may have a better fuel, but mine is cheaper.) There might, of course, be some difficulties in comparing the performance of our machines with equal information— suppose, for example, that my machine has an optical input and yours has an acoustical one; it might turn out (we will come to this later) that for your particular tasks you don't really need an "intelligent" machine, etc. All these questions have to be examined, but at least we are now on solid physical ground. For example, what is your purpose in your reward and punishment technique? Analyzed in term of probability calculus, it might turn out that in your machine you want simply to store a certain frequency in a certain place and that this goal can be much more easily achieved in a different way. It might really be better for you to store two numbers instead of one in that place; if so, probability calculus will tell you what single number you should store if a bigger memory is not available. You might even discover a simpler way that is not duplicated in man for some biological reason. Do not forget that even such a simple thing as the wheel is absent in biological species, since it implies *two* disconnected parts in a single being.

Let me now describe briefly how we applied the above ideas in experimental PAPA machines. The best way to introduce you to our work is probably to show you this little toy (a slide-rule PAPA!) I have here with me.

The slide (Fig. 2) is transparent and consists of 12 rectangles A_1, A_2, A_3, ..., A_{12}. In each rectangle there is a "random" line (partly heavy and partly light). The meaning of the numbers under each rectangle will be explained later. The other part of the toy, where the slider goes, has a reference rectangle in the middle and is essentially an abacus with three rows of beads (Fig. 3).

Assume we want to use this PAPA to recognize the three capital letters Y, E and S as in the word YES. (You see now a little "gimmick" in the toy. The lines in Fig. 2 are not really random: they spell out the sentence "RANDOM LINES?", and the answer "YES" is made up of the letters to be recognized); We start by giving to this PAPA a "past experience" by showing to it 10 examples of Y, 10 examples of E, and 10 examples of S. For example, the ten Y's could be those of Fig. 4.

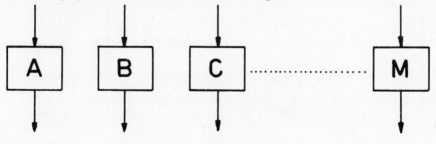

Figure 1

This past experience is processed in the following way. We start writing the first Y of the set of Fig. 4 in the center reference rectangle of Fig. 3. We insert the slide of Fig. 2 so that its rectangle A_1, coincides with the reference rectangle and we look to whether a certain preset, but otherwise arbitrary, condition is satisfied or not. In our toy we say that "yes" (or "1") is the answer when the number of intersections of the letter with the heavy line is greater than the number of intersections with the light line; otherwise, when this number is equal or less, the answer is "no" (or "0"). After repeating this with all rectangles and all examples, we can set up a table of scores as shown in Fig. 5, in which y_1 means that y_1 "yes'es" were scored by the 10 examples of Fig. 4 versus $(10 - y_1)$ "no's" in the first rectangle, etc. Let us now assume that an unknown example X (say a capital Y different from the 10 Y's of Fig. 4) is presented to the machine. Let 100110001001 be the set of 12 one's and zero's that represent that represent the ordered yes-no answers of the twelve rectangles to X. Then the probabilities $p(Y)$, $p(E)$, $p(S)$ that X is the letter Y, E, S respectively, satisfy the relations

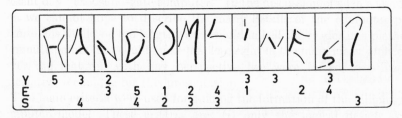

Figure 2

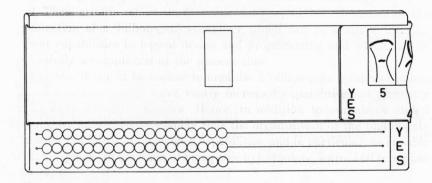

Figure 3

$$\frac{p(Y)}{p(E)} = \frac{y_1(10 - y_2)(10 - y_3)\, y_4 \ldots \ldots y_{12}}{e_1(10 - e_2)(10 - e_3)\, e_4 \ldots \ldots e_{12}}$$

$$= \frac{}{s_1(10 - s_2)(10 - s_3)\, s_4 \ldots \ldots s_{12}} \qquad (1)$$

$$\frac{p(S)}{}$$

according to the computations of a rather poor mathematician that neglects correlations, assuming that the 12 criteria are independent.

With little mathematical manipulations, introducing logarithms to avoid multiplications, rounding up figures to the nearest integer, etc., one can use the abacus of Fig. 3 to compute (1) by adding as many beads as indicated in Fig. 2 for each row of the abacus when the answer is yes, and doing nothing otherwise. The longest row of beads will then give the "guess" by the machine.

I will not describe the various PAPAs we built to perform such operations electronically, the variations on random criteria we used, the theoretical problems and the kind of rather sophisticated patterns we were able to recognize. Most of these questions have already been discussed in the papers published by our group. I prefer here to discuss the possible developments of this approach, as I see it.

First a few remarks. Because an optical input seemed to us the easier to build, all our PAPAs became automatically pattern-recognizing machines. As such they are "intelligent" pattern recognizers. Now, the fact that they are intelligent does not necessarily mean that they are more efficient for special practical purposes. Let me give you an example. I can easily build a PAPA that recognizes small oranges from big oranges, but if I had the problem of separating them in practice I would prefer a much simpler nonintelligent machine (holes of the appropriate size in a conveyor belt). I can easily build a slide-rule PAPA, like the one illustrated in Figs. 1 through 4, that works much more efficiently on the same three letters and with a smaller (< 12) number of carefully selected criteria. In such a case, however, the intelligence would be displayed by me, not by the machine.

In each act of recognition, PAPA behaves intelligently and you don't want to waste intelligence for everything. After all, most of our acts, as humans, are not intelligent—and I do not mean by this to say that the human race is basically stupid. What I mean is simply that after we have reacted intelligently to new situations, we usually select few of the best criteria found—we call them rules—that we then apply automatically without any further thought. This would be a PAPA that automatically discards poor criteria and ends up with the few good ones for that particular purpose.

The best use of PAPA is when new situations are present. Think for example of a big PAPA machine—comparable in size and flexibility to a modern computer—that could handle thousands of examples and examine them with a large number of random criteria of various kinds. To be specific, imagine that the examples are weather maps. An example of class *a* would be a set of weather maps for two successive months, taken from past records. An example of class *b* would also be weather maps for two months, where in the first month we have experimental weather maps as before, but in the second months we have the best (possibly wrong) theoretical forecasts given by a weatherman. Let the random criteria be arbitrary correlations between pressures, winds, temperatures, humidity, etc., in different places. We could then present the machine with a large number of unknown *X* (different weather forecasts for next month as a function of the weather of the month just passed) and pick up the unknown *X* —given as class *a* with the highest probability—as the best forecasts.

Does this mean that PAPAs should never be used for practical special purposes—like reading alphanumeric characters—except perhaps in a preliminary stage to find "good" criteria? I don't think this is true, either. It depends. Nobody would think in this country of building a dam with thousands of men carrying their own small amount of concrete in some primitive container, but in China they are doing so, right now. You can afford to waste (artificial) intelligence for rather primitive tasks, if you can produce simple, unexpensive (and therefore competitive) PAPA devices. I would like to end my talk by illustrating to you just one such device (I call it Papistor). Unfortunately I was unable to get the raw material (fiber optics) in Italy early enough to be able to actually make one in time for this Symposium. So, be satisfied of a description.

A bunch of optical fibers starts from the lower surface *L* and goes to the upper surface *U* of a truncated double cone (Fig. 6). Each fiber connects one point in *L* with one point in *U* through a different "path with loops." One such path is shown in Fig. 6. The device is cut in two parts along the middle section *M*. The pattern to be recognized—of the opaque-transparent type—is introduced in the plane *M* between the two halves of the device.

Figure 4

The surface L is uniformly illuminated. Then in U only those points will be lighted that are connected to L through a fiber that intersects the interposed pattern only in transparent points. For example, in Fig. 6 if the pattern introduced in M is opaque in any one point m_1, m_2, m_3, m_4, or m_5, the light from point l will not arrive in point u. Each point in U (each fiber) will then give a yes-no decision on the basis of whether a certain set of points—like the points m_1, m_2, . . . , m_5 of the above example—of the pattern under examination are all transparent at the same time or not. They are decisions on the overall features of the pattern of the same general type we used before with our random lines.

Now about the memory. Let us assume that we want to teach the Papistor to recognize two classes of patterns—class a versus class b—by presenting 10 examples of each class (a_1, a_2, . . . , a_{10}; b_1, b_2, . . . , b_{10}). To teach the Papistor means to make two photographic (opaque-transparent) slides A and B as follows. Slide A is obtained by superimposing ten snapshots of the surface U as it appears with the ten patterns a_1, a_2, . . . , a_{11} respectively in their place M, with surface L uniformly illuminated. The time of exposure for each snapshot is the same. The film is processed in such a way that slide A will be transparent in all points where no light arrived in all ten snapshots; it will be completely opaque ("opacity" 10) in those points where the light arrived in all ten snapshots; it will have opacity 7, if in 7 out of 10 snapshots the light arrived at those points, etc. Assume for simplicity in the following that the enlargement ratio is 1 : 1 and that there are only 9 fibers in U-quantized in the 3 $\times$ 3 matrix of Fig. 7. The final slide A will then look like Fig. 7, where each number gives the opacity of the corresponding fiber for that class. A similar slide B is obtained with patterns of class b (Fig. 8).

	A_1	A_2	A_3	. . . .	A_{12}
Y	y_1	y_2	y_3	. . . .	y_{12}
E	e_1	e_2	e_3	. . . .	e_{12}
S	s_1	s_2	s_3	. . . .	s_{12}

Figure 5

Let us now consider the slide obtained by superimposing A with the photographic negative, $\bar{B}$, of B (i.e., $\bar{B}$ is the slide whose opacity is the complement to 10 of slide B). The slide $A + \bar{B}$ will then look like Fig. 9 (remember that $8 + 5 = 10$, since 10 represents maximum opacity). Now consider the light passing through the slide $A + \bar{B}$, which is proportional to the opacity of the negative $A + \bar{B}$ (Fig. 10). One notices the interesting fact that no light passes through $A + \bar{B}$ in all those points where the opacity of A is greater or equal to the opacity of B. When the opacity of B is greater than the opacity of A, the amount of light that passes through is equal to that difference. Thus the slide $A + \bar{B}$ is a filter that selects only those fibers that give a preferential "yes" answer to class b and that gives to them a weight proportional to their "goodness" as discriminating criteria. Admittedly, this is not a logarithmic weight, but is still a good approximation. The slide $\bar{A} + B$ operates similarly with the two classes a and b interchanged.

Therefore, splitting by any optical mean the image of U into two images and filtering them with two slides $A + \bar{B}$ and $\bar{A} + B$ respectively, a system is obtained that allows one to decide whether an unknown pattern belong to class a or to class b. The Papistor acts then as a converter from the property "form" to the more easily measurable quantity "light flux."

APPENDIX

The above discussion might have left the impression that PAPA is able to induce only by *interpolating* the unknown X among the examples of its past experiences. That it will not be able to *extrapolate* such past experiences

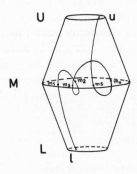

Figure 6

and arrive at really *new* results. That this is not so is most easily shown by considering the following simple (paper and pencil) experiment. Assume that all the patterns under examination are quantized in a 3×3 matrix and have exactly 3 black squares like the examples of Fig. 11.

The decision units (A-units) may also be made out of the same patterns with the addition of the following criterion: the answer is "yes" whenever a pattern has at least one black square in coincidence with the given A-unit; otherwise the answer is "no." The number of different A-units is $\binom{9}{3} = 84$.

Let us assume we want to teach this PAPA the difference between horizontal and vertical bars. An horizontal bar is one of those shown in Fig. 12, but also one of the "noisy" type of Fig. 13. A similar definition may be given for vertical bars. With respect to this class discrimination, the 84 A-units can be divided into three sets α, β, γ as follows:

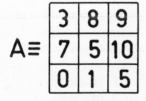

$$A \equiv \begin{array}{|c|c|c|} \hline 3 & 8 & 9 \\ \hline 7 & 5 & 10 \\ \hline 0 & 1 & 5 \\ \hline \end{array}$$

Figure 7

$$B \equiv \begin{array}{|c|c|c|} \hline 4 & 3 & 9 \\ \hline 9 & 8 & 5 \\ \hline 6 & 10 & 4 \\ \hline \end{array}$$

Figure 8

$$A + \bar{B} \equiv \begin{array}{|c|c|c|} \hline 9 & 10 & 10 \\ \hline 8 & 7 & 10 \\ \hline 4 & 1 & 10 \\ \hline \end{array}$$

Figure 9

$$\overline{A + \bar{B}} \equiv \begin{array}{|c|c|c|} \hline 1 & 0 & 0 \\ \hline 2 & 3 & 0 \\ \hline 6 & 9 & 0 \\ \hline \end{array}$$

Figure 10

(α) Useless A-units of the type shown in Fig. 14. They are a total of 42 and are useless, since they give a "yes" answer with equal probability for both classes of horizontal and vertical bars.

(β) Very good A-units of the type shown in Fig. 15, i.e., "perfect" horizontal or vertical bars. The probability of a "yes" answer is very different for the two classes. There are 6 such units.

(γ) Reasonably good A-units of the type shown in Fig. 16, i.e., "noisy" horizontal or vertical bars. The probability of a "yes" answer is different for the two classes, although not as much different as those of set β. They are 36 in number.

Without any loss of generality, assume we have a PAPA with only the 36 A-units of the set γ. Assume we teach the concept of horizontality versus verticality by showing to this PAPA only the noisy set of horizontal and vertical bars. The table of scores for the 18 noisy examples of each class is given in Fig. 17. It is easily verified that every noisy example will then be recognized with a likelihood ratio

$$\left(\frac{14}{13}\right)^{14} \cdot \left(\frac{4}{5}\right)^{4} \cdot \left(\frac{13}{14}\right)^{13} \cdot \left(\frac{5}{4}\right)^{5} = \frac{14}{13} \cdot \frac{5}{4} \sim 1.34 \qquad (2)$$

What happens now if we show to this PAPA—which had only noisy examples in its experience—a "perfect" example, like those of Fig. 12? It is easy to see that it will recognize it with a likehood ratio

$$\left(\frac{14}{13}\right)^{18} \cdot \left(\frac{13}{14}\right)^{12} \cdot \left(\frac{5}{4}\right)^{6} = \left(\frac{14}{13} \cdot \frac{5}{4}\right)^{6} \sim 6.8 \qquad (3)$$

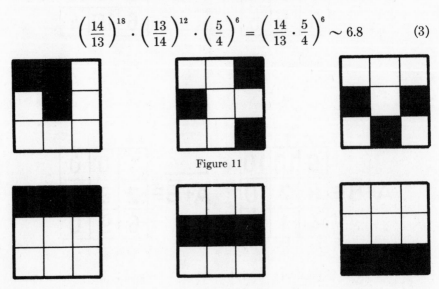

Figure 11

Figure 12

In other words, it will recognize perfect examples with a likelihood ratio *greater* than the one of the noisy examples it has seen before! It says "Boy, these are much better examples than those you showed me before! Why didn't you show me these ones, instead, to teach me what is horizontality and verticality?"

Doesn't this mean also that the formation of concepts—that old problem of Plato's philosophy—is nothing but the extraction of signal from noise, or—to put it in another way—that probability is all there is in intelligence?

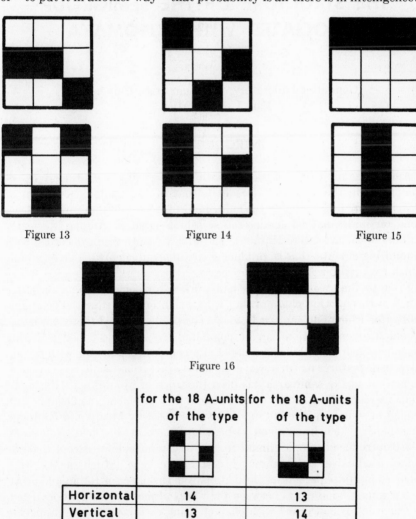

Figure 13   Figure 14   Figure 15

Figure 16

	for the 18 A-units of the type	for the 18 A-units of the type
Horizontal	14	13
Vertical	13	14

Figure 17

9

THE STRUCTURE OF THE SEMIGROUP
ASSOCIATED WITH AUTOMATA

G. P. Weeg

Computer Laboratory, Michigan State University
East Lansing, Mich.

INTRODUCTION

Among the multitude of problems which have arisen with the advent of computers in the past two decades is that of the economical design of switching circuits. Probably the most important work in that area has been done on mathematical models of switching circuits. Among the early authors in the area were Huffman[1] and Mealy.[2] Both were concerned with minimizing circuits, that is, producing circuits equivalent to a given circuit which required fewer memory devices.

Prior to that work, logicians had worked for some time on recursive function theory. One phase of that work has been in the area of computability (for which one can see Davis)[3]. The problem posed there is whether or not a given function can be computed by a device called a Turing machine. Such a machine is a model of a computing machine with certain unrealistic features which however do not detract from its intrinsic interest. Somewhat in the same area has been the work of Moore[4] and Ginsburg,[5] who are concerned with certain decidability problems connected with models of switching circuits similar to those used by Mealy and Huffman. In a paper which has proved to be a landmark in this field, Rabin and Scott[6] introduced a topic similar to that of computability, except that the model used is of the Huffman-Moore-Mealy type. Much of the work reported in this paper has its motivation from the paper of Rabin and Scott.

A common bond exists between the works of most of the authors listed, in that each is concerned with characterising certain structure properties of automata, and with seeing which properties survive certain transformations on automata. Pursuing this common thread, the present author has become concerned with identifying structure properties, transformations of automata, and algebraic properties of those transformations. Although the resulting work appears to be far removed from that of switching theory, two justifications, if any are needed, can be made. First, since switching theory is of great importance, it seems apparent that complete information concerning its mathematical basis should be sought. Second, the work appears to have interest purely as a mathematical investigation.

The object of study in this paper is properties of an automaton, a system (S, I, M) where S is a nonempty, usually finite, set of states of a circuit, I is a semigroup of inputs; and M is a function on pairs, one from S and one from I, into S. Thus, an automaton so described can be recognized as a model of a switching circuit possessing no outputs. These are omitted from consideration to concentrate upon the "structure" of the automaton, that is, the way that the "next-state" function M acts on S under inputs. Associated with this study of automata is a set of permutations of the automaton which leave the next-state function essentially unchanged. The set of all such permutations turns out to be a group, a mathematical structure which has been deeply investigated for at least a century. Moreover, the set of inputs to the automaton, as with a switching circuit, is commonly a set of sequences of basic inputs, and as such is a semigroup. A semigroup, as the name implies, is a mathematical system possessing only some of the properties of a group. The interrelationship of these three mathematical systems, i.e., the next-state function structure, the group, and the semigroup, is the object of study in this and previous papers.

It will be the policy in this paper to try to explain the meaning of certain mathematical terms as they appear. There are two concepts, however, which occur throughout the paper, namely group and semigroup, which are defined here. The definitions become simpler if we define the word "system" first.

A *system* $\{S; *\}$ is a set S and an operation $*$ on S, such that $a * b$ is in S for all a and b in S. The system will often be referred to by the same symbol used to denote the set. Thus we speak of the system $S = \{S; *\}$.

A *group* is a system $\{G; *\}$ such that

(1) $a * b$ is in G for all a, b in G.

(2) $a * (b * c) = (a * b) * c$ for all a, b, c in G.

(3) There is an e in G such that $e * a = a$ for all a in G.

(4) For each a in G there is a b in G such that $b * a = e$.

A *semigroup* is a system $\{G; *\}$ obeying properties (1) and (2) of a group.

STRUCTURE PROPERTIES OF SOME RABIN-SCOTT AUTOMATA

In this section two structure properties are defined, and the preservation of these properties under certain transformations due to Rabin and Scott are briefly studied. The results are primarily intended to provide motivation for the later more detailed work presented in this paper. Certain definitions and conclusions are presented first.

Definition 1. An automaton A is a system (S, M, s_0, F, Σ) where S and Σ are finite nonempty sets; s_0 is a member of S; F is a subset of S; and M is a function on $S \times \Sigma$ (the Cartesian product of S and Σ, i.e., the set of all ordered pairs (s, σ) with s from S and σ from Σ) into S. The set Σ is assumed to be fixed throughout this section.

Definition 2. A *tape* x is a sequence $\sigma_1 \sigma_2 \ldots \sigma_n$, of finite but arbitrary length, of elements σ_i of Σ. The set of all tapes over Σ is denoted T. The function M is also defined on $S \times T$ by

$$M(s, x) = M(s, \sigma_1 \sigma_2 \ldots \sigma_n) = M(M(s, \sigma_1), \sigma_2 \ldots \sigma_n)$$

for all s in S and any tape x in T.

Definition 3. The set $T(A)$ of all tapes x in T for which $M(s_0, x)$ is in F is called the *acceptable set of tapes* for A.

It was shown by Rabin and Scott that the set λ, the set of acceptable sets $T(A)$ for all automata A is a Boolean algebra. Thus for any automata A and B there are automata C, D, and E such that

$$T(C) = T(A) \cup T(B)$$

$$T(D) = T(A) \cap T(B)$$

$$T(E) = T - T(A)$$

The question is now posed: do C, D, and E possess the structure properties of A and B? Attention is focused upon two main properties as defined below.

Definition 4. An automaton $A = (S, M, s_0, F, \Sigma)$ is *strongly connected* if for every pair s and t of elements of S there is an x in T such that $M(s, x) = t$. If in addition, there is a positive integer r such that for every pair s, t of elements of S there is a tape x of length r such that $M(s, x) = t$, then A is said to be *positive*.

The results in this section will be easily visualized if use is made of the connection matrix of an automaton.

Definition 5. The *connection matrix* $C(A)$ for an automaton $A = (S, M, s_0, F, \Sigma)$ for which S is of order n is the $n \times n$ matrix (a_{ij}) whose entry in the ij position is the set of all tapes x of length 1 for which $M(s_i, x) = s_j$. If this set is null, $a_{ij} = 0$.

Returning now to the question posed, the automaton E is just $E = (S, M, s_0, S-F, \Sigma)$. Since S and M are the same for E and A, the structure of the two automata is identical. Next, for the automaton C for which $T(C) = T(A) \cup T(B)$, since λ is a Boolean algebra,

$$T(C) = T - [T - T(A)] \cap [T - T(B)]$$

Hence the properties of C can be deduced by examining automata of the type D and E. Thus only automata of the type D remain to be examined.

Rabin and Scott showed that the automaton D for which $T(D) = T(A) \cap T(B)$ is just the direct product $A \times B$ of A and B.

Definition 6. If $A = (S, M, s_0, F, \Sigma)$ and $B = (T, N, t_0, G, \Sigma)$, then the *direct product $A \times B$ of A and B* is the automaton $A \times B = (S \times T, M \times N, (s_0, t_0), F \times G, \Sigma)$ where $S \times T$ is the Cartesian product of S and T; (s_0, t_0) is a pair in $S \times T$; $F \times G$ is the Cartesian product of F and G; and $M \times N$ is defined by $M \times N((s, t), \sigma) = (M(s, \sigma), N(t, \sigma))$ for any σ in Σ and any (s, t) in $S \times T$.

The actual formation of the direct product of two automata can be tedious. However, the connection matrix $C(A \times B)$ can be formed in a simple way. Define the operation $\times$ on Σ by $\sigma \times \tau = 0$ for $\sigma = \tau$ and $\sigma \times \tau = \sigma$ for $\sigma = \tau$ for any σ and τ in Σ. Also, $\sigma \times 0 = 0$ for any σ in Σ. Moreover, if $a = \{\sigma_1, \sigma_2, \ldots, \sigma_r\}$ is a set of elements of Σ, then by $\sigma \times a$ is meant the set $\sigma \times a = \{\sigma \times \sigma_1, \sigma \times \sigma_2, \ldots, \sigma \times \sigma_r\}$. If $C(B) = (b_{ij})$ is the connection matrix for an automaton B, then define $\sigma \times C(B)$ by $\sigma \times C(B) = (\sigma \times b_{ij})$. Finally, define $C(A) \times C(B) = (a_{ij} \times C(B))$. That is, $C(A) \times C(B)$ is formed in blocks, with the matrix $a_{ij} \times C(B)$ as its ijth block. If $S = \{s_1, s_2, \ldots, s_q\}$ and $T = \{t_1, t_2, \ldots, t_r\}$ then label the rows of $C(A) \times C(B)$ starting at the top row as $(s_1, t_1), (s_1, t_2), \ldots, (s_1, t_r), (s_2, t_1), (s_2, t_2), \ldots, (s_2, t_r)$, etc. Similarly label the columns. Then $C(A \times B) = C(A) \times C(B)$.

EXAMPLE 1

Let $C(A)$ and $C(B)$ be given by

$$C(A) = \begin{bmatrix} 0 & a,b \\ a & b \end{bmatrix} \qquad C(B) = \begin{bmatrix} 0 & a,b & 0 \\ 0 & 0 & a,b \\ b & a & 0 \end{bmatrix}$$

Then

$$C(A \times B) = \begin{bmatrix} 0 & 0 & 0 & 0 & a,b & 0 \\ 0 & 0 & 0 & 0 & 0 & a,b \\ 0 & 0 & 0 & a & b & 0 \\ 0 & a & 0 & 0 & b & 0 \\ 0 & 0 & a & 0 & 0 & b \\ a & 0 & 0 & b & 0 & 0 \end{bmatrix}$$

It should be pointed out that $[C(A) \times C(B)]^n = [C(A)]^n \times [C(B)]^n$. By the nth power of $C(A)$ is meant the ordinary product of matrices, except that addition is replaced by set union; while the multiplication of two sets $a_1 = \{x_1, x_2, \ldots, x_r\}$ and $a_2 = \{y_1, y_2, \ldots, y_s\}$ is defined* as the set $\{x_i y_j | x_i \in a_1$ and $y_j \in a_2\}$. The operation $\times$ is extended to tapes of length greater than one in an obvious way.

Returning now to the structure of $A \times B$, the following lemma can be proved:

LEMMA 1. If $A \times B$ is strongly connected, then both A and B are strongly connected. If $A \times B$ is positive, then A and B are each positive.

Proof. Let $A = (S, M, s_0, F, \Sigma)$ and $B = (T, N, t_0, G, \Sigma)$. If $A \times B$ is strongly connected, then for every pair (s_i, t_j) and (s_k, t_m) of $S \times T$ there is an x in T such that $M \times N(s_i, t_j), x) = (M(s_i, x), N(t_j, x)) = (s_k, t_m)$. From the last equality it follows immediately that A and B are strongly connected.

If $A \times B$ is positive, then there is an integer r such that for every pair of state s_i, s_j in S and t_k, t_m in T, there is a tape x of length r such that

$$M \times N((s_i, t_k), x) = (M(s_i, x), N(t_k, x)) = (s_j, t_m)$$

Hence, A and B are each positive, and the lemma is proved.

Of course, if A and B are each strongly connected or each positive, AxB need have neither property. The automata in Example 1 are both positive, yet the automaton $A \times B$ is not even strongly connected.

Returning now to the automaton C for which $T(C) = T(A) \cup T(B)$ and making use of the fact that $T(C) = T - [T - T(A)] \cap [T - T(B)]$, if C is strongly connected or positive then A and B are strongly connected or positive respectively.

This is all that will be shown concerning $A \times B$. A detailed study of the direct product has been made by Fleck.[7]

STRUCTURE-PRESERVING FUNCTIONS OF AUTOMATA

The structure of $A \times B$ can be markedly different from that of A and B, as was pointed out in the previous section. This leads to certain general considerations of functions on automata. Thus, the direct product is just a special case of a function θ on automata $A_1, A_2, \ldots, A_q$, into a class of automata. It is of interest to ask what classes of functions $\theta(A_1, A_2, \ldots, A_q)$ preserve various structure properties of the original automata $A_1, A_2, \ldots,$

---

*The symbols $\{x|P\}$ is used to mean the set of all x which possess property P. Moreover $a \in A\epsilon$ means that a is a member of set A.

A_q. The question has been extensively investigated by Fleck[7] and to some extent by the author. Since Fleck's work is basic to much of the later results, it will be reviewed here. The definitions made here will be used throughout the remainder of the paper.

Definition 7. An *automaton* A is a triple $A = (S, I, M)$ where S is a non-empty set; I is a semigroup; and M is a function on the Cartesian product $S \times I$ into S, with the property that $M(s, xy) = M(M(s, x), y)$ for all s in S and x and y in I.

The set S may be thought of as the set of states of a switching circuit. An infinite set of states is allowed in this section. The semigroup I is to be thought of as the inputs to the circuit. Once again, it should be pointed out that the input set to a switching circuit is usually the set of all sequences generated from a certain finite basic set of inputs. Since such a set is a *free semigroup*, (i.e., a semigroup I generated by juxtaposition of a finite subset of I) generality is added to the definition by allowing I to be an arbitrary semigroup.

Fleck is concerned with functions on automata, and so as to give a precise meaning to the concepts associated with function, he imposed a topology on an automaton as follows:

Definition 8. A set of state $T \subset S$ of an automaton $A = (S, I, M)$ is *open* if for each s in $T, M(s, x)$ is in T for all x in I.

Thus, an open set contains all the states that can be reached from any state in the set.

Definition 9. An automaton $A = (S, I, M)$ is *not connected* if there exist nonnull open sets R and T in S such that $R \cup T = S$ and $R \cap T$ is null; A is *connected* otherwise.

An automaton $A = (S, I, M)$ is *strongly connected* if, as before, for every s, t in S, there is an x in I for which $M(s, x) = t$.

Definition 10. Let $A = (S, I, M)$ and $B = (T, I, N)$ be two automata. By a *function h* of A into B, written $h : A \rightarrow B$, is meant a function h on S into T.

Certain standard terminology is used: Thus, the *image* $h(X)$ of a set $X \subset S$ is the set $h(X) = \{t | h(x) = t \text{ for } x \in X\}$; while by the *inverse image*, $h^{-1}(Y)$ of a set $Y \subset T$ is meant the set $h^{-1}(Y) = \{s \in S | h(s) \in Y\}$.

Definition 11. A function $h : A \rightarrow B$ for $A = (S, I, M)$ and $B = (T, I, N)$ is continuous if for every open set $Y \subset T, h^{-1}(Y)$ is open.

Several results are proved by Fleck concerning continuous functions. In particular he shows that if $h : A \rightarrow B$ is continuous and onto, and if A is strongly connected (or connected) then B is strongly connected (or connected). Moreover, if $h : A \rightarrow B$ is an onto function and B is strongly connected then h is continuous. Thus, any onto function which preserves strongly connectedness is a continuous function.

An important subset of the set of all continuous functions on automata is introduced by Fleck.

Definition 12. Let $A = (S,I,M)$ and $B = (T,I,N)$ be automata and let $h : A \to B$ be a function from A into B. Then h is said to be operation preserving if $h(M(s,x)) = N(h(s),x)$ for all s in S and x in I.

Since it can be shown that an operation preserving function is continuous, then an onto operation preserving function preserves connectedness and strongly connectedness. What is more, Fleck shows that onto operation preserving functions preserve most of the interesting structure properties of automata. Finally, the set of such functions, properly restricted, constitutes a group.

LEMMA 2.[7] The set of all one-to-one, onto, operation preserving functions $h : A \to A$ where $A = (S,I,M)$, is a group, denoted $G(A)$.

The remainder of this paper is devoted to the relationships between $G(A)$, I, and A for an automaton $A = (S,I,M)$.

SOME PRELIMINARY RESULTS FOR FINITE AUTOMATA

In the remainder of this paper S, the set of states of the automaton $A = (S,I,M)$, is assumed to be finite. Moreover, it will generally be assumed that A is strongly connected. If now $g \in G(A)$, then g is a one-to-one onto function $g : S \to S$, so that, g is just a permutation of S. There are two standard notations for a permutation g on S, and both will be used in this paper. Let $S = \{s_1, s_2, \ldots, s_q\}$. Then $g(s_i)$ is defined for $i = 1, \ldots, q$ and moreover, $g(s_i) \neq g(s_j)$ if $i \neq j$, since g is a one-to-one function. One notation used to represent g is

$$g = \begin{pmatrix} s_1, s_2, \ldots, s_q \\ g(s_1)\ g(s_2), \ldots, g(s_q) \end{pmatrix}$$

and a second notation, the cyclic notation, is

$$g = (s_{i_{0,1}}, s_{i_{1,1}}, \ldots, s_{i_{m_1,1-1,1}})(s_{i_{0,2}} s_{i_{1,2}}, \ldots, s_{i_{m_2,2-1,2}}) \ldots \tag{1}$$

where

$$g(s_{i_{jk}}) = s_{i_{j+1,k}}$$

where the sum $j + 1$ is taken modulo m_k. Each parenthesized set is called a cycle.

If for every power, say g^r, of g, it is the case that $g^r(s) = s$ for some s implies that $g^r(s) = s$ for all $s \in S$, then g is called a regular permutation. In its cyclic representation, all cycles of a regular permutation are of equal length.

It was shown by the author in Ref. 8 that if A is strongly connected then for each $g \, \epsilon \, G(A)$, g is a regular permutation on S. The number of regular permutations on a set S is given in the following lemma.

LEMMA 3. Let R_n be the number of regular permutations on the set $S = \{s_1, s_2, \ldots, s_n\}$. Let the distinct positive divisors of n be denoted by $r_1, r_2, \ldots, r_q$. Further, let $p(\alpha) = n/r_\alpha$. Then

$$R_n = n! \sum_{\alpha=1}^{q} \frac{1}{r_\alpha{}^{p(\alpha)}(p(\alpha))!} \qquad (2)$$

Proof.* Consider the divisor r_α of n. All regular permutations of order r_α are products of precisely $p(\alpha)$ cycles of length r_α. To enumerate all such regular permutations without repetition, select one member $s_1 \, \epsilon \, S$ which will be assigned the first position in the first cycle of every such permutation. Then the remaining $r_\alpha - 1$ positions in the first cycle can be filled in $(n - 1)(n - 2) \ldots (n - r_\alpha + 1)$ distinct ways. Of the remaining $n - r_\alpha$ letters of S, select one, say s_2, which is assigned the first position of the second cycle. The remaining positions of the second cycle can then be filled in $(n - r_\alpha - 1)(n - r_\alpha - 2), \ldots, (n - 2r_\alpha + 1)$ distinct ways. In general, after the first q cycles have been filled, there will be $n - qr$ letters of S left. Select one of those letters, say s_{q+1} to fill the first position of the $(q + 1)$st cycle. There will be $(n - qr_\alpha - 1)(n - qr_\alpha - 2), \ldots, (n - (q + 1)r_\alpha + 1)$ distinct ways to fill the $(q + 1)$st cycle. Hence, the number of regular permutations of order r_α is

$$\frac{(n - 1)!}{(n - r_\alpha)(n - 2r_\alpha), \ldots, (r_\alpha)} = \frac{(n - 1)!}{r_\alpha{}^{(p(\alpha)-1)}(p(\alpha) - 1)!} \qquad (3)$$

$$= \frac{n!}{r_\alpha{}^{p(\alpha)}(s(\alpha))!}$$

Summing the number in Eq. (3) over all α, there follows

$$R_n = n! \sum_{\alpha=1}^{q} \frac{1}{r_\alpha{}^{p(\alpha)}(p(\alpha))!}$$

For a given strongly connected automaton A of n states, the number of regular permutations which are in $G(A)$, however, will not be this large.

---

* The author is indebted to Mr. Robert Bartholemew, an undergraduate National Science Foundation scholarship recipient, for this lemma.

As is shown in the next theorem, the order of $G(A)$ divides n. This theorem is purely a group-theoretic result, and is probably known, although the author has not located it in the literature. Since its proof is short, it is presented here.

THEOREM 1. If G is a group of regular permutations on the set $S = \{1, \ldots, n\}$, then the order of G divides n.

Proof. The group G is either transitive (a group G on S is transitive if for every pair of elements s, t in S, there is a g in G such that $g(s) = t$) or not. If G is transitive then G is a regular (i.e., a transitive group of regular permutations) permutation group. But a regular permutation group is its own regular representation.* The degree of the regular representation of a group G is equal to the order of G. But the degree of G is n in this case, so that the order of G is n.

If G is a nontransitive group on the set $S = \{1, 2, 3, \ldots, n\}$ then separate S into q disjoint sets $S_0, S_1, \ldots, S_{q-1}$. If $a' \in S_i$ then $a \in S_i$ if and only if $f(a) = a'$ for some $f \in G$. Then each $f \in G$ is a product of permutations $f_0, f_1, f_2, \ldots, f_{q-1}$ where f_i is a permutation of the letters of S_i only. The set G_i of permutations f_i for all $f \in G$ is a group, since G is a group. Also, G_i is transitive. Hence each G_i is a regular group, so that the order of each G_i is equal to the number of letters in S_i. But the order of each G_i is the order of G. Hence each S_i is composed of the same number of letters, each G_i has the same order, this order is the order of G, and hence the order of G_i divides n.

Finally, not only is the group $G(A)$ for any strongly connected automaton A a group of regular permutations whose order therefore divides the order of S, but also for every finite group G of regular permutations on the set $S = \{s_1, \ldots, s_n\}$ there is, as shown in Ref. 9, a strongly connected automaton $A = (S, I, M)$ for which $G = G(A)$. Thus, the groups $G(A)$ for strongly connected automata provide a vehicle for studying groups of regular permutations.

Up to this point, concern has centered upon $A = (S, I, M)$ and $G(A)$. Now the connections between $G(A)$ and the input semi-group I will be explored. Some of the results obtained in Refs. 8 and 9 are summarized here.

The object of the first few results is to establish a mathematical relationship between I and $G(A)$. It was shown that there exists a homomorphism from I to $G(A)$ in certain cases, and from a subset of I to $G(A)$ in other cases. [A homomorphism may be described as follows: Let $\{J; *\}$ and $\{K; O\}$ be two systems, where J and K are sets and $*$ and O are closed operations on J and K respectively. An onto function $h : J \to K$ is a homomorphism of the first system to the second system if $h(a*b) = h(a) \, O$

---

* See Zassenhaus, p. 37.

$h(b)$ for all a and b in J. A 1-to-1 homomorphism is an isomorphism.] This is done by establishing an equivalence relation on I, which induces equivalence classes on I. Under a certain operation a subset of these equivalence classes is isomorphic to $G(A)$.

Let $A = (S,I,M)$ be a strongly connected n-state automaton. The relation R_i over I is defined by xR_iy if and only if $M(s_i,x) = M(s_i,y)$; it is easily shown that R_i is an equivalence relation. Thus for each $i = 1, 2, \ldots, n$, R_i establishes a set T_i of n equivalence classes over I, $T_i = \{T_{i1}, T_{i2}, \ldots, T_{in}\}$, where $x \in T_{ij}$ if and only if $M(s_i,x) = s_j$. Since A is a strongly connected automaton it follows that for all $i,j = 1, 2, \ldots, n$, T_{ij} is nonempty; and that $T_{ij} \cap T_{ik}$ is empty for $j \neq k$ and $i = 1, 2, \ldots, n$. Furthermore $\bigcup_{j=1} T_{ij} = I$.

An operation, $*_i$, among the classes of T_i is formally defined.

Definition 13. The operation $*_i$ over a subset of the classes of T_i is defined by $T_{ij} *_i T_{ik} = T_{im}$ if and only if $M(s_i,xy) = s_m$ for all $x \in T_{ij}$ and $y \in T_{ik}$.

It may indeed be the case that $*_i$ is not well defined with respect to certain i, j, k, and m. However, it was shown in Ref. 10 that $*_i$ is always well defined for a certain subset of T_i.

THEOREM 2. If $G(A)$ is the group of the n-state strongly connected automaton $A = (S,I,M)$, then the system $\{T_i^*; *_i\}$, where $T_i^* = \{T_{ig(i)} | g \in G(A)\}$ is a group isomorphic to $G(A)$.

This isomorphism establishes a homomorphism h on a subset of I to $G(A)$. The subset is the subsemigroup $\cup T_{ig(i)}$ for all $g \in G(A)$. The homomorphism $h : \cup T_{ig(i)} \to G(A)$ is defined by $h(x) = g$ if and only if $x \in T_{ig(i)}$. The kernel of the homomorphism h [i.e., the set of all elements $x \in \cup T_{ig(i)}$ for which $h(x) = e$, the identity of $G(A)$] is just T_{ii}, the set of all elements x of $\cup T_{ig(i)}$ for which $M(s_i,x) = s_i$.

Using the isomorphism from $\{T_i^*; *_i\}$ to $G(A)$, an algorithm is presented in Ref. 9 for producing $G(A)$ for a given strongly connected automaton $A = (S,I,M)$. In that same paper, several properties of the input semigroup are discussed. The relative size of the various classes T_{ij} is not determined in that paper. However, it is shown below that each of the classes is of the same cardinality when I is a free semigroup. That is, for each $x \in T_{ij}$ there is a distinct element $y \in T_{ke}$, and conversely for each $y \in T_{ke}$ there is a distinct $x \in T_{ij}$.

THEOREM 3. If $A = (S,I,M)$ is an n-state strongly connected automaton and I is a free semigroup then the cardinality of T_{ij} and T_{kl} is the same for $i, j, k, e = 1, \ldots, n$.

Proof. Let $\sigma : T_{ij} \to T_{ke}$ be defined by $\sigma(x) = yxz$ for any $x \in T_{ij}$ and fixed $y \in T_{ki}$ and $z \in T_{jl}$. This is a 1-to-1 function since if $x \neq u$ then $\sigma(x) = yxz \neq yuz = \sigma(u)$. Hence the cardinality of T_{kl} is at least as great as that of T_{ij}. A similar argument shows that the cardinality of T_{ij} is at least as great as that of T_{kl}, hence T_{ij} and T_{kl} have the same cardinality.

At the end of Ref. 9 a brief introduction to a vexing problem is given. That is, how can one characterize semigroups which can serve as input semigroups for strongly connected automata? Are there broad classes of semigroups which can be identified as input semigroups? It was shown there that certainly not all semigroups can be used as input semigroups for strongly connected automata. It is shown there further that every free semigroup is the input semigroup of a strongly connected automaton of arbitrary order. However, no general conclusions as to input semigroups were reached. Pursuing this problem, the author has been forced to consider certain special cases in an effort to obtain some insight into the problem. In the next two sections two special semigroups are examined.

DIVISIBLE SEMIGROUPS

In order to obtain some insight into semigroups which can be input semigroups for strongly connected automata, rather a natural semigroup to investigate is the system $\{R; \cdot\}$ where R is the set of all positive real numbers with the operation of multiplication. This is a nontrivial semigroup in the sense that it is infinite and its structure is well defined. In fact it may be characterized in part as a system which possesses every nth root of every number in the system. Trying to determine if that semigroup is an input semigroup leads to a more general investigation.

Definition 14.[11]   A semigroup I is *divisible* if for every $a \in I$ and for every positive integer n there is an element $b \in I$ such that $a = b^n$.

Clearly the system $\{R; \cdot\}$ is a divisible semigroup since it is a group and for any element $a \in R$, $a = (^n\sqrt{a})^n$ for any positive integer n.

An automaton may have an input semigroup which though it is not necessarily divisible behaves with respect to the automaton as if it were divisible. This is stated in precise terms as:

Definition 15.   A strongly connected automaton $A = (S, I, M)$ is *divisible* if for every $a \in I$ and every positive integer n there is a b in I such that $M(s, a) = M(s, b^n)$ for every $s \in S$.

Clearly, if I is divisible then the strongly connected automaton $A = (S, I, M)$ is divisible, though the converse need not be true. If A is a divisible automaton, however, the structure of I is seriously restricted. To see this, we make use of a definition of Fleck.[7]

Definition 16.   The binary relation R on I is defined by a Rb if and only if $M(s, a) = M(s, b)$, for all $s \in S$ and arbitrary a and b in I. The set of equivalence classes induced by R is denoted by $I = \{\overline{x}_1, \overline{x}_2, \ldots, \overline{x}_q\}$ for some integer q. Define multiplication between equivalence classes by $\overline{x}\,\overline{y} = \overline{xy}$.

If then A is a divisible automaton and $M(s,a) = M(s,b^n)$ for all s in S, then $b^n \in \bar{a}$. Since $\overline{(b)}^n = \overline{(b^n)}$, then $\overline{(b)}^n = \bar{a}$. This proves the following lemma.

LEMMA 4.   If $A = (S,I,M)$ is a divisible automaton then I is a finite divisible semigroup.

Two examples of divisible automata are presented here:

EXAMPLE 2.

The semigroup I with elements a,b and with an operation defined by

	a	b
a	a	b
b	a	b

is a divisible semigroup. The automaton $A = (S,I,M)$ where $S = \{s_1, s_2\}$ and M is defined by

$$M(s_1,a) = s_2$$
$$M(s_2,a) = s_2$$
$$M(s_1,b) = s_1$$
$$M(s_2,b) = s_1$$

is a divisible automaton. The group $G(A)$ of this automaton is just $G(A) = \{e\}$, for if $(s_1 s_2) \in G(A)$ then $M(s_2,a) = s_1$ which is false.

EXAMPLE 3.

Let $S = \{s_1, s_2, \ldots, s_n\}$ and let I be a semigroup with elements $a_1, a_2, \ldots, a_n$ and some suitable operation. Let $A = (S,I,M)$ where $M(s_i,a_j) = s_j$ for $i,j = 1, 2, \ldots, n$. Clearly $M(s_i,a_j) = M(s_i,a_j{}^q)$ for $i,j = 1, \ldots, n$ and every positive integer q.

The next theorem investigates finite divisible semigroups. It is again a purely semigroup theoretic result, which may be known. Its proof is vital to this study however, so it will be included. It is shown that certain semigroup elements are idempotent; an element a of a semigroup is *idempotent* if $a^2 = a$.

THEOREM 4.   If I is a finite divisible semigroup then each element of I is idempotent.

Proof.   Let $I = \{a_1, a_2, \ldots, a_n, b_1, b_2, \ldots, b_m\}$ where each a_i and no b_j is idempotent. Let $A = \{a_1, a_2, \ldots, a_n\}$ and $B = \{b_1, b_2, \ldots, b_m\}$; it is sufficient to show that B is null. First, since I is divisible then $A_\alpha = A$ where $A_\alpha = \{a_1{}^\alpha, a_2{}^\alpha, \ldots, a_n{}^\alpha\}$, so that $B_\alpha = B$ where $B_\alpha = \{b_1{}^\alpha, b_2{}^\alpha, \ldots, b_m{}^\alpha\}$ for each positive integer α. Then let B' be the set $B' = \{b_1{}^t | \text{for all positive integer } t\}$. Then B' is a semigroup since $b_1{}^t b_1{}^s = b_1{}^{t+s} \in B'$ for any positive integers t and s. Moreover, $B' \subseteq B$, hence must contain no idempotent. But it is well known that every finite semigroup contains an idempotent. This contradiction forces B to be empty, and the theorem is proved.

Corollary 1. No finite nontrivial group is a divisible semigroup.

Corollary 2. If $A = (S, I, M)$ is a divisible automaton with the property that $M(s, xy) = M(s, yx)$ for all x and y in I and all $s \in S$, then S is of order 1.

Proof. Fleck[7] calls such an automaton *abelian*, and he shows that $\bar{I}$ is a group isomorphic to $G(A)$. Hence, $\bar{I}$ must be of order 1. But the order of $\bar{I}$ is greater than or equal to that of S, hence, S is of order 1.

Corollary 3. If $A = (S, I, M)$ is a divisible automaton, then $G(A)$ is of order 1.

Proof. The semigroup $\bar{I}$ is divisible, hence every element $x \in \bar{I}$ is idempotent, so that $M(s, x) = M(s, x^2)$ for every $s \in S$ and $x \in I$. Now select any $g \in G(A)$. Thus for some $s \in S$ and $x \in I$, $M(s, x) = g(s)$. But

$$
\begin{aligned}
g(s) &= M(s, x) \\
&= M(s, x^2) \\
&= M(M(s, x), x) \\
&= M(g(s), x) \\
&= g(M(s, x)) \\
&= g(g(s)) \\
&= g^2(s)
\end{aligned}
$$

But since $g^2 \in G(A)$, then if $g(s) = g^2(s)$ for one $s \in S$ then $g \equiv g^2$. Therefore each g is idempotent, hence $G(A) = \{e\}$.

Because of Corollary 3 the original question becomes obvious. There is clearly no nontrivial strongly connected automaton $A = (S, R, M)$ since R is a divisible abelian semigroup. The following example shows that there is an infinite group however which is the input semigroup for a strongly connected automaton.

EXAMPLE 3.

Let the semigroup I be the system $I = \{J; +\}$ where J is the set of all positive and negative integers and zero, with the operation of addition. If J is to be the input semigroup to a strongly connected automaton $A = (S, J, M)$ since it is abelian, so also must the automaton A be abelian. But then according to Ref. 7, $G(A)$ must be of the same order as S and moreover $\bar{J}$ must be isomorphic to $G(A)$. We need then an equivalence relation on J which partitions J into n equivalence classes; these n equivalence classes must then serve as the classes T_{11}, T_{12}, ..., T_{1n}. But for any positive integer n, use the equivalence relations modulo n encountered in number theory. That is, $i \equiv j$ (modulo n) if and only if n divides $i - j$.

This equivalence induces the set $\bar{J}$ of classes $\bar{J} = \{\bar{0}, \bar{1}, \bar{2}, \ldots, \overline{n-1}\}$ where $k \in \bar{i}$ if and only if $k \equiv i$ (modulo n). Define addition of those classes by $\bar{i} + \bar{j} = \overline{i+j}$, as usual. Then the system $\{\bar{J}; +\}$ so obtained is clearly an abelian group, and a strongly connected automaton $\bar{A} = (\bar{J}, \bar{J}, \bar{M})$ exists where $\bar{M}$ is defined by $\bar{M}(\bar{i}, \bar{j}) = \overline{i+j}$. Using this as a hint, we proceed to define the automaton $\bar{A} = (\bar{J}, J, M)$ where M is given by $M(\bar{i}, j) = \overline{i+j}$. This is clearly strongly connected and has J as input semigroup.

This result is not surprising since $\{J; +\}$ may be considered a free semigroup, since each element of J can be obtained by a finite sum of 1's and -1's.

THE CENTRALIZER OF A GROUP OF REGULAR PERMUTATIONS

A second special semigroup has also been studied as the input semigroup for a strongly connected automaton. The results obtained shed perhaps more light on group theoretic concepts than on automata, yet seem interesting enough to present here.

Let $A = (S, I, M)$ be a strongly connected n-state automaton with group $G(A) = \{g_1, g_2, \ldots, g_q\}$ where $n/q = p$ say, where n, q, and p are positive integers. Let $S_1, S_2, \ldots, S_r$ be a system of transitivity for $G(A)$. That is, $S_1 = \{g(s_1) | g \in G(A)\}$, $S_2 = \{g(s_2) | g \in G(A)$ and $s_2 \neq h(s_1)$ for any $h \in G(A)\}$ and similarly for $S_3, \ldots, S_r$. Let g_{ij} be the product of those cycles of g_i which permute just the set S_j, and let $G_j(A)$ be the set $G_j(A) = \{g_{1j}, g_{2j}, \ldots, g_{qj}\}$. Then it follows that $G_j(A)$ is a transitive group of regular permutations, hence the order of $G_j(A)$ is the same as the order of S_j. Thus, the order of $G_j(A)$ is q and $r = p$—that is, there are p sets $S_1, S_2, \ldots, S_p$ with $pq = n$.

Now consider for $i = 1, \ldots, p$, the automata

$$A_i = (S_i, G_i(A), M_i)$$

where M_i is defined by $M_i(s, g_{ji}) = g_{ji}(s)$ for $s \in S_i$. Certainly A_i is strongly connected. The group $G(A_i)$ of each of these automata is extremely interesting. Let $\pi \in G(A_i)$. Then π is a permutation found in the symmetric group on S_i, and

$$\pi(M_i(s, g_{ji})) = \pi(g_{ji}(s))$$

while

$$M_i(\pi(s), g_{ji}) = g_{ji}(\pi(s))$$

Hence, $\pi \in G(A_i)$ if and only if π commutes with all elements of $G_i(A)$; the set of all permutations in the symmetric group on S_i which commutes with every element of $G_i(A)$ is called the centralizer of $G_i(A)$. Thus the centralizer of a regular permutation group is a group of regular permutations whose order divides that of the regular group.

Moreover, since $G(A_i)$ is the group of operation preserving functions for the strongly connected automaton $A_i = (S_i, G_i(A), M_i)$, there is a homomorphism from a subset of $G_i(A)$ to $G(A_i)$. Let ϕ_{jk} be the set of all elements x in $G_i(A)$ for which $M_i(s_j, x) = s_k$ for $s_j, s_k \in S_i$. Then ϕ_{jk} contains precisely one element. For simplicity sake, suppose $s_i \in S_i$. Since the set $\phi = \{\phi_{i\pi(i)} | \pi \in G(A_i)\}$ with the operation $*_i$ is a group isomorphic to $G(A_i)$ then there is an isomorphism σ between a subset of $G_i(A)$ and $G(A_i)$, given by $\sigma(g_{ji}) = \pi$ if and only if $g_{ji}(s_i) = \pi(s_i)$.

Since σ is an isomorphism then for g_{ji} and g_{ki} in the subset isomorphic to $G(A)$, let $\sigma(g_{ji}) = \pi$ and $\sigma = (g_{ki}) = \lambda$. Then $\sigma(g_{ji}g_{ki}) = \pi\lambda$, hence

$$g_{ji}(g_{ki}(s_i)) = \pi(\lambda(s_i))$$

But
$$\pi(\lambda(s_i)) = \pi(g_{ki}(s_i))$$
$$= g_{ki}(\pi(s_i))$$
$$= g_{ki}(g_{ji}(s_i))$$

Since g_{ji} and g_{ki} are in a group of regular permutations then $g_{ji}g_{ki} = g_{ki}g_{ji}$, so that the centralizer of $G_i(A)$ is commutative.

These results are summarized as:

THEOREM 5. The centralizer for a regular group G of permutations is a commutative group H of regular permutations such that the order of H divides that of G. Moreover, H is isomorphic to a subgroup G' of G.

REFERENCES

1. Huffman, D. A., "The Synthesis of Sequential Switching Circuits," *J. Franklin Inst.*, pp. 161–190. March 1954, vol 57.
2. Mealy, G. H., "A Method for Synthesizing Sequential Circuits" *Bell Syst. Tech. J.*, vol. 34, September 1955, pp. 1045–1079.
3. Davis, M., *Computablility and Unsolvability*, McGraw-Hill, New York, 1958.
4. Moore, E. F., "Gedanken Experiments on Sequential Machines," in *Automata Studies*, Princeton U. P., Princeton, N.J., 1956, pp. 129–153.
5. Ginsburg, S., various papers. See, for example, "On the Length of the Smallest Uniform Experiment Which Distinguishes the Terminal States of a Machine" *J. ACM*, vol. 5, no. 3, July 1958, pp. 266–280.
6. Rabin, M. O., and D. Scott, "Finite Automata and their Decision Problems" IBM *J. Res. Devel.*, vol. 3, April 1959, pp. 114–125.
7. Fleck, A. C., "Isomorphism Groups of Automata" *J. AMC*, vol. 9, no. 4, October 1962, pp. 469–476.
8. Weeg, G. P., "Some Group Theoretic Properties of Strongly Connected Automata" unpublished research paper, Eng. Res. Division, Michigan State University.

9. ——, "The Group and Semi-Group Associated with Automata", Proceedings of the Symposium on Mathematical Theory of Automata, Polytechnic Institute of Brooklyn, 1962.

10. ——, "The Structure of an Automaton and its Operation Preserving Transformation Group" J. of ACM, vol. 9, no. 3, July, 1962, pp. 345–349.

11. Tamura, T., "Commutative Divisible Semi-Groups" *Amer. Math. Soc. Notices*, vol. 10, no. 1, January 1963, p. 87.

10

TEMPORALLY ORGANIZED AUTOMATA AND AN ALGEBRAIC THEORY OF MACHINES

M. J. PEDELTY

The American University, Washington, D. C.

INTRODUCTION

This is a preliminary report on some work which brings out the essential behavioral equivalence between switching circuits operating in a "spatial domain" (e.g., combinatorial switching networks of either "conventional" or threshold logic[†]) and those employing pulse-interval modulation. The latter have been described by MacKay[‡] as "temporally organized automata." The equivalence mentioned takes the form of a common mapping or set of mappings which each automaton can effect between its inputs and its outputs. Much of the latter part of this paper will be concerned, therefore, with properties of mappings, such mappings being, in general, realizable by either kind of network. However, the domain and range of such a mapping can consist of alphabets not necessarily formed from strings of binary digits. Thus we are free to use other than conventional Boolean logic. A major result of the theory is a characterization of machine decomposition problems.

The earlier part of the report is concerned with a description of a particular kind of temporally organized automaton which we shall call a P-machine. Although any such machine can be replaced, in theory, by a combinatorial switching network, the P-machine appears to offer peculiar advantages. These depend on the fact that very sophisticated organization

* Research sponsored by Aeronautical Systems Division, Air Force Systems Command, under Contract AF 33(657)–9195.

† M. J. Pedelty, *An Approach to Machine Intelligence*, Spartan, Baltimore, Md., 1963.

‡ D. M. MacKay, *"Self-Organization in the Time Domain,"* in Yovits et al. (eds.), *Self-Organizing Systems, 1962*, Spartan, Baltimore, Md., 1962.

can thus be obtained from relatively simple structures. Their principle can best be exploited when a cheap form of pulse delay is available. A specific instance of the flexibility of a P-machine is its ability to switch rapidly between mappings, which can be achieved in a normal threshold logic circuit only by rather complicated manipulations of thresholds and coupling "weights".* Such switching will be accomplished in a P-machine simply by selection of words from a "control alphabet" produced by a "generator" (i.e., any device capable of synthesizing appropriate sequences of bits). This generator will be able to select any given mapping from the set of mappings realizable by the machine. (This is, generally, a proper subset of the set of all possible mappings from the input set, α, into the output set, β.) The design of suitable generators will not be discussed here. The set of mappings realizable by the machine will be determined by the machine's structure,† its input alphabet, α, (consisting of sequences of bits forming "data words") and its control alphabet, Q, which is the output of the aforementioned generator.

This paper is intended to be of tutorial value. For this reason, non-essential formalism will be omitted, or relegated to the appendix.

We start with the notion that any finite automaton can be characterized by a mapping: $Q \times \alpha \rightarrow \beta$ (i.e., a set, S', of mappings : $\alpha \rightarrow \beta$), where Q is a "state" set, α, an input alphabet, and β, an output alphabet.‡ The primary advantage of working in terms of mappings is that the theory is equally applicable to conventional combinatorial switching circuits, threshold logic, sequential circuits or any finite state machine (including the case of multi-valued logic). For example, a machine, M, consisting of a single threshold element with n inputs has an input alphabet consisting of up to 2^n n-dimensional binary vectors, an output alphabet, $\{0,1\}$, and its realizable mappings will form a set, S', of all the linearly separable Boolean functions of n variables, if M's weights and threshold are allowed to assume any real value.

Our characterizations of machines yield upper and lower bounds on a machine's ability to distinguish members of its input alphabet. They also lead to certain decomposition results. That is, they enable us to replace a machine, realizing a complex mapping or mappings, with two or more machines each realizing a smaller set of mappings or having smaller alphabets. For example, if M is a threshold device with weights and threshold assuming any real value, it may be possible to replace M with subautomata having fixed weights. The results of this paper will show,

* M. J. Pedelty, *op. cit.*
† i.e., configuration and the values of the delays.
‡ A. Gill, *Introduction to the Theory of Finite State Machines*, McGraw-Hill, New York, 1962. Strictly, a finite state machine has a "next state" function defined at all times.

inter alia, whether any particular collection of subautomata are equivalent to M. These subautomata may be cheaper to build or easier to "train" than M. The results would be equally applicable if some man-machine complex is to be synthesized out of components each of limited capacity. The theory would ensure that the aggregate did, in fact, achieve the required mapping from input to output. (The method of simple enumeration of input symbols is, of course, discarded as being an overwhelming procedure during the design phase.)

The machine decomposition results depend on the facts that (i) a mapping, $\alpha \rightarrow \beta$, may be decomposed into a partition, π, on α, resulting in a map, $\alpha \rightarrow \gamma$, and a further mapping (e.g., on automorphism) $\gamma \rightarrow \beta$; and (ii) any partition π can be formed by taking the greatest lower bound of two (generally less refined) other partitions. These results yield decomposition into series and parallel configurations, respectively.

A partition π induces an equivalence relation on α such that any two elements in α are equivalent if they map onto the same image in γ. Thus, the members of any given block of π are all those elements in α which are pre-images of a single element in γ. The set of all partitions on a set form a lattice, L_π, ordered by the relation, $\leq$, if "$\pi_1 \leq \pi_2$" is equivalent to "any block of π_1 is contained in a block of π_2" (i.e., π_1 is a refinement of π_2), for any π_1, $\pi_2 \in L\pi$.* The greatest lower bound (g.l.b.) of any two partitions π_1, π_2, is a partition, $\pi_1 \wedge \pi_2$, formed by intersecting the blocks of π_1 and π_2.

THE P-MACHINE

In this section, we will describe a temporally organized automaton, consisting of a set of coincidence gates and delays arranged in parallel.

THE COINCIDENCE GATE

The essence of the system we shall describe is that signals are "broadcast" on a "to-whom-it-may-concern" basis. Coincidence gates and delays can then be used to detect certain pulse patterns from the "broadcast alphabet". For instance, the circuit:

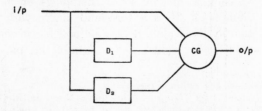

* G. Birkhoff, *Lattice Theory,* American Mathematical Society, New York, 1948.

can be used to detect the pulse train

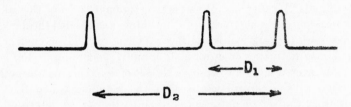

if all input connections to the gate are excitatory. If this is a threshold element with unit input weights (synaptic strengths), then lowering the threshold from 3 to 2 would cause the gate to detect all pulse trains of frequencies $1/D_1$ or $1/D_2$ or integral multiples thereof, in addition to pulse patterns of the type shown above. That is, this circuit would dichotomize the set of all signals arriving at its input terminal into those that did and those that did not correspond to the types mentioned.* Since no "start" time has been defined, all sets of such pulses would be so classified (cf. "prefix" codes). If a "start" time must be defined, it could be provided by a simple "facilitate" connection direct to the c.g. This latter forms a very crude form of "control word".

CONTROL WORDS

Consider the following detector:

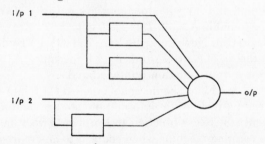

in this arrangement, if the gate has a threshold of 5, both inputs must be activated by suitable pulse-patterns (with coincident starting times). One pattern may be a "control word" from a "control alphabet," which sensitizes this detector to a certain class of "data words" on the other input line. A threshold lower than 5 will produce a more subtle interaction between the data alphabet and the control alphabet.

---

* Actually, there are a few other patterns, such as those associated with $|D_1 - D_2|$, which would also produce an output. The element indicates the dichotomy by either firing a single pulse or remaining quiesant.

D. M. MacKay, op. cit.

Control words can be used in the following way. A network of detectors having the form shown above is arranged such that data words go to all input terminals "1" and control words to terminals "2." For the sake of a label let us refer to this network as a P-machine. Let us label the detectors 1 through n, and the data words, A, B, etc. Then, for a given control word, say C_1, A may activate detectors 1, 3, 5, and 7, for example. For control word C_2, however, a different subset of the set of detectors may be activated by A. That is, the control words alter the mapping which the circuit provides from the set of data words, α, into the set of detector output n- tuples, β.* (The mapping is also from the temporal to the spatial domain, if any data word reaches all detectors simultaneously. The spatial data may, of course, be placed in serial order, if desired.) We shall see presently how this variable mapping may play an important role. (For the time being, we consider only binary responses at the detector output, not sequences.)

AN ALGEBRA FOR P-MACHINES

In order to facilitate the discussion of the behavior of P-machines, we should avoid, as far as possible, working with their direct internal structure. For this purpose we intend to develop an algebra of their behavior. There exists at least one direct correspondence to the theory of finite-state machines. We recall that the behavior of such a machine may be represented by a mapping $Q \times \alpha \rightarrow \beta$, where Q is the set of machine states and α and β are the set of input and output alphabets, respectively. (An equivalent statement is to be found in A. Gill, *Introduction to the Theory of Finite-State Machines*, McGraw-Hill, New York, 1962, p. 7, def. 1.1.) By inspection, it can be seen that the set of control words for a P-machine, $\{C\}$, corresponds to the set Q, in the output function quoted above.

An algebra for P-machines should enable one to (1) relate structure to function, (2) relate function to information storage and environment matching problems, (3) relate function to learning. Two P-machines may form a complete learning machine when coupled to an environment, E:

To facilitate discussion, P-machines should be classified in terms of certain general properties. Certain useful theorems could then be derived taking the general form: for a P-machine of the Kth class, if there exists a mapping, M, and M has the property, p, then there exists mapping M' with p'. If advantage can be taken of the transitive nature of a series of such implications, they may be used to show that a whole family of mappings having the properties p, p', etc., exist for a given P-machine of the Kth class.

---

* The element of β at time t indicates which detectors fired it time t.

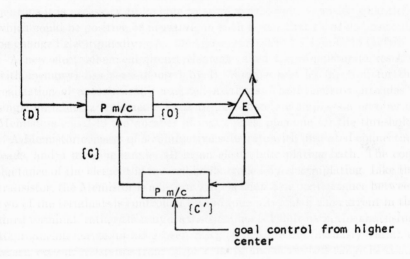

AN ASSOCIATIVE MEMORY

This memory is capable of storing "data words" consisting of bits distributed serially in time. It contains certain "interrogate words" of similar form. The basic storage is recirculating loops taking the form of "conventional" delay lines or neuristor lines.* Such a line may store more than one word. The form of association is as follows: if a data word D is a subset† of an interrogate word, I, and it arrives at certain designated portions of the memory coincidentally with I, then D will be stored in a "D-loop." If these conditions are fulfilled except for I being a subset of D, then the portion of D contained in I will be stored. D will normally be circulated to all loops in the memory, so several copies may be stored, some under identical I-words and others under non-identical I-words. (For all such I's, D must be contained.) We assume that the transmission of D from an input terminal to the loop terminals is subject to a constant delay, possibly different for each loop. This requirement could be dropped, however.

Results, so far, appear to indicate that the memory, when coupled to suitable data-transforming devices (e.g., P-machines) would exhibit many of the properties of human memory. A brief description of the minutiae of its operation will now be given. In the diagram, only one D-loop and one

* H. D. Crane, "Neuristor—A Novel Device and System Concept", *Proc. IRE*, vol. 50, no. 10, October 1962, pp. 2048–2060.

† That is, the D-word consists entirely of pulses coincident with, but of shorter duration than, those comprising the I-word, including the special cases of D-word pulses of zero length or of length equal to that of the corresponding I-word pulse.

I-loop are shown. All lines are delay lines. All unlabeled arrows go to other loops.

Read-in to a particular store is contingent (in part) on the simultaneous arrival of *D* and *I* words at the coincidence gate, shown with threshold 2. Additional differentiation is available by manipulating the "flow-cocks", $\oplus$. Storage could be ensured by inserting the same data word repeatedly. Since over-writing may occur, repeated insertion with a frequency dependent on use might be desirable, the most needed words thus having greatest chance of survival.

Readout could occur for a particular *I*-loop, depending on its cock position and the frequency of this loop relative to that of the *D*-loop. A slow phase drift might cause some difficulty in high-speed retrieval, but it would reduce the over-writing problem. An optimum solution might be slow drifts with a zero average (over a long time interval). If other *I*-loops could interrogate this *D*-loop, this data might (e.g., due to drift) become associated with other *I*-words. This could be disadvantageous, but, if properly controlled, it could also lead to creativity. The problem of hierarchies (transitive associations) could be dealt with by arranging for any *D*-loop to be an *I*-loop for some other loop. Thus, the original distinction between *I*-loops and *D*-loops was made only for clarity of description.

To get "raw" data into suitable form (subset-wise) several different recodings might be employed. This could be done by cycling a P-machine through several mappings by means of a small set of control words, while holding the raw data constant. Thus, entirely different aspects of the raw data could be "highlighted" for association in several ways.

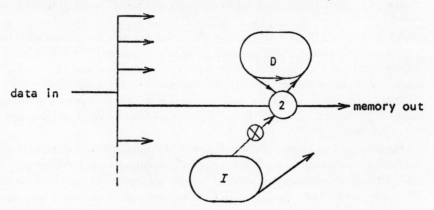

THEORY

A large part of the theory is concerned with sets of mappings (e.g., between alphabets) and it should, therefore, have much wider applicability to automata theory than was originally intended. Partition theory will form a part of the foundation and a succinct discussion of the basic theorems may be found in Hartmanis.*

As we mentioned before, the P-machine is related to the finite-state machine. The similarity is in the output function: $Q \times \alpha \to \beta$, where Q is a state-set and α an input alphabet. The difference, however, is that the finite-state machine's "next state" is uniquely determined by its present state and its present input, whereas the P-machine can adopt a "next state" determined by a "higher center," which may include a human operator.

Examination of the function: $Q \times \alpha \to \beta$, reveals that it can be broken into a number of mappings, $\alpha \to \beta$, one for each member of Q. The study of sets of mappings should, therefore, form an important part of our theory. Actually, a P-machine is behaviorally equivalent to a network of plastic neurons.† However, as mentioned before, the P-machine appears to offer great economy in the use of components. Further, adaptation of a plastic neuron requires changing a number of "weights" or "gains", the physical realization of which is often difficult to achieve. However, corresponding "adaptation" in a P-machine requires merely the selection of another control word from Q, leaving the structure of the machine unaltered. (For the purpose of this paper, "learning" is to be considered synomous with "adaptation", with the above meaning.)

NOTATION

S, set of all maps, $m: \alpha \to \beta$

B_s, Boolean algebra, the elements of which are the set of all subsets of S.

L_π, lattice of all partitions on α ‡

$\pi_i \in L_\pi$

$|\alpha|$, cardinal of set, α, (similarly for any set)

Greatest lower bound (g.l.b.), $\wedge$

Least upper bound, (l.u.b.) $\vee$

R, relationship "having" (e.g., mRp, where p is a defined property. If π_m is an image of m, under $S \to L_\pi$, and if mRp then we say $\pi_m R'p$.)

---

* J. Hartmanis, "Symbolic Analysis of a Decomposition of Information Processing Machines", *Information and Control*, vol. 3, 1960, pp. 154–178, and vol. 4, 1961, pp. 95–96.

† M. J. Pedelty, *An Approach to Machine Intelligence*, Spartan, Baltimore, Md., 1963, pp. 54–58.

‡M. J. Pedelty, *op. cit.*, pp. 84–87.

MAPPINGS

Any given mapping, $m : \alpha \rightarrow \beta$ will partition α into equivalence classes each consisting of all those pre-images of a single element in β. Thus the set, S, maps into L_π, and under this mapping we denote the image of m by π_m.

DEFINITION 1: If two mappings in S have ranges automorphic with one another, they are said to be π-equivalent. Any two such mappings map onto a single element in L_π, under $S \rightarrow L_\pi$. For convenience, any $m \in S$ is π-equivalent to itself.

Using the definition of π-equivalence, we can define a mapping, $L_\pi \rightarrow B_s$, such that if $m \rightarrow \pi_m$ under $S \rightarrow L_\pi$, then the image of π_m under $L_\pi \rightarrow B_s$ is the union (l.u.b.) of every mapping π-equivalent to m.

It might be thought that if a machine could produce one mapping in a particular equivalence class, it would be of no advantage to have it induce another mapping in that same class, since, due to the automorphic relationship implied, each would be a mere relabelling of the other. However, this conclusion is not, in general, valid, depending on the application.

For example, suppose a machine, M, has an input alphabet, $\alpha = \{1,2,3\}$, and an output alphabet, $\beta = \{a,b,c\}$. Let M produce at least two (π-equivalent) mappings, m and m', as shown.

m	m'
$1 \rightarrow a$	$1 \rightarrow b$
$2 \rightarrow b$	$2 \rightarrow c$
$3 \rightarrow c$	$3 \rightarrow a$

Now suppose that the output of M feeds another machine resulting in the (arbitrary) relationship cRb. For example, R may be equivalence under another mapping or the relationship "subset of" of an associative memory. Then the two machines, in cascade, could produce $3R2$ (under m) or $2R1$ (under m'). If M were a P-machine and it produced both mappings (disjoint in time), then both $3R2$ and $2R1$ and, by transitivity, $3R1$. Yet no notion of "subset" need be inherent in the "raw data," 3, 2, and 1.

THE SET $S = \{m_1, m_2 \ldots \}$

Unfortunately, engineers have grown accustomed to the Boolean algebra applied to switching circuits by Shannon* to the almost total exclusion of other Boolean algebras of equal interest. Shannon's Boolean algebra was finite and therefore atomic. We will discuss here, in broader outline, this and other Boolean algebras, especially the algebra whose elements are all the subsets of a set.

---

* C. E. Shannon, "Symbolic Analysis of Relay and Switching Circuits," *Trans. AIEE*, vol. 57, 1938, pp. 713–723.

Every Boolean algebra is a lattice.* Every finite Boolean algebra L is atomic. An atom of a Boolean algebra is an element $p \neq 0$ such that $x \leq p$ implies either $x = p$ or $x = 0$, where $\leq$ is the ordering relation of the lattice. This statement is equivalent to "every atom *covers* zero". Examples of atoms are: (1) the minterms of a "free Boolean algebra", (2) the elements of the set, S, in the algebra whose elements are all the subsets of S. A Boolean algebra is *atomic* if every non-zero element contains an atom. A Boolean algebra is atomic if and only if the unit element is the sum of all the elements that it contains. In the corresponding lattice the unit is the supremum and the zero element the infimum of that lattice. The operation "sum" is "least upper bound."

If the unit element is equated to "true" and the zero to "false", then the preceding statements lead to the conclusion that, in every atomic Boolean algebra, one and only one atom is true (for a given set of consistent propositions, a given "state" of a physical system, a given time, etc).

The complement of an element, x_1, of a Boolean algebra, is an element $x_2 \ni x_1 \cup x_2 = 1$ and $x_1 \cap x_2 = 0$. It is clear that, in general, the complement of an atom is not itself an atom. However, in the algebra with only four elements, $\{1,0,a,b\}$, a and b are necessarily complementary, although atoms. This is because, in every Boolean algebra $\exists$ for any element x_1 a unique complement. 1 and 0 are complementary, therefore so are a and b. However, both are atoms, since if only one covered zero it would, itself, be covered by the other, a condition incompatible with the notion of complementarity, since an element cannot be included in its complement. It should now be clear that if a set S consists of elements called maps, then in the Boolean algebra which is the set of all subsets of S, the complement of a map will not itself be a map, unless the cardinal of S be two.

Free Boolean Algebras

Let B be any Boolean algebra. Let I be a (non-void) subset of B satisfying $\forall (x,y)$: 1) $x \in I$, $y \in I$ implies $x \cup y \epsilon I$, 2) $x \epsilon I$, $t \leq x$, $t \epsilon B$ implies $t \epsilon I$. Then I is called an *ideal* of B. If $I \neq B$, I is called *proper*.

The ideal generated by Y is the smallest ideal of B containing Y, where Y is any subset of B. A principal ideal is an ideal generated by one element, a, and is denoted (a). Obviously, $(a) = \{x : x \leq a, x \epsilon B\}$. In a finite Boolean algebra every ideal is a principal ideal.

A subalgebra of B is a (non-void) subset of B, which is closed under the three Boolean operations. Any such subset contains 0 and 1.

If $X \subseteq B$, X is called a *set of generators* of B if the smallest subalgebra of B containing X, is B itself. X is said to *generate* B.

* M. J. Pedelty, *op. cit.*

The "Shannon algebra" is a *free Boolean algebra* of 2^{2^n} elements generated by a subset X of n elements called *literals*. In application, these literals may be binary variables representing the "state" of a physical element or they may be compound "events" corresponding to subsets of another Boolean algebra. The set X is called a *free set of generators* of B. This set is not constrained, i.e., a no element in X such that its truth value is implied by the truth values of the other elements in X.

RELATIONSHIP BETWEEN S, L_π AND B_s

As before, define $S = \{m_1, m_2 \ldots \}$ to be the set of all mappings, $m_i : \alpha \to \beta$. Let L_π be the lattice of partitions, π_j, on the set α. Let B_s be the Boolean algebra whose elements are the set of all subsets of S.

We have already established that there exists a many-one mapping, $S \to L_\pi$ and that this mapping partitions S.

Now, every non-zero element in B_s can be expressed as a union of maps, m. From this and the foregoing, it can be seen that there exists an order preserving mapping $L_\pi \to B_s$. The image, under this mapping, of some $\pi_k \in L_\pi$ will be the union of all those mappings in S which possess ranges automorphic with one another.[*] However, the domain of the mapping, $L_\pi \to B_s$, does not necessarily contain every $\pi_k \in L_\pi$, since, if the cardinal of β is less than the cardinal of α, not every partition of α could be produced by mappings from α to β.

Definition 2. $S' \subseteq S$ is said to be α-complete if it realizes every partition of α. (Similarly for machine, M.) The domain of the mapping $L_\pi \to B_{s'}$ is then the whole set, L_π.

Notice, a set which is α-complete need not possess *every* $m: \alpha \to \beta$, but those not possessed must be π-equivalent to those which are. We can now state a sufficient condition for two machines in cascade to realize every possible mapping

We have elsewhere[†] defined a "level of awareness" for a machine. This consisted of examination of the number of equivalence classes into which stimuli were divided (each class being defined by exactly one output symbol) in relation to the size of the stimulus alphabet. Maximal awareness was said to occur if each such equivalence class contained one stimulus. In our present context, this constitutes a 1-1 mapping of α onto β, the particular mapping being of no concern. Our Definition 2 is an extension of this idea which specifies a machine, M, capable of mapping α into β so as to satisfy any possible required partition of α. M is then said to be alpha-

---

[*] That is, if $m_i \to \pi_k$, than π_k maps onto an element in B_s. which is the union of all m_j π—equivalent to m_i.

[†] M. J. Pedelty, "Machine Intelligence and its Implications for Design Philosophy," *NAECON*, 1962.

complete. According to the mapping selected (e.g., in a P-machine by selection of a "control word"), any stimulus can be treated as equivalent to any other stimulus, and any required discrimination can be produced. Theorem I, considers such an α-complete machine M_1, and places in cascade a second machine M_2 which can perform any desired relabeling of the output of M_1. In physiological terms, M_1 performs the desired discrimination on the stimulus and M_2 functions as a "motor cortex", i.e., matches the output of M_1 with a particular desired response. It is probable that such a decomposition can greatly shorten learning times when compared to a single machine.

Definition 3. A machine, M, will be said to *contain* a mapping, $m : \alpha \rightarrow \beta$ if α is included in M's input alphabet and β is included in M's output alphabet, every element in α has an image in β, under m, and M realizes m. M is said to contain a set of mappings, $\{m_1, m_2, \ldots, m_n\}$ if M contains m_i for all i $(1 \leq i \leq n)$. Each such m_i has a common domain and a range which is contained in β.

THEOREM I

Let $S_1 = \{m_1, m_2, \ldots, m_i, \ldots, m_n\} \ni m_i : \alpha \rightarrow \gamma$, $(1 \leq i \leq n)$, and let $S_2 = \{m_1, m_2, \ldots, m_j, \ldots, m_m\}$, $\ni m_j : \gamma \rightarrow \beta$, $(1 \leq j \leq m)$. Let $|\gamma| = |\beta|$. Let S_1 be α-complete and let S_2 contain every possible 1-1 mapping of γ onto β. (These mappings will be called automorphisms of γ if $\gamma = \beta$ in terms of the physical representation of their elements.)

Then a sufficient condition for machines M_1 and M_2 in cascade to realize every mapping, $\alpha \rightarrow \beta$, is for M_1 to contain S_1 and M_2 to contain S_2.

INTERESTING SUBSETS OF L_π AND NOTION OF RELATIVE COMPLEMENTARITY

Theorem II concerns maps, which refine a certain discrimination, i.e., subdivide its equivalence classes. Theorem III simply says that an upper bound to any such process of refinement exists because β is finite and thus so is the number of equivalence classes into which α can be divided. (Of course, if α is of a lesser cardinal, any desired refinement can be achieved.) No proofs are provided.

A: IDEALS

Let p be the property, "maps onto π_k, under $S \rightarrow L_\pi$", (for any $\pi_k \in L_\pi$). Let p' be the property, "maps onto any $\pi_j \leq \pi_k$".

THEOREM II

The set of all maps $mR(p \cup p')$ maps onto an ideal, $(\pi_k) \subseteq L_\pi$, generated by π_k.

Definition 4: If p and p' have the definitions given under heading "A: Ideals," above, then $m_i R p'$ is *more refined* than $m_j R p$. Similarly, a refinement of a mapping, $m_j R p$, is any $m R p'$. If we allow m to be an (improper) refinement of itself, then it follows from Theorem II that the set of all refinements of m maps onto (π_m) if $m \rightarrow \pi_m$. This set is, of course, a subset of S, i.e., an *element* of B_s. If it is an *atom*, there exists no proper refinement of m in S. Similarly:

THEOREM III

If p is the property "partitions α into p blocks", and $|\beta| = p$ and m is any mapping α *onto* β then there exists no (proper) refinement of m in S.

THEOREM IV

Let $m_i \rightarrow \pi_k$, $m \pi_j$. If $\pi_k \wedge \pi_j = \pi_k$, then m_i is a refinement of m_j. Similarly, if $\pi_k \wedge \pi_j = \pi_j$, then m_j is a refinement of m_i.

B: SUBLATTICES

Consider a set, $S' = \{m_1, m_2, \ldots, m_n\} \subseteq S$. If for all pairs m_i, $m_j \in S'$ $\exists\, m_k$, $m_l \in S' \ni \pi_{m_k} = \pi_{m_i} \vee \pi_{m_l}$ and $\pi_m = \pi_{m_i} \wedge \pi_{m_j}$, then $S' \rightarrow L_\pi'$ (under $S \rightarrow L_\pi$), where L_π' is a sublattice of L_π.

C: RELATIVE COMPLEMENTARITY

Definition 5. Consider the sublattice, L'_π, with supremum, I', and infinum Φ'. π_1, $\pi_2 \in L_\pi'$ are *relatively complementary* (in L_π') if $\pi_1 \wedge \pi_2 = \Phi'$ and $\pi_1 \vee \pi_2 = I'$. Maps m_1 and m_2 are π-complementary if $\pi_{m_1} \vee \pi_{m_2} = I$ and $\pi_{m_1} \wedge \pi_{m_2} = \Phi$. They are relatively π-complementary (under L_π') if they are contained in S', $S' \rightarrow L_\pi'$ and π_{m_1}, π_{m_2} are relatively complementary (in L_π'). Notice, in general, the π-complement of a map is not unique.

If $\forall \pi \in L_\pi'$ $\exists$ its relative complement $\pi' \in L_\pi'$ then L_π' will be said to be *relatively complemented*.

D: MACHINE DECOMPOSITION

Throughout this portion of the study we have tried to stress the notion of partition as being of fundamental importance in discrimination. If two partitions are complementary, their greatest lower bound is the infimum of the lattice of partitions on the set α. This is the greatest discrimination possible. If two machines are available, each with input alphabets, α, and their maps are π-complementary, then α may be completely resolved by the adjunction of their outputs (i.e., a multi-valued equivalent of an AND-gate)*.

---

* With suitable timing, another P-machine would do, with its "data words" the outputs of M_1 and its "control words" the outputs of M_2. (Spatial to temporal conversion is assumed.)

Of course, complete resolution of α may be unnecessary. In that case we may define a partition, Φ', which is just adequate, and, if, for reasons of economy of learning times or hardware, two machines are to be used to achieve Φ', we merely define a sublattice, infimum Φ', and choose machines yielding mappings which are relatively π-complementary within that sublattice. Thus π-complementarity becomes a basis for machine decomposition, replacing a single machine by a triangular network.

Machine learning has only been implicit in this discussion. In the case of a P-machine, a generator of "control words" would adjust M to the desired mapping by the selection and retention of an appropriate word. Such selection would be eased if only a small set of words were involved. This implies a restricted set of mappings and partitions which M can provide. Thus the decomposition of machines forms a most important topic in this context.

APPENDIX

APPLICATIONS OF PARTITION THEORY

Theorems V through IX show which mappings can guarantee a certain minimal level of discrimination. Theorems X through XIV deal with mappings yielding a certain maximal level of discrimination.

A: Let p_1 be the property "partitions α into at least p blocks".

THEOREM V

If $m_i R p_1$ and m_j π-equivalent to m_i, then $m_j R p_1$.

THEOREM VI

If L_π is ordered by $(\leq)$ and $\pi_k \leq \pi_j$, and if $m_j R p_1 \to \pi_j$, (under $S \to L_\pi$), then if $\pi_k \to x$ $(L_\pi \to B_s)$ and $x = m_1 \cup m_2 \cup \ldots \cup m_i \cup \ldots \cup m_n$ then $m_i R p_1$ for all i: $(1 \leq i \leq n)$. For convenience, we say "$\pi_k R' p_1$."

THEOREM VII

If $p = 1$, then $m R p_1$ V $m \epsilon S$.

THEOREM VIII

If $p = |\alpha|$, then $\exists$ one and only one $\pi_k \epsilon L_\pi$ (namely the infimum of L_π) $\ni \pi_k R' p_1$.

THEOREM IX

If either $\pi_k R' p_1$ or $\pi_j R' p_1$, then $(\pi_k \wedge \pi_j) R' p_1$.

B: Let p_2 be the property "partitions α into at most p blocks."

THEOREM X

If $m_1 R p_2$ and m_j π-equivalent to m_i, then $m_j R p_2$.

THEOREM XI

If L_π is ordered by $(\leq)$ and $\pi_k \leq \pi_i$, and if $m_j R p_2 \to \pi_k$ (under $S \to L_\pi$), then $\pi_j R' p_2$.

THEOREM XII

If $p = |\alpha|$, then mRp_2 ∀ $m \epsilon S$.

THEOREM XIII

If $p = 1$, then ∃ exactly one $\pi_k \epsilon L_\pi$ (namely the supremum of L_π) ∋ $\pi_k R' p_2$.

THEOREM XIV

If either $\pi_k R' p_2$ or $\pi_j R' p_2$, then $(\pi_k \vee \pi_j) R' p_2$.

SUMMARY

As indicated, p_1 is the property "partitions α into at least p blocks." Theorem V states that if one member of any pair of π-equivalent mappings has p_1, then so does the other member. This follows directly from the definition of π-equivalence: "mappings in S with ranges automorphic with one another". Hence the range of one mapping is a one-one relabeling of the other, and both induce the same partition on α. Thus, in Theorem V, the discrimination provided by m_i is identical to that of m_j.

Theorem VI defines π_k as a refinement of π_j. That is, any block of π_k is contained in a block of π_j. Thus, any mapping inducing π_k will provide discrimination among the members of α *at least* equal to that provided by a mapping inducing π_j.

Theorems VII and VIII are the cases provided by the partitions which are, respectively, the supremum and the infimum of L_π. By definition, the supremum "divides" α into one block (an improper dichotomy) and using this and Theorem VI, we have that every partition (and hence every mapping) divides α into at least one block. Obviously, the *infimum* of L_π has exactly one element of α in each block.

Theorem IX says that if either of two partitions has at least p blocks, then so does their greatest lower bound. The g.l.b. of two partitions is formed by intersecting their blocks. It is, therefore, a refinement of both. Theorem VI completes the proof.

In effect, then, Theorems V through IX state that if we have a mapping, m_i, which induces at least a certain discrimination among members of α, then there exists another mapping m_j, which stands in a certain relation to m_i, such that m_j induces at least that discrimination. The particular relation is given by the theorem. Obviously, most of these theorems can be used recursively to define a family of such mappings. Theorem II is one such family.

---

* J. Hartmanis, "Symbolic Analysis of a Decomposition of Information Processing Machines," Information and Control, vol. 3, June, 1960, pp. 156–157.

Theorems X through XIII are the duals of Theorems V through VIII.

Theorem XIV says that if either of two partitions divide α into at most p blocks, then so does their least upper bound.* This is because both π_k and π_j are refinements of $(\pi_k \ \vee \ \pi_j)$. This is the dual of Theorem IX.

In effect, Theorems X through XIV describe a family of maps which can do no better than to yield a certain discrimination. Notice that if p is some cardinal number other than 1, then, of any two maps, m_1, m_2, if m_1 is a member of the family generated by Theorems V through IX and m_2 is a member of the family generated by Theorems X through XIV, we may say that m_1 is a refinement of m_2. This provides a way of comparing machines without recourse to enumeration.

11

A THRESHOLD-CONDITIONED ADAPTIVE TEMPLATE PROCEDURE FOR RECOGNITION OF NORMALIZED CONNECTED PATTERNS

SALOMON KLACZKO-RYNDZIUN

University òf Frankfurt, Frankfurt, Western Germany

PART I

GENERAL CONCEPT

The general structure of a learning-pattern recognizer is known. A function diagram will illustrate its structure. As shown in Fig. 1, a sensor is necessary to transform the energy quality of the input information into the energy quality of the adaptive-pattern recognizer (e.g., optical in electrical or acoustical in electrical energy). The sensor has to transform the energy form without destruction of necessary information (e.g., photomultiplier). For computer handling he can, for example, digitalize an analog electrical signal.

The transducer has to realize a certain form of data processing, without changing the energy form. It has to reorganize the structure and the order of the information, as it appears in the input, and to adapt it for the particular necessities of the adaptive recognizer. While the sensor is purely a physical translator, the transducer is a logical translator. Because of this, the transducer may lose a part of the received information amount if it does not find this information necessary for the recognizer. The transducer is conditioned by the pattern structure, the sensor function and the recognizer requirements. It is specific for each array of pattern recognition devices.

We will assume that the sensor output and the adaptive recognizer will have both a digital code (not necessarily different ones). The adaptive recognizer must have a direct input for reinforcement signals sent by the human operator who controls the function of the device. The signals may be for punishing or rewarding, related to the errors or the success of the recognizer. The reinforcement will provoke the adaption steps. After a certain given quantity of steps related to one single pattern and all its permissible variations, the adaptation process may be closed. However, it can be repeated as often as necessary.

THE MULTIVALUED UNION-INTERSECTION TEMPLATE

The single-template method tests the identity between a given pattern and a stored template. This test allows only two decisions—identity or none. A certain degree of freedom may be introduced if a measure of non-identity is defined. The measure can be given, for example, by the number of noncommon bits between pattern and template. If a threshold equivalent to the maximally authorized number of noncommon bits is introduced the identity test will become a similarity test. We will have now three possible decisions: identity, similarity or none. We will discuss this possibility later. A second degree of freedom is given, if this threshold will be variable under control of the reinforcement signals. A third degree of freedom is definable, if the set-theoretical intersection of all possible similar patterns is used, provided that this intersection is nonempty. It is apparent that a necessary but not sufficient condition for similarity between the pattern and the template consists on the property of the pattern of completely containing the intersection of all similar patterns. But there is another necessary and partial condition for similarity: the pattern must be completely contained in the set-theoretical union of all similar patterns. It can be easily proved that the association of *both* properties is a sufficient condition for similarity. So it is possible to realize practically this approach by construction of two templates—one for the intersection set and the other one for the union set. The union of the two templates will be called a filter. The logical operation to be realized will be no more the equivalence or the antivalence, but the implication. If one pattern has no other similars than itself, the filter will consist on the pattern itself. For practical purposes we will use not the union set itself, but its complementary.

A fourth degree of freedom can be introduced in the testing stage, if we distinguish between training, testing, and application stages. The mean value of correctness of the responses of a filter can be computed. If this mean value lies under a certain threshold—which can be also adjustable—the filter will be excluded from the recognition process and eventually its information will be destroyed.

If the recognizer exists as a special program for a digital computer and it has the abovementioned adaptive capabilities, we will call it an Universal Digital Adaptive Recognizer (UDAR).

The Transducer Problem

We will define the transducer problem as follows: Given is a source-sensor-complex and an adaptive recognizer with reinforcement capabilities, find a transducer which realizes a homomorphism between them. If we work with a digital computer and the sensor belongs to the input equipment of the computer, the solution of the problem is a transducer which transforms the code of the input information into the UDAR-code. This problem is evidently soluble if the number of bits of a filter template is not less than the number of bits of the S-field (input display field of the sensor).

We can prove the following proposition:

1. If an UDAR-code and a set of patterns represented in this code is given it is necessary and sufficient to classify them, that an UDAR with such a structure is used which will distinguish each pair of different patterns and which will not distinguish each pair of similar patterns. The definitions of difference and similarity are given by the human operator arbitrarily, by means of the reinforcement procedures. *The only restriction is that two identical patterns are not defined as different by the operator.*

Proof of Proposition 1:

It is obvious that between each arbitrary source-sensor-transducer array $(s, \bar{s}, t)$ and each arbitrary UDAR, they give a secondary transducer (t') which solved the transducer problem. The set of transducers constitutes a group of transformations by the transducers product. For each t and t' they give a transducer $t'' = t \cdot t'$. The array equivalence $(s, \bar{s}, t) \cdot (t') \equiv (s, \bar{s}, (t \cdot t')) \equiv (s, \bar{s}, t'')$ implies that the UDAR are invariant over the set of all the arrays of the form $(s, \bar{s}, t)$. The existence of a difference d between two patterns p and p' implies, that the difference

$$d = p - p' \neq 0$$

belongs to one of the patterns and to the complement of the other pattern, for example

$$d \subset p$$
$$d \subset \bar{p}'$$

If the two instances are declared similar by the operator, d becomes irrelevant for the invariant part (kernel) of the pattern and will belong only to the set of variations of the pattern. For each pattern p and the kernel k_p there will be a set

$$D^p = d_0^p, d_1^p, \ldots, d_n^p = \{d_i^p\}$$

of all the allowed variations d_i^p of p. A necessary and sufficient condition for the similarity of two patterns p and p' is

1. that they have the same kernel k_p
2. that the differences $d_i^p = p - k_p$ and $d_i^p = p' - k_p$ belong to D^p.

Then, for distinguishing between two different patterns it is sufficient to state that they have not the same kernel. For recognition of the similarity of two patterns with the same kernel k_p it is enough to establish that the complements $\bar{p}$ and $\bar{p}'$ have the same common kernel $k_{\bar{p}} \equiv \overline{k_p + D}$.

Otherwise, if two identical patterns are defined as different by the operator's reinforcement, there will be at least two identical kernels k_p and $k_{p'}'$ which will achieve simultaneously the recognition of one and the same pattern p. But simultaneous achieving of more than one filter by recognition is constructively excluded. So it will be a contradiction.

Some Theoretical Considerations

By the learning experiment we have a system of n different input variables. We can attribute to each variable V_i, also if it is a continuous one, a discret number m of permissible states, representing intervals of the continuous variation field of the variable. It will be convenient to select only values of m which are powers of 2. It is then indifferent if the n variables have different values of m. We find that the number c of combinations or states of the set of variables is

$$c = \prod_{i=1}^{n} m_i$$

When m constant we have obviously

$$c = m^n$$

In a large number of cases we will work with variables where $m = 2$. We can generally assume that a correspondence or mapping

$$M_i = V_i \to p_h$$

between a certain state

$$V_i = x_{i1} v_1, x_{i2} v_2, \ldots, x_{in} v_n = \{x_{ij} v_j\}$$

of the set of variables v_i and a recognized pattern p_h, is learned if this correspondence appears consecutively r times. Otherwise, a learned correspondence will be forgotten, if it appears contradicted more than r' times. The condition

$$r \leqslant r'$$

can be assumed to be correct, if the likelihood of an already learned correspondence

$$M_i = V_i \rightarrow p_h \tag{1}$$

is greater than the likelihood of a new correspondence

$$M_{i+1} = V_i \rightarrow p_h' (p_h \neq p_h') \tag{2}$$

Then, the substitution of Eq. (1) by Eq. (2) may be accepted, only if Eq. (2) appeared $r + s$ times ($s = 1, 2, 3 \ldots$). The substitution of Eq. (2) by a correspondence

$$M_{i+2} = V_i \rightarrow p_h'' \tag{3}$$

may be accepted only if (3) appears $r + 2s$ times. This will represent a learning model with a component s of positive learning inertia. If s becomes negative, we will have a learning model with negative inertia, i.e., high adaptability. In certain cases it can be necessary to consider for the series

$$\{M\} = M_i, M_{i+1}, M_{i+2}, \ldots, M_{i+n}, \ldots$$

the correspondent series

$$\{S\} = s_i, s_{i+1}, s_{i+2}, \ldots, s_{i+n}, \ldots$$

not as a constant, but as a monotonic increasing or decreasing series. This will imply that the series $\{M\}$ will have a nonlinear increment function. The case of nonlinear increasing or decreasing of $\{S\}$ will have no practical interest. The punishing may be realized in two forms: Only by decreasing $t(M_i)$ or by doing this with a simultaneous increase of $t(M_{i+1})$. This variable is the number of successive times that M_i (respectively M_{i+1}) was registered. (We will call it certainly coefficient.) The second case will imply that for each state V_i there exist parallel both patterns p_h and p_h', i.e., M_i and M_{i+1}. Only one of them will then be accepted as the available, while the other may remain in reserve. The possibility that more than one M_{i+n} will be in reserve simultaneously may be theoretically interesting. But in practice this is excluded, if the reinforcement of the operator is single- and not multi-valued. In the first case—only a reduction of $t(M_i)$—the first stage for relearning will be to "forget," and the second stage, sequentially separated, to learn the new statement. It is obviously not ever necessary to count $t(M_i)$ out of the interval

$$o \leqslant t(M_i) \leqslant r$$

but we can do it under certain special conditions.

First Practical Conclusions

The above theoretical discussion and the proof of Proposition 1 has practical importance, because they show which elements we have to consider for the concrete realization of an UDAR. We can distinguish now:

1. A set V of variables v_i.

2. A scanning field (S-field) of v_i variables, i.e., the set V plus a certain topological array of the variables, realized, for example, on a digital memory device.

3. A certain topological and numerical structure of the single variable, as an array of two-valued elements (flip-flops). In the simplest case, by two-valued variables, a variable itself will be represented by a flip-flop.

4. A set of as many filters as patterns are recognizable, each filter consisting of two masks of bits. The first mask must contain the kernel k_p of the filter, inscribed over a reproduction of the S-field. The second mask must contain the complementary kernel $k_{\bar{p}} = \overline{k_p + D^p}$, also inscribed over a reproduction of the S-field.

5. A set of counters, one for each filter, for counting the variable $t(M_i)$.

6. A set of counters, one for each filter, for counting the variable r, if $\{S\}$ is not a constant but a monotonic varying series.

7. A given series $\{S\}$ if Item 6 is attempted, or a given constant s if not.

8. A set of output variables p_h (patterns).

9. An identifier register that stores by punishing the name of the correct pattern.

10. An output register that stores the number or name of the recognizing filter.

Further, we can design the function diagram of the UDAR, the black box called Adaptive Recognizer in Fig. 1. In Fig. 2 we have included the S-field in the UDAR as input. The filters are not explicitly included. Instead we have represented Learning Building Blocks (LBB), each of which includes respectively the filters, the computing circuit for $t(M_i)$ and the comparing circuit for the threshold r and $t(M_i)$ as said in Fig. 3.

We have then developed a first approach to the basic concept of an universal pattern-recognition system, and the discussion resulted in three function diagrams, the second and third explaining the internal structure of the black box in the preceding one.

We have accordingly the possibility of studying in detail in the further chapters the fine structure problems resulting from the above functional concept of the system.

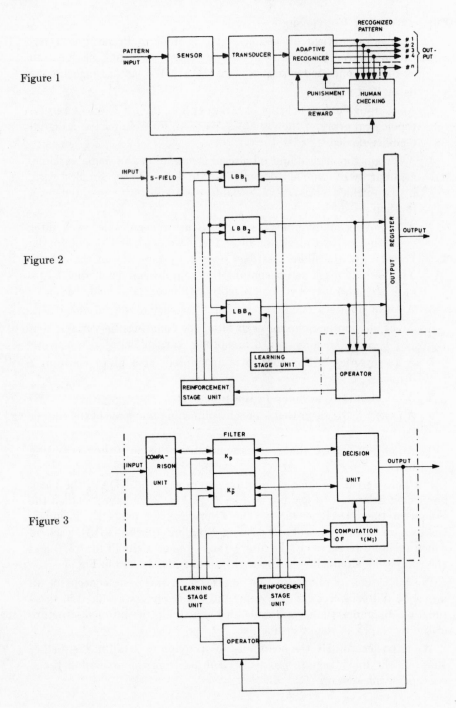

Figure 1

Figure 2

Figure 3

PART II

SOME DIFFICULTIES WITH THE MODEL

Further development of the system concept creates certain basic difficulties due to exceptions to the general case provided by the algorithm. Before we continue it will be necessary to study these exceptions and to find functional or theoretical solutions for them. The method followed will be the same as that in Part I—first a theoretical discussion and then the practical conclusions for an optimal realization of the system.

THE PROBLEM OF THE CO-CONTAINED PATTERNS

The recognition algorithm introduced before is not suitable to distinguish between two different patterns p_h and p_h' if one of them—say p_h'—accomplishes

$$k_p \subset p_h' \subset \overline{k_p + D^p} \tag{4}$$

It is then necessary to enclose in the learning stage a supplementary procedure. The set D^p must be divided in two subsets $^1D^p$ and $^2D^p$, which have not necessarily the same kernel. For the formulation of a precise classification criterion between the elements of D^p in one of the two new classes, it would be necessary to introduce a topological measure and certain additional conditions of maximality. But generally it can be stated that the two new resultant patterns of p_h—we call them p_j and p_k—and the pattern p_h' will be handled and recognized as three different features. Out of the output we can then join p_j and p_k by a logic disjunction, to identify them. But both must be so selected that they have a maximal topological difference with p_h'.

It can be calculated for a given S-field, a kernel k_p and a variations set D^p, by means of the above mentioned metric, how many series

$$P_0 = p_h, p_h', p_h'', p_h''', \ldots, p_h^{(n)}$$

there are, by which each pair of successive elements $(p_h^{(i)}, p_h^{(i+1)})$ accomplishes the property of Eq. (4). With the same data it is possible to determine the length of each P_i chain respectively throughout the mean length value of the chain set.

THE PROBLEM OF THE CERTAINTY COEFFICIENT COMPUTATION

For the computation of the certainty coefficient $t(M_i)$ Steinbuch (1961) gives a procedure which requires to store the results of the n last experiments related with a given M_i. He forms the algebraic sum of the truth values $w(M_i)$ of the consecutive M_i experiments (1 if confirmed and -1 if rejected). It is clear that

$$\sum_{j=1}^{n} |w_j(M_i)| = n$$

To project $t(M_i)$ over the interval

$$-1 \leqslant x \leqslant 1$$

he divides

$$\frac{\sum_{j=1}^{n} w_j(M_i)}{\sum_{j=1}^{n} |w_j(M_i)|} = \frac{\sum_{j=1}^{n} w_j(M_i)}{n} = t(M_i)$$

We can obtain a similar result without storage of the n former results, by recursive computation. Given $t_j(\leqslant_i)$ we can obtain $t_{j+1}(\leqslant_i)$ by the following procedure:

$$t_{j+1}(M_i) = t_j(M_i) + \frac{w_{j+1}(M_i)}{n}$$

For projection over the interval

$$-1 \leqslant x \leqslant 1$$

it is sufficient to divide it by the maximal value function of the $t_{j+1}(M_i)$:

$$\text{Max } t_{j+1}(M_i) = 1 + \frac{1}{n} = \frac{n+1}{n}$$

The value n must be, of course, a positive integer. Assumed that the procedure is applied at first for $t_0(M_i) = 0$ and that $t_j(M_i) = \pm 1$ for each j, the recursive conditions are sufficiently defined. For projection over the interval

$$0 \leqslant x \leqslant 1$$

we can utilize the formula

$$t_{j+1}(M_i) = \frac{1}{2} \cdot [t_j(M_i) + w_{j+1}(M_i)]$$

for $t_0 = 0.5$ and $w_j = 0$ (reject of M_i) or $w_j = 1$ (confirmation of M_i). Further we can utilize the formula

$$t_{j+1}(M_i) = \frac{1}{2}\left[t_j(M_i) + \frac{1 + w_{j+1}(M_i)}{2} \right]$$

for $t_0 = 0.5$ and $w_j = -1$ (reject) or $w_j = 1$ (confirmation).

Instead of the Steinbuch procedure it seems to be more practical to select the interval $0 \leqslant x \leqslant 1$—also utilized by Rosenblatt (1958)—because of the direct interpretability of $t_j(M_i)$ as a probabilistic value; and to choose for $w_j(M_i)$ the values 0 (reject) and 1 (confirmation) because of the direct interpretability as a logical truth value. We will then utilize the recursive function

$$t_0(M_i) = 0.5$$
$$t_j(M_i) = \frac{1}{2}[t_{j-1}(M_i) + w_j(M_i)]$$

for computing the actual value of $t_j(M_i)$ at each instant during the learning stage of the system. At the same time we can then consider the threshold $r = 0.5$ as a constant value or vary it in the interval

$$0 \leqslant r \leqslant 1$$

if necessary. The given recursive function is not a trivial averaging, because of the initial value, which assumes a previous history of the system, with an asymptotic behavior. But it is very easy to compute because of the simple structure of the step function. The distinction between the computation of $t(M_i)$ and the determination of the threshold r is a further advantage of the above system over the single counting of $t(M_i)$.

The Problem of the Disjunctive Co-signification

A limitation of the defined recognizing algorithm is the necessary condition for the similarity of two patterns, that they have a common part, i.e., a nonempty topological intersection. This condition is necessary at the filter level, because of the former explained monovalency of the kernel k_p of the pattern. If we will assume the permissibility of more than one kernel over one single filter, and each two kernels k_p and k_p' accomplishes

$$k_p \cap k_p' = 0 \tag{5}$$

then we will obtain two or more disjunctive filter masks for scanning. By n disjunctive kernels over one filter, we will have a $n + 1$-valued decision, one supplementary decision for the case of a "nonrecognizable pattern." This will imply that the filter must be constructed with at last n-valued basic cells, one value for each possible kernel.

The number m of necessary flip-flops for realizing technically the desired basic cells, will be

$$m = [\log_2 n]$$

only if the condition, Eq. (5), is rigorously accomplished. But if there are exceptions, we must accept the expensive solution

$$m = n$$

The expression

$$a = [b]$$

implies: a equal to the lowest integer containing b. A way for solving this problem consists in the consideration of each disjunctive kernel of the same pattern as a different pattern at the filter level. For n disjunctive patterns we will have n different filters. Since each filter gives a 2-valued decision, the n filters will give a $2n$-valued one. The inequation

$$N = R \sum_{i=1}^{m} n_i \leqslant Rm \left[\log_2 (n_i \max + 1)\right] = M \qquad (6)$$

must be accomplished to assure, that the solution with one filter for each disjunctive kernel of the same pattern is not more expensive than the single filter with $n + 1$-valued basic cells for each pattern; N and M being the sum of bits over the complete filter set for each of the two solutions. R will be the number of bits of one filter. If

$$\bar{n} = \left[\left(\sum_{i=1}^{m} n_i \right)/m \right]$$

is the integer average value of n_i, then inequality, Eq. (6) implies

$$\bar{n} \leqslant [\log_2 (n_i \max + 1)]$$

and, with certain restrictions

$$2^{\bar{n}} - 1 \leqslant n_i \max (\bar{n} = 1, 2, 3, \ldots)$$

The higher $\bar{n}$, the lower obviously the probability that the inequality of Eq. (6) will be accomplished. The above discussion is realized under the assumption that the number R of bits of each filter is the same as in the S-field, as a condition for comparing them.

The discussion allows to give a criterion for deciding between one $n + 1$-valued filter for each pattern and n bivalued filter for each disjunctive kernel of the pattern. A simple means of programming may introduce in the last case the possibility of disjunctive mapping of the different filters over one common output channel. The operator may then define the similarity of two arbitrary different signal classes with no common characteristics by means of reinforcement.

The Problem of Partial Punishing

There are two forms of punishing for reinforcement. The trivial one consists on the total punishing of a class of learned patterns, which are the only ones registered in one filter. It is solved by repeated diminishing of the respective $t(M_i)$. The other case consists in the punishing only of one subclass or one single pattern of the class belonging to one filter, but conserving on the filter the rest of the registered patterns. We will then call it the partial punishing case.

The problem in this case is equivalent to the following set theoretical:

PROBLEM 1: Given the union and the intersection of an overset of point sets, and given one single point set or subset of the overset, determine the union and the intersection of the rest of the overset.

It is possible to prove that this problem has no general solution. The proof is based on the constructive properties of the set theoretical union and intersection. These properties are of a combinatorial nature related to the construction pathways, by successive building of the union and the intersection of pairs of sets; the intermediately formed union and intersection sets being considered also as sets.

This procedure is reversible only under the condition that all the original sets are available for a successive reconstruction of the desired rest overset. A construction pathway is uniquely determined by a given permutation of the rest overset, representing the formation steps of the desired union and intersection. Given such a permutation, the union and intersection of the overset are also uniquely determined. But the inverse proposition is not true: thus given the intersection and the union of an overset, the power of the set of possible point sets that generates this intersection and union, is a combinatorial function of the power of the intersection and the union itself.

For our practical purpose, it is equivalent with the following

PROPOSITION 2. Given a filter consisting of the union set $(D + k_p)$ and the intersection set k_p of a set of similar (co-significative) patterns, the set of patterns is not uniquely determined. The number of possible sets of patterns capable of generating the given filter is calculable by combinatorial means as a function of the number of bits of both, $D + k_p$ and k_p. If d is the number of bits of D then there are 2^d different possible patterns; 2^{d-1} different pairs of complementary patterns generating D; and

$$\sum_{n=1}^{d} (2^{d-1} + 2^{d-2} + \cdots + 2^{d-n})$$

n-tuples of n-adic complementary patterns generating D. In other words: given a filter we cannot reconstruct its formation history. Consequently we cannot assure that there was no p_1 under the forming patterns which contained completely the pattern q, the only one that we will punish. Then we cannot correct the union set $D + k_p$. Also we cannot prove that there was no pattern p_2 contained completely in the pattern q that we will punish. Thus we cannot correct the intersection set (kernel) k_p. (see Fig. 4) We see then, that the exposed problem may have many common points with the problem of the co-contained patterns as discussed above.

THE KERNEL RESTORING ALGORITHM FOR PARTIAL PUNISHING

A statistical approximation to the solution of the partial punishing problem for the union set is given by construction of the difference set $q - k_p$ between the punished pattern q and the kernel k_p; further by adding this difference to the complement $\overline{D + k_p}$ of the union set; and then by repetition of the learning stage for the pattern class P, q being excluded from Fig. 5 gives an example of construction of the set

$$\overline{D + k_p} + q - k_p \tag{7}$$

The discussion of the partial punishing problem shows that the construction of new union and intersection sets giving only the punished pattern, is not possible. Then the new union and intersection would be constructed by repetition of the full learning process, after erasing the former union and intersection on the filter. We would then start again from the initial point.

An alternative is given by starting from an advanced point of the learning way that accomplishes the following conditions:

1. At this point the union set does not contain completely the punished pattern q and will then reject it.
2. The union set must contain at least the intersection k_p, and will then recognize at least one part of the patterns $p_i \, \epsilon \, P$.

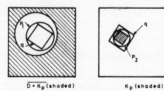

D + K$_p$ (shaded)   K$_p$ (shaded)

Figure 4

D + K$_p$ + q - K$_p$

Figure 5

Condition (1) is accomplished by subtracting q from $D + k_p$ and condition (2) by adding $k_p \, \epsilon \, q$ to the difference

$$(D + k_p) - q \tag{8}$$

Since

$$q \cap D = q - k_p \neq q$$

the difference

$$D - q$$

has in our case no sense algebraically, and Eqs. (7) and (8) are not associative.

Then the further relearned process will act not over the complete filter, but only over the set $q - k_p$. If the correction c introduced in this set by relearning is not equal to the set itself, the reject condition for q is accomplished, and also the partial punishing as desired. Similarly we can correct the intersection set k_p by adding to it the set $q - k_p$. This implies the substitution of the kernel k_p by a new kernel $k_p' = q$, for further statistical reduction of $q - k_p$ by relearning. With n different patterns of the class B, one bit of k_p symbolizes n bits, one for each pattern. With m bits of the set D, each of them symbolizes as a mean value $\bar{n}$ different patterns. We define $\bar{n}$ as

$$\bar{n} = \frac{\sum_{i=1}^{n-1} \overline{V}_i (n - i)}{m} = \frac{\sum_{i=1}^{n-1} \overline{V}_i (n - i)}{\sum_{i=1}^{n-1} \overline{V}_i} < n \tag{9}$$

V_i being the respective number of bits of D, symbolizing $n - i$ different patterns simultaneously.

Thus the correction of one single bit of k_p implies a greater loss of learned information than the correction of one single bit of D. Since by correcting D for the union set and k_p for the intersection, the same set $q - k_p$ is added, the total amount of loss of learned information is greater by the second correction procedure than by the first one. This may imply that eventually the correction of D only is more advantageous than both corrections because of the lower loss of information by partial punishing.

THE NEIGHBOR CONDITION FOR SET RESTORING

If we are concerned only with connected patterns (as numbers or letters, except i and j) whose sizes are smaller than those of the S-field, we can also study the particular case that the punished pattern q is topologically a neighbor either of the intersection k_p or of the complementary union $\overline{D + k_p}$.

This implies that the pattern q is connected with k_p or with $\overline{D + k_p}$ respectively. Only in this case we can assume that the pattern q itself has possibly reduced the size of k_p or of $D + k_p$ during the learning stage (see Fig. 6).

Given two not necessarily unparallel limit axes for area growth of the intersection set k_p and the complementary union set $D + k_p$, we can promote the reincreasing of both sets to a greater size than the original. By relearning, the newly added excess area will disappear partially and will then be approximated to the desired value. It may be meaningful to apply before relearning the kernel restoring procedure as above explained, since after growing the union and intersection sets are automatically out of the neighbor condition case.

THE CLASSIFICATION PROBLEM FOR NONRECOGNIZABLE PATTERNS

In the preceding sections we have assumed that there are for each UDAR not only a set $\{P_i\}$ of recognizable classes P_i of patterns but also a non-empty class P_o of not recognizable—i.e., meaningless—patterns. $\{P_i\} + P_o$ will be then the set of all 2^n possible patterns representable on a S-field of n binary valued elements. But in certain cases P_o may be divided in certain characteristic subclasses. Some of such subclasses P_{oi} consisting of only one pattern, may have a great similarity with at least two recognizable pattern classes P_i and P_j. Our classification problem consists in finding a procedure to discriminate, if P_{oi} belongs to P_o, or not, and if not, to what P_i it belongs. Certain approaches are well known. If the probability of noise by the input devices of the patterns is not negligibly small we can assume that the pattern P_{oi} is really not a P_o but either a P_i or a P_j. A measure

$$d = \frac{d(P_i) - d(P_j)}{2}$$

can be introduced in the sense of Hamming distance and the condition

$$\left| d(P_{oi}) - d(P_i) \right| \leqslant d$$

may decide that the similarity with class P_i is greater than the similarity with class P_j.

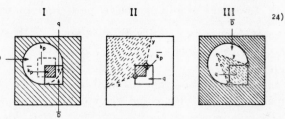

Figure 6

If we define

$$d = \max \frac{d(P_i) - d(P_j)}{2} \tag{10}$$

for all the pairs i and j $(i \neq j)$ of $\{P_i\}$, then d is a threshold value of the UDAR. We can then compute the correlations between the pattern P_{oi} and each of the patterns of $\{P_i\}$. This will imply that we have to correlate for each P_i with the respective value variations of Eq. (9):

$$f(V_i, i) = \frac{\sum_{i=1}^{n-1} V_i(n - i)}{\sum_{i=1}^{n-1} V_i} = 0 \tag{11}$$

$$1 \leqslant f(V_i, i) \leqslant n \tag{12}$$

$$f(V_i, i) = n \tag{13}$$

If g is the internal sum of V_i (as shown above) divided by the number n of V_i's, i.e.,

$$g = \sum_{j=1}^{n} \frac{(x_{ij} \cdot V_j)}{n}$$

then g_0 may be the partial internal sum over the variables of case (11), g_1 of Eq. (12) and g_n of Eq. (13). In principle we will have

$$\begin{aligned} g_0 &= 0 \\ 0 \leqslant g_1 &\leqslant 1 \\ g_n &= 1 \end{aligned} \tag{14}$$

But we can accept certain tolerances in these values because of the input noise assumption. The degree of tolerance given by a value over a certain measure space is another threshold of the system.

Certain forms of adaptivity promote learning by varying this last threshold. Generally they subdivide the sets defined by the filter in basic blocks (for example, associative elements) each one having its own tolerance threshold. This is very practical if all the associative elements (A-elements) process in parallel the pattern information. By using an universal digital computer, parallel work of many hundred A-elements is excluded. Further, the computing time will be increased considerably by numerical simulation of a majority (threshold) decision. The methods developed until now for threshold-dependent pattern recognition were not oriented for application in digital computers as a part of the computer software. The efforts were concentrated on the problem of recognizing "Gestalts," i.e., spatial patterns, shapes or features characterized only by their topological properties and generally independent from size, position or orientation on the display (generally a 2-dimensional) field.

From the point of view of our scheme in Fig. 1, the solution of the problem of Gestalt recognition must be searched at the level of the transducer. Certain approaches to this problem allow to support this assumption (Buell, 1961; Stevens, 1961). But the Gestalt recognition is concerned with optical patterns exclusively. Nonoptical patterns have no need of spatial dependent invariance recognition. An effective UDAR will then be independent of the specific invariance problems of a certain physical kind of patterns. It will concentrate its capabilities on the activity of inductive logical inference, as a more general cogniscibility problem than the spatial invariance detection, and will then be free of the handicap of confusion between the logical inference problem and the problem of the invariance related to specific spatial transformations.

Nevertheless, the approach intended in this work, is dependent from the specifical spatial properties of the S-field. But the invariance detection method is very simplified because it is only oriented to the logical inference activity.

We have said that the classification problem for nonrecognizable patterns is related with the existence of a threshold in the system. Then, the classification problem must be also solved in dependency of the specific properties of the S-field, as in the invariance detection. The solution must take into account the serial processing mode of the digital computers and the need for reducing arithmetic computation to save time.

For our purposes, a convenient solution is possible by extension of the abilities of a digital computer, allowing it to realize majority decisions over a connected set of bit sets of the accumulator. One example is given in the switching diagram of Fig. 7. This example accomplishes a majority decision over 36 bits in 3 microprogram steps. By varying the threshold of the majority decision elements (MD-elements) we introduce a degree of freedom in the system. The MD will be performed over the 36-bit pattern resulting from building either the intersection or the logical identity (negated exclusive or) between a 36-bit group of the filter and the correspondent bit group of the S-field. The trivial case is given when the MD-elements have a threshold equal to 6. A separate register may count the number of 36-bit groups that exceed the threshold. The obtained number will imply a correlation coefficient between the pattern read and the respective filter. If the maximal coefficient is greater than $\bar{d}$, the pattern

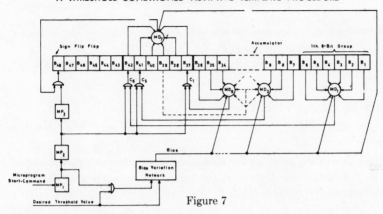

Figure 7

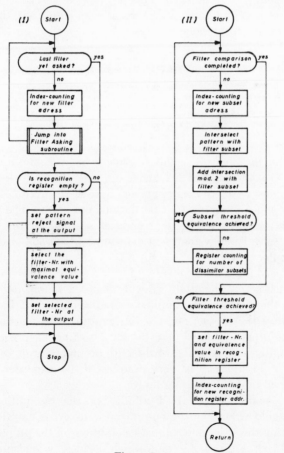

Figure 8

will become recognizable and identical to the filter mask with the maximal coefficient. The proposed network for MD allows also to realize other logical operations, like conjunction, disjunction, mask building, asking for zero, etc.

FURTHER PRACTICAL CONCLUSIONS

We can now state precisely certain consequences of the above considerations.

(a) We need an algorithm for establishing whether or not the kernel k_p is completely contained in the pattern displayed over the S-field. With arbitrary sets of bits this can be proven easily by a successive realization of a bit-wise conjunction (i.e., logical intersection) between p and mask m and a bit-wise "exclusive-or" between intersection and mask. If the result is an empty set, the implication is proven. In symbolic notation:

$$p \supset m \leftrightarrow (p \cap m) \oplus m = 0 \qquad (15.1)$$
$$\leftrightarrow \overline{(p \cap m)} \oplus m = 1 \qquad (15.2)$$
$$\leftrightarrow (p \cap m) \overline{\oplus} m = 1 \qquad (15.3)$$
$$\leftrightarrow \overline{(p \cap m)} \overline{\oplus} m = 0 \qquad (15.4)$$

In this formulae $\oplus$ is the "exclusive-or" (i.e., addition modulo 2) and $\overline{\oplus}$ is the negated "exclusive-or" (i.e., the equivalence). Further, 1 implies that the correspondent part of the accumulator contains only one's; 0 implies that it contains only zeros. The programming facilities of the respective computer selected for the realization of the recognizing system, will determine which one of the four given formulae will be selected, since they are all equivalent.

(b) We need a partition in subsets of the set of bits composing a filter in such a way that the retrieval of such a subset and his transport into the accumulator implies no redistribution of the internal bit order of the subset; i.e., the retrieval must be only a transport of an information word but no data sorting or processing. For a computer with a single word-length accumulator of 48 bits a subset size of 36 bits may be very practical if the computer is not purely decimal in its internal structure.

To permit a certain flexibility of the recognition process, a threshold value like the one introduced earlier may be defined for limiting the strict deterministic conditions of the propositions (15.1) to (15.4). A threshold value which decides by inaccuracies of more then 10 percent has no practical application. A maximal error of

5 percent may be meaningful. This will imply a 1-bit difference in 20, i.e., a negated threshold of value 1, for 20 inputs being equivalent to each other. As an example the proposed network of Fig. 7 will identify a threshold of 1 to 36, 1 to 18 or 1 to 12, depending upon that the threshold of the MD-element of the 7th bit-group is 1, 2 or 3; provided that the majority decision is realized not over the L-outputs but over the 0-outputs of the flip-flops of this bit-group. In this sense a technological limit for MD-elements must remain in order to achieve reliability. Six or eight inputs for a MD-element and the respective threshold interval are possible. Then the bit-groups can not be greater. The number of bit-groups will be subject to the same limitations. Because of the advantages of octal representation of binary numbers it can be more interesting to operate with bit-groups of 6 or 9 bits than with groups of 8 bits.

The size of a filter-subset will be generally the square of the size of a single bit-group and a size of a filter will be a multiple of the size of a single subset. Though the size of the S-field of a UDAR will be not only a function of the type of pattern to be recognized but also of the internal organization of the selected computer.

(c) We need a register to count the total number of subsets which do not accomplish the threshold condition in a given filter. This number will be the equivalence value.

(d) After the learning stage of the system we have to compute the two above mentioned thresholds. Particularly we can consider each filter as a pattern itself and determine for each one the two other filters having the greater similarity with it. The number of not common bits, divided by two, will determine a local distance between each of two very similar filters. By letters, e.g., we can determine that the two more similar letters for "E" are "L" and "F." The filter of "E" will then have two registers, each for one similar pattern indicating his name and the not-common bit-number, divided by two. If a given pattern shows the same equivalence values for two different filters, the numerical relation to the not-common bit-set of the two filters may provide a supplementary criterion for recognitive decision.

(e) We need an index-register for address modification of the filters, another for address modification of the subsets belonging to one single filter and a third for address modification into that recognition register where those filters are listed which have recognized a certain pattern.

The above conclusions permit the design of the flow-diagram for the recognition process of a pattern as shown in Fig. 8.

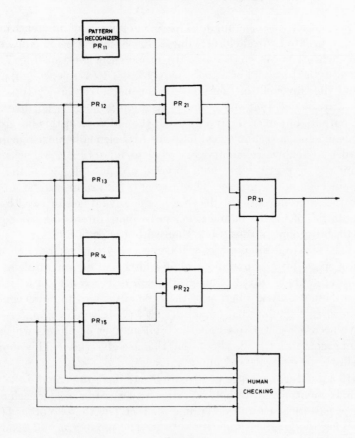

Figure 9

PART III
CONVERGENCE PROCEDURES

Free Convergence Behavior

Take a pattern A_0 whose filter is generated by the subset

$$g(A_0) = \left\{ a_i \right\}_{i=1}^{n} = a_1, a_2, a_3, \ldots a_i, \ldots a_n \tag{16}$$

of all the variations a_i of A_0. The conditions

$$a_i \neq a_j \longleftrightarrow i \neq j; \quad n > 1 \tag{17}$$

are necessary and sufficient to accomplish

$$\bigcup_{i=1}^{n} a_i = \bigcap_{i=1}^{n} a_i \tag{18}$$

Let us now define

$$\overline{D}_0 = \bigcup_{i=1}^{n} a_i - \bigcap_{i=1}^{n} a_i$$

It is easy to prove that $\bar{D}_0$ is also of the form

$$\overline{D}_0 = \bigcup_{i=1}^{n} \bigcup_{j=1}^{n} (a_i - a_j) = \bigcup_{i=1}^{n} (a_i - \bigcap_{i=1}^{n} a_j)$$

but A_0 itself is a class consisting of the patterns

$$A_0 = \left\{ a_i \right\}_{i=1}^{2^{D_0}} = \left\{ a_i \right\}_{i=1}^{n} + \left\{ a_i \right\}_{i=1+n}^{2^{D_o}} = g(A_0) + P_0 \tag{19}$$

where D_0 = order of $\bar{D}_0$, given in a certain metric (e.g., the number of bits involved), such that $2^{D_0} = 0(A_0) =$ order of A_0. In other words, A_0 is able to recognize by construction not only the learned $g(A_0)$ but also the unlearned set P_0.

A certain threshold value may be introduced to bound 2^{D_0} as a function of $n = 0 \ (g(A_0))$ in the form

$$n.k \geqslant 2^{D_0}$$

The decision to take either $k \geqslant 1$ or $1 > k > 0$ may depend on some considerations related with the class of patterns we like to analyze. We have now in fact a certain extrapolation capability of A_0, as this filter is able to recognize the pattern variations of the unlearned subset

$$\text{subset } P_0 = \left\{ a_i \right\}_{i=n+1}^{2^{D_0}}.$$

This ability is interesting because it implies the distribution of a nonarbitrary likelihood among the set of the nonlearned patterns. We have then a certain pre-classification of the set of nonexplicitly classified, i.e., nonperceived patterns. Even this is also a danger, since some patterns could be classified in P_0 although they belong to a class of patterns other than A_0. Thus, a procedure to restrict the set P_0 may be desirable.

Since the reconstruction of $g(A_0)$ for a given A_0 is impossible (see Part II, The Problem of Partial Punishing), it is also impossible to construct P_0 itself, as P_0 is the complement of $g(A_0)$ in A_0. On the other hand, it is possible to restrict A_0 by constructing an $A_1 \subset A_0$, such that

$$A_1 = \left\{ a_i \right\}_{i=\beta_{1,1}}^{\beta_{n(1),1}} + P_1$$

is generated by an arbitrarily chosen subset $g(A_1)$

$$= \left\{ a_i \right\}_{i=\beta_{1,1}}^{\beta_{n(1),1}}$$

of A_0 with $0(g(A_1)) = n(1) \leqslant n$. For a subset A_j we will substitute $i = 1$, $2, \ldots, n$ by the index series $i = \beta_{1,j}, \beta_{2,j}, \ldots \beta_{n-1(j),j}, \beta_{n(j),j}$. Iterating the procedure, we will get a sequence of subsets of A_0 forming a *convergence chain*

$$\overline{A}_{m,h} : A_0 \supseteq A_1 \supseteq A_2 \ldots \supseteq A_m = a_k \tag{20}$$

where a_k is a single element of A_0 and where

$$A_j = \left\{ a_i \right\}_{i=\beta_{1,1}}^{\beta_{n(j),i}} + P_j$$
$$A_m = a_k; \qquad P_m = \varphi; \qquad \beta_{n(m),m} = \beta_{1,m} = k \tag{21}$$

Proposition 3:

The order m of any convergence chain for $D_0 > 1$ is

$$0(A_{m,h}) = m < n = 0(A_0)$$

The proof uses the condition in Eq. (17). This implies that there are at least two elements $a_i, a_j \epsilon A_0$ with $i \neq j$ such that

$$(\overline{D}_0 \cap a_i) \cap (\overline{D}_0 \cap a_j) = \varphi; \qquad a_i \neq \overline{D}_0 \neq a_j \tag{22}$$

for $D_0 > 1$. This is true because a given chain cannot contain both a_i and a_j with the property $A_m = a_i; A_{m+r} = a_j$ unless $a_i \supseteq a_j$, but this last condition is in contradiction to the condition in Eq. (22). So, $m \neq n$ and $m < n$ (QED).

The set $|A| = \{A_{m,h}\}$ has an homomorphic mapping over A_0, i.e., a chain determines one and only one element of A_0 by mapping; while

$0(|A|) > 0(A_0)$, since $|A|$ is a set of lattices of A_0 elements. We call the explained procedure *free convergence* of $A_0 \rightarrow a_k \epsilon A_0$.

The velocity of convergence will in such a case be an inverse function of the orders of the successively generated subsets A_i and of the probability that the event

$$A_i = A_{i-1} \tag{23}$$

will occur. Convergence behavior can then be studied as a function of the distribution of the event [Eq. (23)] and of the orders $0(A_i)$ over the chain. In this sense it is meaningful to the distribution over the chain, of the ratios

$$r = \frac{0(A_i)}{0(A_{i-1})} \leqslant 1$$

of pairs of successive chain elements, where $r = 1$ implies no convergence.

Non-Free Convergence Behavior

It is possible to introduce some restrictions in the convergence procedure to get special properties of convergence. Let set $g(A_1)$ not be a random set, but a set of elements $a_i \epsilon A_0$ which was tested after the learning stage of the automaton and found to be correct. So, the set $g(A_1)$ contains supplementary information; these elements were not only learned but also confirmed. We can provide a procedure of convergence which takes advantage of such a kind of generator subset. It is possible to generate with a given $g(A_1)$, instead of A_1 itself, a subset $h(A_1) \subseteq A_0$ such that for a given metric and a threshold π, the difference between an element of $h(A_1)$ and an element of the generator will be less than the threshold in this metric. In other words, we will have an homomorphismus h of $h(A_1)$ *into* $g(A_1)$ such that $a_i - \Theta \subseteq ha_{j,i} \subseteq a_i + \Theta$ for $a_i \epsilon g(A_1)$ and $ha_{j,i} \epsilon h(A_1)$. So, if A_1 is now the subset of A_0 generatred by $h(A_1)$ we have instead of Eqs. (21) and (19) an element of the form

$$A_1 = \left\{ a_i \right\}_{i=1}^{n} + \theta \left\{ a_i \right\}_{i=n+1}^{s} + \left\{ a_i \right\}_{s+1}^{2D_0}$$

$$= \left\{ a_i \right\}_{i=1}^{n} \theta_s + \left\{ a_i \right\}_{s+1}^{2D_0}$$

$$= g(A_i)\} \; \theta_s + P_1 = h(A_1) + P_1 \tag{24}$$

It is obvious that $g(A_1)$ may be only of order 1, i.e., it may consist just of the single pattern $a_k \epsilon A_0$. Using the above notation Equation (24) could, in such a case, be written in the form

$$A_1 = a_k \} \theta + P_1$$

The chain of the convergence $A_0 \to a_k$ is itself not interesting in this case, but some subchains converging to a subset $A_m \supset a_k \neq A_m$ may be generated varying the threshold θ. This will affect the order s of $h(A_1)$ since s is a direct function of θ under the condition

$$\left\{ a_i \right\}_{i=1}^{n} \cap \left\{ a_i \right\}_{i=n+1}^{s} = \phi$$

which implies $\theta > 1$, and has the advantage of avoiding ambiguities. This special variant of the general procedure will be called *positive convergence*, and is equivalent to the reward methods of reinforement by learning.

An equivalent of the punishing methods is also possible. Let

$$g(A_1) = \left\{ a_i \right\}_{i=1}^{n}$$

be a set of patterns $a_i \epsilon A_0$, proved at the testing stage to be incorrect. It would be interesting to "erase" $g(A_1)$ from A_0. Thus we can now apply the kernel restoring algorithm (see Part II) for partial punishing.

Defining

$$A_1 = A_0 - g(A_1)$$

we can apply either free or positive convergence to the subset $A_1 \subseteq A_0$. In the first case we will speak about *negative convergence* and in the second about *negative threshold convergence*. Equations (24) will now have the form

$$A_1 = \left\{ a_i \epsilon g(A_1) \right\}_{i=1}^{t} + \theta \left\{ a_i \right\}_{i=t+1}^{s} + \left\{ a_i \right\}_{i=s+1}^{2^{D_0}}$$

$$= \left(\left\{ a_i \right\}_{i=1}^{t} - \left\{ a_i \right\}_{i=1}^{n} \right) + \theta \left\{ a_i \right\}_{i=t+1}^{s} + \left\{ a_i \right\}_{i=s+1}^{2^{D_0}}$$

$$= \left(\left\{ a_i \right\}_{i=1}^{t} - \left\{ a_i \right\}_{i=1}^{n} \right) \} \theta_s + \left\{ a_i \right\}_{i=s+1}^{2^{D_0}}$$

$$= (g(A^t) - g(A_1)) \} \theta_s + P_1 = h^t(A_1) + P_1$$

where $g(A') - g(A_1)$ will have only positive values or none, and where $g(A')$ will be such a subset of A_0, that

$$g(A') \cap g(A_1) \neq g(A')$$

REFERENCES

1. Stevens, M. E., "Abstract Shape Recognition by Machine," Proc. Eastern Joint Computer Conference, 1961.
2. Bell, D. N., "Chrysler Optical Processing Scanner," Proc. Eastern Joint Computer Conference, 1961.
3. Steinbuch, K., "Automat and Mensch," Springer-Verlag, Berlin, Germany, 1961.
4. ———, "Lernende Automaten," in *Kybernetik*, vol. 1, no. 1, Springer-Verlag, Berlin, Germany, 1961.
5. Rosenblatt, F.; "Principles of Nevrodynamics," Report No. 1196-G-8, March, 1961, Cornell, Aeronautical Laboratory, Buffalo, N.Y.

12

PATTERN-RECOGNIZING CONTROL SYSTEMS

BERNARD WIDROW AND FRED W. SMITH

Stanford University, Stanford, Calif.

INTRODUCTION

For the past several years the properties and applications of adaptive threshold-logic elements and means of physical realization of these elements have been under study at Stanford University. It is the purpose of this paper to present an up-to-date summary of this work, and in particular, to show how adaptive logic networks have been used in an automatic control system.

ADALINE, AN ADAPTIVE LOGIC ELEMENT

A basic building block of the systems to be considered is an adaptive threshold element, sometimes called an adaptive "neuron." For the past several years, we at Stanford University have called this element Adaline (adaptive linear neuron). A functional diagram of this element is shown in Fig. 1. It includes an adjustable threshold element and the adaptation machinery which automatically adjusts the variable weights. It has been demonstrated experimentally and theoretically that this element can be trained to react specifically to a wide variety of binary input signals and that it can be trained to generalize in certain ways, i.e., to react as desired with high reliability to inputs that it has not been specifically trained on.

In Fig. 1 the binary input signals on the input lines have values of $+1$ or -1 rather than the usual values of 1 or 0. Within the neuron shown, a linear combination of the input signals is formed. The weights are the gains $w_1, w_2, \ldots$, which could have both positive and negative values. The output signal is $+1$ if this weighted sum is greater than a certain threshold, and -1 otherwise. The threshold level is determined by the setting of w_0, whose input is permanently connected to a $+1$ sorce. Varying w_0 varies a constant added to the linear combination of input signals.

For fixed gain settings, each of the 2^n possible input combinations would cause either a $+1$ or a -1 output. Thus, all possible inputs are classified into two categories. The input-output relationship is determined by choice of the gains $w_0, \ldots, w_n$. In the adaptive neuron, these gains are set during the training procedure.

In general, there are 2^{2^n} different input-output relationships or truth functions by which the n input variables can be mapped into the single output variable. Only a subset of these, the linearly separable logic functions, can be realized by all possible choices of the gains. Although this subset is not all inclusive, it is a useful subset, and it is "searchable," i.e., the "best" function in many practical cases can be found iteratively without trying all functions within the subset. An iterative search procedure has been devised and is described below. This procedure is quite simple to implement, and can be analyzed by statistical methods that were originally developed for the analysis of adaptive sampled-data systems.[1]

An adaptive pattern classification machine has been constructed for the purpose of illustrating adaptive behavior and artificial learning. A photograph of this machine, which is an adjustable threshold element (called "KNOBBY ADALINE"), is shown in Fig. 2.

During a training phase, simple geometric patterns are fed to the machine by setting the toggle switches in the 4×4 input switch array. All

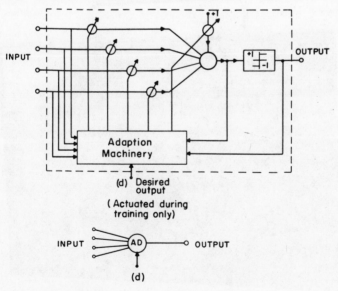

ADALINE (Adaptive Linear " neuron ")

Figure 1

gains, including the threshold level, are to be changed by the same absolute magnitude such that the analog error (the difference between the desired meter reading and the actual meter reading) is brought to zero. This is accomplished by changing each gain in the direction which will diminish the error by $\frac{1}{17}$. The 17 gains may be changed in any sequence, and after all changes are made, the error for the present input pattern is zero. The weights associated with switches up ($+1$ input signals) are incremented by rotation in the same direction as the desired meter needle rotation, the weights connected to switches in the down position are incremented opposite to the desired direction of rotation of the meter needle. The next pattern and its desired output is then presented, and the error is read. The same adjustment routine is followed and the error is brought to zero. If the first pattern were reapplied at this point, the error would be small but not necessarily zero. More patterns are inserted in like manner. Convergence is indicated by small errors (before adaption), with small fluctuations about stable weights. A least-mean-square adaption procedure (LMS) requires that adaption be made even if the quantized neuron output is correct. If, for example, the desired response is $+1$, the neuron is adapted to bring the analog response closer to the desired response, even if the analog response is more positive than $+1$.

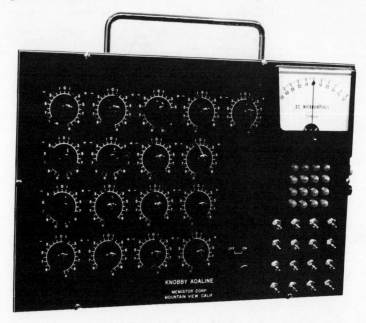

Figure 2

The iterative training routine is purely mechanical. Electronic automation of this procedure will be discussed below.

The results of a typical adaption on six noiseless patterns is given in Fig. 3. During adaption, the patterns were selected in a random sequence, and were classified into 3 categories. Each T was to be mapped to $+30$ on the meter dial, each G to 0, and each F to -30. As a measure of performance, after each adaptation, all six patterns were read in (without adaptation) and six analog errors were read. The sum of their squares denoted by Σe^2 was computed and plotted. Figure 3 shows the learning curve for the case in which all gains were initially zero.

It is shown in Ref. 2 and 3 that making full correction with each adaption using the LMS procedure is in effect a stable "performance feedback" process having an adaptive time constant equal to the number of weights. In the experiment of Fig. 3, the time constant is 17 adaptions. It is also shown that changing each weight by the same magnitude in the appropriate

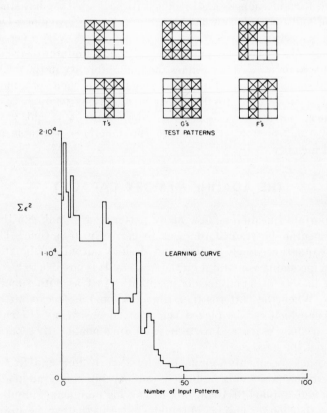

Figure 3

directions is equivalent to utilization of the method of steepest descent on a mean square error surface. A number of other steepest descent adaption procedures have been devised by W. C. Ridgway III[4] and C. H. Mays.[5][6] These proceedures have been analyzed by Mays with regard to proofs of converoence and bounds on the number of adaptions required for convergence. The decision to adapt may be based on one of the following rules: adapt only if the response is incorrect; or adapt only if the response is incorrect or within a "dead zone." If the decision to adapt is made, then the increment size might be fixed or might be proportional to the analog error, the difference between the analog sum and the desired output. These procedures are described in detail in Mays' Ph.D. thesis, along with bounds on the number of adaptions needed for convergence.

The effects of adaptive feedback in Adaline networks on their ability to self-heal by adapting around internal defects are analogous to the effects of feedback in amplifiers and control systems in making system performances insensitive to gain changes and nonlinearities. P. R. Low has studied by simulation and by analysis what he calls "defective" Adalines. One such Adaline has a set of weights whose integration speeds vary over a 5-to-1 ratio. These speeds are randomly selected from a uniform distribution of speeds. It was found that sometimes the nonuniformity in the adapt rates hinder and sometimes help, but on the average, this wide variation among the speeds increases the total number of adaptions required to achieve convergence, but by only 5 percent. The resultant weight values are essentially unaffected by this, as are the functions realizable and the statistical memory capacity.

THE ADALINE MEMORY CAPACITY

An important question is, how many patterns or stimuli can the single adaptive neuron be trained to react to correctly at a time? This is a statistical question. Each pattern and desired output combination represents an inequality constraint on the weights. It is possible to have inconsistencies in sets of simultaneous inequalities just as with simultaneous equalities. When the patterns (i.e., the equations) are picked at random, the number which can be picked before an inconsistency is created is a random variable. As few as 4 patterns can form a nonlinearly separable set, regardless of the pattern size.

A series of experiments was devised by J. S. Koford and R. J. Brown where patterns containing unbiased random bits and random desired responses were applied to Adalines with varying numbers of inputs. It was found that the average number of random patterns that can be absorbed by an Adaline is equal to twice the number of weights. This is one basic meas-

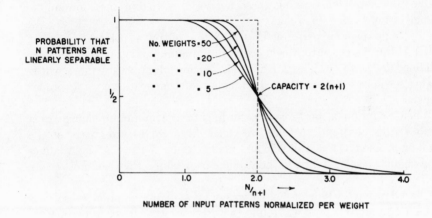

Figure 4

ure of memory capacity. It was recently proven by Brown that this experimental result is rigorously correct. Analytical curves showing the probability of being able to train-in N patterns as a function of $N/(n + 1)$ are presented in Fig. 4. Notice the sharpening of the break point of these curves at exactly the average capacity as the number of inputs to the Adaline increases.

Derivation of the capacity formula and of the curves in Fig. 4 will be presented in a Ph.D. thesis by Brown.

MADALINE, A PARALLEL NETWORK OF ADALINES

Storage capacity in excess of that of a single Adaline can be readily achieved by use of parallel multi-Adaline networks. Several Adalines can be used to assist each other in solving problems by automatic load-sharing.

The configuration in Fig. 5 shows a Madaline (multiple Adalines) of 5 Adalines with parallel-connected inputs in the first layer. In the second layer of fixed logic the Adaline outputs are connected to a majority-rule element whose output is the system output. The "job assigner," a purely mechanical device, automatically decides which Adalines if any need adaption. There are a variety of fixed-logic schemes that could be used on the second layer. M. E. Hoff, Jr., in his doctoral thesis,[7] described convergent adaption procedures that can be used with all possible fixed-logic second layers.

One procedure for training these networks is to use the "minimum-change" rule. Under this rule:

(*i*) No adaption is performed if the system output is correct.

(*ii*) If the system output is in error, a minimum number of the incorrect Adalines are adapted. The Adalines chosen for adaption are those whose analog responses require the least amount of change to give the proper response.

When adaption is performed according to the minimum-change rule, various Adalines tend to take "responsibility" for certain parts of the training problem. Thus, this rule produces load sharing among the Adalines by assigning responsibility to the Adaline or Adalines that can most easily assume it.

The adaptive system of Fig. 5 was suggested by common sense, was tested by simulation, and was found to work very well. It was subsequently proven by Ridgway in his doctoral thesis that this system will converge on a solution if a set of weights exists that will solve the training problem. The essence of the proof lies in showing that the probability of a given Adaline taking responsibility for adaption to a given pattern, desired-response pair is greatest if that Adaline had taken such responsibility during the previous adapt cycle in which the pattern was presented. The division of responsibility stabilizes at the same time that the responses of the individual Adalines to their share of the load stabilizes. In the case that the training problem is not perfectly separable by this system, it can be shown that the adaptation process tends to minimize error probability.

The memory capacities of Madaline structures utilizing both the majority element and the OR element have been measured by Koford. Although the logic functions that can be realized with these output elements are different, both types of elements yield structures with the same statistical storage capacity. The average number of patterns that a Madaline can be adapted to equals the capacity per Adaline multiplied by the number of Adalines. The memory capacity is therefore equal to twice the number of weights.

GENERALIZATION EXPERIMENTS WITH ADALINES AND SIMPLE NETWORKS OF ADALINES

With suitable pattern-response examples and the proper training procedures, generalizations can be trained into Adalines. The kinds of generalizations to be considered here are concerned with the training of Adalines to be statistically insensitive to noise, and to be sensitive or insensitive to translation, rotation, and size. Adalines can be forced to react consistently to a training set of patterns for all possible positions, for example, and then they will react consistently in all positions with high reliability on new patterns.

GENERALIZATION WITH RESPECT TO NOISE

Statistical separation of patterns consisting of a finite set of basic "prototypes" and noisy versions of these basic patterns can be readily accomplished by the single Adaline after training on the basic patterns and/or samples of the noisy patterns. A new pattern would be associated with one of the prototype classes by proximity in a Hamming distance sense.

With the objective of minimizing the probability of incorrect classification, there is an optimum set of weights that would result from training on a

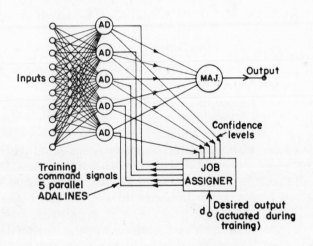

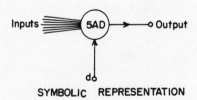

SYMBOLIC   REPRESENTATION

Figure 5

very large sample. The effect of training on a small sample set can be summarized with the following formula, derived in Ref. 2 and 3.

$$M = \frac{(n + 1)}{N} \tag{1}$$

The number of training samples is N, randomly selected from all possible samples, and the total number of weights is $(n + 1)$. The quantity M is called the "misadjustment." It is the per unit increase in error probability, based on a minimum error probability attainable by training on a very large sample. This formula leads directly to the idea that the number of patterns required to train an Adaline to discriminate noisy patterns is about five times (making M only 20 percent) the number of weights. The number of training patterns required to produce this form of generalization is of the order of twice the statistical memory capacity.

GENERALIZATION WITH RESPECT TO ROTATION OF PATTERNS

Insensitivity to rotation by 90° is a characteristic that can be perfectly trained into an Adaline. An experiment was made as depicted in Fig. 6 by using the 4 × 4 KNOBBY ADALINE shown in Fig. 2. C's rotated in all four positions were trained-in to give the $+1$ response, while T's were trained-in to give the -1 response in all four rotations. The initial weights were set to zero, and during training, the minimum mean-square error adaption procedure with an adaptive time constant of 32 patterns was utilized. The process converged with the desired responses trained-in precisely, and the set of weights shown in Fig. 6 resulted. Without further training, new patterns totally unrelated to the training patterns were inserted, and it was observed that not only were the decisions made by the Adaline perfectly consistent for each pattern over the four rotations, but the four meter readings (confidence levels or analog outputs) for each pattern were identical. The reason for this is simple: Rotation of the weights by 90° yields an identical set of weights. Let the a-matrix represent the set of weights (not including the threshold weight). The threshold weight remains the same for all rotations. The superscript R represents rotation by $+90°$.

$$[a] = [a]^R = \left[[a]^R \right]^R = \left[\left[[a]^R \right]^R \right]^R \tag{2}$$

Other training patterns and other numbers of training patterns were used in this experiment, and in each case, after convergence, the same

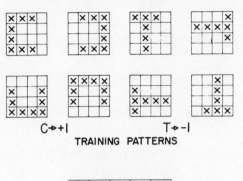

C→+1   T→-1

TRAINING PATTERNS

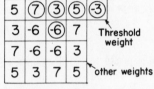

RESULTING WEIGHTS
AFTER TRAINING

Figure 6

symmetry expressed in Eq. (2) resulted automatically. Adaptation with a time constant, long compared to the number of training patterns, allows the neuron to retain responses to all the training patterns essentially equally. Minimization of mean-square error forces the response voltage to each training pattern in all four rotations to be consistent even when it might not be possible for this voltage to be precisely +1 or −1. This forces the symmetry of Eq. (2).

An interesting question is, how many specific responses on the average can be trained in and yet have the neuron trained to be insensitive to 90° rotation for all patterns. The 4 × 4 neuron has a capacity of 32 patterns. Eight basic patterns on the average can be trained in, since each basic pattern must be inserted in all four rotations. Another point of view on this question was suggested by Hoff. The four encircled weights and the threshold shown in Fig. 6, once chosen, set the rest of the weights when the constraint of Eq. (2) is followed. There are 4 "degrees of freedom" plus the threshold freedom. The number of basic patterns that can be discriminated therefore corresponds to the capacity of a 4-input neuron which is 8 patterns.

The same training procedure could be used to train-in a direct sensitivity to rotation, rather than an insensitivity. The experiment was remade, with a C mapped $+1$ and a T mapped -1, however with a rotated C mapped -1, and a rotated T mapped $+1$, etc., the following set of weights resulted.

$$
\begin{array}{cccc}
-11 & +9 & -2 & +11 \\
+\,2 & 0 & 0 & -9 \\
-9 & 0 & 0 & +2 \\
+11 & -2 & +9 & -11
\end{array}
\qquad 0
$$

threshold weight

The symmetry in the weights can be described by

$$[a] = -[a]^R = -\Big[[a]^R\Big]^R = -\Big[-\Big[-[a]^R\Big]^R\Big]^R \tag{3}$$

Rotation of any input pattern by 90^0 causes a sign reversal in the confidence level, and therefore an opposite decision.

GENERALIZATION WITH RESPECT TO LEFT-RIGHT TRANSLATION

Perfect solutions to the problem of training an Adaline to be insensitive to left-right pattern translation exist. A solution requires the columns of the a-matrix to be identical. On a 4×4 input array, there is a choice of 4 independent weights, each choice setting a row of weight values. It follows that the statistical discrimination capacity subject to the constraint of insensitivity to left-right translation is that of a 4-input Adaline or 8 basic patterns. The total capacity of the 4×4 Adaline is 32 patterns, and this corresponds to the four positional possibilities for each of the 8 basic patterns. Patterns can be placed in four positions by considering the input pattern space to be continuous and folded over a cylinder having a vertical axis.

By symmetry, the same training procedures apply to training for insensitivity to up-down motion. If both left-right and up-down insensitivity is desired, the only perfect solution is the relatively trivial one, all weights in the a-matrix being equal. Discrimination is based on pattern "area," the number of $+1$ pattern bits. More sophisticated discrimination based on pattern features other than area has been made by using two Adalines and an OR output element in the form of a simple Madaline.

An experiment was made to train a KNOBBY ADALINE to give a sign reversal for left-right motion and, at the same time, to give a sign reversal for rotation by $90°$. The pattern T on a 3×2 grid was trained in to produce $+1$ in the vertical left position, -1 in the vertical right position, etc. The following set of weights resulted. Notice the symmetries and sign alternations.

8	−5	5	−8	−2
5	−1	1	5	
5	1	−1	−5	
−8	5	−5	8	

It was found that approximately 85 percent of new patterns would consistently produce sign alternation for all possible left-right, up-down, and rotation by 90° motions. The remaining 15 percent of patterns would be consistent in most situations, perhaps be incorrect in only 2 out of 16 cases. Symmetrical patterns would be perfectly consistent.

GENERALIZATION WITH RESPECT TO PATTERN SIZE

An Adaline can be trained to be highly insensitive to pattern size. The training procedure again requires slow minimum mean-square-error adaption. In Fig. 7, a set of "small" and "large" patterns is shown that comprised examples for the training experiment. On a 3 × 3 array in the upper left hand corner of a 4 × 4, a T and a C were inserted as shown. In the full 4 × 4 array, expanded versions of these patterns were trained-in to give corresponding responses. After training, it was found that new patterns gave widely fluctuating analog responses. For about 90 percent of new pattern inputs, the same binary response resulted for the small as for the large versions, and the corresponding confidence levels were extremely close.

To be perfectly insensitive to size, the weights of an Adaline must be such that an element of area of the small pattern "sees" the same total weight (input patterns are thought of as continuous two-dimensional functions and weights are thought of as continuous distribution functions) as the corresponding area element of the large pattern that it maps into. It can be shown that perfect solutions result when the weight function radiates from a point and has an intensity that decays with an inverse-square law. These general effects can be detected in the weights of Fig. 7.

APPLICATIONS OF PATTERN CLASSIFICATION PRINCIPLES TO SYSTEMS PROBLEMS

In addition to an application to automatic control systems which will be described in detail in the next section, the above principles have been applied to weather forecasting, speech recognition, and diagnosis of EKG waveforms.

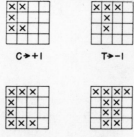

C ⇒ +1   T ⇒ -1

TRAINING PATTERNS

2	1	-5	-1	1
7	-7	-1	-1	
8	-1	-1	-1	
1	1	1	-1	

RESULTING WEIGHTS

Figure 7

WEATHER FORCASTING

One of the highly successful applications of Adaline-type trainable threshold networks has been to weather forecasting. This work has been performed mainly by M. J. C. Hu, a graduate student at Stanford, with the cooperation of Mr. H. E. Root of the U.S. Weather Bureau at the San Francisco International Airport.

Measurements of sea-level barometric pressure at a number of points around San Francisco were applied, after appropriate encoding, to the inputs of a network of Adalines. The desired outputs to which the network was trained was whether or not it rained during some future interval at San Francisco. Both two-level and multilevel input Adalines have been used for these experiments.

Consider the results obtained from an illustrative experiment. A three-Adaline system was used to give three separate forecasts, covering three successive 12-hour periods in the future. One Adaline was trained to indicate whether or not it rained from 8 a.m. to 8 p.m. on the day when the pressure map was made (the map was made at 4 a.m.). The other two Adalines were trained, using the same data, to forecast whether or not it rained from 8 p.m. of the same day to 8 a.m. of the next day, and from 8 a.m. to 8 p.m. of the next day, respectively.

The experiment utilized three types of weather information. The three-Adaline system was trained to recognize 33 patterns of each of the following types.

1. Today's 4 a.m. PST (Pacific Standard Time) Surface Pressure Map.
2. Today's 4 a.m. PST and yesterday's 4 a.m. PST Surface Pressure Maps.
3. Today's 4 a.m. PST Surface Pressure Map and the difference between today's and yesterday's pressure (dp/dt).

The three-Adaline system was then tested on 18 patterns from each of the types mentioned above. The performance of the three-Adaline system was then compared with the official forecast for those 18 days. The results are tabulated below:

	Percent Right		
	Today 8 a.m.–8 p.m.	Tonight 8 p.m.–8 a.m.	Tomorrow 8 a.m.–8 p.m
Official forecast	78	89	67
Adaline forecast using			
1. 4 a.m. PST Map	72	67	67
2. Today's and yesterday's 4 a.m. PST Maps	78	78	78
3. Today's 4 a.m. PST Map and dp/dt	78	89	83

The success of this work, particularly considering that only barometric pressure was used for generating the Adaline forecasts, has resulted in growing interest, both at Stanford and among local meteorologists, in this technique.

SPEECH RECOGNITION

A small-scale, real-time, trainable speech recognition system has been built and studied extensively by L. R. Talbert, G. F. Groner, and J. S. Koford, P. R. Low, and R. J. Brown, with the advice of Dr. Dorothy A. Huntington of the Speech Pathology and Audiology Department at Stanford. This system consists of a microphone-input speech preprocessor, which feeds a speech waveform of normalized amplitude into eight bandpass filters spaced throughout the audio spectrum. The detected outputs of these filters (proportional to spectral energy) are then quantized, digitally coded, and sampled for application directly to a simulated Adaline network.

In a typical experiment the output of each of the bandpass filters is quantized into four levels, and is then represented by a simple three-bit linearly separable code (this will be explained in the next section). Ten samples of each quantized output are then taken at equal intervals throughout the duration of a spoken word. Thus, each spoken word is represented by $8 \times 3 \times 10$, or 240, bits. k-simulated Adalines are used to provide classification for 2^k words. Thus, for recognition of the spoken digits 1 to 10, four simulated Adalines of 240 inputs each were used.

In use, training samples of the particular voice to be recognized are first taken, and the Adalines are trained to correctly classify these training samples. After convergence on the training samples, new spoken samples can be used to test the ability of the network. After training on ten samples of each spoken word from one individual, the network can typically classify new samples of the same spoken word by that individual with 98 percent accuracy or better. If tested on a new individual, this accuracy averages 90 percent or better.

VECTORCARDIOGRAM DIAGNOSIS

Networks of Adalines have been applied with encouragingly good success by D. F. Specht with help, advice, and data supplied by Drs. J. G. Toole and J. Von der Groeben of the EKG Department, Stanford University, School of Medicine to the diagnosis of heart defects from examination of vectorcardiograms. A vectorcardiogram differs somewhat from the usual 12-track electrocardiogram in that only three sets of data are recorded, but they are recorded simultaneously, so that significant phasé information among them is preserved. The input patterns to an Adaline network are formed by sampling the vectorcardiograms at 5-millisec intervals. During training on approximately 100 sample patterns, the desired outputs were based on an electrocardiologist's diagnosis. The following table indicates the sort of success which has been obtained in preliminary experiments.

Recognition Rate on the Testing Set

	True Normals, % (27 cases)	True Abnormals, % (30 cases)
Clinical EKG	95	54
Generalized adaptive approach	89	73

APPLICATION TO CONTROL SYSTEMS

The state of a dynamic system can be completely described at any instant by the values of the state variables of the system. (The state variables of a control system are such quantities as the error, the error derivative, etc.) A control decision therefore need depend only on the present values of the state variables. The value of each state variable can be encoded as a sequence of binary digits. The collection of these encoded state variables forms a pattern. Proper control of a dynamic system by an Adaline or Madaline becomes a matter of the proper classification of the patterns which represent the different states of a dynamic system. Just as an Adaline can be taught to classify patterns into two groups, it can also be taught to control a dynamic system in a "bang-bang" or $+1$, -1 manner.

When the state variables are encoded using what has been called a "linearly independent code," the task of learning control strategies is quite natural for an Adaline.

i. The large sets of patterns representing the control strategy for all possible regions of state space are often either linearly separable, or separable with simple Madaline structures. Then umberof patterns which the Adaline is able to correctly classify is generally a norder of magnitude or more greater than its statistical capacity.

ii. The Adaline generalizes in a known and predictable way. Namely, the Adaline can correctly classify all the patterns of a control strategy after learning to correctly classify only the patterns bordering on the switching surface.

Because of this strong generalizing property and because of the special interrelationships among the many patterns, the Adaline is much easier to train than it would be for a similar number of random or near random patterns.

THE TRAINABLE CONTROLLER

Figure 8 shows in block diagram form the general situation in which a Madaline would be used as a trainable controller for a dynamic system. The state variable $y_1, \ldots y_m$ are assumed to be the system error.

The teaching controller supplies the desired output to the Adaline during the training process. This controller could be an automatic controller or possibly a human. The Adaline controller and the teaching controllre need not have the same inputs, provided both receive the same or related information. For instance, the Adaline controller could be receiving the state variables as electronic signals while a human teacher could be receiving information about the system by actually watching its motions.

For the purposes of discussion the teacher will be assumed to be represented by a function $f(y_1, \ldots, y_m)$. The switching surface $f(y_1, \ldots, y_m) = 0$ describes the transition where the teacher changes his reaction from "force plus" to "force minus." During the training, the Adaline analog output $\hat{f}(y_1, \ldots, y_m)$ is adjusted so that its switching surface $\hat{f}(y_1, \ldots, y_m) = 0$ is made to approximate the switching surface of the teacher.

The Adaline controller consists of an encoder and an Adaline. For simplicity, a single Adaline is shown here in the controller; more typically a Madaline might be used. The Adaline with its encoder is basically a trainable function generator which forms the function $\hat{f}(y_1, \ldots, y_m)$. The pattern inputs to the Adaline change continually as the state variables change. The encoder produces patterns by quantizing or dividing the range over which each of the state variables varies into a finite number of zones. Each zone of a state variable y_i is represented by binary number or *partial pattern*. The m partial patterns make up the total pattern which represents a particular hypercube of state space.

Figure 9 illustrates the quantization of a two-dimensional state space. Each square in the figure is represented by a particular pattern for the Adaline. The continuous curve $\widehat{f}(y_1, y_2) = 0$ represents a typical desired switching surface (a curved line in this case). The jagged curve $\widehat{f}(y_1, y_2) = 0$ is the switching curve that an Adaline controller might use to approximate the teaching controller.

The system has two modes of operation:

i. During the training mode, the teaching controller controls the dynamic system. The adapt logic in the Adaline continuously compares the binary output of the Adaline with that of the teacher. Whenever they differ, the Adaline is adapted in the direction which would make them agree. Because the patterns change rapidly, there may not be time for a full

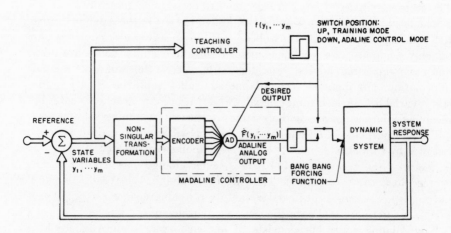

Figure 8

correction. However, the pattern is bound to recur, at which time adaption can be continued. During the training mode the Adaline controller "watches" the teacher zero the error after various large disturbances or initial contions.

ii. During the Adaline control mode the teaching controller is not used and may be completely removed from the system.

CODING

The choice of codes used to represent the values of the state variables largely determines how well the Madaline controller will be able to imitate its teacher. Figure 10 illustrates two possible "linearly independent codes." A linearly independent code is any code which has a nonsingular *partial pattern matrix*. This matrix has the partial patterns as rows plus a column of ones (if necessary). The partial pattern matrix for the codes of Figs. 10*a* and *b* are respectively:

$$\begin{bmatrix} 0 & 0 & 0 & 1 \\ 0 & 0 & 1 & 0 \\ 0 & 1 & 0 & 0 \\ 1 & 0 & 0 & 0 \end{bmatrix} \qquad \begin{bmatrix} 1 & 1 & 1 & 1 \\ 1 & 1 & 1 & 0 \\ 1 & 1 & 0 & 0 \\ 1 & 0 & 0 & 0 \end{bmatrix}$$

Both matrices are obviously invertible. When linearly independent coding is used, the Adaline will be able to exactly imitate (except for quantization effects) any teacher whose function does not contain cross-product terms, i.e., terms of the form $y_i y_j$, $i \neq j$, regardless of the number of patterns.

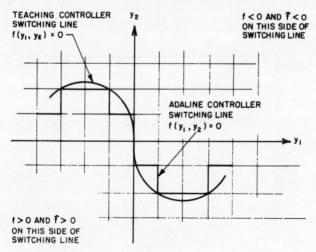

Figure 9

The proof that an Adaline using linearly independent coding has such classifying power can be given by demonstrating of how the Adaline matches its function to that of the teacher. The analysis an Adaline is much simpler for the class of classification problems in which a decision is based on the encoded values of state variables than for most problems. The simplification occurs because the Adaline can be fully described in terms of the m state variables instead of the n binary inputs, ($n \gg m$ generally). The weights for the inputs used to encode a particular state variable are considered not as separate entities but as a single function of the state variable. The abilities and limitations of a single Adaline in pattern classification and generalization become apparent. Also, the weights can often be calculated in many seemingly complicated problems.

This new interpretation of the Adaline is for analytical purposes only. The Adaline is trained in the usual way. The function matching to be described goes on automatically "inside" the Adaline.

Let the schematic of the Adaline be redrawn as in Fig. 11. Only the method of summing has been changed so as to allow the quantities $f_i(y_i)$, $i = l, \ldots, m$, to be defined. The threshold weight w_0 is figuratively considered to be divided into m thresholds w_{i0}, where

$$\sum_{i=1}^{m} w_{i0} = w_0 \tag{4}$$

Each partial sum $\hat{f}_i(y_i)$ is a function of only the state variable y_i. The switching surface for the Adaline is

$$\hat{f} = \sum_{i=1}^{m} f_i(y_i) = 0 \tag{5}$$

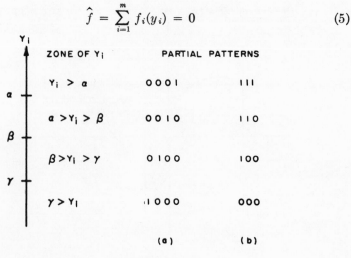

Figure 10

This function has no cross product terms and cannot approximate teaching functions with cross-product terms. Thus, the Adaline can imitate only teaching functions of the form

$$f = \sum_{i=1}^{m} f_i(y_i) = 0 \tag{6}$$

This is a consequence of encoding each state variable independent of the others.

If the switching surface of the Adaline controller is to imitate that of the teaching controller, $\hat{f}$ must be proportional to f, and furthermore, because the y_i can vary independently, each $\hat{f}_i(y_i)$ must be proportional to $f_i(y_i)$. (Assume a proportionality constant of one here.) Thus the coding of the state variables into patterns can be studied by examining how a *single* variable is encoded.

Consider the state variable y_i. When y_i is in a particular quantum zone the partial sum $\hat{f}_i(y_i) = (\vec{a})^T \cdot (\vec{W}_i)$. The vector $(\vec{a})$ is the partial pattern associated with that zone, augmented by a $+1$ "threshold input" as its first entry. The vector $(\vec{W}_i)$ contains the weights associated with y_i in Fig. 12. The threshold weight w_{i0} is the first entry. If $\hat{f}_i(y_i)$ is to match $f_i(y_i)$, then they should be equal somewhere within each quantum zone. Thus:

$$(\vec{a})^T \cdot (\vec{w}_i) = f_i(y_i)$$

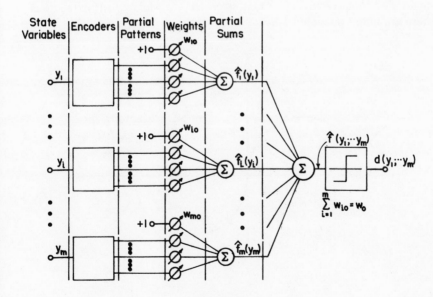

Figure 11

somewhere within each quantum zone. These equations (one from each quantum zone) must have a simultaneous solution. They can be rewritten more compactly

$$[A]\ (\vec{w}_i) = (\vec{f}_i) \tag{7}$$

$[A]$ is the partial pattern matrix described above. The $(\vec{f}_i)$ is a vector containing values of $f_i(y_i)$ at which $\hat{f}_i(y_i) = f_i(y_i)$.

When the equations $[A](\vec{w}_i) = (\vec{f}_i)$ are consistent $\hat{f}_i(y_i) = f_i(y_i)$ is possible and the Adaline partial sum will be able to "exactly" imitate the partial sum of the teaching function, $f_i(y_i)$. "Exactly" is meant in the sense that $\hat{f}_i(y_i) = f_i(y_i)$ for at least one value of y_i in each zone of y_i. If each of the $\hat{f}_i(y_i)$ is "exactly" equal to its corresponding $f_i(y_i)$ for all i, then $\hat{f}(y_1, \ldots, y_m)$ will equal $f(y_1, \ldots, y_m)$ somewhere within each hypercube of state space. Furthermore, the hypercube, and its pattern, will have the same sign as $f(y_1, \ldots, y_m)$ at this point. (These points of equality are indicated in Fig. 13.)

If $f_i(y_i)$ is an arbitrary function, then the only way in which the equations $[A]\ (\vec{w}_i) = (\vec{f}_i)$ can be guaranteed to be consistent is to choose partial patterns so that $[A]$ has a left inverse. To minimize the number of weights $[A]$ must also have a minimum number of columns. The only form of $[A]$ which satisfies both of these criteria is an $[A]$ which is square and invertible. Thus, for an arbitrary $f_i(y_i)$ the partial patterns representing y_i must be such that $[A]$ has an inverse. Then, $\vec{w}_i = [A]^{-1}(\vec{f}_i)$ for any $f_i(y_i)$. Obviously, there are many possible $[A]$'s.

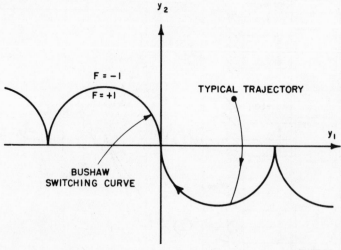

Figure 12

Two possible ways of encoding the state variables have been illustrated in Fig. 10. The "single spot" code of Fig. 10a is easy to analyze mathematically because most of the weights would have zero coefficients. If the threshold weight is not used, the weights are:

$$\begin{bmatrix} w_1 \\ w_2 \\ w_3 \\ w_4 \end{bmatrix} = (\vec{f_i})$$

The "multispot" code of Fig. 10b is illustrated because it is usually quite easy to instrument and also because this code usually allows the weights of the Adaline to be quite small. Other authors[5] have shown that, in general, the smaller the magnitudes of the weights (after proper normalization) the easier it will be to train the Adaline.

The use of linearly independent coding shows that it is sufficient to guarantee that the Adaline function generator will be able to "exactly" imitate a teaching function that has no cross-product terms. By a more involved argument, it can be shown that linearly independent coding is necessary if the Adaline controller is to have a minimum number of weights while "exactly" imitating a teaching function with no cross terms. A proof of necessity is hardly needed, however, when the nonstatistical capacity of an Adaline using linearly independent coding is considered. For in-

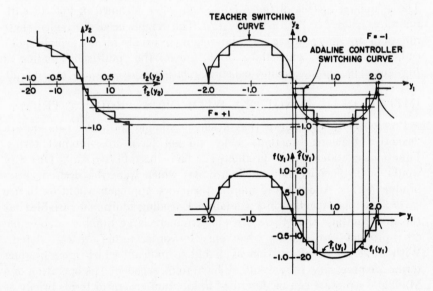

Figure 13

stance, when each of the state variables is quantized into n' zones, there are $(n')^m$ possible patterns. The statistical capacity of this Adaline is approximately $2mn'$.

Consider the values $n' = 5$; $m = 4$. Then $(n')^m = 625$ patterns can be correctly classified while the statistical capacity is only $2mn' = 40$. The actual capacity in this typical case is more than an order of magnitude greater than the statistical capacity.

AN EXAMPLE OF AN ADALINE CONTROLLER

The above ideas can best be illustrated by showing how an Adaline controller would control the oscillatory undamped second-order system with differential equation

$$\ddot{y}_1 + y_1 = F, \quad F = \pm 1, \quad y_2 = \dot{y}_1 \tag{8}$$

The minimum-time optimum-switching curve is the well-known Bushaw[8] switching curve shown in Fig. 12. This switching surface was chosen for an example because it gives appreciably faster response than a linear switching line, and because it is highly nonlinear.[9] A typical trajectory of the minimum time optimum controller is also shown in Fig. 12. The optimal controller makes no "wrong" decisions but instead moves right to the origin with one reversal of F. A controller containing one Adaline is capable of closely approximating the nonlinear function of the optimum controller. The switching surface of the Adaline controller is shown in Fig. 13 with functions $f_1(y_1)$, $f_1(y_1)$, $\hat{f}_1(y_1)$, and $f_2(y_2)$. The weights needed to realize these functions are shown in Fig. 14. The weights of (a) are for the "single spot" coding of Fig. 10a, while those of (b) are for the "multispot" coding of Fig. 10b. The porportionality constant relating $\hat{f}(y_1, y_2)$ and $f(y_1, y_2)$ is 20.

IMITATION OF FUNCTIONS WITH CROSS-PRODUCT TERMS

Previously it was shown that a single Adaline controller can imitate "exactly" teaching functions which do not have cross-product terms. Functions containing cross products can be realized in two ways. One way would be to encode additional variables which were the desired cross-product terms. Another and more satisfactory approach would be to use several Adalines together in a Madaline. Encoding additional variables has the disadvantage that there are an extremely large number of possible cross-product terms (even when only low-order terms are considered). With no *a priori* information available to indicate which cross-product terms are necessary, they would all have to be encoded. The operation of a Madaline structure can be described in function-generator terms briefly as follows: The quantizers at the Adaline outputs and the fixed logic element which combines these outputs perform nonlinear operations which can introduce the necessary cross-product terms. A Madaline does not need a weight for every cross-product term because it can organize its total structure in such a way as to take into account the most significant cross-product terms while ignoring the rest.

The situation illustrated in Figs. 15a, b, and c demonstrates the ability of a Madaline structure to imitate a teaching function with cross-product terms. The teaching function is a rotated ellipse with equation:

$$5y_1^2 - 6y_1y_2 + 5y_2^2 - 2 = 0 \tag{9}$$

This curve was chosen as a familiar nonlinear function. Two Adalines are used. Adaline I in Fig. 15b has the U shaped switching line which approximates the switching line of half of the teaching function. Adaline II in Fig. 15c has the inverted U-shaped switching line which approximates the other half of the teaching function. The Adaline outputs are combined in an OR circuit. The logic of the OR circuit is: both Adaline outputs −1 then Madaline output −1 otherwise Madaline output +1. With the polarity of the Adaline outputs as shown on the figure the OR circuit causes the interior of the ellipse to be −1 as desired. The functions approximated by the individual Adalines can be shown to contain no cross terms.

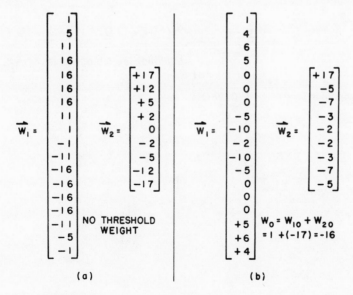

Figure 14

"BROOM-BALANCING MACHINE"

To demonstrate the ideas presented thus far in this chapter a relatively complex dynamic system with an Adaline controller has been assembled. The dynamic system is a motorized cart carrying an inverted pendulum. The controller for the system is required to keep the pendulum balanced and keep the cart within certain bounds by applying a horizontal force to the cart. An actual memistor Adaline is used in the trainable controller. This form of physical realization of adaptive logic circuits will be explained below. Figure 8 gives a block diagram of the dynamic system and its controllers. The nonsingular transformation in Fig. 8 is the identity transformation in this case.

The cart and pendulum system is an undamped and inherently unstable fourth-order dynamic system. The four-state variables are the angle of the pendulum from vertical, θ; the rate of change of angle θ; the position of the cart, x; and the rate of change of position x. These and other relevant

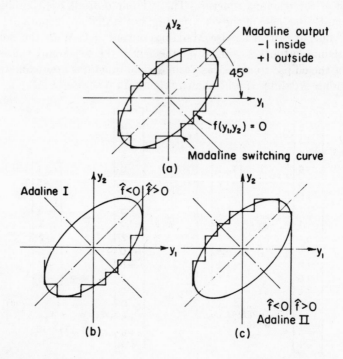

Figure 15

quantities are defined in Fig. 16. The linearized differential equations representing this system are:

$$\ddot{\theta} = \frac{3g}{4l}\theta - \frac{3}{4lM}F$$

$$\ddot{x} = \frac{1}{M}F \tag{10}$$

It is assumed that there is no damping, and that the reaction of the pendulum motions on the cart is negligible.

The teaching controller being used in these experiments has a linear switching surface of approximately

$$f = -2.0\,\dot{\theta} - 1.0\,\theta + 1.0\dot{x} + 1.0x \tag{11}$$

The Adaline controller contains one 24-input Adaline. The range of each of the state variables is divided into seven approximately equal zones. The state variables are encoded into 6-bit partial patterns using a linearly independent code similar to the one illustrated in Fig. 10b. The controller is taught by having it observe the teacher return the system to the origin of state space after it has received various large disturbances.

"SELECTIVE BOOTSTRAPPING"

The Adaline controller illustrated in Fig. 8 is a trainable adaptive system, but not a self-optimizing one. A teacher must exist in some form to serve as an example for the imitating Adaline. An alternative self-optimizing

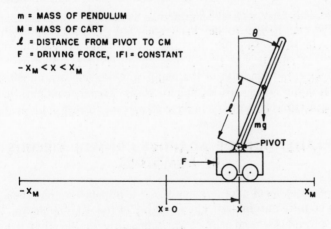

m = MASS OF PENDULUM
M = MASS OF CART
l = DISTANCE FROM PIVOT TO CM
F = DRIVING FORCE, |F| = CONSTANT
$-x_M < x < x_M$

Figure 16

technique for the training of an Adaline controller, that of "selective bootstrapping," has been studied by E. C. Fraser. Using this method, the Adaline controller is allowed to operate with the Adaline weights set to any arbitrary initial values—thus realizing an arbitrary control function. The performance of the system, when operating in this manner, is observed and evaluated. When, in the judgment of the observer, the performance over long chains of decisions is acceptable, the Adaline is adapted to reinforce such decisions; conversely, if the performance is unacceptable, the Adaline is adapted to reverse the decisions as they are being made. If the observer is uncertain, no change is made in the Adaline weights. In this way, training information is obtained directly from the performance and does not depend on any knowledge of the dynamic system configuration. That the system be in a stable operating condition is not a requirement of this technique since information about a system's performance can be obtained even though it is at the moment unstable. This is similar to a person trying to balance a broom on his finger; even though he may drop it (the system undergoes an unstable runaway), he learns something from the experience which aids him to do a better job the next time. Of course, systems to which this technique is applicable must be such that they can be stopped and restarted whenever the output gets out of bounds (i.e., the broom falls over).

It can be shown that, for second-order systems at least, when this technique is employed, the system will converge to a stable configuration if the performance evaluations of the observer are correct greater than 50 percent of the time. For higher-order systems this limit may be somewhat higher. The average rate of convergence is related to the observer's performance and is maximum when he is 100 percent correct and becomes zero when he is 50 percent correct. For values less than 50 percent, the system tends toward unstable configurations.

Experimental evidence has been collected to verify the convergent properties of this technique. In experiments conducted with computer-simulated systems it was found that an observer familiar with control system theory, but ignorant of the plant configuration, would consistently produce training sequences leading to stable system configurations. The observer was found to range from 55 to 62 percent correct in his evaluations.

REALIZATION OF ADAPTIVE CONTROL CIRCUITS BY MEMISTORS

In large networks of adaptive neurons it is imperative that the adaptive processes be fully automated. The structure of the Adaline neuron and the adaption procedures used with it are sufficiently simple, that it has been possible to develop electronic automatically adapted neurons which are reliable, contain few parts, and are suitable for mass production. In such neurons it is necessary to be able to store weight values, analog quantities which could be positive or negative, in such a way that these values could be changed electronically.

A new electrochemical circuit element called the Memistor (a resistor with memory) has been devised by B. Widrow and M. E. Hoff for the realization of automatically adapted Adalines. The Memistor provides a single variable gain element. Each neuron therefore employs a number of Memistors equal to the number of input lines, plus one for the threshold.

A Memistor consists of a conductive substrate with insulated connecting leads, and a metallic anode, all in an electrolytic plating bath. The conductance of the element is reversibly controlled by electroplating. Like the transistor, the Memistor is a 3-terminal element. The conductance between two of the terminals is controlled by the time integral of the current in the third terminal, rather than by its instantaneous value, as in the transistor. Reproducible elements have been made which are continuously variable, which vary in resistance from 50 to 2 ohms, and cover this range in about 15 sec with several tenths of a milliampere of plating current. Adaptation is accomplished by direct current, while sensing is accomplished nondestructively with alternating current.

Although the Memistor is still an experimental device, it is in limited commercial production. Figure 17 shows how they are made, 21 at a time on a common substrate. Each cell has a volume of about 2 drops. The entire unit is encapsulated in epoxy.

The broom-balancer has been controlled by an adaptive machine called Madaline I, containing 102 Memistors. This machine was constructed hastily over a 1½-month period. The Memistors were not tested before installation in the machine, and some were defective when first made. A number of wiring errors existed; some weights were adapting to diverge rather than converge. There were a number of short circuits, open circuits, cold solder, joints, etc. This machine worked very well when first turned on, and has functioned with very little attention over the past year and a half. After several weeks of experimentation the individual weights were checked. Twenty-five percent of them were not adapting. Yet the machine was able to adapt around these internal flaws and was able to be trained to make very complex pattern discriminations. Self-repairing control systems are a very real and vital possibility.

ACKNOWLEDGMENTS

This work was performed under Office of Naval Research Contract Nonr 225 (24), NR 373 360, jointly supported by the U.S. Army Signal Corps, the U.S. Air Force and the U.S. Navy (Office of Naval Research), under

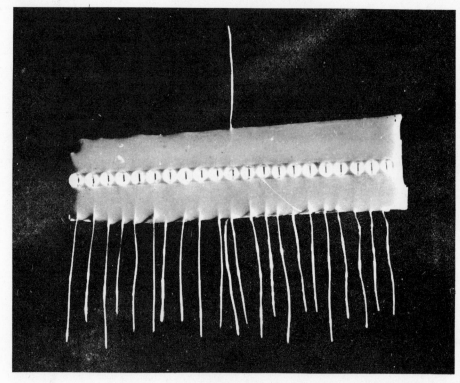

Figure 17

Air Force Contract AF33(616)7726 supported by Aeronautical Systems Division, Air Force System Command, Wright-Patterson Air Force Base, and under Contract DA–04–200–AMC–57(Z) supported by the U.S. Army Zeus Project Office, Redstone Arsenal, Huntsville, Alabama.

REFERENCES

1. Widrow, B., "Adaptive Sampled-Data Systems—A Statistical Theory of Adaption," 1959 WESCON Convention Record, Part 4.
2. ———, and M. E. Hoff, "Adaptive Switching Circuits," 1960 WESCON Convention Record, Part IV, Aug. 23, 1960, pp. 96–104.
3. ——————, "Adaptive Switching Circuits," Technical Report No. 1553–1, Stanford Electronics Laboratories, Stanford University, Stanford, Calif., June 30, 1960.
4. Ridgway, W. C., III, "An Adaptive Logic System with Generalizing Properties," Technical Report No. 1556–1, Stanford Electronics Laboratories, Stanford University, Stanford, Calif., April 1962.
5. Mays, C. H., "Adaptive Threshold Logic," Technical Report No. 1557–1, Stanford Electronics Laboratories, Stanford University, Stanford, Calif., April 1963.

6. ———, "Effects of Adaptation Parameters on Convergence Time and Tolerance for Adaptive Threshold Elements," submitted to *IEEE Trans. Electronic Computers.*

7. Hoff, M. E., Jr., "Learning Phenomena in Networks of Adaptive Switching Circuits," Technical Report No. 1554–1, Stanford Electronics Laboratories, Stanford, Calif., July 1962.

8. Pontryagin, L. S., V. G. Boltyanskii, R. V. Gamkrelidze, and E. F. Mishchenko, "The Mathematical Theory of Optimal Processes," (translation), Interscience, New York 1962.

9. Smith, Fred B., Jr., of Minneapolis-Honeywell Regulator Company has independently done some similar work using a threshold logic element to implement nonlinear minimum time switching surfaces. This work was reported in "A Logical Net Mechanization for Time-Optimal Regulation," NASA Technical Note D–1678; December 1962.

13

LEARNING CONTROL SYSTEMS

K. S. Fu

School of Electrical Engineering,

Purdue University, Lafayette, Ind.

INTRODUCTION

Recently the concept of introducing learning to automatic control systems has been proposed.[1,2] A learning control system can be considered as a system which modifies its control parameters to maintain a good performance as a result of its experience, in the presence of unpredictable changes of environment. From this viewpoint, a learning (control) system is certainly also adaptive in the sense of conventional adaptive control systems. Moreover, a learning system will be benefited from its past experience to improve its performance. The system performance can be expressed in terms of several different ways—for example, in terms of adaptation time, a prescribed index of performance, etc. The adaptive system is designed to modify itself in the face of a new environment so as to optimize its performance. A learning system, on the other hand, is designed also to recognize familiar patterns in a situation and then, from its past experience, to react in an optimum manner. In the former, emphasis is placed on reacting to a new situation, while in the latter the emphasis is on recognizing old situations and utilizing the system experience.

An adaptive system, as we know, will optimize a slowly time-varying plant for a given index of performance, usually through a hill-climbing technique, by modifying the controller or plant parameters. Thus if sufficient time is available for parameter adjustment, the adaptive system will become optimum for a given index of performance. A basic constraint is that the plant should vary so slowly that the adaptive system is able to search the minimum of the index of performance and maintain good performance. In some instances, the plant parameters vary so fast that the

318

adaptive system cannot maintain optimum performance through adaptive action. It is in this type of situation that a learning system is preferable. Because the learning system gains more *a priori* information as time proceeds, it can, in theory, react more rapidly. On the other hand, for the same amount of time, the learning system should approach more closely to the optimum by properly utilizing its stored experience.

No learning control systems are known to be in field operation at the present time. Krug and Letskii have suggested the application of a learning technique for the optimum control of slow but complex dynamic processes, such as chemical processes.[3] They suggest that the optimum control might be determined by a systematic evaluation of input and output data and an index of performance. The system as outlined is very general and a probabilistic approach is proposed for organizing the memory for optimum-search procedure. A human operator is needed to make the final decision about the satisfactoriness of the system performance. Widrow has proposed a model for learning control systems based on the boss-worker analogy.[4,5] His broom-balancing machine can learn from a human trainer how to balance an unstable pendulum.[6] Mesarovic has proposed a model for multilevel multigoal system for self-organizing control systems.[7] He considers that adaptation and learning as an operation on uncertainty set. The learning process is considered as completed when the uncertainty set becomes void. Several learning control systems are currently under study in the Control and Information Systems Laboratory of Purdue University. Preliminary results have shown very impressive progress.[8-9]

One requirement for learning control systems is the learning process must take place not only during the training phase but also during the operation phase. They will be expected to accomplish learning "on line" and while responding to normal command inputs. System learning in the operation phase is possible by a continuous check of the index of performance. This system will be designed so that it will recognize and store the patterns of the plant parameters which are varying or the patterns of the environment parameters causing the variation. It also stores in memory the best index of performance obtained by a hill-climbing technique and the corresponding corrections necessary to obtain this performance. Thus when a previously occurring patterns of plant parameters are again encountered, the current best corrections would be immediately set from the information stored in memory and the hill-climbing procedure carried out from that point on. The system will, of course, be designed so that the memory contents will be continuously updated with the current best results of the corrections. Because of the finite memory capacity, the environmental patterns would necessarily be classified properly in a finite number of classes within the limitation of the system memory.

The performance of a learning system can be expressed by a set of learning curves. A learning curve is a plot of a certain quantity such as response entropy, adaptation time, system error, or index of performance versus the number of occurrences for the same situation. The concept of learning curves has been applied to describe the behavior of a learning system by various authors.[6,9] The system will be said to learn if the curve is monotonically approach the optimum value of the quantity. The "rate of learning" may be measured by the time rate of change of the quantity. The "learning time" may be expressed as the number of trials required to bring the quantity to its optimum value (or a certain percentage of its optimum value) multiplied by the time required for each trial. For example, if the plot of adaptation time versus the number of trials is used to describe the performance of a learning system, the optimum value of the adaptation time is its minimum. The system will be said to learn if the slope of the curve is always negative. The rate of learning is the time rate of change of adaptation time—that is, the value of the slope. The learning time is the time required to bring the adaptation time to its minimum (or a certain percentage of the minimum).

DESCRIPTION OF A CLASS OF LEARNING CONTROL SYSTEMS

In general, the operation of a learning system can be illustrated by a block diagram as shown in Fig. 1. In response to an input stimulus the system makes one of several possible responses. It remembers what decision were made in choosing this response. Shortly thereafter, the Trainer sends to the system a signal L, which may be called a learning operator, this directs the improvement of the system performance. In a conventional adaptive control system, the system consists of a plant and an adaptive controller. Thus, Fig. 2 can be considered as a block diagram of a learning control system. The combination of controller and Trainer will be called the "learning controller." A learning controller must be able to perform the following three functions:

(1) recognition of plant-parameter patterns or environmental patterns,
(2) search of optimum control-parameter values for a given index of performance, and
(3) continuous improvement of the system performance as a result of its past experience.

The first step is essentially a problem of pattern recognition. The second basic element of learning control is the process of searching optimum which has been treated extensively in adaptive and self-optimizing control systems research. The third part involves the efficient use of memory capacity and the continuous updating of memory contents.

Since the problem of optimum-searching has been treated by various authors,[11] our discussion here will be limited only to those functions of pattern recognition and memory modification. One of the important problems in pattern recognition is how to select a good set of features to represent various possible patterns and how to measure those features. In control of a plant, the learning controller would have to measure a set of features which describe the patterns of environment characteristics. This set of features may be a set of plant parameters; the states of the plant, or

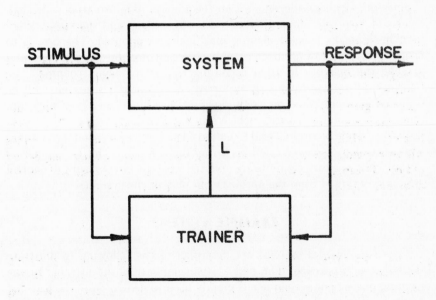

Figure 1

some parameters characterizing the environment.* The feature space (or measurement space) is partitioned into a finite number of regions of which each represents a specific pattern class. The partition may be obtained either from the *a priori* knowledge of various pattern classes or from a learning procedure. The number of pattern classes will be usually the same as the number of control strategies if it is known. If the number of control strategies is unknown or not finite, the number of pattern classes may be determined from a learning process subject to the limitation of memory capacity. Each region in the feature space corresponds to a particular pattern class of environmental situation, and corresponding to each environmental situation there is a control strategy which is so far the best for a given index of performance. The controller will have to recognize the environmental situation and react with the best control strategy.

Since practical considerations limit the amount of information which can be stored, two procedures similar to the "refreshing and the "forgetting" used in Samuel's checker-playing machine[12] are adopted. The first is to count the number of occurrences of each environmental pattern class and arrange the memory location according to the frequency counted. The information for less frequently occurred environmental situations will be removed gradually as soon as the memory locations have been filled up. New environmental situation which has not happened again will be soon forgotten, while environmental situations which have occurred many times will be remembered even if not occurring thereafter for a fairly long period of time. The memory contents are updated with the latest results of control strategy, obtained from the optimization part of the system.

EXAMPLE SYSTEMS

Two experimental systems are described in the following to illustrate the proposed approach. The first system emphasizes the learning in the training phase. The second one is mainly used to demonstrate the learning in the operation phase. Both systems have been simulated on an IBM 1710-GEDA hybrid computer facility and results from simulation are considered very satisfactory.

System I. The problem is to design a learning controller which will learn how to drive a second order plant from any set of initial conditions to the vicinity of the origin in the state space by applying a control signal with either $+1$ or -1 to the plant.

In this system, the feature space is essentially the state space with possible additions of environmental parameters. The number of control

---

* Here we simply call them environmental patterns.

strategies is two (corresponding to $+1$ or -1 control signal). The major part of the problem is to design a learning controller which will learn to establish the boundary of partition, or optimum switching boundary in this case, in the state space under a particular environmental condition. This corresponds to the case of learning in the training phase. Then the learning controller will be also designed to extend the same technique for learning optimum switching boundaries under various environmental situations, i.e., learning in the operation phase.

To start with the two-dimensional case, the feature space is partitioned by constructing circular sets of a prescribed radius D. (The sample-set approach used here is similar to the one proposed by Sebestyen for recognition of speakers.[13]) Each set of feature measurements (x_1, x_2) can be considered as a vector in the feature space (state vector in this case). Two feature vectors are considered in the same set if the distance between them is less than D. Each set is characterized by a set vector (center of the set) which is the mean of the first n (in this particular example, $n = 10$) members of the set. If the distance between two feature vectors is greater than D, a new set must be established, and the feature vector which is inside the new set is assigned as the set vector. Sets are only established in the vicinity of measured feature vectors. Thus, memory is not wasted in establishing sets in regions where measurements never occur. In addition to the set vector, each set has been associated with a probability of choosing $+1$ as the control signal, P_i. Initially the probability P_i is assumed $\frac{1}{2}$ and the proper value will then be learned by a simple reinforcement technique for a given index of performance.[14] A block diagram of the system is shown in Fig. 3. As learning progresses, the probability of choosing $+1$ as the control signal for a given measurement (x_1, x_2) will either approach 1, 0, or vary between these two values. If after a finite period of learning, P_i lies between two thresholds, (say 0.9 and 0.1), it is quite likely that part of the set will corresponds to $+1$ as optimum control signal and part of set to -1 as optimum control signal. This indicates the set is actually on the switching boundary. Sets with this property are further partitioned into subsets with smaller radius. This gives the advantage of fine quantization near the switching boundary without the extremely large increase in memory capacity. A typical distribution of sets and subsets for a second order plant is shown in Fig. 4.

The technique of partitioning the feature space according to certain control strategy can be easily extended to include the environmental parameters as additional dimensions of the feature space. In general, the plant may be higher order, nonlinear, or time-varying, the number of control strategies may be more than two, and no limitations need be put on the types of hypersurface as the boundary in this example of partition.

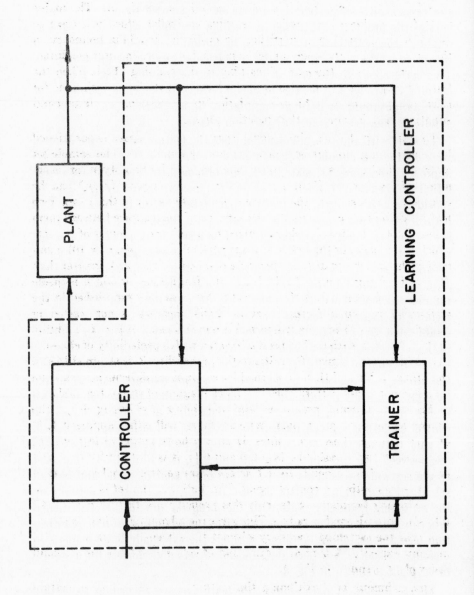

Figure 2

It is noted that the learning controller, is similar to a pattern recognition device with the ability of learning the optimum partition in the feature space under various environmental conditions. (Appendix A.)

APPENDIX A

PATTERN RECOGNITION IN LEARNING CONTROL SYSTEMS

INTRODUCTION

A learning (control) system is designed to recognize familiar features and patterns in an environment and then from its past experience or learning behavior to react in an optimum manner. The recognition of various environmental patterns becomes an important function which must be performed by a learning system. A general pattern recognition scheme for learning control system is proposed. By employing the feature-extraction technique, a set of parameters, say $(x_1, x_2, \ldots, x_n)$, must be first chosen to describe various environmental patterns. In this case, for a given plant, the environmental situation at time t may be described by the values of all the plant state variables at t, a sequence of values of plant output state variable from t_0 to $t(t_0 < t)$, or the values of a set of other parameters (e.g., ζ and ω_n for a second-order plant). Each set of parameter values can be considered as a point in an n-dimensional vector space. Suppose we can divide the vector space (called parameter space or feature space) into finite number of regions so that each represents an environmental pattern class. This is illustrated in Fig. 8 for number of parameters $n = 2$. These regions may not be necessarily simply-connected or linearly separable (separable by hyperplanes). The recognition scheme must be able to evaluate the parameter measurements and classify them according to the region in which they are contained.

Without loss of generality, suppose we only consider two environmental patterns E_1 and E_2. In order to minimize the probability of misrecognition, a set of parameter measurements will be more likely a member of E_1 than of E_2 if [10]

$$P(E_1) \, p(x_1, \ldots, x_n/E_1) > P(E_2) \, p(x_1, x_2, \ldots, x_n/E_2) \tag{1}$$

or

$$P(E_1/x_1, \ldots, x_n)/P(E_2/x_1, \ldots, x_n) > 1 \tag{2}$$

where $P(E_1)$ and $P(E_2)$ are the *a priori* probabilities of E_1 and E_2. If the *a priori* probabilities are unknown, the functional form of the decision rule remains unchanged. Equation (1) may be written in terms of the likelihood ratio λ which is to be compared with a constant as shown in Eq. (3).

$$\lambda = \frac{p(x_1, \ldots, x_n/E_1)}{p(x_1, \ldots, x_n/E_2)} > \frac{P(E_2)}{P(E_1)} = K \tag{3}$$

The boundary between the regions E_1 and E_2 is the locus where λ equals K. Thus the region of the space within which inputs are classified as members of a specific pattern class is the region in which the conditional probability density of members of that class exceeds by K the density of members of any other class.

METHODS OF COMPUTING UNKNOWN DENSITIES

Unfortunately, the conditional probability densities $p(x_1, \ldots, x_n/E_1)$ and $p(x_1, \ldots, x_n/E_2)$ are usually unknown and environmental patterns are known to the decision maker only through a finite number of their samples. That the pattern-recognition machine attempts to define a decision for each point of the vector space, from knowledge of the correct decision at only a finite number of points through learning is one approach. Another approach is to compute the densities based on the assumption that the region occupied by members of E_i can be approximated by the union of circles representing equiprobable contours of Gaussian processes.[13] This is illustrated in Fig. 9. For simplicity, these are shown to have equal variances in all directions and are assumed to have uncorrelated variables. Thus, the probability ratio $P(E_1/x_1, \ldots, x_n)/P(E_2/x_1, \ldots, x_n)$ in Eq. (2) can be

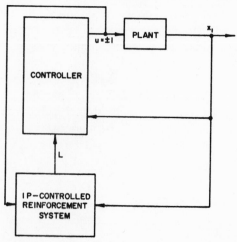

Figure 3

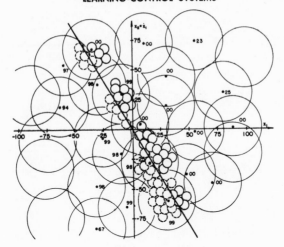

Figure 4

written as

$$\frac{P(E_1/x_1, \ldots, x_n)}{P(E_2/x_1, \ldots, x_n)} = \frac{\sum\limits_{i=1}^{k_1} P(E_{1i})\, p(x_1, \ldots, x_n/E_{1i})}{\sum\limits_{i=1}^{k_2} P(E_{2i})\, p(x_1, \ldots, x_n/E_{2i})} \tag{4}$$

where

$$p(x_1, \ldots, x_n/E_{1i}) = \frac{1}{(\sqrt{2\pi}\,\sigma)^n} \exp\left\{ -\frac{1}{2\sigma^2} \sum_{j=1}^{n} [x_j - m_j(E_{1i})]^2 \right\} \tag{5}$$

Note that k_1 and k_2 are the number of E_1 and E_2 subclasses, and $m_j(E_{1i})$ is the jth coordinate of the mean of the E_{1i} subclass. $P(E_{1i})$ is proportional to the number of samples M_i observed in the neighborhood of $m_j(E_{1i})$. Thus $(x_1, x_2, \ldots, x_n) \in E_1$, if

$$\sum_{i=1}^{k_1} M_i \exp\left\{ -\frac{1}{2\sigma^2} \sum_{j=1}^{n} [x_j - m_j(E_{1i})]^2 \right\} >$$

$$K \sum_{i=1}^{k_2} M_i \exp\left\{ -\frac{1}{2\sigma^2} \sum_{j=1}^{n} [x_j - m_j(E_{2i})]^2 \right\} \tag{6}$$

RECOGNITION UNDER THE SITUATION OF INCOMPLETE OBSERVATION

In many practical situations, all n parameters are not always measurable (It is true especially if we select all the state variables as the set of parameters and all the information gathered is not sufficient for estimating all the state variables from the observable state variables). Suppose there are only k out of n parameters measurable, it can be shown that the optimum decision based on k variables is based on the k-variate marginal-probability densities. The resulting decision is given by Eq. (7).

$$(x_1, \ldots, x_k) \text{ is in } E_1 \text{ if } \frac{P(E_1/x_1, \ldots, x_k)}{P(E_2/x_1, \ldots, x_k)} > 1 \tag{7}$$

where

$$\frac{P(E_1/x_1, \ldots, x_k)}{P(E_2/x_1, \ldots, x_k)} = \frac{\sum_{i=1}^{k_1} P(E_{1i}) \, p(x_1, \ldots, x_k/E_{1i})}{\sum_{i=1}^{k_2} P(E_{2i}) \, p(x_1, \ldots, x_k/E_{2i})} \tag{8}$$

RECOGNITION BASED ON REPEATED OBSERVATIONS

If a recognition of input can be based on the cumulative evidence collected from r repeated observations, the probability of correct recognition can usually be increased over that obtained with recognitions based on a single observation. If $x(k) = x_1(k), x_2(k), \ldots, x_n(k)$ represents the set of n parameters measured (or estimated) at the kth instant, and if the different measurements are statistically independent, the optimum procedure for recognizing the set of r repeated measurements being more likely a member of class E_1 or E_2 is given by Eq. (9).

$$(x_1, x_2, \ldots, x_n) \, \epsilon \, E_1$$

if

$$\frac{P(E_1)}{P(E_2)} \frac{\prod_{k=1}^{r} p\{x_1(k) \, x_2(k), \ldots, x_n(k)/E_1\}}{\prod_{k=1}^{r} p\{x_1(k) \, x_2(k), \ldots, x_n(k)/E_2\}} = \frac{P(E_1)}{P(E_2)} \prod_{k=1}^{r} \lambda_k > 1 \tag{9}$$

It is easily shown that the error probability of the pattern recognition machine will be decreased as the number of repeated observations, r, increases.[10,13]

APPENDIX B

INTRODUCTION TO MATHEMATICAL LEARNING THEORY[15,16]

K. S. Fu

Introduction

Any systematic change in behavior with a certain specified goal is considered to be learning. Our purpose here is to describe learning processes using mathematical models. In order to describe behavioral change, we must distinguish among various kinds of responses. In general, r mutually exclusive and exhaustive classes of responses are considered. Let the r response classes be represented by a set of alternatives $A_1, A_2, \ldots, A_r$. A set of probabilities, $p_j, j = 1, 2, \ldots, r$, are chosen as an index of behavior, one for each alternative or class of responses. p_j is the probability that the jth class of response will occur on a particular trial. Then

$$\sum_{j=1}^{r} p_j = 1, \quad \text{and} \quad 0 \leq p_j \leq 1. \tag{1}$$

We consider the behavioral change being the change of the set of probabilities $\{p_j\}$. In order to specify what factors in the learning process change the set of probabilities, we begin with a general view: whenever certain events $E_1, E_2, \ldots, E_m$ occur, the probabilities are altered in a determined way. We assume that every time a response occurs it has an outcome, and a particular outcome following a given response changes the set of r probabilities in a unique way which is independent of earlier events in the process. In other words, if we are given a set of probabilities $\{p_j\}$ on trial n, the new set on trial $n + l$ is completely determined by the response occuring on trial n and its outcome. Earlier events will, of course, determine the $\{p_j\}$ on trial n.

Now we can describe a learning process consisting of a sequence of trials, on each of which one and only one response occurs. Each response occurrence has an outcome which alters the probabilities of various responses. Let the set of r probabilities, for the r response classes be represented by a column vector p:

$$p = \begin{bmatrix} p_1 \\ p_2 \\ \cdot \\ \cdot \\ \cdot \\ p_r \end{bmatrix} \tag{2}$$

We then define a "learning operator" T, which is an $r \times r$ matrix:

$$T = \begin{bmatrix} u_{11} & u_{12} & \cdots & u_{1r} \\ u_{21} & u_{22} & \cdots & u_{2r} \\ \cdot & \cdot & & \cdot \\ \cdot & \cdot & & \cdot \\ \cdot & \cdot & & \cdot \\ u_{r1} & u_{r2} & \cdots & u_{rr} \end{bmatrix} \tag{3}$$

When this matrix operator T is applied to p we obtain a new column vector $T\,p$, which represents the new set of r probabilities for the r response classes.

Two Alternatives or Response Classes

In this case, $r = 2$

$$p = \begin{bmatrix} p_1 \\ p_2 \end{bmatrix} = \begin{bmatrix} p \\ q \end{bmatrix} \tag{4}$$

and

$$T = \begin{bmatrix} u_{11} & u_{12} \\ u_{21} & u_{22} \end{bmatrix} \tag{5}$$

where $p + q = 1$.

When the operator T is applied to p, the new probability vector is given by

$$T\,p = \begin{bmatrix} u_{11}p + u_{12}q \\ u_{21}p + u_{22}q \end{bmatrix} \tag{6}$$

Since $T\,p$ is also a probability vector, we must have

$$(u_{11}p + u_{12}q) + (u_{21}p + u_{22}q) = 1$$

or

$$(u_{11} + u_{21})p + (u_{21} + u_{22})q = 1 \tag{7}$$

Equation (7) must hold for all values of p and q consistent with the condition that p and q sum to unity, and so in particular for $p = 1$ and $q = 0$ we have

$$u_{11} + u_{21} = 1 \tag{8}$$

whereas for $q = 1$ and $p = 0$, we obtain

$$u_{12} + u_{22} = 1 \tag{9}$$

Equations (8) and (9) assert that the column sums of the matrix T must each be unity, that is, T must be a stochastic matrix.

Let $a = u_{12}$ and $b = u_{21}$, then

$$T = \begin{bmatrix} 1 - b & a \\ b & 1 - a \end{bmatrix} \tag{10}$$

For occurrences of the ith event ($i = 1, 2, \ldots, m$),

$$T_i = \begin{bmatrix} 1 - b_i & a_i \\ b_i & 1 - a_i \end{bmatrix} \tag{11}$$

and

$$T_i\,p = \begin{bmatrix} (1 - b_i)\,p + a_i q \\ b_i p + (1 - a_i)\,q \end{bmatrix} \tag{12}$$

Let

$$T_i\,p = \begin{bmatrix} Q_i p \\ \overline{Q}_i q \end{bmatrix} \tag{13}$$

where

$$Q_i p = (1 - b_i)\,p + a_i q \tag{14}$$

$$\overline{Q}_i q = b_i p + (1 - a_i)\,q \tag{15}$$

and

$$Q_i p + \overline{Q}_i q = 1 \quad (i = 1, 2, \ldots, m)$$

Equation (14) may be rewritten as

$$Q_i p = \alpha_i p + (1 - \alpha_i)\lambda_i \quad (i = 1, 2, \ldots, m) \tag{16}$$

where $\alpha_i = 1 - a_i - b_i$ and $\lambda_i = a_i/(1 - \alpha_i)$. Equation (16) is called the "fixed-point" form. If it should happen that $p = \lambda_i$, we find that $Q_i p = \lambda_i$ from Equation (16). Conversely, if we require that $Q_i p = p$, we have $p = \lambda_i$ provided only that $\alpha_i \neq 1$. Therefore, λ_i is a fixed point of the operator Q_i. If p should ever equal λ_i, the operator Q_i would not change p. A geometrical interpretation of the various parameters in Eq. (16) may be seen in Fig. 10. We have plotted the function $Q_i p$ against p. If the value of p is to the left of λ_i ($p < \lambda_i$) and we apply Q_i to p, the new value $Q_i p$ will be greater than p. When p is to the right of λ_i ($p > \lambda_i$) $Q_i p$ will be less than p. Hence the effect of the operator Q_i is to generate a new value $Q_i p$ in the direction of λ_i from p.

If we have a sequence of identical events, we need to compute the effect of a repetitive application of a single operator Q_i. From Eq. (16),

$$Q_i^2 p = Q_i(Q_i p) = \alpha_i(Q_i p) + (1 - \alpha_i)\lambda_i$$
$$= \alpha_i^2 p + (1 - \alpha_i^2)\lambda_i \tag{17}$$

Similarly, $Q_i{}^3p = \alpha_i{}^3p + (1 - \alpha_i{}^3)\lambda_i$ and in general,

$$Q_i{}^np = \alpha_i{}^np + (1 - \alpha_i{}^n)\lambda_i \qquad (18)$$

$$\lim_{n \to \infty} \quad Q_i{}^np = \lambda_i \qquad (-1 < \alpha_i < 1) \qquad (19)$$

The plot of $Q_i{}^np$ against n, as shown in Fig. 11, is the learning curve of the described process with specified parameter values.

Since the values of Q_ip must lie in the closed interval [0, 1], the requirement places some restrictions on the allowed values of the parameters a_i, b_i, α_i and λ_i. Rewrite Eq. (14) as

$$Q_ip = p + a_i(1 - p) - b_ip$$

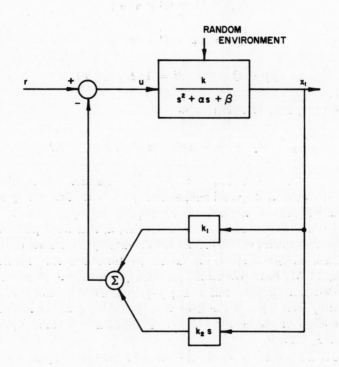

Figure 5

Consider first the situation when $p = 0$, $Q_i p = a_i$, hence

$$0 \leq a_i \leq 1 \tag{20}$$

Then consider the situation when $p = 1$, $Q_i p = 1 - b_i$, hence

$$0 \leq b_i \leq 1 \tag{21}$$

In order to prove the sufficiency of these two conditions, we first note that for any allowed p, the expression $p + a_i(1 - p) - b_i p$ assumes its largest value when a_i is as large as possible and when b_i is as small as possible. Thus, for a given p, the probability $Q_i p$ will be the largest $(= 1)$ when $a_i = 1$ and $b_i = 0$. Furthermore we note that, for a given p, the probability $Q_i p$ will be the smallest $(= 0)$ when $a_i = 0$ and $b_i = 0$. Therefore, the restrictions on a_i and b_i, (20) and (21), are also sufficient for $0 \leq Q_i p \leq 1$.

The parameter α_i also has a restricted range of values. Since a_i and α_i cannot be chosen independently in this situation, we consider the following two cases: (1) $\alpha_i > 0$, $Q_i p$ has a maximum value of $a_i + \alpha_i$ when $p = 1$, hence

$$a_i + \alpha_i \leq 1$$
$$\alpha_i \leq 1 - a_i$$

Also $Q_i p$ has a minimum value of a_i when $p = 0$, hence $a_i \geq 0$, (2) $\alpha_i < 0$, $Q_i p$ has a maximum value of a_i when $p = 0$ and so $a_i \leq 1$. Also $Q_i p$ has a minimum value of $a_i + \alpha_i$ when $p = 1$ and so

$$0 \leq a_i + \alpha_i$$

or

$$-a_i \leq \alpha_i$$

Hence the restriction on α_i is

$$-a_i \leq \alpha_i \leq 1 - a_i \tag{22}$$

In the normal learning situation, $\alpha_i \geq 0$. This means that the slope of the line $Q_i p$ versus p must be positive or zero.

The restriction on λ_i can easily be obtained from Eq. (16)

$$0 \leq \lambda_i \leq 1 \tag{23}$$

Generalization to r *Alternatives*

In this case, $r > 2$. For each of the m possible events we define a matrix operator

$$
T_i = \begin{bmatrix}
u_{11,i} & u_{12,i} & \cdots & u_{1r,i} \\
u_{21,i} & u_{22,i} & \cdots & u_{2r,i} \\
\cdot & & & \\
\cdot & & & \\
\cdot & & & \\
u_{r1,i} & u_{r2,i} & \cdots & u_{rr,i}
\end{bmatrix}
\tag{24}
$$

$$
(i = 1, 2, \ldots, m)
$$

When we apply the operator T_i to the probability vector p of Eq. (2), we obtain the probability vector:

$$
T_i\, p = \begin{bmatrix}
\sum_j u_{1j,i}\, p_j \\
\cdot \\
\cdot \\
\cdot \\
\sum_j u_{r,j,i}\, p_j
\end{bmatrix}
\begin{array}{l}
(i = 1, 2, \ldots, m) \\[4pt]
(j = 1, 2, \ldots, r)
\end{array}
\tag{25}
$$

The elements of this new vector give us the r probabilities for the r response classes after the application of T_i, and so these elements must sum to unity also.

$$
\sum_{k=1}^{r} \sum_{j=1}^{r} u_{kj,i} p_j = 1
\tag{26}
$$

We now wish to introduce one further restriction on our operators. If r classes of responses are initially defined and if the experimenter later decides to treat any two classes in identical manner, it should be possible to combine those two classes, thereby obtaining the same results that would have been obtained had only the $(r - 1)$ classes been defined initially. Formally, we may think of this combining of two classes as the collapsing of an r-dimensional vector sapce into an $(r - 1)$-dimensional vector space. Since the restriction is automatically fulfilled when we have only two classes of responses, let us first examine the implications of this restriction for $r = 3$.

$$
p = \begin{bmatrix}
p_1 \\
p_2 \\
p_3
\end{bmatrix}
\tag{27}
$$

We wish to combine classes 1 and 2 to form a new class c where $p_c = p_1 + p_2$. The probability vector in the collapsed space is resrepresented by

$$c\,p = \begin{bmatrix} p_c \\ 0 \\ p_3 \end{bmatrix} \tag{28}$$

and c, called the "projection operator", is given by

$$c = \begin{bmatrix} 1 & 1 & 0 \\ 0 & 0 & 0 \\ 0 & 0 & 1 \end{bmatrix} \tag{29}$$

Now if an event occurs,

$$c(T\,p) = \begin{bmatrix} (u_{11} + u_{21})\,p_1 + (u_{12} + u_{22})\,p_2 + (u_{13} + u_{23})\,p_3 \\ 0 \\ u_{31}p_1 + u_{32}p_2 + u_{33}p_3 \end{bmatrix} \tag{30}$$

Since the components of $c(T\,p)$ must not depend on p_1 and p_2 but only upon their sum p_c, we demand that

$$u_{31} = u_{32} = u_3$$

and $\tag{31}$

$$u_{11} + u_{21} = u_{12} + u_{22}$$

These restrictions assure that $u_{31}p_1 + u_{32}p_2 = u_3 p_c$ and $(u_{11} + u_{21})\,p_1 + (u_{12} + u_{22})\,p_2 = (u_{11} + u_{21})\,p_c$.

If we combine classes 1 and 3, we obtain in similar manner

$$u_{21} = u_{23} = u_2, \qquad u_{11} + u_{31} = u_{13} + u_{33} \tag{32}$$

Or, if we combine classes 2 and 3,

$$u_{12} = u_{13} = u_1, \qquad u_{23} + u_{33} = u_{22} + u_{32} \tag{33}$$

The restrictions (31), (32), and (33) reduce our original operator T to the form

$$T = \begin{bmatrix} u_{11} & u_1 & u_1 \\ u_2 & u_{22} & u_2 \\ u_3 & u_3 & u_{33} \end{bmatrix} \tag{34}$$

Since each column of T must sum to unity, then T can be written as

$$T = \begin{bmatrix} 1 - u_2 - u_3 & u_1 & u_1 \\ u_2 & 1 - u_1 - u_3 & u_2 \\ u_3 & u_3 & 1 - u_1 - u_2 \end{bmatrix}$$

$$= (1 - u_1 - u_2 - u_3) \begin{bmatrix} 1 & 0 & 0 \\ 0 & 1 & 0 \\ 0 & 0 & 1 \end{bmatrix} + \begin{bmatrix} u_1 & u_1 & u_1 \\ u_2 & u_2 & u_2 \\ u_3 & u_3 & u_3 \end{bmatrix} \qquad (35)$$

Let $\alpha = 1 - u_1 - u_2 - u_3$ and $\lambda_j = u_j/(1 - \alpha)$, $(j = 1, 2, 3,)$, then

$$T = \alpha I + (1 - \alpha) \Lambda \qquad (36)$$

where I is the identity matrix, and

$$\Lambda = \begin{bmatrix} \lambda_1 & \lambda_1 & \lambda_1 \\ \lambda_2 & \lambda_2 & \lambda_2 \\ \lambda_3 & \lambda_3 & \lambda_3 \end{bmatrix} \qquad (37)$$

The form of T in Eq. (35) is a direct consequence of the combining classes restriction. When we apply T to p we obtain

$$T p = \alpha I p + (1 - \alpha) \Lambda p = \alpha p + (1 - \alpha) \lambda \qquad (38)$$

where

$$\lambda = \begin{bmatrix} \lambda_1 \\ \lambda_2 \\ \lambda_3 \end{bmatrix} \qquad (39)$$

The above arguments can be directly extended to the case of more than three response classes and will lead to the following general operator

$$T = \alpha I + (1 - \alpha) \Lambda$$

where

$$\alpha = 1 - \sum_{j=1}^{r} u_j \qquad (40)$$

Λ is an $r \times r$ matrix given by

$$\Lambda = \begin{bmatrix} \lambda_1 & \lambda_1 & \dots & \lambda_1 \\ \lambda_2 & \lambda_2 & \dots & \lambda_2 \\ \cdot & \cdot & & \cdot \\ \cdot & \cdot & & \cdot \\ \cdot & \cdot & & \cdot \\ \lambda_r & \lambda_r & & \lambda_r \end{bmatrix}, \; \lambda_j = \frac{u_j}{(1 - \alpha)}, \; \sum_{j=1}^{r} \lambda_j = 1 \qquad (41)$$

The general element of $T'p$ can be expressed by

$$p_j' = \alpha\, p_j + (1 - \alpha)\, \lambda_j \qquad (j = 1, 2, \ldots, r) \tag{42}$$

In the case of a repetitive application of a single operator T_i, we first consider

$$T_i\, T_i = T_i^2 = [\alpha_i\, I + (1 - \alpha_i)\, \Lambda_i]\, [\alpha_i\, I + (1 - \alpha_i)\, \Lambda_i]$$
$$= \alpha_i^2\, I + (1 - \alpha_i^2)\, \Lambda_i \tag{43}$$

since $I^2 = I,\ I\,\Lambda_i = \Lambda_i\, I = \Lambda_i$, and $\Lambda_i^2 = \Lambda_i$. Similarly,

$$T_i^3 = \alpha_i^3\, I + (1 - \alpha_i^3)\, \Lambda_i$$

and, in general,

$$T_i^n = \alpha_i^n\, I + (1 - \alpha_i^n)\, \Lambda_i \tag{44}$$

Finally, when we apply T_i^n to p we obtain

$$T_i^n\, p = \alpha_i^n\, p + (1 - \alpha_i^n)\, \lambda_i \tag{45}$$

and

$$\lim_{n \to \infty} T_i^n p = \lambda_i \qquad (-1 < a_i < 1) \tag{46}$$

Sequence of Events

Because effects of events are represented by the application of operators and because the events usually occur successively, we are concerned with sequences of operators that are applied to the probability vector. In the case of two response classes and two events, the sequence of operators may be expressed by a general form $(Q_2^v\, Q_1^u)^n$. Since $Q_1^u p = \alpha_1^u p + (1 - \alpha_1^u)\lambda_1$, then

$$Q_2^v\, Q_1^u p = \alpha_1^u\, \alpha_2^v p + \alpha_2^v (1 - \alpha_1^u)\, \lambda_1 + (1 - \alpha_2^v)\, \lambda_2 \tag{47}$$

Rewrite $Q_2^v Q_1^u$ as a new operator $Q_{u,v}$,

$$Q_{u,v} p = \alpha_{u,v} p + (1 - \alpha_{u,v})\, \lambda_{u,v} \tag{48}$$

where

$$\alpha_{u,v} = \alpha_1^u \alpha_2^v \tag{49}$$

and

$$\lambda_{u,v} = \frac{\alpha_2^v (1 - \alpha_1^u)\lambda_1 + (1 - \alpha_2^v)\lambda_2}{(1 - \alpha_1^u \lambda_2^v)} \tag{50}$$

Apply $Q_{u,v}$ to p a total of n times, we get

$$Q_{u,v}^n\, p = (Q_2^v\, Q_1^u)^n p = \alpha_{u,v}^n\, p + (1 - \alpha_{u,v}^n)\lambda_{u,v} \tag{51}$$

$\lambda_{u,v}$ is the fixed point. It is worth noting the behavior of $\lambda_{u,v}$ when u or v becomes large. First, if u is fixed and v tends to infinity, we have

$$\lim_{v \to \infty} \lambda_{u,v} = \lambda_2, \qquad \alpha_2 \neq 1 \tag{52}$$

On the other hand, if v is fixed and u tends to infinity, we have

$$\lim_{u \to \infty} \lambda_{u,v} = \alpha_2^v \lambda_1 + (1 - \alpha_2^v)\lambda_2, \qquad \alpha_1 \neq 1 \tag{53}$$

The asymmetry in this pair of results, (52) and (53), comes from the fact that Q_2 is applied after Q_1, and that the more recent applications usually have relatively greater effects on the final outcome.

Another interesting problem is the commutativity of the operators. For example, if Q_1 is applied when reinforcement is given and Q_2 is applied when reinforcement is withheld, would their order make any difference? Would it matter whether the reinforcements were scattered randomly through the sequence or all bunched together at the beginning or at the end? If it does not matter, the operators should commute. Suppose we apply Q_1 first, then Q_2, using the fixed-point form of the operators:

$$Q_2(Q_1 p) = \alpha_1 \alpha_2 \, p + \alpha_2(1 - \alpha_1) \, \lambda_1 + (1 - \alpha_2) \, \lambda_2 \tag{54}$$

On the other hand, applying Q_2 first and then Q_1 gives

$$Q_1(Q_2 p) = \alpha_1 \alpha_2 \, p + \alpha_1(1 - \alpha_2) \, \lambda_2 + (1 - \alpha_1) \, \lambda_1 \tag{55}$$

The difference between (54) and (55) is

$$(Q_1 Q_2 - Q_2 Q_1) + = (1 - \alpha_1) \, (1 - \alpha_2) \, (\lambda_1 - \lambda_2) \tag{56}$$

From Eq. (56) we can see that the operators Q_1 and Q_2 commute if any of the following three conditions holds:

$$\begin{aligned} \alpha_1 &= 1 \\ \alpha_2 &= 1 \\ \lambda_1 &= \lambda_2 \end{aligned} \tag{57}$$

Similarly, we can generalize the results to the case of two matrix operators T_1 and T_2. Consider

$$T_1 = \alpha_1 \, I + (1 - \alpha_1) \, \Lambda_1 \tag{58}$$

$$T_2 = \alpha_2 I + (1 - \alpha_2) \Lambda_2 \tag{59}$$

then

$$T_2 T_1 = \alpha_1\alpha_2 I + \alpha_2(1 - \alpha_1) \Lambda_1 + \alpha_1(1 - \alpha_2) \Lambda_2 + (1 - \alpha_1)(1 - \alpha_2) \Lambda_1 \Lambda_2 \tag{60}$$

and

$$T_1 T_2 = \alpha_1\alpha_2 I + \alpha_1(1 - \alpha_2) \Lambda_2 + \alpha_2(1 - \alpha_1) \Lambda_1 + (1 - \alpha_1)(1 - \alpha_2) \Lambda_1 \Lambda_2 \tag{61}$$

The difference between (60) and (61) is

$$T_1 T_2 - T_2 \dot{T}_1 = (1 - \alpha_1)(1 - \alpha_2)(\Lambda_1 \Lambda_2 - \Lambda_2 \Lambda_1) \tag{62}$$

Since

$$\sum_{j=1}^{r} \lambda_{ij} = 1 \qquad (i = 1, 2)$$

then

$$\Lambda_1 \Lambda_2 = \Lambda_1 \qquad \text{and} \qquad \Lambda_2 \Lambda_1 = \Lambda_2$$

Therefore, T_1 and T_2 will commute if any of the following three conditions holds:

$$\begin{aligned} \alpha_1 &= 1 \\ \alpha_2 &= 1 \\ \Lambda_1 &= \Lambda_2 \end{aligned} \tag{63}$$

System II. For a linear second-order plant, assume the transfer function of the plant has the form

$$G(s) = \frac{k}{s^2 + \alpha s + \beta}$$

where α and β are two time-varying parameters. Let the input be a square wave with period τ. α and β are assumed varying slowly compared to the period τ so that at least one adaptive or hill-climbing step may be completed before α and β change significantly. For a given set of α and β, and for a free terminal time T, the optimum control signal u to minimize the index of performance

$$IP = \int_0^T (x'Qx + u^2)\, dt, \qquad x = \text{state vector}$$

is a linear combination of the state variable.* A simple block diagram is shown in Fig. 5. The problem is to design a learning controller for the given plant and the index of performance.

* This is formulated as an optimum regulator problem but it is equivalent to the optimum step response problem by setting the steady state errors to zero.

For this particular system, plant parameters α and β are considered as the features to describe the environmental patterns (i.e., the effect of environment on the plant characteristic patterns). Since the number of possible control strategies is unknown, a simple but crude classification of (α, β) is to quantize, at first, α and β into a finite number of levels, say five, this is corresponding to dividing the feature space into twenty-five regions. (Assume the probable ranges of α and β are known). For each set of (α, β), k_1 and k_2 are adjusted by a two-dimensional hill-climbing technique in order to minimize the performance index. Memory is used to store the current best estimate of k_1 and k_2 for a given set of (α, β) values. When a new set of (α, β) is recognized, the memory is interrogated for the best values of k_1 and k_2 and these values are set before hill-climbing proceeds. Adaptation then proceeds and better values of k_1, k_2 and performance index replace the old values in the memory. A typical plot of performance index versus time is shown in Fig. 6. If the values of performance index when (α_1, β_1) occurs are extracted from Fig. 6, a nonincreasing learning curve will be obtained as shown in Fig. 7.

In order to exercise the "refreshing" and the "forgetting" procedures on computer memory capacity, only the 16 most probable (α, β) sets out of a

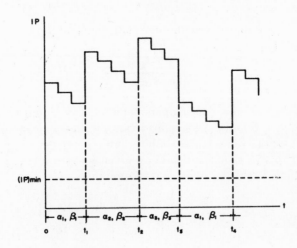

Figure 6

possible 25 will be allowed to have corresponding values of k_1, k_2, and IP stored with them. A continuous check of the number of occurrences of each (α,β) pair will determine the 16 most probable (α,β) combinations. Whenever a new set of (α,β) occurs, the parameter values of k_1 and k_2 supplied by the learning controller will be those that were the optimum values for the old (α,β) set that most closely resembles the existing one and it is improbable that they will be very far from the true optimum values. It is hoped that, by applying a learning process, the 25 regions in the feature space will be finally partitioned into only 16 regions or even less such that all the information may be stored within the allowable memory capacity.

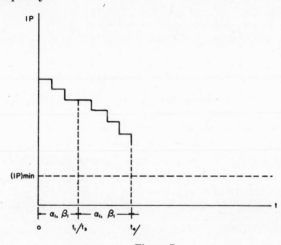

Figure 7

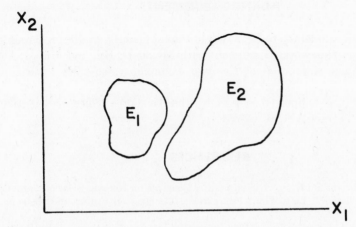

Figure A1

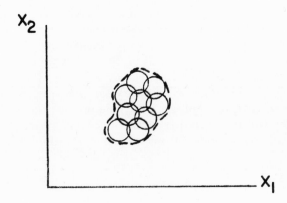

Figure A2

CONCLUSIONS

An informal introduction of learning control systems has been presented. A class of learning control systems has been described in detail and the basic functions of a learning controller have been discussed. Two example systems have been given to illustrate the proposed approach. A complete analytic design procedure of learning control systems is still under investigation. This paper is by no means a complete discussion on the design of learning control systems.

ACKNOWLEDGMENTS

The author is indebted to Dr. J. E. Gibson for his support and encouragement through this work. Discussions with Mr. J. D. Hill and Mr. M. D. Waltz on their simulation of the two example systems are especially helpful.

The work was supported in part by the Air Force Office of Scientific Research, Contract AFOSR 62-351.

REFERENCES

1. Tou, J. T., and Fu K. S., "Digital Control Concepts for Nervous System Synthesis and Simulation," Proc. Third International Congress on Cybernetics, Belgium, 1961.
2. Fu, K. S., "A Learning System Using Statistical Decision Functions," AIEE Winter General Meeting, 1962.

3. Krug, G. K., and Letskii E. K., "A Learning Automaton of the Tabular Type," *Automation and Remote Control*, vol. 22, no. 10, March 1962.

4. Widrow, B., "Adaptive Sampled-data Systems," Tech. Rept. No. 2104–1, Stanford Electronics Laboratories, Stanford University, Stanford, Calif., July 15, 1960.

5. Sklansky, J., "Adaptation and Feedback," Symposium on Discrete Adaptive Processes, 1962 JACC, New York.

6. Widrow, B., "Pattern Recognition and Adaptive Control," Symposium on Discrete Adaptive Processes, 1962 JACC, New York.

7. Mesarovic, M. D., "Self-Organizing Control Systems," Symposium on Discrete Adaptive Processes, 1962 JACC, New York.

8. Gibson, J. E., "Adaptive Learning Systems," Proc. 1962 National Electronics Conference, Chicago.

9. Group Report No. 1, "Philosophy and State of the Art of Learning Control Systems," Control and Information Systems Laboratory, School of Electrical Engineering, Purdue University, Lafayette, Ind., AFOSR-5144.

10. Fu, K. S., "A Statistical Approach to the Design of Intelligent Machines—Pattern Recognition and Learning," Cybernetica, No. 2, 1962.

11. Chang, S. S. L., *Synthesis of Optimum Control Systems*, McGraw-Hill, New York, 1961.

12. Samuel, A. L., "Some Studies in Machine Learning Using the Game of Checkers," *IBM J. of Res. and Dev.*, vol. 3, no. 3, July 1959.

13. Sebestyen, G. S., "Pattern Recognition by an Adaptive Process of Sample Set Construction," *Trans. IRE Inform. Theory*, vol. IT–8, September 1962.

14. Fu, K. S., "Introduction to Mathematical Learning Theory," Class Notes, EE 681—Artificial Intelligence, Spring 1963, Purdue University. (Part of the notes is presented in Appendix B.)

15. Bush, R. R., and Mosteller, F., "Stochastic Models for Learning", Wiley, New York, 1955.

16. Suppes, P., and Atkinson, R. C., "Markov Learning Models for Multiperson Interactions," Stanford University Press, 1960.

14

A PROBLEM SOLVER WITH
FORMAL DESCRIPTIVE INPUTS*

DAVID J. KUCK and GILBERT K. KRULEE

The Technological Institute, Northwestern University

INTRODUCTION

In the research to be discussed in this paper, we have designed a system that attempts to solve problems which have initially been presented to it in the form of descriptive statements in ordinary English. The total system falls into two major divisions. The first of these, which has been described elsewhere,[5] accepts the verbal statements as inputs and produces as output a formal description of the problem. This description contains two kinds of elements: logical *predicates* for summarizing qualitative relationships and *functor expressions* for the representation of quantitative data. The second subsystem takes this description as its input and proceeds deductively to obtain a solution. In this paper, we shall begin with these formalized descriptions as inputs and describe only the problem solving portion of the larger system. In designing this system we have limited ourselves to certain classes of problems, namely, those that can be described algebraically and that represent quantifiable physical situations with an unknown. Elementary problems in mechanics and electrical circuits are perhaps the best examples.

We can also contrast this problem solving system with the current computer methods for obtaining solutions to physical problems. Normally, a machine user must first abstract from the real world a formal model of a

* This research is being supported through Grant G–17951 from the National Science Foundation and is part of a larger program of studies on the simulation of human behavior. The present status of the system is that the design has been substantially completed. The system is currently being programmed using the IPL-V list processing language of Newell, Shaw, and Simon[9].

physical system. Secondly, he must derive an algorithm which will compute the unknown values in his model. Even if he uses a problem-oriented language as input, he will still present to the computer some data and an algorithm. Under these circumstances the physical problem to be solved no longer has any relevance for the machine. In our problem solver we shall present to the computer formal descriptions of the physical world. It will be up to the machine to derive implicitly its own algorithm.

This procedure in some senses is not unlike that followed by an engineer when given an adequate description of a physical system. Even though he may not be familiar with all the necessary equations, he can look up formulas in a handbook, perform algebraic manipulations on them, substitute actual numbers for variables or parameters, and eventually obtain a numerical solution. Thus, in some sense, the scheme we are attempting to mechanize has the same overall characteristics as a human problem solver and it might be viewed as an artificial intelligence model. However, we make no claims for this system as a model of psychological processes.

The paper is organized into three main parts. In the first, our use of formal representations of physical problems will be discussed. In the second part, we will describe the functioning of the problem solver. Finally, we will discuss some formalisms used in programming the system.

SYSTEM ORGANIZATION

In the field of linguistics it is a standard practice to distinguish between semantics and syntactics, while in studies of the foundations of mathematics, one talks about *theory* and *metatheory* or *system* and *metasystem*.* In either case, one is in a position to employ at least two related methods of representation. One set of symbols refers to objects while the other refers to permissible relationships among classes of objects. This principle of two or more representations, arranged in a hierarchy, is also employed in the design of this problem solving system—it is a critical feature of its structure and operation.

For example, in metamathematics one may abstract from some informal mathematical theory, a formal system that expresses symbolically all of the pertinent relationships, such that by purely syntactic methods, i.e., no interpretations needed, at least some of the theorems of the informal theory can be derived. To manipulate the formal system, another informal system

---

* Throughout, we will have occasion to use words like "formal system" or "formal theory" and "metasystem" or "metatheory." The distinction between "theory" and "system" will be that the former is completely abstract and the latter is a machine representation of this abstraction. This distinction is not important, so we can on some occasions use either term, interchangeably.

is used which consists of only very conservative mathematical techniques (e.g., finitary methods, constructive proofs, etc.). This is called the meta-theory and the formal system under study is its object theory.*

Thus we can speak of three distinct theories: (1) the original informal theory, (2) the formal system abstracted from (1) which is the object theory of (3) the informal metatheory (Fig. 1). Further, the metatheory can be quasiformalized to be used like a formal system by the meta-mathematician, or it can be formalized completely and be made the object theory of study by an informal metametamathematical system.

It should be clear that this picture will be quite useful when we think about the digital computer as a problem solver. In our case, the original informal system will be the physical world which is the subject of all of our problems. We wish to map problem statements about the real world into a set of formal representations. With these formalisms, we must be able to express anything that we wish to say about the outside world. With a metasystem, we will want to manipulate the formalisms of the object system in such a way as to lead to the numerical problem solution.

In order to obtain formal representations of the real world, we have several choices open to us. We could equip the machine with some sort of direct input devices, e.g., meters of all sorts, from the reading of which the machine could formalize a picture of the outside world. We could also have unknown meters such that the machine knew their location and purpose but not their reading, and thus have it solve for these. Information about all sorts of physical configurations and side conditions would also come in via meters. Alternatively, we as observers could write down directly this information in the formal terms which the machine is prepared to accept. It is this latter course of action which we have chosen to follow. (See Fig. 2).

With the formal representation of a problem at hand, a set of formal metatheoretical rules will be applied. The metasystem employs a number of heuristic procedures and resembles in some important respects the systems of Newell, Shaw, and Simon for theorem proving and general problem

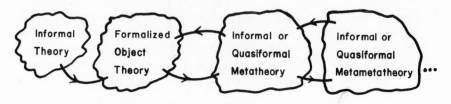

Figure 1

* This is described in Kleene,[4] Art. 15.

solving.[10] This metasystem operates in a formal way and makes one or more attempts to derive a solution to a problem. It distinguishes the unknown, the given numerical data, and the accompanying physical relations that make up the input problem. It tries to use these in forming a logical *deduction* that leads to the correct answer. The metasystem will operate on the input problem statement and the deduction string. It has also at its disposal some physical, logical, and algebraic formalisms. In its operation, there is no guarantee that it will solve any given problem. For relatively simple problems, we can argue convincingly that the system will be effective. For more complex problems, there is no alternative to empirical studies of effectiveness with the computer system.

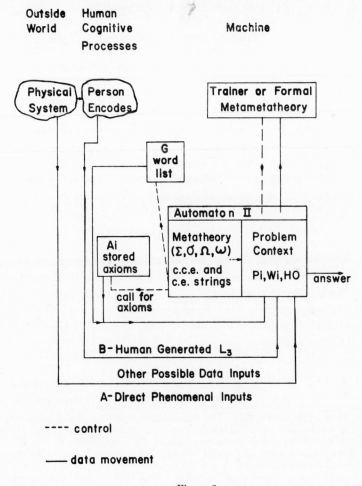

Figure 2

RELATIONS

The first formalism which we discuss will be used to express the qualitative data conveyed by a problem statement. We choose for this purpose to use standard first (and possibly higher) order predicates, which are well known in symbolic logic. For the present we shall consider only constants as arguments but later will introduce bound variables. Our predicates will all be two place predicates wh'ch express a *relation* between the two arguments. For example the sentence 'Harry runs the race' expresses the relation of running given by the verb 'runs,'* between the two arguments 'Harry' and 'the race.' Formally then, 'runs' is the relation and we write:

$$\text{relation (argument 1, argument 2)}$$

as:

$$\text{runs (Harry, the race)}$$

In general the arguments are an ordered pair, although this ordering may be relaxed in some cases.

FUNCTORS

We will use *functors* as a second kind of formal representation for the expression of quantitative data. Functors are defined and used in slightly different ways by several writers† but can be thought of as a generalization of the standard mathematical function. We will define a functor to be a class of consistent quantities given by a mapping of some domain (D) into some range (R) written:

$$\text{functor [argument(s)]} = \text{value}$$

Distinguishing numerical and nonnumerical domains and ranges, there are four possible kinds of functors. If D and R are both sets of numbers (or symbols for numbers) then we have the ordinary definition of a mathematical *function*, e.g., $+(3,5) = 8$, where $+$ is the function. If the domain is extramathematical‡ but R is as above, then we have the class of physical *fluents*, e.g., pound weight (oranges) = 5, where the weight in pounds is a fluent. We shall write functors with physical dimensions as

$$\text{functor}_{\text{dimension}} \text{ (argument)} = \text{value}$$

---

* Single quotation marks will be used to distinguish object language from metalanguage when both are English. The many other object languages used at several levels will be distinguished only by their form and context to avoid unnecessary pedantry. We will persist in using double quotation marks in the colloquial sense.

† For three points of view see Carnap,[1] Menger,[8] and Reichenbach.[11] We choose an eclectric definition drawn from these.

‡ See Menger[8] for a discussion of this point. Note that functors with nonnumerical mathematical domains are commonly called functionals.

Thus, this example could be written:

$$\text{weight}_{\text{pounds}} \text{ (oranges)} = 5$$

The third possibility is an extramathematical D and R is

$$\text{first member (orange, apple)} = \text{orange}$$

or

$$\text{color (orange)} = \text{green}$$

All functors have an *intension* and an *extension*. The intension is concerned with what is meant by, or what is intrinsic in, the functor itself, i.e., it is concerned with the operator of the left-hand side. The entire left-hand side is called a *functor expression* (f. ex.). In our examples the intensions are the operation of addition, the weight in pounds, first-place membership, and physical color, respectively. The extensions in each case are the "values" or right-hand side members. Note that any n-place functor can be replaced by an $(n + 1)$-place predicate, but not vice versa.* Moreover, the extension of a fluent can be substituted for its functor expression, but in predicate form this substitution property of equation form is lost. We will explicate this further in subsequent applications. In what follows, we will use the term "functor" to refer to any of these formalisms.

THE PROBLEM SOLVER

We now turn to an informal description of our problem-solving system. The inputs to this system will always be a set of relations and functor equations which serve to define a particular problem. For convenience, we will use the name $L3$ to refer to the set of all possible problem inputs.

ANALYTIC PROBLEMS

The first and simplest class of problems considered will be amenable to solution by analytic methods. If a problem statement contains all that is necessary for its solution, we term it an analytic problem statement. Since $(\lambda x_1, x_2, x_3, x_4)(x_{1_{x_2}}(x_3) = x_4)\ (a, b, c, d)$ is a representation of many different functor equations in $L3$, depending on a choice of parameters a, b, c, and d, we call manipulation in terms of these, parametric methods.† In particular

---

* This point is discussed by Carnap (Ref. 1, p. 74). Note also that the only functors for which general substitution is allowed are the functions, as shown in the very interesting paper by Menger.[8]

† The lambda notation of Church is used in logic to explicate the use of arguments by a *form* and thus defines a *function* by binding the form's variables. For example, $x_1^2 + x_2 x_1$ is a *form* which, if used as a function and applied to the argument pair $(2, 3)$, would lead to ambiguity. To clarify the correspondence of entries in the argument vector to variables we write: $(\lambda x_1, x_2)\ (x_1^2 + x_1 x_2)\ (2, 3) = 10$, while $(\lambda x_2, x_1)\ (x_1^2 + x_1 x_2)$ $(2, 3) = 15$. In general, where $x^{(n)} = x_1, x_2, \ldots, x_n$ (with x_i uninterpreted symbols), we call $f(x^{(n)})$ a *form* and $(\lambda y^{(n)})\ (f(x^{(n)}))$ a *functor*, where $y^{(n)}$ is some permutation of $x^{(n)}$.

we shall be concerned with those parameters representing the three parts of the left-hand side, namely f_i, d_i, and arg_i. In terms of these parameters we will be able to plan heuristically some steps in our problem-solving attempt. We will point these out in detail after considering an example.

Example 1

Consider the English sentences:

(1-1). 'The price of an orange is 10¢.'

(1-2). 'What is the price of five oranges?'

In $L3$ these become:

f.e.1: price_ξ (orange) $= 10$

f.e.2: price_{d_2} (5 oranges) $= x$

The answer deduction string could be as follows* (the deduction string entry is followed by its explanation in all examples):

$(A1)$ price_{d_2} (5 oranges)	$= x$	: f.e.2, given question
$(A2)$ price_ξ (orange)	$= 10$	: f.e.1, given data with same f_i as $(A1)$
$(A3)$ price_ξ (5 oranges)	$= x$	: replace d_2 of $(A1)$ with ξ of $(A2)$
$(A4)$ $*(5, \text{price}_\xi \text{ (orange)})$	$= x$	: follows $(A3)$ by homogeneity of 'price'
$(A5)$ $*(5, 10)$	$= x$	: substitute RHS for LHS of $(A2)$ in $(A4)$
$(A6)$ 50	$= x$	: carry out* operation

As a general rule we start with the unknown f.e. as $(A1)$. Then, scanning the given data for something parametrically similar to $(A1)$, we find f.e.2 which gives $(A2)$ in this case. In this case, we chose to make d_2 correspond to the dimension of f.e.1, and carried out this parameter replacement in $(A3)$. In $(A4)$ we took advantage of a property of a number of functors† which is the same as the homogeneity of linear transformations, $f_{i_{d_i}}(\text{nbr}_i \ \text{arg}_i) = *(\text{nbr}_i, f_{i_{d_i}}(\text{arg}_i))$, where nbr_i is any number (or corresponding word) and juxtaposition of the parts of the left hand side's argument implies numerical quantification (e.g., 'five eggs,' '3 oranges'). We will call these homogeneous functors. Next, in the deduction, we substituted the numerical value of f.e.1 into $(A4)$ to get $(A5)$. Carrying out the indicated operation, in $(A6)$ we got the desired numerical result. Notice that here where the dimension of the answer was not explicitly specified in the problem statement, we are justified in either normalizing or tentatively assuming anything we wish. However, it would be necessary

---

* Deductions will be given in a typical fashion, but they are not intended to be (and certainly are not) unique solution procedures.

† Later in this chapter we will formally present all of these rules. The homogeneity rule will be applicable to f.e. with functors which are marked 'homogeneous' in our stored glossary.

to print out the final axiomatic functor equation represetationn of x, namely $(A3)$ here, to indicate what has been done. We can interpret the results as something like 'The price of five oranges is 50¢.'

Notice that in the introduction of the homogeneous functor we make use of the mathematical function as a special kind of functor having both a mathematical domain and range. In our computing we shall need first the arithmetic functions (r.5 will be discussed below):

$$(r.5a) \quad (\lambda x_1, x_2)(+(x_1, x_2))(a,b) = a + b \qquad \text{sum}$$
$$(r.5b) \quad (\lambda x_1, x_2)(-(x_1, x_2))(a,b) = a - b \qquad \text{difference}$$
$$(r.5c) \quad (\lambda x_1, x_2)(*(x_1, x_2))(a,b) = a * b \qquad \text{product}$$
$$(r.5d) \quad (\lambda x_1, x_2)(/(x_1, x_2))(a,b) = a / b \qquad \text{quotient}$$

where a and b are either numbers or functor expressions. Also we assume the ability of the system to evaluate these functors for numerical arguments. When a and b are functor expressions we can observe some useful heuristics. Consider the following cases:

$$(1\text{-}3) \quad (\lambda x_1, x_2)(+(x_1, x_2))(f_{1_{d_1}}(\text{arg}_1), f_{1_{d_1}}(\text{arg}_2)) = f_{1_{d_1}}(\text{arg}_1) \pm f_{1_{d_1}}(\text{arg}_2)$$
$$= f_{1_{d_1}}(\text{arg}_1 \cup \text{arg}_2)$$

$$(1\text{-}4) \quad (\lambda x_1, x_2)(\pm(x_1, x_2))(f_{1_{d_1}}(\text{arg}_1), f_{2_{d_1}}(\text{arg}_1)) = f_{1_{d_1}}(\text{arg}_1) \pm f_{2_{d_1}}(\text{arg}_1)$$
$$= f_{3_{d_1}}(\text{arg}_1)$$

$$(1\text{-}5) \quad (\lambda x_1, x_2)(*/(x_1, x_2))(f_{1_{d_1}}(\text{arg}_1), f_{2_{d_2}}(\text{arg}_1)) = f_{1_{d_1}}(\text{arg}_1) */ f_{2_{d_2}}(\text{arg}_1)$$
$$= f_{3_{d_1}} */ d_2(\text{arg}_1)$$

where the connectives are $+$ or $-$ in (1-3) and (1-4), and $*$ or $/$ in (1-5). In (1-3) we have a pair of expressions with identical functor and dimension but with different arguments. When these are added (or subtracted) we get an expression with the same dimension, the same or a related functor, i.e., f_2 may be identical to f_1, and an argument corresponding to the union of the two component arguments. For example: (1-3') cost$_\ell$ (apple) $+$ cost$_\ell$ (orange) $=$ cost$_\ell$ (apple and orange). This corresponds to the additivity property of a linear operator and such functors will be called additive. Since we have seen that such functors as 'cost' or 'price' satisfy both additivity and homogeneity, we will call them linear functors. In (1-4) we have a pair of expressions with common dimension and argument that are added or subtracted. Here the resulting expression has the same *argument* and *dimension*, but the functor is usually different than either of the input pair. An example of this would be: (1-4') Selling price$_\ell$ (apples) $-$ purchase price$_\ell$ (apples) $=$ profit$_\ell$ (apples) or the corresponding statement with addition. In (1-5) we have different functors and dimensions but a common argument for the two expressions. These combine under $*$ or $/$ to give a new functor, retaining the same argument, but with a dimension corresponding to the juxtaposition (product or quotient) of the constituent dimensions. For example: (1-5') voltage$_{volts}$ (resistor A) = *(resistance$_{amps}$ (resistor A), current$_{ohms}$ (resistor A)). We can condense (1-3), (1-4) and (1-5) in the following table which shows common parameters versus the algebraic connective of a pair of functor expressions:

Algebraic connective		Argument	Common parameters, argument and dimension	Functor and dimension
	$+$		(1–4)	(1–3)
	$-$		(1–4)	(1–3)
(1–6)	*	(1–5)		
		(1–5)		

With this example, we can see at least intuitively how a solution can be guaranteed from its $L3$ problem description. At this point, we will turn to consideration of how this problem solving procedure will be organized.

DEDUCTIVE SYSTEM*

Recalling that the nonnumerical side of our extensional functor equation was called the functor expression (f. ex.), we will occasionally write f. ex.$_i$ for $f_{i_{d_i}}(\arg_i)$. We define as *formulas* of our formal system:

(f.1) $f_{i_{d_i}}(\arg_i) = f_{j_{d_j}}(\arg_j)$ or x : intensional functor equation† (i.f.e.)
(f.2) $\text{pred}_i(\arg_i, \arg_j)$: relational predicate (rel.)

When a problem is mapped into $L3$, we will get a number of such formulas. When these are used in a formal deduction, we call them *assumption formulas*. Also, the input problem will give a number of extensional functor equations; we will call these formulas the *assertions* of a functor expression:

(f.3) $f_{i_{d_i}}(\arg_i)$ = number   : extensional functor equation (e.f.e.)

Thus, we can use = to show equality between f.e. and assume that we are trying to solve for the right-hand side; = is in a sense, then, a directed relation. On the other hand, ≡ simply identifies a functor expression with

---

* The definitions in this section are modeled after the formal systems of logic; see Kleene.[4]

† We adopt the nomenclature, intensional and extensional functor equations, to denote functor equations with functor expressions on both sides of the '=', and with a number on one side and a functor expression on the other side, respectively.

a number. In examples we will use = in all cases for simplicity.* We also define some *axioms* that have the form of (f.1) type formulas and which we discussed as (1-3), (1-4), and (1-5) above:†

$$(\text{ax. 1}) \quad f_{1_{d_1}}(\text{arg}_1) \pm f_{1_{d_1}}(\text{arg}_2) = f_{1_{d_1}}(\text{arg}_1 \cup \text{arg}_2)$$

$$(\text{ax. 2}) \quad f_{1_{d_1}}(\text{arg}_1) \pm f_{2_{d_1}}(\text{arg}_1) = f_{3_{d_1}}(\text{arg}_1)$$

$$(\text{ax. 3}) \quad f_{1_{d_1}}(\text{arg}_1) \, */ \, f_{2_{d_2}}(\text{arg}_1) = f_{3_{d_1}} \, */ \, d_2(\text{arg}_1)$$

These axioms will be used to generate new formulas from old ones in a way to be discussed shortly. Other stored axioms will be used later.

In order to generate a solution to a problem we will form a *deduction* string of formulas $A1, A2, \ldots, An$ which yields or deduces the conclusion An from $A1, \ldots, An - 1$ (we symbolize this: $A1, A2, \ldots, An - 1 \vdash An$) in the following way. For each Ai, $1 \leq i \leq n - 1$, we require that either Ai is an assumption formula, or Ai is an axiom which, for example, is introduced by supplying arguments to the lambda notation functions (1-3), (1-4) and (1-5) to yield formulas of the type (ax. 1), (ax. 2) and (ax. 3), respectively, or Ai is a consequence of preceding formulas (Aj, $j < i$) according to the formal *rules of inference* (r.o.i.). Useful arguments will be chosen for (ax. 1), (ax. 2), and (ax. 3) from the preceding Ai of the deduction string, or they may be left temporarily as free variables (mnemonic assignments) to be bound by the context later.

The rules of inference are metatheoretical rules that operate on the deduction string. The symbols used in these rules are metatheory symbols that represent deduction string formulas. We now detail some of the rules of inference (r.o.i.) to be used.

Rule 1 corresponds to the symmetry of the equality relation and will be used when the "solved for" part is reversed:

$$(\text{r.1}) \quad (\text{f.e.}_i = \text{f.e.}_j) \rightarrow (\text{f.e.}_j = \text{f.e.}_i) : \text{symmetry}$$

The arrow notation for all rules of inference means that of the formula(s) or functor expression(s) to the left of the arrow appear(s) preceding Ai in a deduction, we can use the right hand member of the arrow as formula $Ai + 1$ in the deduction string. Rule 2 is the transitivity of equality:‡

$$(\text{r.2}) \quad (\text{f.e.}_i = \text{f.e.}_j) \, \& \, (\text{f.e.}_j = \text{f.e.}_k) \rightarrow (\text{f.e.}_i = \text{f.e.}_k) : \text{transitivity}$$

---

* While the distinction between = and ≡ will be useful in the mechanization of this system, it seems overly pedantic to employ it in this presentation.

† Note that some of these could be generalized to longer strings of functor expressions on the LHS of a particular axiom. We will have no use for these, however.

‡ We shall use the symbol & as the logical 'and'.

By *substitution* of an extensional functor equation in a functor expression, we shall mean replacing the LHS of the e.f.e. (f.ex. part) by the RHS of the e.f.e. (number) at all occurrences of the LHS of the e.f.e. in the f. ex. The next rule of inference is analogous to modus ponens in the predicate calculus and we shall call it detachment:

$$(r.3) \quad (f.e._a) \ \& \ (f.e._a = f.e._b) \rightarrow (f.e._b) \qquad : detachment$$

To use detachment we require that f.e.$_a$ be asserted. This means that all functor expression components f.e.$_i$ of f.e.$_a$ must appear as e.f.e., f.e.$_i$ = number, in previous formulas in the deduction (cf. f.3). Then, from the i.f.e.

$$f.e._a = f.e._b$$

we can infer that f.e.$_a$, with all numbers substituted in, is a number such that

$$number = f.e._b$$

which asserts or detaches f.e.$_b$. Also, we have for homogeneous functors:

$$(r.4) \quad (f_{i_{d_i}}(number \ ^*arg_i)) \rightarrow (^*(number, f_{i_{d_i}}(arg_i))) \qquad : homogeneity$$

$$f_i \ \epsilon \ \{homogeneous \ functor \ set\}$$

Also we must have the ability to evaluate arithmetic operations (cf. *r.5a, b, c, d* above):

$$(r.5) \quad (f.e._i = f_i(number_1, number_2)) \rightarrow (f.e._i = resulting \ number)$$
$$f_i \ \epsilon \ \{+, \ -, \ ^*, \ /\}$$

For manipulating relational predicates with nonoriented relations (e.g., those signifying physical juxtaposition—hooked, joined) we have:

$$(r.6) \quad (jux. \ pred_i(arg_i, \ arg_j)) \rightarrow (jux. \ pred_i(arg_j, \ arg_i)) \qquad : commutativity$$

For choosing the argument of an f.e. arising from a relation:

$$(r.7) \quad (rel. \ i: pred_i(arg_1, \ arg_2)) \ \& \ (f_{i_{d_i}}(rel. \ i) = RHS)$$
$$\rightarrow (f_{i_{d_i}}(arg_1) = RHS) \ \vee \ (f_{i_{d_i}}(arg_2) = RHS)$$

This $\vee$ is in the inclusive sense (i.e., both may be the case), but we will generally only want one, depending on the context.

We also will want to be able to bind formally free arg, d, and f variables in terms of standards or earlier deduction string entries. Thus for standard binding:

$$(r.8) \quad (standard) \ \& \ (\lambda f, d, arg)(f_d(arg) = number_i)(x_1, x_2, x_3)$$
$$\rightarrow (\lambda f, d, arg)(f_d(arg) = nbr_i)(y_1, y_2, y_3)$$

where one or perhaps more of the x_i are free and the corresponding y_i's are bound with respect to the standards. The remaining x_i and corresponding y_i are identical. We are here using x_i and y_i as English words and arg, d, and f as mnemonic aids. Since we sometimes bind with respect to other elements of the deduction string, we have also:

$$(\text{r.9}) \quad (\lambda f, d, \arg)(f_d(\arg) = \text{nbr}_i)(x_1, x_2, x_3) \ \& \ (\lambda f, d, \arg)(f_d(\arg)$$
$$= \text{nbr}_j)(y_1, y_2, y_3) \rightarrow (\lambda f, d, \arg)(f_d(\arg) = \text{nbr}_k)(z_1, z_2, z_3)$$

where the x_i are all bound in an earlier Ai, some (usually one) of the y_i are free and are to be bound with respect to the x_i in the corresponding z_i. The remaining (bound) y_i and corresponding z_i are identical. The particular use of (r.8) and (r.9) will always be clear in context and will be referred to as binding. Other rules will be introduced as required in subsequent examples.

SYNTHETIC PROBLEMS

The category of problems that we have been discussing was called (parametric) analytic because we manipulated formulas in terms of f_i, d_i and $\arg_i$ (parameters) and because the problem statement was "self-contained." Only the formulas given in the problem statement were used in its solution. Now we turn to the (parametric) synthetic case where some formulas which are necessary for the deduction of a solution will not be contained in the given problem statement. While the above problems required a good deal of formalized metatheory in their solutions, we never had to "know" anything about the problem contexts. Much human problem solving in realistic cases requires some previous knowledge or training. In particular, in solving engineering problems or even in elementary algebra "story problems" the solver is usually required to supply some key information in order to succeed. As examples, we may need to know empirically determined equations like Ohm's law or Kirchhoff's equations in electricity, or in an algebra problem we may be required to supply the fact (in equation form) that everyone who finishes a race runs the same distance. We shall discuss first examples similar to the use of Ohm's law for the simple parametric synthetic case.

Before considering an example, a brief digression will be made in order to distinguish Ohm's law type equations from the equation type of the other two cases mentioned above. Notice first that Ohm's law applies only to a fixed physical system and it relates only three fluents in the physical system. While the magnitudes of these fluents may be varied (within limits) and the law reapplied, the number of fluents in a single application is fixed at three. On the other hand, Kirchhoff's equations and the distance equation are based on indices and can be used in formulas representing any number of fluents. (Note that while every man that finishes a 100-yard dash runs the same 100 yards, a separate fluent is associated with each of them, e.g.: distance$_\text{yards}$ (Harry) = 100 is not the same as distance$_\text{yards}$ (Fred) = 100.)

In both the fixed and indicial cases, we shall be using intensional functor equations that relate a number of functor expressions that have related domains. As Menger* points out, the domain (set of arguments) of such an i.f.e. is a distinguished subset of the Cartesian product of the domains of all of the functor expressions involved. In the case of Ohm's law, for example, the domain is any particular series-parallel combination of electrical resistance elements such that the current under consideration enters and leaves the network at two distinguished points and that the voltage under consideration is applied across these same two points. Elsewhere we have made this network definition rigorously explicit by a set of recursive definitions.[5]

EXAMPLE 2

This second example is an elementary problem in electrical circuits.† We give first the original problem statement in English and then its $L3$ representation.

(2-1)   A current of 15 amp flows through an electrical appliance of 30 ohms resistance and a lamp of 190 ohms resistance.

The $L3$ transform of the problem is:

(rel. 1): flow (current, electric appliance and lamp)
(e.f.e. 1): (1) current$_\text{amp}$ (rel. 1) = 0.5
(e.f.e. 2): (2a) resistance $_\text{ohm}$ (rel. 1) = 30
(e.f.e. 3): (2b) resistance$_\text{ohm}$ (rel. 1) = 190
(i.f.e. 4): voltage$_{d_4}$ (lamp) = x

The deduction string always starts with 'x' (i.f.e. and e.f.e. are intensional and extensional functor equation(s) abbreviations, respectively, and a.f. is assumption formula abbreviation):

($A1$)   voltage$_{d_4}$ (lamp)   = x : a.f., i.f.e. 4.
($A2$)   voltage$_\text{volt}$ (lamp) = x : bind d_4 in ($A1$) with standard

Since a scan reveals no parametric possibilities on the e.f.e. directly, we start to manipulate them from the beginning:

($A3$)   (1) current$_\text{amp}$ (rel. 1) = 0.5   : a.f., e.f.e. 1
($A4$)   flow (current, el. app. and lamp)   : a.f., rel. 1 (need for ($A3$))
($A5$)   current (el. app. and lamp) = 0.5 : r.7   on   ($A3$)   with   ($A4$)
                                             (choose second arg because
                                             f_i are not eligible as f. ex.
                                             arguments)

---

* See Menger[8] for an illuminating exposition of functors in physical applications.

† This problem is taken from Schaum.[12] Many other problems from the elementary physics review book were used for hand simulation of the system.

The parenthesized comments are simply aids to the reader. These are the kinds of considerations that will have to guide the development of a meta-theory. It is characteristic of the English form of these problems that if nothing is explicit, one assumes that the components are connected in series; this is the case in the present problem. Since the argument in $(A5)$ is partly like that of our objective $(A2)$, we will explore splitting this functor expression. As a matter of fact we are again faced with another new situation which we shall call a *nonadditive functor** and which can be operated on by the following rule of inference: (the $\vee$ is inclusive)

$$(r.19) \quad (f_{id_i}(\text{arg}_j \ \& \ \text{arg}_k) = \text{number}_i) \rightarrow (f_{id_i}(\text{arg}_j) = \text{number}_i)$$
$$\vee \ (f_{id_i}(\text{arg}_k) = \text{number}_i)$$

This rule will be applicable only to a distinguished set of functors and the notation assumes that the subscripted words are constant throughout. Since 'current' with series arguments will belong to this nonadditive functor set, we are free to use (r.19) on $(A5)$:

$(A6)$ current$_{\text{amp}}$ (lamp) = 0.5   : r.19 on $(A5)$ (choosing the argument of our objective, $(A2)$)

This is a potentially useful (and will be necessary) but not sufficient e.f.e. to solve our problem. Continuing to explore the given data:

$(A7)$ $(2a)$ resistance$_{\text{ohm}}$ (rel. 1) = 30   : a.f., e.f.e. 2
$(A8)$ resistance$_{\text{ohm}}$ (el. app.)   = 30   : r.7 on $(A7)$ with $(A4)$
$(A9)$ $(2b)$ resistance$_{\text{ohm}}$ (rel. 1) = 190   : a.f., e.f.e. 3
$(A10)$ resistance$_{\text{ohm}}$ (lamp)   = 190   : r.7 on $(A9)$ with $(A4)$.

$(A10)$ exhausts the given data and has an interesting argument but we still have no hope of solving the problem. Thus Example 2 is clearly synthetic and we turn to the stored axioms, looking for one with voltage in it, and one that also has the functors of $(A6)$ and/or $(A10)$, since these "interesting due to argument" functors are the only analytic data with which the deduction procedure has been provided. Fortunately, we find:

$(A11)$ *(current$_{\text{amp}}$ (arg$_i$), resistance$_{\text{ohm}}$ (arg$_i$)) = voltage$_{\text{volt}}$ (arg$_i$)
                                                            : stored axiom

---

* This name is used to distinguish these functors from the algebraically additive functor which has the same kind of LHS, but whose RHS is the algebraic sum:

$$(f_{id_i} \ (\text{arg}_j \ \& \ \text{arg}_k) = \text{number}_i) \rightarrow (f_{id_i} \ (\text{arg}_j, + \ f_{id_i} \ (\text{arg}_k) = \text{number}_i)$$

rather than the logical sum as in $(r. 10)$.

We can adapt this to the present problem and conclude the solution:

$(A12)$ *current$_{amp}$ (lamp), resistance$_{ohm}$ (lamp))
        = voltage$_{volt}$ (lamp) : bind arg$_i$ of $(A11)$ using $(A2)$

$(A13)$ *(.5, 190) = voltage$_{volt}$ (lamp)   : r.3 on $(A12)$ with $(A6)$ and
                                          $(A10)$

$(A14)$ 85 = voltage$_{volt}$ (lamp)   : r.5 on $(A13)$

$(A15)$ $85 = x$: r.2 on $(A2)$ and $(A14)$

This solution was rather straightforward and we had no need for a recursive definition of a valid circuit.

REPRESENTATION OF PROGRAMS

We have now discussed two sample problems and how they might be solved by a person using a formal set of rules. Our next task is to show how these rules and their use might be mechanized. Before turning to the details of a system, let us mention some attributes that it should possess.

The programming language should be flexible and useful in a wide variety of problem contexts. The language should have a concise and readable representation that will be easy for people to use. Programs should be formally translatable into equivalent computing procedures and there should be formal means for deciding the equivalence of two apparently different procedures. There should be a way of concatenating several parts of a program and of breaking up one part into several. It should be possible to have a metasystem that can determine the input and output requirements, constraints, etc. that will be required for program concatenation. The programs must be locally and globally reorganizable in an easy way, i.e., it should be possible to exhibit *learning* and self-organizing properties in programs. Subjectively, since our data structure is already fixed, the system should be able to handle functors and relations in a deduction string context.

It is quite clear that the lack of metatheory surrounding the traditional one dimensional machine code, most problem oriented languages, and the two dimensional flow chart representations makes them inadequate for this task. McCarthy[6] has suggested requirements similar to some of the above and has given a very good start on building a system which has some of these attributes. In our system, we are interested in the implicit derivation of an algorithm. Our intermediate results are made up of a vector that has a step of this algorithm applied to it for each metatheoretic proposition that is true in the context of the vector. Thus we can think of our desired result as an element of the free *semigroup* over the set of possible computing steps in the problem solving metatheory. We shall first discuss the problem of program control and the relevance of conditional expressions as a method of program control. We will introduce a second control procedure and apply both to the problem solving situation of the previous section.

CONDITIONAL EXPRESSIONS

McCarthy's conditional expressions[6] can be used in a variety of ways. We shall use them in the following form:*

$$\text{c.e.}_i(x^{(n)}) = [p_{i1}(x^{(n)}) \rightarrow e_{i1}(x^{(n)}), \ldots, p_{im}(x^{(n)}) \rightarrow e_{im}(x^{(n)})] \qquad (1)$$

In each *conditional expression* (c.e.), each p_{ij} is a logical proposition with truth values T or F. In general, when $x^{(n)}$ is any n-dimensional argument vector, we will say that c.e.$_i$ has the "value" e_{ij} if p_{ij} is the first proposition on j in c.e.$_i$ that is true with respect to $x^{(n)}$. The several uses we make of conditional expressions depend on the form taken by the e_{ij}'s. They may be object level words such that the $x^{(n)}$ argument vector does not affect the form of the e_{ij} selected. They may be operators which transform $x^{(n)}$ into $x^{(n)\prime}$ or they may be other conditional expressions. In this latter case we transfer control to the new e_{ij}. We also allow mixed uses of conditional expressions such that a single expression may combine the functions of command and control. Notice that explicit control statements need never be given.

In examining the possible usefulness of these expressions, we want to consider the effects of reordering the $p_{ij} \rightarrow e_{ij}$ pairs in a particular c.e.$_i$.

First, the c.e. can be used as an n-way branch, transferring control in a way that depends on the particular truth values. We assume that only one p_{ij} is true. In this case, the order of testing will be logically irrelevant. The time for serial processing would of course depend on the order. This will be called Type 1.

With Type 2 expressions, there may be several true propositions, p_{ij}, for some $x^{(n)}$, the extreme case being when all predicates are the same. However, the first proposition examined will dictate the value. For this case, rendering by some metasystem will change the value of the conditional expression. We might use this case when a number of effective procedures are available. We might order the choices according to previous popularity, thus controlling the choice of a procedure.

We could use Type 3 expressions to set up a logical condition which is a function of all the p_{ij}'s for a given c.e.$_i$. For this use, the expression will

---

* As originally defined by McCarthy, the value of a conditional expression might be undefined if an undefined p occurs before a true p or if all p's are false or if the e corresponding to the first true p is undefined. We shall use a more restricted definition such that the value of the expressions will always be defined.

not be reorderable. We assume that more than one p_{ij} is true for some $x^{(n)}$, otherwise our Type 3 expression would be equivalent to Type 1.

Thus, for possible applications, we have Type 1, the n-way branch; Type 2, the preferred and logical selection from an equivalence class; and Type 3, the logical function. We emphasize that for all types and for any use, only one e_{ij} results from the evaluation of a conditional expression.

CONTINUED CONDITIONAL EXPRESSIONS

We will now discuss a formalism that is an extension of the c.e. For this case more than one e_{ij} can result from the application of a single formalism. We shall refer to these formalisms as *continued conditional expressions* (c.c.e.) and write them as:

$$\text{c.c.e.}_i(x^{(n)}) = \; < p_{i1}(x^{(n)}) \to e_{i1}(x^{(n)}), \ldots, p_{in}(x^{(n)}) \to e_{in}(x^{(n)}) > \qquad (2)$$

Given an argument vector $x^{(n)}$, as above, a single c.c.e. generates an output string in general. The e_{ij} can have the same interpretations as they had with the conditional expression. When the outputs of c.c.e.$_i$ have either *object* or *command* significance, for any index of c.c.e.$_i$, if p_{ij} is true, then e_{ij} is entered in the output string and control is transferred to index $j + 1$. That is, $p_{i,j+1}$ is tested just as p_{ij} was. If p_{ij} is false, then nothing enters the output string and control transfers to $j + 1$. When the last term in a c.c.e. is reached, control ascends a level in a *pushdown control* list. In the control case, where e_{ij} contains another c.c.e., we must record our current location in a pushdown control list and transfer to the new c.c.e. We then reapply these rules.

Note that if only one p_{ij} is true in some c.c.e.$_i$, then the c.c.e.$_i$ is effectively equivalent to a c.e.$_i$ of Type 1. Thus the c.c.e. will be useful only when several p_{ij} are true at one time. We have then, recalling our c.e. type consideration, only the two remaining kinds of cases (Types 2 and 3) to study: ordered and not ordered c.c.e. with several true p_{ij}.

Let us consider first the case of the reorderable continued conditional expression. A particularly useful application might be that of sifting data with respect to several attributes.

Thus, a c.c.e. applied to some argument could list a subset of a particular attribute set which the argument satisfies. This would be an object language data processing application. This case is similar in range to c.e. Type 1 in that it gives attributes (but can give any number of them, whereas c.e. Type 1 picks out a unique answer). It is also similar in domain to c.e. Type 2 in that it can be used on some kind of equivalence class of attributes, i.e., to respond to physical properties of individuals. In this sense, c.c.e. Type 1 can be reordered without any difficulties arising.

We shall now turn our attention to a class of possible applications in which reordering is not possible, at least not in the most general sense. Consider now the elements e_{ij} to be members of some order code set E. Then each c.c.e. is essentially the producer of an algorithm. The generation proceeds by subjecting the entry of any step into the algorithm to the condition that its associated p_{ij} be true with respect to some $x^{(n)}$. The resulting string of e_{ij} will be called a *partial algorithm string*. Let us use the notation p.a.s. for partial algorithm string in the proper (partial) sense and when a string (completely) computes a useful output we will call it an algorithm string (still in the set of partial algorithm strings). Thus a c.c.e. with all its $p_j \equiv T$ (identically T) *is* a p.a.s., that is, if:

$$\text{c.c.e.}_i = \; < T \to e_{i1}, T \to e_{i2}, \ldots, T \to e_{in} > \; \equiv \; < e_{i1}, e_{i2}, e_{i3}, \ldots, e_{in} >$$
$$= \text{p.a.s.}_i.$$

A c.c.e. with some $p_{ij} = T$ and some $p_{ij} = F$ after testing (and some $p_{ij} \equiv T$) *generates* a p.a.s. depending on truth values along the way. Notice that this string can be explicitly generated (compiled) and later run, or it can be executed step by step (interpreted) with perhaps some future tests in the generation dependent on earlier e_{ij} execution. Thus, in the interpretive mode the input $x^{(n)}$ to c.c.e.$_i$ will be transformed into $x^{(n)'}$ by e_{i1} if $p_{i1}(x^{(n)})$ is true. This $x^{(n)'}$ will be used as the argument in test p_{i2}, etc. This kind of process would seem to be very useful in programming goal seeking, teleological types of processes, because we can posit an operation (i.e., make a guess) and observe the results immediately, allowing for correction or modification if the results do not appear to be desirable. Note that we can think of this procedure as a feedback type process with respect to a c.c.e. or a set of c.c.e.$_i$, with the $x^{(n)'}$ output reentering the metasystem at the next stage in the logical process. This case then is one of generating (command and control) statements of a program to be executed. It is clear that, in general, gross permutations of the order of the c.c.e. steps will destroy the logic of the resulting program. We could, however, allow local reordering within certain substrings of the c.c.e. (e.g., "fetch a, then add b" is equivalent to "fetch b, then add a").

We now have discussed possible uses of c.e. and c.c.e. It is clear that each can have special use in a programming system. In particular, since they can both be used recursively and can transfer control to any other c.e. or c.c.e., we shall in general write arrays of c.e. and c.c.e. (including p.a.s.) to serve as programs. The e_j will be chosen from commands and other c.e.–c.c.e. names in the array. In this sense we note that the c.e.–c.c.e. arrays can be considered as the context of a computer programming metatheory. Whether or not a step should be executed is based on some extra-programmatic decision; it is then executed or control moves on. We also comment that such a c.c.e.–c.e. array together with a pushdown control list, can serve as a general model of an interpretive system with an arbitrary number of subroutine levels.

STATE DIAGRAM REPRESENTATIONS

The c.c.e. and c.e. linear strings (simple or mixed) may also be given a graph theoretic two dimensional representation. In this context, if we make the command e_j explicitly o_j output elements, the o_j can be identified with the outputs of a sequential machine* where the graph is a *state diagram* of the sequential machine. The internal states are represented by the vertices of the graph and the p_j of the linear language are propositions associated with the vertices. The notation a/b associated with each are means that, following the arrows, if an input a is given where we are in some vertex-state at the tail of an arrow, we proceed to the vertex at the arrow head and give output b. φ is the empty output (no operation).

Cases A and B of the example given is Figure 3 contrast the graphs of the same computing scheme for both the c.e. and the c.c.e. representations. The inputs here are '1' for true and 'φ' for false, when a p_{ij} is applied to $x^{(n)}$. Notice the more desirable form of graph A compared to graph B. We can manipulate the graph of A in ways that correspond to linear language (and their corresponding list structure) manipulations. For example, we can concatenate another graph to the output of A. We can split vertices with respect to input and output arcs and introduce new graphs in a way corresponding to operations on the linear format. Similarly, we can remove subgraphs and allow the remaining exposed nodes to coalesce analogously to the extirpation of p,e strings in c.c.e. It is clear that in B, operations of this nature would not be simple, due to the distributed nature of the o_j. For example, note that o_j appears on four distinct arcs due to the distributed logic of the conditional expression. We will refer to this property of the conditional expressions, that c_k is the output if p_k is true and p_j false for all $j < k$, as distributed logic. By way of contrast, the continued conditional expressions have localized logic. Although in the graphs shown, each vertex stands for a single test in the linear expression and each operation has a single link image in the graph, this one for one relationship does not hold in general, (cf. appendix). In the general case a particular test in the linear representation will appear at several places in the graphical representation (many for one). This means that arrays of c.e. and c.c.e. are in general a rather compact notation.

---

* See Gorn,[3] for example, for his discussion of sequential machines. His discussion is particularly interesting because of his references to language.

SYSTEM ORGANIZATION

We have considered the c.e. and c.c.e. to be operating on some vector $x^{(n)}$. In the problem solver this vector will have to be associated with the deduction string or strings, with the input problem, and with the stored axioms. When the e_j correspond to o_j outputs, we have referred to the o_j as steps of an algorithm. In fact this will usually be the name of a rule of inference which operates on $x^{(n)}$. The application of it will lead to a new entry in the deduction string. It will be the case that $x^{(n)}$ is the entire

P_1	P_2	P_3	output
T	T	T	$e_2\ e_3\ e_1$
T	T	F	$e_2\quad e_1$
T	F	T	$e_3\ e_1$
T	F	F	e_1
F	T	T	ϕ
F	T	F	ϕ
F	F	T	ϕ
F	F	F	ϕ

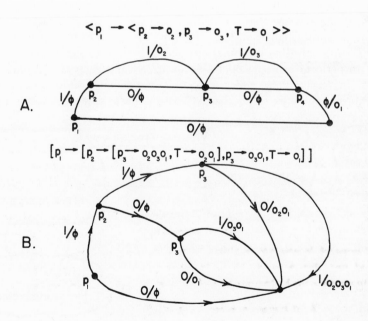

Figure 3

problem solving context within the computer. The o_j may also be some kind of a nonstring-oriented housekeeping chore, but these can be thought of as generalized r.o.i. Thus the input vector to the next state of the problem solving system will in general be different from the input to the present state (Fig. 4).

We now see that the c.e.–p.a.s.–c.c.e. arrays will be used for the representation of the metatheory that guides the development of a deduction string. The p.a.s. will be used for known, effective partial algorithm strings. The c.c.e. will be used for introducing a string of steps conditionally and the c.e. will be used within them to generate logical functions, to search among equivalents, and for n-way branching. We note again that no control statements need be made explicit when using this notation. This is clearly useful for flexible formal manipulation of strings as mentioned in the opening statements of this section. Once a human user understands the parenthesis use, he can work easily with these arrays. With respect to learning, we have discussed permutation and augmentation of certain strings. For c.c.e. that do a particular job, it is desirable that they be no longer than necessary, i.e., that at number of tests don't consistently fail in the preparation for the execution of certain tasks. This suggests the technique of Selfridge[13] to split popular strings. Suppose that c.c.e.$_1$ has five p,e pairs and that the total expression is very popular. If we monitor it for awhile, suppose that we learn that pairs 1, 3, and 4 are frequently giving T and being executed at the same time, and at other times 2 and 5 are T, and that other combinations seldom occur. We would then be foolish not to perform a fission operation on c.c.e.$_1$ and generate two new c.c.e. with the respective sets of $p,e,$ pairs. If our monitor showed a number of uses beside these we could also save c.c.e.$_1$. These new c.c.e. would have to

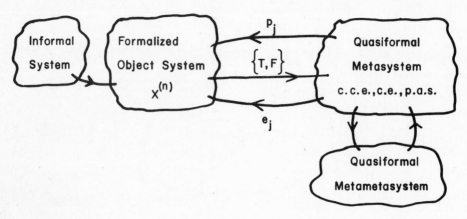

Figure 4

have appropriate entry conditions associated with them, i.e., they would have to be entered through the old paths that led to c.c.e.$_1$ under several conditions, now divided into two (or more) sets. Our monitor could also expunge unused strings. Note also that as a fail-safe procedure we can attach all sorts of unpopular equivalence class members to the end of c.e. and c.c.e. While the above gives formalism to the metatheory, note that the operations on the c.c.e. and c.e. strings have been only discussed informally. We may have to write some kind of quasiformal metameta-theory, i.e., a program that we change from time to time to carry out different learning and self-organizational schemes. This metametatheory would have the problem solving metatheory as its object theory.

PROBLEM SOLVING SYSTEM

The problem solving system requires that we organize the total set of machine locations into a number of functional areas. These will contain all of the usable data, including the evolving deduction strings themselves. The areas we shall refer to are: $P = \{Pi\}$, the problem element set containing the e.f.e., i.f.e., and rel. of a given problem; $A = \{Ai\}$, the stored axiom set; G, the glossary of English words; $W = \{Wi\}$, the set of deduction strings being evolved in the Wi pushdown lists; and HO, the pushdown accumulator which holds intermediate results. We also have at our disposal a pushdown store of arbitrary capacity. This is the pushdown control list which permits us to make nested, *recursive* use of the c.e.–c.c.e.–p.a.s. arrays. We shall refer to the above areas collectively as (P, A, G, W, HO). This is the problem context (Fig. 5).

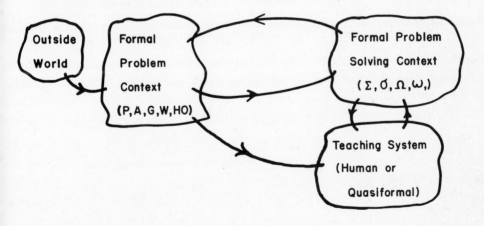

Figure 5

We next define a problem oriented language that operates on this problem context. $(\Sigma, \sigma, \Omega, \omega)$ is an $L3$ oriented language made of an array of arbitrarily nested c.e., p.a.s., and c.c.e. strings. This is the problem solving metasystem which guides the solution of problems in (P, A, G, W, HO). We will speak of the context of $(\Sigma, \sigma, \Omega, \omega)$ as the problem solving context. (Σ, σ) operates on the total (P, A, G, W, HO) context, while (Ω, ω) operates only on the W context. Σ and Ω contain gross operators that in general are composed of elementary strings σ and ω, respectively. The fundamental operations performed within all of $(\Sigma, \sigma, \Omega, \omega)$ are made up of primitives which are defined symbolic functions and predicates, and the rules of inference, (r.o.i.).

The new operators that we shall want are defined in such a way that they will be useful in operating on $L3$ statements and will be mechanizable with IPL-V operations. The operations to be carried out fall into several general categories. The symbolic operations take a symbolic input and give a symbolic output (i.e., they are functors with object level arguments), or they move symbols from one location to another as a result of their application (i.e., they are machine commands). They are:

lhs(s) = symbol on left-hand side of = in s
rhs(s) = symbol on right-hand side of = in s
load(Wi): puts upper symbol of HO on top of Wi
bring(s, Wi): puts s on top of Wi
bindim(s, t): binds dimension of s with respect to dimension of t
bindarg(s, t): binds argument of s with respect to argument of t
bindfunc(s, t): binds functor of s with respect to functor of t

Notice that we are here mechanizing r.8 and r.9, the binding rules described earlier.

Other operations are given by predicates that have symbolic arguments and truth value (T, F) extensions. These may also perform some data movement, particularly in the case of T results. An 'n' in front of any of these denotes the negation of the predicate and the truth values are thereby complemented. We have here the predicates:

$$\text{eq}(s, t) = \begin{array}{l} T \text{ is } s \text{ and } t \text{ are identical } (s, t \text{ are i.f.e. or e.f.e.}) \\ F \text{ otherwise} \end{array}$$

$$\text{comarg}(s, R) = \begin{array}{l} T \text{ if } s \text{ and expression in } R \text{ have same argument} \\ F \text{ otherwise} \\ \text{also brings the expression in } R \text{ to } HO \text{ if } T \end{array}$$

$$\text{comfunc}(s, R) = \begin{array}{l} T \text{ is } s \text{ and expression in } R \text{ have the same functor} \\ F \text{ otherwise} \\ \text{also brings the expression in } R \text{ to } HO \text{ if } T \end{array}$$

$$\text{comdim}(s, R) = \begin{array}{l} T \text{ if } s \text{ and expression in } R \text{ have the same dimension} \\ F \text{ otherwise} \\ \text{also brings the expression in } R \text{ to } HO \text{ if } T \end{array}$$

$$\text{intarg}(s, R) = \begin{array}{l} T \text{ if } s \text{ and expression in } R \text{ have intersecting argument} \\ F \text{ otherwise} \\ \text{also brings the expression in } R \text{ to } HO \text{ if } T \end{array}$$

$$\text{intdim}(s, R) = \begin{array}{l} T \text{ if } s \text{ and expression in } R \text{ have intersecting dimension} \\ F \text{ otherwise} \\ \text{also brings the expression in } R \text{ to } HO \text{ if } T \end{array}$$

$$\text{intfunc}(s, R) = \begin{array}{l} T \text{ if } s \text{ and expression in } R \text{ have intersecting functor} \\ F \text{ otherwise} \\ \text{also brings the expression in } R \text{ to } HO \text{ if } T \end{array}$$

$$\text{frearg}(Wi) = \begin{array}{l} T \text{ for free argument in top of } Wi \\ F \text{ otherwise} \end{array}$$

$$\text{fredim}(Wi) = \begin{array}{l} T \text{ for free dimension in top of } Wi \\ F \text{ otherwise} \end{array}$$

$$\text{frefunc}(Wi) = \begin{array}{l} T \text{ for free functor in top of } Wi \\ F \text{ otherwise} \end{array}$$

$$\text{val}(s, t) = \begin{array}{l} T \text{ if value of e.f.e. } s \text{ is } t \text{ (puts } s \text{ in } HO) \\ F \text{ otherwise} \end{array}$$

$$\text{homog}(Wi) = \begin{array}{l} T \text{ if } f_i \text{ in top of } Wi \text{ is homogeneous} \\ F \text{ otherwise} \end{array}$$

$$\text{adit}(Wi) = \begin{array}{l} T \text{ if } f_i \text{ in top of } W_i \text{ is additive} \\ F \text{ otherwise} \end{array}$$

$$\text{simpfunc}(R) = \begin{array}{l} T \text{ if } f_i \text{ is simple functor} \\ F \text{ otherwise} \end{array}$$

$$\text{simparg}(R) = \begin{array}{l} T \text{ if arg i in } R \text{ is simple argument} \\ F \text{ otherwise} \end{array}$$

$$\text{simpdim}(R) = \begin{array}{l} T \text{ if } d_i \text{ in } R \text{ is simple dimension} \\ F \text{ otherwise} \end{array}$$

$$\text{epty}(R) = \begin{array}{l} T \text{ if } R \text{ is empty location or area} \\ F \text{ otherwise} \end{array}$$

$$\text{assert}(R) = \begin{array}{l} T \text{ if LHS is asserted} \\ F \text{ otherwise} \end{array}$$

When used as arguments, f_i and rel.$_i$ represent themselves. We also use f.e., arg, rel, and f as operators, which when applied to some argument stand for 'the functor expression of,' 'the argument of,' 'the relation of,' and 'the functor of,' respectively. These operators also bring the designated symbols to HO, when found.

We now describe $(\Sigma, \sigma, \Omega, \omega)$. This is a formal model of the problem solving system which is written in terms of an array of conditional and continued conditional expressions. The predicates used are drawn from those defined above and the operators consist of rules of inference. These are the r.o.i. previously defined plus the special operations given above. As mentioned above, the (σ, ω) level strings are made directly from the primitives and the (Σ, Ω) strings are made of these lower level strings. These are given in Figs. 6 and 7. We also recall the important point that control statements are not given in these expressions, in general, and the control is implicit in the definition of the various strings. We do however allow some control statements, given in capital letters, viz. STOP, which causes all further computation to cease. With respect to Figs. 6 and 7 we make several comments. The context of the system is assumed to be the top of pushdown list $W1$, unless otherwise noted. By the notation, $W1_i$, we mean the ith cell in $W1$'s pushed down stack. Also, auxno refers to the number in parentheses before certain functors, and arg i is the ith argument of a relation. Finally, ω_7 contains an abbreviation of all of the requirements associated with the rules of inference for algebraic manipulation.

To illustrate the use of this system, we present a simple example in Fig. 8. This example is the mechanization of Example 1 and the steps followed here are precisely those that were previously given. The notation followed in Fig. 8 is that p.c.l. is the pushdown control list which here

$$
\begin{aligned}
\Sigma &= <\sigma_1, \Sigma_0, \Sigma_5, ...> \\
\Sigma_0 &= <\Omega_7, \sigma_7, \Sigma_6, \sigma_6, \Omega_0, \Sigma_4> \\
\Sigma_4 &= [\text{nepty}(\text{f.e.}(\text{Pi}) \rightarrow <\text{br}(\text{f.e.}(\text{Pi})), \Sigma_0>] \\
\Sigma_5 &= <\sigma_5, \Omega_7, \Omega_1> \\
\Sigma_6 &= <\text{nsimparg}(W1) \rightarrow [\omega_2(W1) \rightarrow (\text{Pi}), \Omega_1>, \omega_8] \\
\sigma_1 &= [\text{val}(\text{Pi}, x) \rightarrow \text{load}(W1), T \rightarrow \text{STOP}] \\
\sigma_2 &= [\sigma_7, \text{comfunc}(W1_i, W1_i) \rightarrow \text{bindarg}(W1_i, W1_i)] \\
\sigma_3 &= [\text{comarg}(W1, \text{Pi}) \rightarrow [\text{nsimpdim}(HO) \rightarrow \omega_1, T \rightarrow \text{bind}(W1, \text{std})], \\
&\quad \text{intarg}(W1, \text{Pi}) \rightarrow <\text{comfunc}(W1, \text{Pi}) \rightarrow \omega_4>, T \rightarrow \text{bind}(W1, \text{std})] \\
\sigma_4 &= [\text{comdim}(W1, \text{Pi}) \rightarrow \text{bind}(W1, \text{Pi})] \\
\sigma_5 &= <\text{comfunc}(W1_x, \text{Ai}) \rightarrow \text{br}(\text{Ai}), \omega_7> \\
\sigma_6 &= <\text{nepty}(\text{Pi}) \rightarrow [\text{comarg}(W1, \text{f.e.}(\text{Pi})) \rightarrow \sigma_8, \text{comdim}(W1, \text{f.e.}(\text{Pi})) \rightarrow \\
&\quad \sigma_8, \text{intarg}(W1, \text{f.e.}(\text{Pi})) \rightarrow \rightarrow \sigma_8]> \\
\sigma_7 &= [\text{eq}(\text{arg}(W1), \text{rel}(\text{Pi})) \rightarrow \omega_6] \\
\sigma_8 &= <\text{load}(W1), \Sigma_0>
\end{aligned}
$$

FIG. 6

starts from the top and p.u.o. is the pop-up order which shows when each step is popped up.

This illustrates the operation of $(\Sigma, \sigma, \Omega, \omega)$ in a simple case. The comments at the right are to aid the reader. Note that the p.u.o. numbers can be consulted to determine which processes are subprocesses of others. A process uses those below it which have lower p.u.o. ordinals than it has. For this reason we also enter c.e. names.

SUMMARY AND DISCUSSION

Having completed a description of this problem solving system, we shall summarize briefly its operation and discuss some possible extensions. Unlike most programming systems, this problem solver does not require an algorithm for the solution of problems as its input. Rather, it accepts

$\Omega_0 = \; <\omega_5, \Omega_4>$

$\Omega_1 = \; <\omega_3, r_5, r_2>$

$\Omega_4 = \; <\Omega_7, \Omega_6, \Omega_1>$

$\Omega_6 = \; [\omega_3, <\Omega_7, \Omega_6>]$

$\Omega_7 = \; <\text{frearg} \to \sigma_2, \text{fredim} \to \sigma_3, \text{frefunc} \to \sigma_4>$

$\omega_1 = \; <\text{load}(W1_1), [\text{intd}_s(W1_1, W1_2) \to \text{bindim}(W1_1, W1_2), T \to \text{pop } W1_1]>$

$\omega_2 = \; <\text{homog} \to r.4>$

$\omega_3 = \; [\text{asert} \to r.3]$

$\omega_4 = \; <\text{load}(W1), \text{bind}(W1_1, W1_2)>$

$\omega_5 = \; [\text{comarg}(W1_i, W1_j) \to [\text{comdim}(W1_i, W1_j) \to r.4,$
$\quad \text{nsimpdim}(W1_i, W1_j) \to r.5, \text{comfunc}(W1_i, W1_j) \to [\text{comdim}(W1_i,$
$\quad W1_j) \to r.3]]$

$\omega_6 = \; <\text{br(rel.i)}, \text{neg(arg(rel.i)} f_i) \to \; <\text{eq}(\text{auxno}, 1) \to$
$\quad \text{bind}(Wi_j, \text{arg1 (rel.i)}), \text{eq}(\text{auxno}, 2) \to \text{bind}(Wi_j, \text{arg 2(rel.i)}) > >$

$\omega_7 = \; [\text{neq}(f(1\text{hs}(W1_x)), f(1\text{hs}(W1_1))) \to \; <\{r.10, r.11, ..., r.18\}, \omega_7>]$

$\omega_8 = \; [\text{nadit}(W1) \to r.19]$

FIG. 7

p.u.o.	p.c.l.	coments
12	Σ	start
1	σ_1	find problem A1
11	Σ_0	
4	Ω_7	
3	σ_3	free dimension
2	ω_4	A2, A3
5	σ_7	
10	Σ_6	compound argument
6	ω_2	homogeneous f_i, r.4 $\to$ A4
7	ω_2	
9	Ω_1	r.5 $\to$ A6: solution
8	ω_3	assertion, r.3 $\to$ A5

FIG. 8

descriptive statements in the form of relational predicates for qualitative data and functors for quantitative data. On the basis of these inputs, the system derives its own algorithm and computes a numerical result.

The significance of this choice of a descriptive formalism is twofold. On the one hand, this class of inputs has considerable breadth and may properly be described as "multicontext." On the other hand, this same formalism has helped us in the definition of a language-processing system, which accepts natural language statements and which produces suitable inputs for our problem solver.[5]

We have described how this system operates for two classes of problems. Certain problems are defined as *analytic* when the descriptive input contains all the information necessary for the solution of the problem. Certain other problems which are not self-contained are defined as *synthetic*; in solving these some knowledge must be added, usually in the form of a physical law. For these situations we provide the system with a set of appropriate formulas and the ability to retrieve them when necessary.

With problems of either kind, the problem solver carries out a series of logical deduction steps on the original problem statement. This process makes use of a number of axioms and rules of inference with which the system is provided. The system operates heuristically. First it isolates what is unknown and tries to implicitly derive an algorithm that will relate this unknown to a series of known quantities. If successful in its derivation, the system concludes by executing the required arithmetic operations in order to obtain an answer.

Finally, we have described how the problem solver can be mechanized. For reasons of clarity and precision, we have maintained a sharp distinction between two levels of representation in the problem solving system. The object level of representation in the system is the problem context. It contains the formal representation of a given problem, a set of stated axioms, a glossary of English words, the set of deduction strings as they are evolved, and a pushdown accumulator for holding intermediate results.

It is the problem solving metasystem that operates on this problem context; this is an array of conditional expressions and continued conditional expressions which makes unnecessary any explicit provision for program control. These arrays provide us with a very compact method for program representation. We have discussed a number of important attributes of these expressions and noted that they may also be represented by state diagrams. We have also suggested some of the problem solving metasystem's features which appear to be context-independent and which justify its use as a multicontext procedure.

Now that the design of this system has been completed, a number of possible extensions remain for further consideration. Most important is the demonstration of a machine system that performs in the way described. For a given class of problems, we need to explore in depth the ability of the system to perform in a satisfactory manner. We need also to consider a variety of classes of problems in order to explore the limits of one problem solver as a *multicontext system*. In addition, expansion and modification in order to achieve more efficient operation will be desirable.

There remains a most interesting question of providing the system with the ability to learn from its experiences. One possibility would be to use a human trainer in order to reorganize the system, in which case the learning program would remain external to the system. However, after experimenting with the system in a number of contexts, we would expect the problem solving metasystem to begin to display rather interesting behavior. After some teaching methods have been developed, they could be formalized into an array of conditional expressions, continued conditional expressions, and partial algorithm strings. This new array would constitute a quasi-formal metametasystem. This metametasystem would need to observe both the problem context and the problem solving context. Its relationship to the original system is expressed diagrammatically in Fig. 5.

The teaching system would take inputs from both the problem and the problem solving contexts. It would operate on the problem solving context in order to improve its behavior. Thus a problem solving automaton has, by definition, a problem context and a problem solving metasystem. A problem solving automaton with learning has, by definition, the structure of the original automaton plus a teaching system that is a metametasystem with respect to the problem context and a metasystem with respect to the problem solving context.

APPENDIX

This appendix presents some details of a study of arrays of conditional and continued conditional expressions. We shall use a result of Chomsky and Schutzenberger from their algebraic theory of language[2] in order to represent explicitly all possible algorithms generated by an array. We write the disjunction of all possible strings where juxtaposition represents the concentration of commands applied from the left. Thus we have:

$$\text{c.e.} = [p_1 \to e_1,\, p_2 \to e_2,\, \ldots,\, p_n \to e_n] = e_1 + e_2 + \cdots + e_n$$

$$\begin{aligned}
\text{c.c.e.} = \ &<p_1 \to e_1,\, p_2 \to e_2,\, \ldots,\, p_n \to e_n> = e_1 + e_2 + \cdots + e_n \\
&+ e_1 e_2 + e_1 e_3 + e_1 e_2 e_3 + e_1 e_4 + \cdots + e_1 e_2 e_3,\, \ldots,\, e_n \\
&+ e_2 e_3 + e_2 e_4 + e_2 e_3 e_4 + \cdots + e_2 e_3 e_4,\, \ldots,\, e_n \\
&\quad \bullet \\
&\quad \bullet \\
&\quad \bullet \\
&+ e_{n-2} e_{n-1} + e_{n-2} e_n + e_{n-2} e_{n-1} e_n + e_n
\end{aligned}$$

These are the ordered strings derived from the power set (except φ) of the e_6 of the c.c.e.

In the case that control transfers within a c.c.e. we must record our present position in a pushdown control list (p.c.l.). This allows subprogram nesting to an arbitrary depth. We can use metalinguistic arrows to indicate p.c.l. activity, for example:

$$\text{p.a.s.} = \ <ce_1, ce_2> \ = \ \downarrow ce_1 \uparrow \ \downarrow ce_2 \uparrow$$

In general, for nested c.c.e., arrows will build up at the ends and have no benefit for our purposes. Instead the pairings will be denoted by $*$; thus we have:

$$\text{p.a.s.} = ce_1 * ce_2$$

where $*$ indicates p.c.l. activity that leads to a new expression (control transfer) in the array.

Notice that the polynomial generated in this way will show the total number of ways a particular string can be generated. This is obtained by the rule: $ms_1 + ns_1 = (m + n)s_1$ where the s_1 is an operator string and m and n are integers. The coefficients of the strings denote this number of possibilities.[2]

We are interested in the question of many-for-oneness—that is, why do some graphs necessarily contain more than one image of parts of the expressions? The problem obviously is centered in the fact that the meta-theoretic p.c.l. information is not available in the one-for-one graph. However, the mere necessity of a p.c.l. is not sufficient to lead to difficulties. This state diagram ambiguity arises when, within a c.c.e., some terminating expression can be reached at more than one control point in the p.c.l. The manifestation of the problem is that we will reach some terminal operation in an expression and not know how to leave the node. The p.c.l. information is necessary. We conjecture that in general the intuitively obvious solution, two interacting state diagrams, will be effective. Now we give a graphical expression of the problem and the algebraic way to determine such state diagram ambiguity.

Consider the simple example:

$$\text{p.a.s.}_1 = \ <\text{c.e.}_1, \text{c.e.}_2> \qquad \text{c.e.}_1 = [p_{11} \rightarrow \text{c.e.}_2, \ p_{12} \rightarrow e_{12}]$$
$$\text{c.e.}_2 = [p_{21} \rightarrow e_{21}, \ p_{22} \rightarrow \text{c.e.}_1(e_{22})]$$

We attempt a 1-1 image with a graph in Fig. 9a. The solid graph represents c.e.$_1$, the first step of p.a.s.$_1$, and is 1-1 with the formalism. At node 3, c.e.$_1$ will terminate. We then wish to go to c.e.$_2$, which could be done by transitioning automatically to p_2 following dashed arc 1. When c.e.$_2$ terminates we will also be at vertex 3 and then wish to stop (or go on if p.a.s.$_1$ is longer). This would require following arc 2. The problem arises at vertex 3 in not knowing which way to leave.

Figure 9b is another construct of A which connects the outputs of the first step of p.a.s.$_1$ to p_2, to start c.e.$_2$. The difficulty arises, obviously, in that this graph never terminates, as it should on the completion of c.e.$_2$, since when c.e.$_2$ finishes, we are again at p_2.

Note that in Fig. 9c we also show a one-for-many graph that does represent the formalism as a connected sequential machine; however, this is A iterated twice (the second image having a different input point than the first). The symbolic c.e.–c.c.e. program notation is thus quite econom-

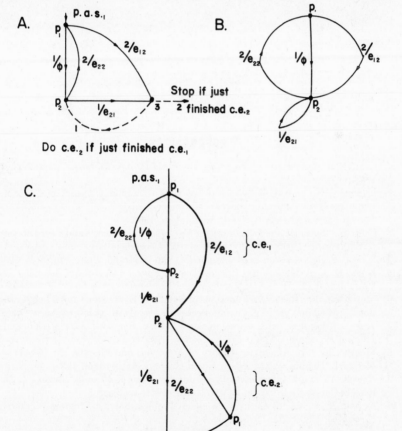

Figure 9

ical of space in that a flow chart's symbolic formalism would be, in general, much larger due to its many-for-one relation with this formalism.

The weakest algebraic rule is obvious. Write the power series of the language with the metalinguistic *. If an operator occurs immediately before the * at more than one place (or at the final position) in the string, state diagram ambiguity results. We illustrate with the above example (suppressing strings with no *).

$$p.a.s._1 = c.e._1 + c.e._2 + c.e._1 * c.e._2$$
$$c.e._1 = c.e._2 + e_{12}$$
$$c.e._2 = e_{21} + e_{22}\, c.e._1$$

Thus:

$$p.a.s._1 = (c.e._2 + e_{12}) * (e_{21} + e_{22}\, c.e._1)$$
$$= c.e._2 * e_{21} + c.e._2 * e_{22}c.e._1 + e_{12} * e_{21} + e_{12} * e_{22}c.e._1$$
$$= (e_{21} + e_{22}c.e._1) * e_{21} + (e_{21} + e_{22}c.e._1) * e_{22}(c.e._2 + e_{12})$$
$$\qquad\qquad + e_{12} * e_{22}(c.e._2 + e_{12})$$
$$= e_{21} * e_{21} + e_{22}c.e._1 * e_{21} + e_{21} * e_{22}c.e._2 + e_{21} * e_{22}e_{12}$$
$$\quad + e_{22}c.e._1 * e_{22}c.e._2 + e_{22}c.e._1 * e_{22}e_{12}$$
$$\quad + e_{12} * e_{22}c.e._2 + e_{12} * e_{22}e_{12}$$

Thus at level two we have difficulties with both e_{21} and e_{12} as was observed in the state diagram.

REFERENCES

1. Carnap, R., *Introduction to Symbolic Logic and Its Applications.* Dover, New York, 1958.
2. Chomsky, N., and M. P. Schutzenberger, "The Algebraic Theory of Context-Free Languages," in P. Braffort and D. Hirschberg (eds.), *Computer Programming and Formal Systems*, North-Holland, Amsterdam, 1963.
3. Gorn, S., "Specification Languages for Mechanical Languages and their Processors," *Communications of the ACM*, vol. 4, no. 12, December 1961.
4. Kleene, S., *Introduction to Metamathetics*, Van Nostrand, Princeton, N.J., 1950.
5. Kuck, D. J., *A Multicontext Problem Solving System with Natural Language Inputs*, Unpublished Ph. D. thesis, Northwestern University, 1963.
6. McCarthy, J., "Recursive Functions of Symbolic Expressions and Their Computation by Machine, Part I," *Communications of the ACM*, vol. 3, 4, April 1960.
7. ————, "Programs with Common Sense," Proc. *Symposium on Mechanization of Thought Processes*, HMSO, vol. 1, London, 1959.
8. Menger, K., "An Axiomatic Theory of Functions and Fluents," in *The Axiomatic Method* L. Henkin, et al., (eds.), North-Holland, Amsterdam, 1959.
9. Newell, A., et al., *Information Processing Language V Manual, Sections I, II.* The RAND Corporation Papers P–1897 and P–1918, 1960.
10. Newell, A., et al., "Report on a General Problem Solving Program," *Information Processing*, UNESCO, Paris, 1960.
11. Reichenbach, H., *Elements of Symbolic Logic*, Macmillan, New York, 1947.
12. Schaum, D., *Theory and Problems of College Physics.*, Schaum, New York, 1954.
13. Selfridge, O., "Pandemonium: A Paradigm for Learning," in *Proc. Symposium in Mechanization of Thought Processes*, vol. I, HMSO, London, 1959.

15

DYNAMIC PROGRAMMING, LEARNING, AND ADAPTIVE PROCESSES*

RICHARD BELLMAN

The RAND Corporation, Santa Monica, Calif.

INTRODUCTION

The recent intensive study of biological, medical, psychological, engineering, and computer processes has uncovered large numbers of problems which not only escape solution by means of classical mathematical techniques, but even pose problems of formulation.

In order to see what some of the difficulties are, it is necessary to understand the essential features of the classical approach to descriptive and variational processes. We shall briefly review the essentials of this approach and then indicate some of the ways in which dynamic programming furnishes a natural bridge between classical and modern theories.

Finally we shall indicate some of the major problems which are encountered in the study of adaptive processes and suggest some directions of research.

DETERMINISTIC DESCRIPTIVE PROCESSES

Let S be a physical system under examination and let us introduce a set of variables $x_1, x_2, \ldots, x_N$ describing the *state* of the system at any time t. The vector $x(t) = (x_1(t), \ldots, x_N(t))$ is called the state vector. To determine

* This research is sponsored by the United States Air Force under Project RAND— contract No. AF 49(638)–700 monitored by the Directorate of Development Planning, Deputy Chief of Staff, Research and Development, HqUSAF. Views or conclusions contained in this Memorandum should not be interpreted as representing the official opinion or policy of the United States Air Force.

the behavior of the system over time, we further postulate an equation of the form

$$\frac{dx}{dt} = g(x(s)), \qquad -\infty < s \leq t) \tag{1}$$

where the notation indicates that the function g depends upon the entire past history of the process. In many situations, we can assume that Eq. (1) has the form of an ordinary differential equation

$$\frac{dx}{dt} = g(x), \qquad x(0) = c \tag{2}$$

See [Ref. 1] for the more general case.

The study of the properties of the system S has thus been reduced to the study of the analytic behavior of the solutions of a differential equation, a considerable reduction in difficulty.

STOCHASTIC DESCRIPTIVE PROCESSES

It was soon recognized that this concise description of a physical process was either not available or not applicable in a large number of significant situations. Either the functions $g(x)$ were not known, or if precisely known, of such complicated form as to be unusable due to the high dimension of the vector x. In other cases, the initial state was not known.

To circumvent these difficulties, which at first sight appear to be major obstacles to progress, random variables were introduced, with average behavior replacing unique behavior over time.

Thus Eq. (2) might be replaced by

$$\frac{dx}{dt} = g(x(t), r(t)), \qquad x(0) = c \tag{3}$$

where c is a random variable and $x(t)$ is a random function of t. In some cases, as in quantum mechanics, the random variables are not explicit and the equations are of the type shown in Eq. (2) with the components representing probabilities or functions from which probabilities are generated.

DETERMINISTIC VARIATIONAL PROCESSES

In the study of control processes in engineering and economics, we encounter, in a very natural fashion, the problem of minimizing functionals of the form

$$J(x) = \int_0^T g(x, x', t) \, dt \tag{4}$$

where x is subject to various initial and terminal conditions and local and global constraints.

In mathematical physics, these questions arise in connection with alternative formulations of the behavior of systems.

DISCUSSION

In pursuing this classical route, we tacitly assume detailed knowledge of the following:

(a) number of state variables
(b) cause and effect
(c) values of state variables, initially and throughout the process   (5)
(d) probability distributions—if random variables are present
(e) criteria—if the processes are of variational type

How do we proceed if this information is not available?

LEARNING AND ADAPTIVE PROCESSES

Since we are treating new types of processes and problems, it is reasonable to expect that we will introduce some new concepts and some new analytic tools. The new concepts are those of learning and adaptation and the new tools are dynamic programming and adaptive control. Just as the boundary between learning and adaptation is not precise, so there is considerable overlap between dynamic programming and adaptive control.

It is clear that there is little to be done about ignorance in the short run. Hence we focus our attention upon multistage processes where information is obtained at each stage. The basic problem is that of using this information so as to improve decision making.

Fortunately, a fundamental idea from the field of engineering, feedback control, provides the essential clue. A mathematical abstraction of this leads to the theory of dynamic programming.[2,3,4]

With this mathematical apparatus we can handle a number of processes which arise in psychology, biology, medicine, economics and industry—all fields where learning, adaptation and feedback play primary roles.

The feedback to mathematics itself is in the form of new ideas and new fields in which to roam.

ITERATION AND TRANSFORMATIONS

Let us begin at the classical level with the concept of a transformation. Let p, a point in phase space, denote the state of a system S and let $T(p)$

denote the state a unit time later. Then the behavior of the system over time is equivalent to the study of the iterates, $p_1, p_2, \ldots, p_n, \ldots$, where

$$p_1 = T(p), \; p_2 = T(p_1), \ldots, p_{n+1} = T(p_n) \tag{6}$$

DYNAMIC PROGRAMMING

Let us now extend this idea in the following way. Instead of keeping the transformation fixed over time, let us suppose that we have a choice of the transformation to be applied at each stage. If q denotes the choice variable, or control variable, we have

$$p_1 = T(p,q_1), \; p_2 = T(p_1,q_2), \ldots, p_{n+1} = T(p_n,q_n), \ldots. \tag{7}$$

The q_i are to be chosen so as to minimize a given criterion function

$$R(p,p_1, \ldots, q_1,q_2, \ldots) \tag{8}$$

A set of q_i is called a *policy* and a set which minimizes is called an *optimal policy*.

If we assume that R has a separable structure,

$$R = g(p,q_1) + g(p_1,q_2) + \cdots \tag{9}$$

and introduce the function

$$f(p) = \min_{(q)} R \tag{10}$$

then the principle of optimality[2,3,4] yields the functional equation

$$f(p) = \min_{q_1} [g(p,q_1) + f(T(p,q_1))] \tag{11}$$

In the continuous case, the analogue of Eq. (11) yields as a by-product the Euler equation and the entire set of classical conditions of the calculus of variations.[5]

ABSTRACTION AND EXTENSION

Since we have carefully avoided defining the phase space to which p belongs, nothing prevents us from taking p to be a point in an infinite-dimensional space or from choosing as components of p probability distributions, past histories, and so on.

We thus have a quite general formulation of multistage decision processes. It remains to apply this formalism to the study of learning and adaptive processes.

ADAPTIVE PROCESSES AND LEARNING

The fundamental tool for treating ignorance is probability theory. If we do not know the value of a parameter, we assume that it is a random variable with a given probability distribution. If we do not know the probability distribution, we take it to be a random probability distribution, an element of a family of probability distributions. If we do not know the family . . . and so on. In this way, we are led quite naturally to the consideration of hierarchies of uncertainties; see the discussion in Ref. 6.

The generalized state of a system S in an adaptive process consists then not only of the usual physical state, but contains also the best current estimates of unknown quantities. These estimates may be numbers, e.g., expected values and variances, or they may be probability distributions.

At each stage of the decision process we must make a decision, a choice of q, and we must estimate the new state $T(p,q)$ on the basis of new information. Note that in many cases, part of the decision process is the determination of how much effort is to be devoted to obtaining additional information.

For analytical details, see Refs. 4 and 7.

"Learning" can now be interpreted on several levels, consistent with the concept of hierarchies of uncertainty. It is first of all the ability to estimate efficiently at each stage so that ultimately the unknown elements become known. It is secondly the ability to estimate inabilities to estimate on the basis of a model of simple uncertainties and to introduce more sophisticated uncertainties, and so on.

We see then that we are led to the concept of levels of intelligence, an idea which is quite important in connection with the construction of automata.

APPLICATIONS

Let us note that these ideas can be applied to the construction of simulation processes, both in the business area[8] and in the field of psychiatry.[9] They afford a simple and flexible framework for the study of many multistage processes and have many immediate uses in modern control theory.[4]

COMPLEXITY

As far as obtaining numerical answers to numerical questions is concerned, we are nowhere near a satisfactory situation. If the dimension of p is small, we have efficient routine techniques using digital computers; if the dimension is large, e.g., 10, or if p has components which are functions, these methods fail. Although a number of approximate methods exist which enable us to treat many additional classes of problems, e.g., polynomial approximation, stochastic approximation, we have not really come to grips with complexity.

In particular, we have no idea at the present of how the human mind handles situations involving huge masses of data, conflicting information, and imprecise criteria and makes a decision.

It seems quite clear that when we understand the neurophysiological basis of the human memory, or memories, and the human data retrieval system, then we shall make progress in other areas. Furthermore, when we emancipate ourselves from the restriction of universally true theorems and theories and study approximations in logical space, then we shall develop powerful approximation methods in science.

REFERENCES

1. Bellman, R., and K. L. Cooke, *Differential-difference Equations*, Academic, New York, 1963.
2. Bellman, R., *Dynamic Programming*, Princeton U. P., Princeton, N.J., 1957.
3. Bellman, R., and S. Dreyfus, *Applied Dynamic Programming*, Princeton U. P., Princeton, N.J., 1962.
4. Bellman, R., *Adaptive Control Processes; A Guided Tour*, Princeton U. P., Princeton, N.J., 1961.
5. Dreyfus, S., "Dynamic Programming and the Calculus of Variations," *J. Math. Anal.*, vol. 1, no. 2, 1960, pp. 228–239.
6. Bellman, R., *Dynamic Programming, Intelligent Machines, and Self-organizing Systems, Mathematical Theory of Automata*, Polytechnic Press of the Polytechnic Institute of Brooklyn, New York, 1963, pp. 1–12.
7. Tou, J. T., *Optimum Design of Digital Control Systems*, Academic Press, New York, 1963.
8. Bellman, R., C. Clark, C. Craft, D. Malcolm, and F. Ricciardi, "On the Construction of a Multiperson, Multistage Business Game," *Operations Research*, vol. 5, 1957, pp. 469–503.
9. Bellman, R., M. B. Friend, and L. Kurland, *Psychiatric Interviewing and Multistage Decision Processes of Adaptive Type*, The RAND Corporation, RM–3732–NIH, 1963.

16

PRE-REQUISITES OF SELF-ORGANIZATION

A. M. Andrew

Cybernetic Research Unit
Science in General Management, Ltd.
London, England

By self-organization is meant any process by which an assemblage of initially undifferentiated elements may change its own internal state, and thereby come to show behavior which is useful and possibly intelligent. This definition is not rigorous without the precise definition of various terms appearing in it. It may, in fact, be impossible to arrive at a rigorous definition which will be universally acceptable, since as Ashby[1] and others have pointed out, a system may appear to be self-organizing according to the mode of description used by one observer and not according to the equally valid mode used by another. The fact that the term resists rigorous definition is no reason for abandoning it. The term "learning" is also impossible to define in a completely satisfactory manner, yet when people ask me in the next few weeks whether I learned anything from the COINS symposium, I shall be able to reply unambiguously without requiring them to rephrase the question in rigorous terms.

Self-organization implies the spontaneous improvement of the system's performance in some task or function. In achieving the improvement the system must interact with its environment, and it has sometimes been suggested that there can be no such thing as a self-organizing system, since no system will exhibit the property in isolation. However, since the property is of greatest interest when it remains effective in a wide range of environments, it is appropriate to regard it as being mainly a function of the system studied rather than of the environment. There are some self-improving systems which operate by adjusting the values of continuously variable parameters; these are termed self-optimizing controllers, and it is suggested that the term "self-organizing" should not be applied to them. A system should only be so described if it is capable of changing its own internal structure, and not merely of adjusting parameters. It is not possible to draw a sharp line of distinction here, since the establishment of a new connection within a system may be alternatively described as a change in structure, or as a change of a parameter from zero to a finite value. Here again we must fall back on a subjective, and consequently imprecise, definition, by saying that a system is self-organizing if the spontaneous changes by which it improves its performance are most readily described as changes in structure.

The words "useful" and "improvement" have been used here as though they could always be rigorously defined, though this is not always possible, as discussed by Ashby.[1] Here the difficulty will be circumvented by assuming throughout that some goal for the system is unambiguously defined and that a measure of the degree of goal-achievement is available. In the terminology of Selfridge,[2] adopted by Andrew [3] this is called "hedony"; Wiener[4] has used the term "affective tone."

THE HYPOTHESIS OF UBIQUITY

It is postulated here that self-organization is not an inevitable feature of an assemblage of interacting elements. In other words, it is suggested that there are prerequisite conditions for self-organization to occur; self-organization is not ubiquitous. On the other hand, Ashby[1] has stated "every dynamic system generates its own form of intelligent life, is self-organizing in this sense."

He has, in fact, shown that some degree of adaptation to the environment will occur in virtually any complex system, the only prerequisite being a very large number of equilibrial states. It is only necessary that the states which show better adaptation are also the more stable ones, to ensure that the system will move to a better adapted state when exposed for a sufficient time to any set of environmental conditions.

This mechanism of adaptation is a slight generalization of what is generally thought to happen during evolution. Mutations allow sampling of the desirability of new states to which the species might transfer. If the new state is, in fact, preferable, and the species is living under competitive conditions, the whole species moves to it.

Some biologists have argued that the process of random mutation and natural selection is insufficient to account for evolutionary changes as they have occurred, and that some other guiding principle must play a part. Whether or not this is so will not be argued here but, whatever the mechanism, natural evolution is a slow and wasteful process. In an individual animal further adaptation to the environment occurs during its lifetime due to learning. This is a process of self-organization of the nervous system.

Many useful and interesting things could be done by artefacts embodying this facility of self-organization.

Ashby has suggested that self-organization of this faster kind is also a process of selection from the set of all possible states of the system. It is certainly true that any given system has a finite number of states, and if there is a state which meets a particular requirement it can, in principle, be found by searching through them. However, the number of possible states is so enormous that for a system to organize itself by selection is like trying to obtain a Shakespearian sonnet from monkeys hammering on typewriters. This paper is a selection from the set of all possible sequences of a few thousand English words, but it was of no value whatever to consider the set when preparing this particular sample. The useful states of organization of a system must be found by some other approach than selection.

Some consideration of the number of possibilities for a large system will I think, convince anyone that this is so. For the nervous system it is impossible to compute the number of states without knowing more than we do about the mechanism of memory, but it is certainly greater than for any existing computer. There is no great difficulty in calculating the number of possible states of a computer. The number is, of course, vast. Even the amount of storage equal to that of a single punched card (12 rows by 80 columns giving 960 bits) has a number of states greater than the *cube* of Eddington's cosmic number! (This number, representing the number of particles in the universe, is given as the product of four factors $N = abcd$, where $a = 2$ if the particles are protons and electrons, $b = 0.75$, $c = 136$ and $d = 2^{256}$. Hence $N < 2^{265}$ and $N^3 < 2^{795}$. The number of possibilities for the punched card is 2^{960}.)

When the number of possible states for this moderate amount of storage is so vast, there is little point in calculating the number for a computer. Even if the count is of programs rather than instantaneous states, the number is still supercosmic. In the study of actual working self-organizing systems, supercosmic numbers are effectively infinite, and self-organization cannot be viewed as a process of selection.

Ashby's arguments for the ubiquity of self-organization break down, and it is relevant to ask what are the prerequisites of self-organization.

THE REQUIREMENTS

Certain task can be learned by treating separately every discriminable configuration of inputs from the environment. For instance, a machine could learn to play "noughts and crosses" (tick-tack-toe) by trying the different possible moves for each configuration which can arise in a game, and arriving at a "best" move with which to meet each one. Other task environments do not lend themselves to this kind of treatment since the number of possible situations is enormous. If the system is to learn to perform the more complex tasks, it must be able to detect and utilise invariant properties, or regularities, of the environment. It may then learn in a reasonable time, without excessive demands on storage capacity, and may be able to respond appropriately to configurations of its inputs which have not occurred previously. Examples of regularities which might be detected are the following:

(a) Metrical continuity of the environment.

(b) In character recognition, invariance under translation, rotation and dilation. In human beings the appreciation of this regularity is an offshoot of the general facility by which sensory data are used to form an image of the three-dimensional world. The formation of this facility, in the first instance, must have resulted from the detection of regularities in sensory data.

(c) Logical rules governing the occurrence of events. Suppose a system receives binary input signals $x_1, x_2, \ldots, x_n$, and a further binary signal x_{n+1} is a function of these. One way in which the system might learn to predict x_{n+1} from the others would be by exhaustive classification. That is to say, the appropriate values of x_{n+1} associated with each of the 2^n input patterns would be listed. An artefact which can learn by such exhaustive classification has been described by Uttley.[5] A human being would only use this method as a last resort, and would first try to find a way of expressing x_{n+1} as a logical function of the others. Unless the environment is singularly disordered it is also advantageous for an artefact to be able to detect logical relationships. Ways in which a self-organizing system might detect regularities under (a) and (c) will be considered.

UTILIZATION OF CONTINUITY

In the acquisition of manual skills, human beings utilize the metrical continuity of their environment. It is unthinkable that a person learning to ride a bicycle would know what action to take when the machine tilted to 8° from the vertical, and to 10° and yet have no idea what to do when the tilt was 9°.

There are two main ways in which a system may utilise continuity in improving its own performance in a task. Let the sensory data from the environment consist of the continuously variable signals $a\ (t)$, $b\ (t)$, $c\ (t)$ and let the effector signals, by which the system acts on the environment, be d (t) and e (t). Then, one way in which the system could operate would be to let d and e be computed as polynomial functions of a, b, c, say

$$d = K + La + Mb + Nc + Pa^2 + Qab + \dots \tag{1}$$

and a similar equation for e.

The system can improve its performance by adjusting the values of the parameters K, L, M, $\dots$ in order to maximize the measure of hedony h. This can be done by superimposing fluctuations on the parameter values and correlating these with h. If there is significant correlation a parameter value is altered in a direction determined by the sign of the correlation.

Another way in which the system could operate would be to let the signals a, b, c define a phase-space of input signals. Values of the output signals d and e would be stored in association with a number of "key points" in the phase-space. These stored values would be used to determine the output signals $d(t)$ and $e(t)$ as the operating point moved through the phase-space. A suitable interpolation procedure would be used when the operating point was not coincident with one of the key points. It is not difficult to devise a procedure by which such a system may improve its own performance by superimposing fluctuations on the output signals $d(t)$ and $e(t)$, correlating these with h, and letting the correlation values influence the stored values of d and e associated with the key points nearest to the recent trajectory.

These two ways in which a system may operate to improve its own performance in a continuous environment are both subject to serious limitations. Neither requires the system to be self-organizing since the improvement results from parameter adjustment without change of structure. The range of control policies which can be achieved by the first method is severely constrained since the form of the control equation is unalterable. Similarly, in the second method there are severe constraints because the pattern of key points is unalterable. The constraints become less severe when the number of terms in the equations, or the number of key points, is increased but then the demands on storage capacity and the time taken to learn also increase.

In acquiring manual skills, human beings exploit continuity without restricting themselves as do the types of system discussed above. A human being is quite capable of learning a task where the appropriate response to a tilt of 9° is quite different from that obtained by interpolating between the responses to 8° and 10°. Human beings have the best of both worlds; they exploit continuity but retain flexibility in their range of control policies.

For a self-optimizing system to have the same advantages, it must be able to override the restrictions previously stated; that the form of the control functions or the distribution of key points, is unalterable. It is possible to derive criteria[3,6] for the insertion of new terms in the polynomial or the establishment of new key points. Criteria for the elimination of unnecessary terms can also be devised. If separate elements of the system are used to compute the terms of the polynomial, or to store the information relating to a key point, these criteria provide a means of self-organization of the system. A unit which is spare can be allocated to compute a particular term, or to be associated with a point in the phase-space, whenever the criterion for the establishment of a new term or point is satisfied. When a term or point is shown to be unnecessary, the corresponding unit becomes available for reallocation. Each of the units contains the means of adjusting a parameter associated with it; this is either the coefficient of the polynomial term or the stored value of d or e. By introducing the principle of self-organization it is possible to exploit continuity while keeping the flexibility as great as possible with the number of units available.

LOGICAL FUNCTIONS

The type of system which utilizes a polynomial function has been adapted to deal with logical functions[7]. In this case, the input variables $x_1, x_2, x_3, \ldots$ (corresponding to $a, b, c,$ in Eq. 1) were restricted to the two values 0 and 1, and the output was made to be 1, if the polynomial sum was positive or zero, and 0 if the sum was negative. A computer programme was written embodying this system. Groups of eight binary digits were generated by a pseudo-random generator, and formed the inputs $x_1, x_2, \ldots, x_8$. Some function of these was computed by another part of the program: this was the "correct" answer. From the current form of the polynomial the self-organizing system formed a "machine" answer which was compared with the "correct" answer. The result of the comparison was indicated to the self-organizing system as a hedony signal. Figure 1 shows a block diagram of the arrangement. The goal of the self-organizing system was to improve the agreement between its "machine" answers and the "correct" answers. This it could do by adjusting the polynomial equation. For instance, if the "correct" answer was determined by the identity relationship

$$x_1 \equiv x_2 \tag{2}$$

the "machine" answer would agree when determined by the sign of the polynomial

$$2x_1x_2 - x_1 - x_2 + 0 \tag{3}$$

A self-organizing system was in fact programmed which would adjust its own polynomial to Eq. (3) when the "correct" answer was given by (2), provided the term x_1x_2 was inserted manually. Starting from the form $x_1x_2 + 0$ the system would itself arrive at Eq. (3). The method used to adjust parameters and insert new terms was somewhat different from that suggested for the continuous case. The latter made use of fluctuations superimposed on the parameter values, which were then correlated with the variations in hedony. For the system dealing with logical functions, it is not necessary to impose fluctuations and the parameter changes are determined by triple correlations between h, m and p where h is the hedony, m the machine answer, and p the product of the inputs (e.g., the product x_1x_2) appearing in the term.

This alternative form of operation without parameter fluctuations is possible when the system is able to determine whether its output has erred on the high or low side. In the case of the system giving a binary output, the sign of the error can certainly be determined, since if the "machine" answer was 1 and was wrong, the "correct" answer must have been 0, and vice versa.

There are other circumstances in which the sign of error can be determined, including any case where the goal of the self-organizing system is prediction of some quantity which later becomes accurately known. Self-organization is then possible without the use of test fluctuations in the output signals of the system.

A system which adjusts internal parameters in this general way has been described by Donaldson[8] under the heading of Error Decorrelation. Foulkes[9] has described a system which does, in fact, self-organize but with somewhat restricted applicability.

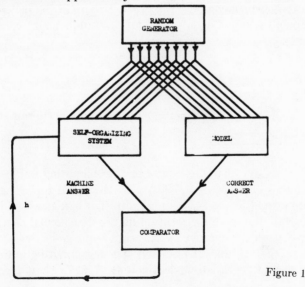

Figure 1

HIERARCHICAL STRUCTURE

Systems which optimize a polynomial function, even one with many terms, or which adjust stored values associated with points in a phase-space, cannot learn really complex tasks. Such tasks cannot be learned in any feasible length of time by attempting to correlate every small variation of the control policy with a single measure of hedony. If a machine is learning a game such as chess, for example, to try to correlate intermediate decisions with eventual outcomes of complete games is not practical.

In order to learn complex tasks a system must be capable of forming a hierarchical structure where higher-order parts form subgoals, which lower-order parts try to achieve. The subgoals are subject to adaptive modification and can be introduced and annihilated like the terms in the polynomial equation. Such a system could be said to be forming new concepts, and to require a different "language" for its description at different stages of the self-organization process. Pask[10] has discussed concept formation and metalanguage. The higher levels of the hierarchical structure are, in effect, using a metalanguage to treat the same phenomena as are treated in greater detail by the lower levels.

PROPOSALS

The principles which have been devised for altering the form of a polynomial expression allow the construction of a simple form of self-organizing system. The idea can be generalized to include computing units other than those which compute the product terms of the polynomial. For example, given the input signals, $a(t)$, $b(t)$, $c(t)$ units might compute

$$A \max (a,b)$$

or

$$A |a|$$

where A is an adjustable parameter, as well as product terms such as

$$Aab, \quad Aab^2, \quad Ac^3 \quad \text{etc.}$$

It is not necessary that the inputs to the computing units be the raw signals from the environment $a(t)$, $b(t)$, $c(t)$. Any signal appearing anywhere in the system could be used as an input. In that case it would be possible to dispense with units forming terms of higher than second degree; higher-degree terms could be formed by successive multiplications in separate units. The precise criteria for insertion of new computing units have not been given here; they are discussed in Refs. 3, 6, 7. They depend on the computation of measures of correlation which can equally well refer to internal signals of the system or to its input data.

This general approach allows the construction of a particular kind of self-organizing system. At present it is at a single level but further study will show how to modify the basic units so that hierarchies can be developed. According to the view that self-organization depends fairly critically on the properties of the elements of the system, the establishment of a set of sufficient conditions is extremely useful, since it allows the construction of self-organizing systems for study. It would be even more interesting to know the set of necessary conditions, but this is a long way ahead. It is suggested that the general approach discussed here provides a "way-in" to the study of self-organizing systems.

The following are some general conclusions which can be drawn about properties of a system conducive to self-organization:

(a) The criterion for the introduction of a new computing unit at any point in the system depends on the detection of correlations between signals. The number of correlation measures which might prove to be significant is enormous, and it would be impossible to monitor all of them continuously. There must, therefore, be some form of sampling which measures the correlation between different pairs of variables at different times. This might be achieved by special "wandering correlators" but it is probably more convenient to let these correlations be computed within existing units, along with the measures which determine changes in the units' own parameters. The units must then incorporate a facility for random selection of variables, external to themselves, to be correlated.

(b) If there is significance in one of the correlation measures computed to indicate the need for a new unit, then either the unit which detected the correlation must split into two, a new unit must be produced in some other way, or an idle one summoned. Foulkes allows his units to split. If the total number is constant, an idle one must be summoned.

(c) Since the number of correlation measures which could prove significant is large, it may be advantageous to have a means of recording and reiterating a section of the history of the system. During the successive reiterations, different correlations could be tested. If the changes in structure and parameter-values of the system are termed long-term memory, this other facility could be termed its short-term memory. (There is a suggestion of dual memory mechanisms even in the earthworm, since the temporal characteristics of its learning are changed when a part of its nervous system is removed, as reported by Ratner and Miller.[11])

(*d*) The system must embody criteria for deciding that a unit is serving no useful purpose, whereupon it is either annihilated or becomes available for reallocation. If, as was suggested above, units can be inserted which use any signals appearing in the system as inputs, there can be some difficulty in deciding whether a unit is indeed serving no useful purpose. The purpose for which the unit was originally inserted may have become unimportant, but its output may have come to be used as input by some other unit. To ensure that a unit in such a situation is not removed, it is necessary to have some mechanism by which pathways carrying important information are protected. A "feedback of significance" along the information pathways, which preserves the units in the path from annihilation or reallocation is needed.

(*e*) The formation of hierarchical structures may be aided by departing from the original condition that the elements of the system should initially be entirely undifferentiated. A certain diffuse differentiation is inevitable if the pathways for incoming and outgoing information make localized connections in the system. Regions near the outgoing connections are likely to form the lower levels of the hierarchy, while those near to the pathway indicating hedony are likely to form higher levels. The adaptive changes which occur in the system should happen more slowly at the higher levels than at the lower, since a variation in high-level policy cannot be evaluated until the lower-level parts have had time to achieve the new subgoals presented to them. The different time-scales at different levels could be a further result of self-organization, since time-constants, as well as the parameters already discussed, can be subject to adaptive modification. The automatic adjustment of parameters such as time-constants can be termed "learning-to-learn."

CONCLUSIONS

The approach to self-organizing systems outlined here provides a basis for theoretical and practical investigations. Systems showing interesting properties have been programmed,[7,9] but digital computers have limitations in the simulation of really complex systems since the separate units must be treated sequentially in the program and the amount of computer time required to show interesting results can become prohibitive. The use of special purpose machinery is, therefore, being considered. Since the separate computing units are rather elaborate, they probably have to consist of electronic circuits, rather than deposited iron threads, crystals, etc. There is considerable scope for ingenuity in finding ways of letting spare units by summoned to sites at which they are required, either by moving bodily, or by forming connections. The provision of the postulated "feedback of significance" is also a challenging technical problem.

REFERENCES

1. Ashby, W. R., "Principles of the self-organizing system," in H. Von Foerster and G. W. Zopf (eds.), *Principles of Self-Organization*, Pergamon, New York, 1962, p. 255.
2. Selfridge, O. G., "Pattern Recognition and Learning," in E. C. Cherry (ed.), *Information Theory*, Butterworth, London, 1956.
3. Andrew, A. M., "Learning machines," in *Mechanization of Thought Processes*, H.M.S.O., London, 1959, p. 473.
4. Wiener, N., *Cybernetics*, Wiley, New York, 1948, p. 150.
5. Uttley, A. M., "The Design of Conditional Probability Computers," *Information and Control*, vol. 2, no. 1, 1959.
6. Andrew, A. M., "Self-optimizing Control Mechanisms and Some Principles for More Advanced Learning Machines," *Automatic and Remote Control* (Proc. I.F.A.C. Congress), Butterworth, London, 1961, p. 818.
7. ———, "An Experimental Comparison of Some Algorithms for Self-organizing Systems," *IRE Trans. Inform. Theory*, vol. IT–8, no. 5, September 1962, p. 163.
8. Donaldson, P. E. K., "Error Decorrelation: a Technique for Matching a Class of Functions," Proc. 3rd. Int. Conf. on Medical Electronics, London, 1960, p. 173.
9. Foulkes, J. D., "A Class of Machines which Determines the Statistical Structure of a Sequence of Characters, ' *IRE WESCON Convention Record*, pt. 4, p. 66, 1959.
10. Pask, A. G., "Contribution to Panel Discussion on Artificial Intelligence," I.F.I.P. Congress, Munich, 1962.
11. Ratner, S. C., and K. R. Miller, "Effects of Spacing of Training and Ganglia Removal on Conditioning in Earthworms," *J. Comp. Physiol. Psychol.*, 52, 1959, p. 667.

17

A UNIFIED THEORY OF LEARNING*
AND INFORMATION

MIHAJLO D. MESAROVIC

Systems Research Center
Case Institute of Technology

INTRODUCTION

The objective of this paper is to propose a conceptual basis for a unified
theory of learning and information and to develop an essential formalism
for further development of such a theory. It is characteristic for the proposed theory that many essential concepts such as information content of
a message, heuristic in a learning process, etc., are not uniquely defined in
the general formalism. However, the relation of these concepts with others
must satisfy certain basic requirements. Therefore in order to apply the
general formalism proposed in this paper one must supplement it with the
specifics of the class of systems under consideration.

It is felt that the absence of uniqueness in defining the mentioned basic
concepts in learning and information does not represent the inadequacy of
the proposed approach but, on the contrary, might well represent one of its
strong points. Namely, the basic problem of decision making on which the
whole theory relies has, as its major characteristic, the fact that its solution
is not unique. Consequently the derived concepts of learning and information can not be made unique either.

Underlying the proposed theory are the following two conjectures:

1. The learning process in a system and its information exchange and
   processing have meaning only in relation to each other. In other
   words, one cannot talk about information content without taking
   into account the learning heuristic used by the system. It is very

* This study has been supported in part by ONR Contract No. 1141 (12).

important, then, to make this fact clearly apparent in the very definition of these two processes. One can thus talk of learning only in conjunction with the flow of information; on the other hand, the flow of information would exist only in conjunction with the system that has the ability to learn from the messages received.

2. We shall be interested in the behavior of a given system in a given learning situation and its ability to utilize the information received and not with the behavior of the class of such systems. The basic activities of the system described are then of logical and heuristic character. Statistical techniques might be used by the system as a possible heuristic, but this is not an essential condition for the learning process itself.

In developing the proposed approach we had in mind descriptive as well as normative applications. Although the statistical models of learning are used successfully to describe learning behavior of certain living systems on an input-output basis it is felt that the same experimental situations can also be described by using the proposed learning model with the additional advantage of providing some understanding of the structure of the learning system and consequently offering some insight as to the behavior of the system in a changed environment. Normative value of the proposed model stems from the fact that the problems underlying the theory sufficiently reflect realistic situations.

BASIC PROBLEM IN DECISION-MAKING

Both learning and communication processes are related via the process of deciding on the proper course of action. We are not interested here in the decision-making process *per se* and will discuss that problem only to the extent essential for the understanding of the learning process.

In essence the general problem of decision making can be formulated in the following way:

GIVEN:

A1. The image of the situation in which the decision maker has to interfere—a model of the system,

$$\bar{y}(t) = T * [\overline{m}(t), \bar{u}(t)] \tag{1}$$

where $\overline{m}(t)$ = decision variable

$\bar{y}(t)$ = outcome of the decision

$u(t)$ = uncertainty variable expressing the recognized uncertainty, doubt, ignorance which the decision maker has about the system.

T = transformation relating m and u to y

Notice that both T and $\bar{u}$ reflect the viewpoint of the decision maker and, of course, not necessarily the actual situation. In other words, the actual system might have a different transofrmation T and the uncertainty variable might be different than that assumed by the decision maker.

A2. Utility function (performance functional)

$$q = q\,[\overline{m}(t),\bar{y}(t)] \tag{2}$$

Again this is the utility function used by the decision maker at the given decision time and is not necessarily a specified, unchangeable function nor is it necessarily truly beneficial to the decision maker.

A3. Set of decision variables Ω_m.

A4. Uncertainty set $u \, \epsilon \, \Omega_u$. This is the key concept for further development of the learning and information theory. It is essential to consider this set in the broadest possible sense. It includes all the hypothesis the decision maker made (or cares to make) about the possible behavior of the unknown or doubtful subsystems or environment. It should be considered initially rather abstractly without assuming that the set is structured in any way. Elements of Ω_u can be points in an arbitrary space and can represent numbers, subsets, functions, families of subsets, relations, etc.

A5. Tolerance functional α specifying the tolerance in the performance the decision maker would accept $\alpha = \alpha\,[\bar{u}(t)]$. It is explicitly defined as a functional on Ω_u.

A6. Relation between q and α.

$$R\,[q,\alpha] \tag{3}$$

A relation of sufficient generality is the inequality

$$|q| < \alpha \tag{4}$$

The problem of decision making is the following:

Find an $\overline{m} \, \epsilon \, \Omega_m$ so that $R\,[q,\,\alpha]$ is satisfied for all $\bar{u} \, \epsilon \, \Omega_u$.

In other words, the decision-making problem consists in finding an appropriate decision variable so that performance of the system will be within the tolerance limit regardless of which element of the uncertainty set occurs.

LEARNING PROCESS IN DECISION-MAKING SITUATION

We shall start the development of the learning theory from the decision-making problem defined in the previous section. We note initially that in order to formulate a learning problem one has to assume, or to be given, the uncertainty set Ω_u.

Conceptually the most difficult problem in decision-making, as discussed in previous sections, results from the existence of the uncertainties. In order to improve the decision-making process one has to remove the "doubt" as much as possible and to reduce uncertainty of the actual outcome of the unknown effects. In essence the learning process is viewed here as being aimed at the removal of this doubt. The learning process can be defined in general in the following way:

Learning is the activity of a decision-making system aimed at the reduction of the uncertainty set Ω_u.

There are two features of this approach that need emphasizing. 1) In order to formulate a learning problem, the uncertainty set Ω_u has to be assumed; 2) The learning process is aimed at the reduction of this set but whether the reduction will actually be accomplished depends upon the action of the environment or in general upon the adequacy of the learning heuristics used in the given situation.

The learning process can be descriptively explained in the following way. The uncertainty set is assumed Ω_u; new evidence is presented X_T; by using learning heuristics L the set Ω_u is transformed into a new, supposedly reduced, set Ω_u'.

Learning is therefore specified by the triplet

$$<\Omega_u, X_T, L> \tag{5}$$

where Ω_u = uncertainty set

$X_T = [x_{1T}, x_{2T}, \ldots, x_{nT},]$, sequence of events representing the evidence as to the outcome of events.

L = learning heuristic; i.e., mapping that generates the new set Ω_u' from the old set Ω_u;

$$\Omega_u' = L[\Omega_u, X_T] \tag{6}$$

It can be argued that the essence of the learning process is in the problem of generalization. The formulation of this problem is as follows:

GIVEN:

A sequence of elements $X_T = [x_{1T}, \ldots, x_{nT}]$ belonging to a set Q i.e.: $x_{jT} \in Q$ for all j's

FIND:

The class property of the set Q that is characteristic for all the elements of Q including, of course, those in the sequence X_T.

In order to develop an appropriate heuristic the generalization problem can be formally specified in the following way:

(A) *Assume*: The existence of:

    1. A universe—uncertainty set Ω_u

2. A subset, $Q \subset \Omega_u$
3. Characteristic function $y(x)$ for the set Q, i.e.,

$$[y(x) = 1] \leftrightarrow [x \in Q] \tag{7}$$
$$[y(x) = 0] \leftrightarrow [x \notin Q]$$

(B) *Given*:
   1. A sequence of elements of Q

$$X_T = [x_{1T}, \ldots, x_{nT}] \tag{8}$$

   2. Bounded characteristic function defined on the set X_T;

$$[y_T(x) = 1] \leftrightarrow [(x \in X_T) \cap (x \in Q)] \tag{9}$$
$$[y_T(x) = 0] \leftrightarrow [(x \notin X_T) \cap (x \notin Q)]$$

(C) *Find*:

The characteristic function $y(x)$ defined on Ω_u as assumed in (A3).

It is apparent that there can not exist a unique "best" method for solving the generalization problem. Depending upon the nature and structure of the sets Ω_u and Q as well as the sequence X_T different generalization method can be advantageous. This is why any of these methods is properly called a heuristic.

Similarly, the adequacy of a selected learning heuristic L for a learning process as specified by the triplet (Ω_u, X_T, L) depends upon Ω_u, X_T as well as on Q. This implies that the very nature of the learning process makes the study of the properties of the learning heuristic very difficult and thus the general conclusions which can be drawn are rather scarce. However, the properties of a given class of learning heuristics can be more readily attainable. In the next section a class of rather general learning heuristics will be considered. This is to be considered only as an illustration for deeper investigations.

LEARNING HEURISTICS

The process of learning as developed in preceding sections consists in eliminating those subsets of Ω_u which, on the basis of the presented evidence, appear to be irrelevant and can be safely omitted from the uncertainty set. In this section we shall present a general class of learning heuristics and discuss some of its basic properties.

In general, the heuristic for learning discussed in this section is specified by the following process:

Initially, the uncertainty set Ω_u is given. The evidence set X_T is then generated sequentially in time, i.e., evidence x_{jT} is presented at time $t = t_j$. After each presentation of the new evidence the reduction of the uncertainty set ensues.

Consider the situation after the first evidence is presented x_1. Several different partial orderings of the set Ω_u are then introduced that induce respective partitions.

$$\overline{P}^1 = [P_1^1, P_2^1, \ldots, P_n^1] \tag{10}$$

where:

$P_1^1 = [P_{11}^1, \ldots, P_{1m_1}^1]$ is the first partition proposed at $t = t_1$

$P_n^1 = [P_{n1}^1, \ldots, P_{nm_1}^1]$ is the nth partition proposed at $t = t_1$

$P_{11}^1, \ldots, P_{1m_1}^1$ subsets of the first partition

$P_{n1}^n, \ldots, P_{nm_1}^n$ subsets of the nth partition

One of the available partitions is then selected—e.g., P_j^1, and a new set is generated from that partition P_j^1 and Ω_u.

$$S_1 = F[N(\Omega_u), M(P_j^1)] \tag{11}$$

New evidence is then presented x_2, and a new set of partitions is proposed

$$\overline{P}^2 = [P_1^2, \ldots, P_n^2] \quad \text{where } P_i^2 = [P_{i1}^2, \ldots, P_{im_2}^2] \tag{12}$$

It is required that $m_1 < m_2$, i.e., that any partition given at $t = t_2$ has larger number of equivalence classes than partitions at $t = t_1$. In other words, partitions at $t = t_2$ are "finer" than partitions at $t = t_1$. A new uncertainty set is then generated in a similar way:

$$S_2 = F[N(S_1), M(P_i^2)] \tag{13}$$

where P_i^2 is the selected partition at $t = t_2$.

Partition P_i^2 is selected from all the partitions available at $t = t_2$ on the basis of the evidences x_1 and x_2. A method of how P_i^2 might be selected will be discussed later in this section.

Proceeding in a similar way a recursive formula for the set S_i is obtained

$$S_i = F[N(S_{i-1}), M(P_k^i)] \tag{14}$$

It is in general required that

$$m_1 < m_2 < \cdots < m_{i-1} < m_i$$

This should give the basis for the selection of continually smaller sets S_i by using an appropriate learning heuristic. However to specify this heuristic even further it is necessary:

1. to select transformation F
2. to select transformation M
3. to select transformation N
4. to define the method for generating a family of partitions at any given time t_j.
5. to define the method for selecting a given partition at $t = t_i$ from the set of partitions $\bar{P}^i$.

In this paper we shall further explore the first three problems. For the fourth problem of generating partitions the approach proposed by R. Banerji[2] seems to be most suitable.

A convenient method of selecting a partition can be derived if the elements inside the equivalence classes can be ordered. After the evidence x_i is presented that partition from the class of partitions $\bar{P}^i$ is selected for which the presented, evidences $x_1, \ldots, x_i$ fall "furthest" from the extreme elements of the respective subsets. For example if only two partitions are considered and each of them has a subset that includes the presented evidence x_i but in one partition the evidence x_i is the largest element in that subset (according to the given ordering) while in another partition the same evidence x_i falls inside the subset, the second partition will be accepted. This method of selection is based on the assumption that if the evidence is on the limit or close to it there is greater chance that the next evidence x_{i+1} will fall outside the selected subset.

Two general classes of learning heuristic will now be considered.

(A) INTERSECTION HEURISTIC

In this heuristic one uses the intersection for F and recursive relation becomes

$$S_i = N(S_{i-1}) \cap M(P_j^i) \qquad (14a)$$

Four different heuristics of this type are under investigation:

A1. The selected partition at $t = t_i$ has n_i subsets. A union of all the subsets P^i_{jk} that include at least one element of the evidence sequence X_{iT} is formed.

$$P_j^i(x) = \bigcup_k P_{jk}^i \qquad (15)$$

and the intersection of the set P_{ji} and a transformed set S_{i-1} is taken. The recursive relation is now

$$S_i = N(S_{i-1}) \cap P_j^i(x) \qquad (15a)$$

A2. Further specification can be obtained if the transformation N is defined in such a way as to eliminate those subsets of the set S_{i-1} which are furthest from the subsets that include the elements of the sequence X_T. Recursive relation for generating set S_i is now

$$S_i = P_h^{i-1}(x) \cap P_j^i(x) \tag{16}$$

where

$$P_h^{i-1}(x) = \bigcup_k P_{hk}^{i-1}$$

A3. Another variation of the same type of heuristic is obtained starting from (15a) and taking the transformation N to be identity. The recursive relation is then

$$S_i = S_{i-1} \cap M(P_j^i) \tag{16a}$$

A4. More specifically the transformation M can be given an interpretation as similar to that given to N in A2. Namely, one would form a union of all the subsets of P_j^i which include at least one evidence and also of the neighboring subsets (properly defined) omitting therefore only those subsets that are furthest from the subsets that include the evidence. The recursive relation is now

$$S_i = S_{i-1} \cap P_j^i(x) \tag{17}$$

Let us now consider the behavior of a system which uses the learning heuristic of A4.

The problem we consider here is the following: What are the conditions that the equivalence classes (subsets of the selected partitions P_j^1, P_i^2, etc.) should satisfy so that the learning process converges toward the set to be learned. In other words, we want to consider the convergence of the learning process to the limit

$$\lim_{n \to \infty} S_n = Q \tag{18}$$

Existence of this limit would guarantee a perfect learning in the limit and a sufficiently good learning in a finite period of time.

Assume that initial set is Ω_u and that the sequence X_T is generated from a given subset $Q \subset \Omega_u$.

To find the conditions that assure existence of the limit in Eq. (18), consider the sequence of sets S_i generated by the recursive relation A4.

$$S_1, S_2, S_3, \ldots, S_i, \ldots$$

Using the A4 heuristic one obtains, by using the recursive relation for the ith set,

$$S_i = \Omega_u \cap P_j^1 \cap P_j^2 \cap \cdots \cap P_j^i \tag{19}$$

or

$$S_i = \Omega_u \cap \left[\bigcup_k P_{jk}^1 \right] \cap \left[\bigcup_k P_{jk}^2 \right] \cdots \cap \left[\bigcup_k P_{jk}^i \right]$$

The solution to this problem for heuristic A4 is given in the form of the following theorem:

THEOREM

If the set Ω_u is complete a sufficient condition for perfect learning behavior, as defined by Eq. (18) when using A4 heuristic, is that

$$_{ijk} \underset{s}{\exists} \, [P_{lh}^5 \supset P_{jk}^i] \tag{20}$$

In other words, for every subset P_{jk}^i selected at the time t_i there is at least one class P_{lh}^s selected at $t = t_{s1}$ that includes p_{jk}^i.

Proof. Using the distributive law one can present the recursive relation for S_i as the union of two sets L and K

$$S_i = L \cup K \tag{21}$$

Set L is the union of sets $L_1, \ldots, L_k$

$$L = L_1 \cup L_2 \cup \cdots \cup L_k \tag{22}$$

Every set L_h is the intersection of i subsets one from every partition selected at the respective decision times

$$L_h = \Omega_u \cap P_{jh}^1 \cap P_{jh}^2 \cap \ldots \cap P_{jh}^i \tag{23}$$

In addition, L_h has the property that there exists a sequence of subsets satisfying the condition. b

$$\Omega_u \supset P_{jh}^{i_1} \supset P_{jh}^{i_2} \supset P_{jh}^{i_3} \supset \cdots \supset P_{jh}^{i-1} \supset P_{jh}^i \tag{24}$$

Set K includes all the subsets which do not contain a sequence of the form of Eq. (24).

Assume now that $i \to \infty$. Set L_h is the intersection of infinite sequence of subsets satisfying the condition $P^i{}_{jh}{}^{-1} \supset P_{jh}{}^i$ for all i's.

According to the Cantor theorem,[6] the intersection L_h is then not empty.

$$L_h = \bigcap_\infty P_{jh}^i \neq 0 \tag{25}$$

According to A4 it includes at least one element of the sequence X_T. For every element $x_i \epsilon \, Q$ we shall have at least one set of the type L_h. Union of all sets L_h will include, therefore, all the elements of Q. Furthermore, if the conditions of the theorem are satisfied the limit of the sets K is an empty set. This completes the proof.

The given theorem can be used as a guide for generating a learning heuristic in the following way:

Whenever presented with the new set of partitions: $\bar{P}^i = [P_1{}^i, \ldots, P_n{}^i]$ one considers only those partitions that satisfy Eq. (20)—i.e., whose sets are subsets of $P_j{}^{i-1}$. If the newly presented evidence x_i is such that none of the partitions in $\bar{P}^i$ satisfy this condition with respect to $P_j{}^{i-1}$ one checks earlier partitions $P_j{}^{i-2}, P_j{}^{i-3}, P^{i-4}{}_j$ etc., until a partition is found for which the conditions of the theorem are satisfied. A new sequence of sets $P_j{}^k$ is then assumed.

$$S_i = \Omega_u \cap \overset{1}{P_j} \cap \overset{2}{P_j} \cap \cdots \cap \overset{s}{P_j} \tag{26}$$

where $P_j{}^s$ is the first set whose equivalence classes have sets from $P_j{}^i$ as subsets.

(B) Union Heuristic

Another general heuristic under consideration is defined by the recursive relation

$$S_i = N(S_{i-1}) \cup M(P_j^i) \tag{27}$$

The new uncertainty set is now the union of the transformed set S_{i-1} and a set obtained from the partition selected at t_i. Preliminary study of this type of heuristic indicates that it represents a more conservative approach than the (A) heuristic in the sense that the convergence can be slower—and, moreover, the process can converge in the limit to a set that includes not only the subset to be learned but some additional elements as well.

A CASE STUDY

In order to be able to assess the descriptive as well as normative value of the theory proposed in this paper we shall analyze the behavior of a learning system on an analytical basis. We are interested in stimuli-response characteristic of the system. We shall assume that the decision making as well as the learning process of the system is known and shall derive the learning curve analytically.

The decision-making problem of the system is specified by the following:

1. A linear system is given

$$\bar{z}(t) = A\bar{z}(t) + B\overline{m}(t) + Lk\bar{u}(t) \tag{28}$$

where $\bar{z}(t)$ = state variable
　$\overline{m}(t)$ = decision variable
　$\bar{u}(t)$ = disturbance
A, B, L = constant matrices
　k = scalar

2. A quadratic utility functional is used

$$q = \frac{1}{2} \int_{t_0}^{T} \left[\bar{z}(t)^T \, Cz(t) + \overline{m}(t)^T \, D\overline{m}(t) \right] dt \tag{29}$$

3. Set of decision variables:
　Ω_u = class of continuous functions defined on (t_0, T)
4. Uncertainty set Ω_u

　$\Omega? = \{$value of disturbance amplitudes, $k\}$

which can vary within the range $[O, K]$
Assume further that:

a) The decision is made on the basis of the assumption that the disturbance will take on maximum value K. Performance functional q is then minimized

$$\min_{m \, \epsilon \Omega_m} \quad q[K, \overline{m}(t)] \tag{30}$$

b) The actual disturbance has the amplitudes within the range $[O, l]$ where $l < K$.

Let us first find the optimal decision variable $\overline{m}(t)$. Conditions necessary for the optimal decision are:

$$H = \bar{p}^T \dot{\bar{z}} - \frac{1}{2} \bar{z}^T C\bar{z} + \overline{m}^T D\overline{m} \tag{31}$$

where $p(t)$ is an auxiliary vector-valued variable

Following Pontryagin maximum principle we set $\dot{\bar{P}} = - \nabla \bar{z} H$ one obtains and

$$\dot{\bar{p}} = C\bar{z} - A^T \bar{p} \tag{32}$$

The equation for the optimal system becomes

$$\begin{bmatrix} \dot{\bar{z}} \\ \dot{\bar{p}} \end{bmatrix} = \begin{bmatrix} A \\ C \end{bmatrix} \begin{bmatrix} BD^{-1}B^T \\ -A^T \end{bmatrix} \begin{bmatrix} \bar{z} \\ \bar{p} \end{bmatrix} + \begin{bmatrix} Lk\bar{u} \\ 0 \end{bmatrix} \tag{33}$$

The solution of this equation is given by

$$
\begin{bmatrix} \bar{z}(t) \\ \bar{p}(t) \end{bmatrix} = \exp N(t,t_0) \begin{bmatrix} \bar{z}(t_0) \\ \bar{p}(t_0) \end{bmatrix} + \int_{t_0}^{t} \exp N(t,t_0) \begin{bmatrix} Lk\bar{u}(t) \\ 0 \end{bmatrix} dt \tag{33a}
$$

The matrix, $\exp N(t,t_0)$, can be partitioned in the following way

$$
\exp N(t,t_0) = \begin{bmatrix} \phi_{11}(t,t_0) & \phi_{12}(t,t_0) \\ \phi_{21}(t,t_0) & \phi_{22}(t,t_0) \end{bmatrix} \tag{34}
$$

We introduce the notation

$$
\int_{t_0}^{t} \phi_{11}(t - \tau)\, Lu(\tau)\, dt = \psi_1(t)
$$
$$
\int_{t_0}^{t} \phi_{21}(t - \tau)\; u(\tau)\, dt = \psi_2(t) \tag{35}
$$

and obtain for the solution, from Eq. (33a)

$$
\bar{z}(t) = \phi_{11}(t,t_0)\, \bar{z}(t_0) + \phi_{12}(t,t_0)\, \bar{p}(t_0) + k\psi_1(t)
$$
$$
\bar{p}(t) = \phi_{21}(t,t_0)\, \bar{z}(t_0) + \phi_{22}(t,t_0)\, \bar{p}(t_0) + k\psi_2(t) \tag{36}
$$

From the maximum principle one obtains further

$$
\nabla_m H = D\bar{m}(t) - B^T\bar{p}(t) = 0
$$
$$
\bar{m}(t) = D^{-1}B^T\bar{p}(t) \tag{37}
$$

Imposing the condition $\bar{z}(T) = 0$ one obtains from Eq. (37), that

$$
\bar{p}(t_0) = -\phi_{12}^{-1}(T,t_0)\, [\phi_{11}(T,t_0)\, \bar{z}(t_0) + k\psi(T)]
$$

From Eqs. (36) and (37) one obtains finally for the decision variable

$$
\bar{m}(t) = D^{-1}B^T[\psi_3(t,t_0)\, \bar{z}(t_0) + k\psi_2(T)]
$$
$$
= \psi_6(t,t_0)\, \bar{z}(t_0) + k\psi_7(T) \tag{38}
$$

where

$$
\psi_3(t,t_0) = \phi_{12}(t,t_0) + \phi_{22}(t,t_0)\, \phi_{12}^{-1}(T,t_0)
$$
$$
\psi_6(t,t_0) = D^{-1}B^T\psi_3(t,t_0) \quad : \quad \psi_7(T) = D^{-1}B^T\psi_2(T) \tag{39}
$$

For the state variable one obtains

$$\bar{z}(t) = \phi_{11}(t,t_0)\,\bar{z}(t_0) - \phi_{12}(t,t_0)\,\phi_{12}^{-1}\,(T,t_0)\,\phi_{11}(T,t_0)$$
$$\bar{z}(t_0) - \phi_{12}(t,t_0)\,\phi_{12}^{-1}\,(T,t_0)\,k\psi_1(T) \tag{40}$$

or

$$\bar{z}(t) = \psi_4(t,t_0)\,\bar{z}(t_0) - k\psi_5(t,t_0) + l\psi_1(t,t_0) \tag{41}$$

where

$$\psi_4(t,t_0) = \phi_{11}(t,t_0) - \phi_{12}(t,t_0)\,\phi_{12}^{-1}\,(T,t_0)\,\phi_{11}(T,t_0)$$
$$\psi_5(t,t_0) = \phi_{12}(t,t_0)\,\phi_{12}^{-1}\,(T,t_0)\,\psi_1(T) \tag{42}$$

Assume that the decision variable Eq. (38) has been implemented in the time interval (t_0,t_i). The performance functional is then

$$q = \frac{1}{2}\int_{t_0}^{t_i}\{[\psi_4(t,t_0)\,\bar{z}(t_0) - k\psi_5(t,t_0) + l\psi_1(t,t_0)]^T\,C[\psi(t_0,t)\,\bar{z}(t_0)$$
$$- k\psi_5(t,t_0) + l\psi_1(t,t_0)] + [\psi_6(t,t_0)\,\bar{z}(t_0) + k\psi_7(T)]^T$$
$$D[\psi_6(t,t_0)\,\bar{z}(t_0) + k\psi_7(T)]\}\,dt \tag{43}$$

Finally, the performance of the system can be represented in the form

$$\int_{t_0}^{t_i}\{[N_1 - kN_2 + lN_3]^T\,C[N_1 - kN_2 + lN_3]$$
$$+ [N_4 + kN_5]^T\,D[N_4 + kN_5]\}\,dt \tag{44}$$

where $N,\ldots,N_4$ are appropriately defined vector valued time functions independent of the elements of the uncertainty set Ω_u.

Assume now that the decision-making system under consideration is using learning heuristic as outlined earlier, namely:

At a given decision time t_i a partition is assumed which has twice as many subsets as the partition selected at t_{i-1}. Assume that at t_i we have a sequence of i evidences; $k_1, k_2, \ldots, k_i$. A neighborhood is then defined for each evidence

$$\epsilon(k_j) = [k_j \pm \Delta k_j] \tag{45}$$

and the union of the minimal number of subsets is taken from partition P^i so that all the neighborhoods $\epsilon(k_j)$ are subsets of L_i

$$\epsilon(k_j) \subset L_i \qquad \text{for all } j\text{'s} \tag{46}$$

To obtain the new uncertainty set S, the intersection is now taken with S_{i-1}

$$S_i = S_{i-1} \cap L_i \qquad (47)$$

or with the first previous S_j that satisfies conditions from the theorem so that the learning process is convergent. The lowest upper bound of the set S_i is then used as k in expression for the optimal decision variable. [Eq. (38)]

The behavior of the overall system can be now described in the following way:

At $t = t_0$ system decides on $m(t)$ by using upper limit of the uncertainty set k as the disturbance amplitude. However, the actual amplitude is l_1. The process now evolves until $t = t_1$ when enough evidence is collected for the system to reduce the uncertainty set to (O, k_1); $k_1 < k$. The new decision variable is then determined $m(t_1 k_1)$ and applied until $t = t_2$ when the limit is again reduced on the basis of additional evidence.

The plot of the learning curve of the system has been calculated and given in Fig. (1). Points in Fig. (1) present the actual behavior. A learning curve of the classical asymptotic form relating stimuli and responses can be fitted through these points.

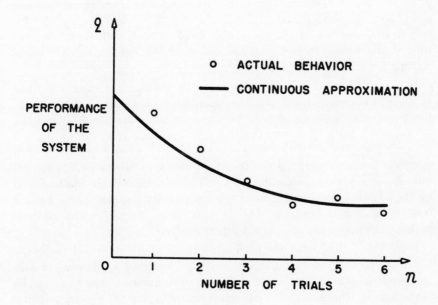

Figure 1

DESCRIPTIVE AND NORMATIVE APPLICATION
OF THE PROPOSED THEORY

The proposed theory of learning requires certain knowledge of the structure of the system under consideration and consequently it illuminates the learning process in a considerably different way than the studies based on the stimuli-response—i.e., input-output observations. Such a deeper knowledge of the learning process becomes necessary if one wants to be able to predict the behavior of the system under conditions different than those in a previously conducted experiment. Namely, stimuli-response description of a learning system gives the information only about the behavior of the same or similar system under the same conditions and gives very little, if any insight into the learning behavior of the system under different conditions—e.g., for different stimuli.

To show more clearly the usefulness of the proposed approach for descriptive purposes, consider the example of an animal (a rat) subjected to a pair of stimuli. The first stimulus, light, is applied a short period in advance of the second stimulus, electric shock. The animal can escape from the area under electric voltage by fleeing across a barrier. By repeating experiments a learning curve for the animal can be obtained by plotting escape time versus number of experiments. A typical learning curve is given in Fig. (2). Disregarding some transients, the learning curve has a sharp discontinuity. It roughly indicates the time when the animal discovers the coupling of the light and shock stimuli and starts running toward the escape barrier immediately after the light appears without waiting for the shock to be applied.

It is apparent that in order to describe the discontinuous learning curve in Fig. (2) one cannot use the same stimuli-response transformation from the continuous learning curve. Therefore, if one wants to explain the behavior of a learning system under different conditions, one has to have a better knowledge of the learning process in the system itself. In such a situation a model based on the theory proposed in this paper has its full meaning as a descriptive method. If one is able to discover the method used by the system for the reduction of the uncertainty set, one should be in a position to describe behavior of the system for a variety of conditions even without the previously conducted experiments.

From this follows also the normative value of the proposed theory of learning—namely, when building a complex adaptive system one would like the system to be successful in a variety of different conditions in the environment. This can be accomplished by specifying the general learning heuristic for the reduction of the uncertainty set regardless of the nature of the elements of the set itself.

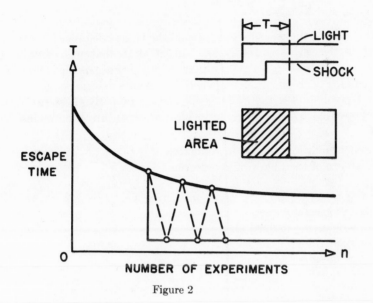

Figure 2

THEORY OF INFORMATION AND THE LEARNING PROCESS

A formalism for a theory of information can be now developed that relies on the learning theory proposed in this paper. As mentioned earlier our starting viewpoint is that a theory of information should presume the existence of a learning system. In this section we shall develop the basic formalisms for such a theory.

We start from the uncertainty set for a decision making system Ω_u. Furthermore a measure is defined on Ω_u with the following properties:

1. To every subset of Ω_u there is associated a real number $\delta(\Omega_x)$.
2. The empty set is the only subset of Ω_u with the measure zero.
3. The measure of a subset cannot be larger than the measure of the set

$$[\Omega_x^1 \subset \Omega_x^2] \to [\delta(\Omega_x^1) \leq \delta(\Omega_x^2)]$$

4. The existence of the mapping $\delta(\Omega_x)$ is a topological invariant—i.e., it cannot be changed by homeomorphic transformations.

Of course there are many different ways to define a measure that satisfies these properties. Final selection will actually depend upon the decision problem at hand. For example, a convenient measure is the norm

$$\delta = \max_{\Omega_x} |y - z| \tag{48}$$

where $y \in \Omega_x$ and $\delta \in \Omega_x$

In other words, the measure δ represents the largest distance for any two elements of the set. Apparently any subset of Ω_x that will contain the furthest element from Ω_x will have the same measure as Ω_x. This measure is convenient for decision problems where one wants assurance that the in the worst possible case the system will behave properly. Less restrictive cases represented by the elements inside the set Ω_x are then of less importance.

Necessary conditions for the introduction of the measure of information is the existence of the following quadruple:

where $$<\Omega_x, \delta, L, \gamma> \tag{49}$$

Ω_x = uncertainty set
δ = measure defined on Ω_x
L = learning heuristic
γ = message

The measure of information content is then given by the ratio

$$i(\gamma) = \frac{F[\delta(\Omega_x)] - F[\delta(\Omega_x^\gamma)]}{F[\delta(\Omega_x)]} \tag{50}$$

where Ω_x is the uncertainty set before the message and Ω_x^γ is the uncertainty set after the message; F is a monotonic function.

Selection of Ω_x is important here; namely, Ω_x should be the uncertainty set that would exist at $t = t_i$ if the message γ had not been received. It is, in general, different from the Ω_x that existed at the preceding decision time t_{i-1}, since the uncertainty in general would incrdase with time. For example, if a dynamic process is involved and if no information is received regarding its behavior, the uncertainty regarding the actual state of the system will increase with time and the importance of the message becomes larger the longer it is delayed.

At this point it is instructive to compare the proposed information measure with the so-called semantic theory of information. Comparison with the approaches in Refs. 1, 4, 8, and 7 indicates the following two basic differences regarding the approach proposed in this paper:

1. The information measure is not defined by using statistical tools.
2. Information is not related to the ultimate success of decision making but rather to the facilitation of the decision making process—i.e., to the removal of doubts in the decision maker's mind.

FURTHER EXTENSION OF THE THEORY

Developed formalism requires that the message contains the information that will allow the contraction of the uncertainty set. In many realistic situations this condition is not satisfied. It is necessary therefore to extend the theory to cover the following two situations:

1. Information received indicates that the evaluation of the uncertainties was too optimistic so that the uncertainty set, after the message, has to be increased rather than decreased. To cope with this situation an appropriate definition for the set Ω_x in Eq. (50) has to be found. In general the occurence of a message that would require redefinition of the uncertainty set corresponds to a change of the framework of the decision problem considered.

2. In complex situations, especially those involving humans, there exists a number of decision problems that are simultaneously under consideration. Since only one action can be taken at a given time, the decision problem with the highest priority will be considered. A message can then change the priority of the decision problems and reactivate the decision process that would not have been considered at that time. In human communication problems this would correspond, for example, to information about an accidental event that completely changes the priority of the problems under consideration.

REFERENCES

1. Ackoff, Russell, "Towards a Behavioral Theory of Communication," *Management Sciences*, vol. 4, April 1958.
2. Banerji, R. B., "An Information Processing Program for Object Recognition," *General Systems*, 5, 117, 1960.
3. Banerji, R. B., "Computer Programs for the Generation of New Concepts from Old Ones," *Proc. Conf. Deutsche Arbeitsgemeinschaft Kybernetic*, Karlsruhe, April 1963.
4. Bar-Hillel, Y., "Semantic Information and its Measures," in H. Von Foerster (ed.), *Cybernetics*, Y. Macy Foundation, 1955.
5. Bellman, R., "Adaptive Control Processes," Academic, New York, 1961.
6. Fraenkel, A., "Axiomatic Set Theory," North-Holland, Amsterdam, 1953.
7. Marshak, J., "Towards an Economic Theory of Organization and Information," in R. Thrall (ed.), *Decision Processes*, Wiley, New York, 1954.
8. Mesarović, M. D., "Self-Organizing Control System," Proc. Symposium on Discrete Adaptive Systems, AIEE, 1962.
9. ———, "General Systems Theory," Proc. Second Systems Symposium at the Case Institute of Technology, Wiley, New York, 1964.
10. Pontryagin, L. S., et al., "Mathematical Theory of Optimal Processes," Wiley, New York, 1962.

18

NEW PROBLEMS IN ADAPTIVE CONTROL*

Peter H. Greene

Committee on Mathematical Biology
The University of Chicago, Chicago, Ill.

INTRODUCTION

This is a review paper which points out a few of the issues that must be faced in designing highly adaptive systems. One point of the paper is to show that it is not sufficient to interconnect a number of elementary systems or programs with specified rules for modifying individual connections in order to obtain all the forms of adaptive behavior one desires.

This is so because one needs to allow for meaningful relations among a number of abstract structures related to the functioning of these elements, and the engineer may have to prepare himself just to *perceive* these structures preparatory to learning how to implement them. An immediate purpose of this discussion is to give some examples of such structures and a language in which to think about them. Theoretical preparation of this type is also necessary in order to know what to look for in the biological laboratory.

The primary objective is, of course, to develop and apply specific theorems to particular situations, but there is at present a dearth of experimental situations prepared with these issues in mind, and it is the aim of this paper to stimulate research to uncover raw material for something better than the present list of abstract possibilities. However, a less ambitious purpose which may be served by this discussion in present form, is to provide a concise and systematic way to organize computer programs

* This research was supported by the Information Systems Branch of the Office of Naval Research under Contract No. Nonr-2121(17) NR 049–148, and some parts were conducted in conjunction with work performed as consultant to the Artificial Intelligence Staff, System Development Corporation, Santa Monica, California. Reproduction in whole or in part is permitted for any purpose of the U.S. Government.

and data for certain types of adaptive system. It was, in fact, the need for such organization of a computer program (Greene and Ruggles[8]) that prompted the present studies.

It cannot be overemphasized that these ideas are not in any way intended to compete with the elements of adaptive systems which have been developed by others; rather, they are intended to indicate new possibilities for incorporating these elements into various kinds of systems. In particular, much of the discussion will presuppose the successful operation of devices, such as those described in other papers in this symposium, which can make gradual adjustments in·parameters so as to achieve some criterion of satisfactory performance. It will be assumed that ideal examples of such devices will be attached to all variables to be considered in certain of the examples. In regard to the following treatment of regulatory systems, someone may ask whether the same regulation cannot be accomplished by feedback (or some other well-understood mechanism). The answer is that of course it is assumed that the regulation actually *is* being accomplished by a standard process such as feedback operating in conventional ways which will not be described, and that the purpose of this paper is to characterize just what it is that this successfully operating feedback is accomplishing, from our point of view.

AN EXAMPLE FOR REFERENCE

As in Greene and Ruggles,[8] the systems to be considered are in part collections of devices which when activated run through innate or acquired repertoires of acts, which have to be modified and coordinated through learning. The systems are supposed able to remember a few relatively undifferentiated acts which work well in some particular circumstance, and not so badly within a range of related circumstances. A basic problem is to piece together these partial acts, defined on overlapping ranges of circumstances, into an integrated act which could be performed in a wide range of circumstances, and which might utilize any number of partial acts, all harmoniously adjusted. This procedure must be revised as more highly differentiated movements and discriminations of ranges of circumstances become possible. These ideas are most adequately formulated mathematically, and the resulting mathematical issues directly involve the behavioral level, rather than the subbehavioral, and the structural, rather than the enumerative, aspects of behavior.

It may be said in general that the performance of a particular behavioral task will impose a specific structure upon the system, and the significant relationships within this structure may hold among elements which cannot directly be seen. An example will illustrate this point and introduce some of the matters to be treated mathematically. The hand and arm can move anywhere, and the eye can look anywhere: what more is there to say about behavioral structure? But look instead at a typical *behavioral* task: learning coordination by moving the hand while keeping vision focussed upon it. We may think of the line of sight as a rigid rod pivoted at the eyeball and extending out into space. The arm and hand become part of a linkage having in effect a slider at the hand, which slides along the rod. The lengths of the links are determined by body dimensions and depth of focus. We have, in effect, the kinematic equivalent of a five-bar linkage, about which much can be said mathematically, whereas all that can be photographed by an observer is a set of freely moving bars which can be in any position whatever. A different task would introduce entirely different "invisible" relations among movements of the system. Our problem is to fit all these elements into purposeful acts.

Thus we must look directly at the *acts*, and not just the movements which happen to comprise them at a given moment, in order to see the significant structure. Let us see, in a preliminary way, what are some of the components of the structure imposed by an extremely simple action of oversimplified mechanical hands. This example will provide a point of view to motivate the subsequent mathematical discussion, and the features described are those which will be referred to from time to time. Space will ultimately be saved and clarity gained by collecting all these features in a single problem which is immediately solvable, since it is so elementary.

We assume that the task is to pick up or move an object which is located on a straight line going from left to right in front of the subject. We suppose that the first step in so doing is to bring either hand, regarded as a point which can move along the same line, to a particular point on the object— i.e., to a specified distance from some reference point on the object. The position of this reference point relative to the subject (to be referred to as the position of the object) will be given by a number representing distance from the origin, which is directly in front of the subject, positive numbers representing distances to the right, and negative numbers representing distances to the left. The location relative to the object of whichever hand is being used to approach the object will be represented by a number corresponding to the same size of distance unit, positive and negative numbers signifying hand positions to the right or left of the object, respectively. Next, suppose that the location of each hand is determined by the value of a single parameter representing the "excitation" of a single "muscle" in its respective arm. These muscles are so constituted that a muscle excitation of zero in an arm causes its hand to be located, let us say, three distance units towards its side, relative to the position immediately in front of the subject. That is, zero excitation of the right arm muscle places the right hand at position 3 on the scale representing positions relative to the subject, and zero excitation of the left arm muscle places the left hand at position -3. Finally, suppose that each positive unit of excitation of a muscle places the respective hand one distance unit further outwards, i.e., further away from the origin, and each negative unit places the hand one unit further inwards, toward the origin. Then a muscle value of -2 would place the right hand at 1 or the left hand at -1, relative to the subject. If the object happened to be at -1, then muscle values of -2 would place the right hand at 2 or the left hand at 0, relative to the object. We shall assume that the subject may choose to use his right hand to approach any position to the right of -1, and his left hand to approach any position to the left of 1. Thus, he could use either hand for the same simple "purpose" on the interval $(-1, 1)$.

Now we may describe the situation in terms that would be silly if this were the only task we should ever have to control, but which are highly significant if we are to devise general methods which computers or other control systems can apply to a wide variety of tasks not known to them in advance.

We suppose that it is the function of some control system to choose one of the two muscles and to specify a value for the excitation of that muscle which will bring the corresponding hand to a desired position relative to the object. We shall examine the structure of a space representing all possibilities of choice for all positions of the object, without regard to which choice will actually be made. All we know about this control system is that because of its past history of success and failure in touching the object, it will not use a hand which, owing to its hypothesized limits of movements, could not actually touch the object, even though at present the system may be required to touch some point to the left or right of the object. It has already learned how to touch the object, and it is now trying to modify this behavior so as to achieve slightly more complicated facts of coordination. If it sees an object to the right of $+1$, the right arm will be activated, and if it sees an object to the left of -1, the left arm will be activated, for it is not yet sophisticated enough to know that for some purposes the opposite arm is better. Thus, we are considering a system in a typical intermediate stage of learning. If the object is between -1 and 1, some control system which we are not describing will make the decision which hand to use. The control system which we are describing will have to supply one value of the excitation if it is going to choose the right hand and another value if it will choose the left hand, and we shall specify the relations between these values. When we have specified these relations, we have described the structure of the purposeful act, since no matter how the muscle excitations are chosen by the decision system, in accordance with these relations, the same goal will be achieved.

We are thus not trying to describe the mechanisms which maintain the relations and perform the act. We assume that they are given in some form, and try to characterize the structure of whatever it is that any such mechanisms must be achieving, however they accomplish it. Of course, the structure in this example is an extremely simple one.

Let us denote the position of the object relative to the subject by x, and an amount of excitation which could be supplied to a particular muscle under consideration by m. Let h denote the resulting position of the hand relative to the object, given x and m. Then a given output m from the muscle control system will in general correspond to two different values of h, depending upon which muscle received this output, for values of x between -1 and 1. Conversely, a desired value of h will in general correspond to two different values of m if x is such that $-1 < h + x < 1$, the conditions on the two values, m_1 and m_2 being $m_1 + m_2 = -6$, and $-4 < m_1, m_2 < -2$. The first condition arises from the particular task, and the second expresses our overall hypothesis about the range of common action of the hands.

The situation we are describing may be visualized graphically in a number of ways, one such being illustrated by Fig. 1. The value of this particular choice of representation, or of any other, would depend upon our momentary purpose in viewing the system as a whole. The horizontal scale at the bottom labeled X represents all possible locations x of the object relative to the subject. The vertical scale on the left, labeled M, represents all possible values m of excitation supplied to whichever muscle the decision system selects. The vertical scale on the right labeled H, represents all possible values of h, the position of the utilized hand relative to the object. The rectangular region labeled E, above the line X, represents a portion of the product space $X \times M$. Within E, each vertical line represents a subspace of potential situations corresponding to a particular potential value of x. The lines corresponding to integral values of x have been indicated in the diagram. Each horizontal line represents a possible value of m, without indicating for which arm this is destined, and these are depicted for integral values of m. Each slanting line represents a locus of points of equal h, those lines slanting upwards to the right corresponding to use of the right arm, and those slanting upwards to the left corresponding to use of the left arm, and the appropriate values of h have been used to label the representative loci depicted. These loci have been drawn to conform to the hypotheses we have made. According to these hypotheses, if the right hand is to be used, the control system must provide a value $m = h + x - 3$, and if the left hand is to be used, the value $m = -h - x - 3$.

Each sloping line corresponds to a point of the line H, and we may regard this correspondence as establishing two different families of mappings of portions of H into portions of E. In the mapping corresponding to the use of the right hand, the image of H sweeps upwards and to the right, starting at the line over $x = -1$, and in the mapping corresponding to use of the left hand, H is turned upside down and its inverted image sweeps upwards and to the left, starting at the line over $x = +1$.

Let us continue to look for obvious features of this trivial example, which in more complicated situations have analogues which are not obvious. Suppose that the task set for this system is to transfer an object from a point several units to the left of center to a point several units to the right of center. This action corresponds to any of a class of movements. The control system must (by feedback, etc.) produce the correct m to place the point (x_0, m), where x_0 is the initial location of the object, on the left-hand locus corresponding to $h = 0$, and the system must then obviously decrease m so as to move the object to the right (assuming that the object is firmly grasped). Then, at any point over the interval $-1 < x < +1$, the object may be switched to the right hand, provided that the appropriate transformation is made from $m = -x - 3$ to $m = x - 3$, and that m subsequently increases until x has reached its desired final value. We might (with no particular advantage in this simple situation) redraw our picture of E by making two separate pictures, one of them E_1 showing the region over

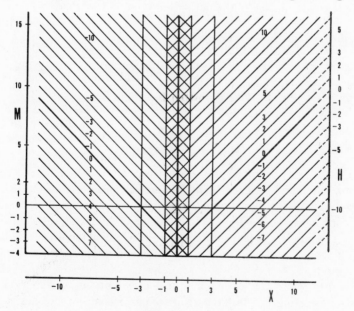

Figure 1

points $x > -1$ with the right-hand loci drawn in, and the other E_2 showing the region over $x < +1$ with the left-hand loci. Then if we turned E_2 face-down by inverting it about the line $m = -3$, we could make E_2 overlap E_1 in such a way that the lines of constant h matched in the overlapping region corresponding to $-1 < x < +1$. In the resulting composite, the action we have described would then consist of moving along the continuous straight line corresponding to $h = 0$, starting at a specified initial point. A modification of this action, in which the hand moves relative to the center of the object, as it transfers the object from left to right, would be represented by a smooth curve which is not a straight line. Finally, suppose that the object is elongated, like a pencil, and that the way the system has learned to pick up such an object which lies along the left-right line we have been considering is to grasp it with the left hand at the left-hand end or, with the right hand at the right-hand end. Let the length of the pencil be $2l$ distance units. Then in terms of our first diagram, the task of moving the pencil from left to right would require starting with the left-hand m appropriate to $x = x_0$ and $h = -l$, and switching to the right-hand locus for $h = +l$ somewhere in the region of overlap. In terms of our second representation, obtained by pasting together two overlapping spaces E_1 and E_2, the spaces would be the same as for the original task, but they would be pasted together differently in the overlapping portions, so that the left-hand $-l$ locus matched the right-hand $+l$ locus in the overlap. Specifically, E_2 would have to be reflected about the line $m = -3 + l$.

This concludes the presentation of our sample system. It will prove useful to summarize some properties which can be seen instantly from Fig. 1, for more valuable application in later contexts. We observe that we have a space E, in which certain subspaces, the vertical lines, correspond to points in the space X. In this example, points in X represent potential positions of the object. Thus, these points and the lines above them represent potentialities which are mutually exclusive. Nonetheless, they are combined in our diagram, which shows structural relations involving the totality of forms the act could take. Corresponding to a set of overlapping regions of X, there are spaces E_i, each mapped into its corresponding region in X (vertical lines into the points beneath them). There is a space H, part of which is mapped into E by families of maps, one family for each region of X, and one map in each family for each point in its region of X. There was a rule which told how the families of maps differ where more than one was defined. The same rule could be viewed as a rule for fastening together the spaces E_i. The system may be regarded as containing subsystems (the arms), each of which might be activated over some range of conditions, each system when activated possessing a certain repertoire of performances (the values of m). This is the type of model discussed by Greene and Ruggles.[8] An engineer studying this system, or a physiologist studying a biological example, might express the position of each hand as a function of muscle excitation. This result would be very useful for answering questions about the mechanisms (e.g., feedback loop transfer functions) which cause the arms to move. However, this result concerns only what happens within one of the vertical lines, and does not tell about the effect of the movement with regard to the purpose of the action, picking up or moving the pencil. This information was embodied in the way the individual slices were fastened together, and the rule for fastening, or equivalently, for mapping H into E, was derived from behavioral considerations (distance from the goal) rather than from the physical nature of the control mechanisms. Different actions, in this example, corresponded to different ways of fastening together the same collection of slices. More generally, for example, if the hand position depended upon another parameter in addition to m, the slices themselves might be modified for some purpose in a systematic way we should like to characterize.

Suppose that the system must do something with the pencil it has picked up, assuming that the system possesses additional effector mechanisms which we have not mentioned up to now. Then the particular movements controlled by the new system in relation to its goal depend upon the position of the pencil and the system configuration resulting from the first act. Thus, the second act is representable by some such structure as has been discussed in regard to the first act. If, as the engineer or physiologist might do, we look only at the two movements actually performed, and perhaps introduce rules for changing probabilities or strengths of performance of these movements in the future, we have overlooked the additional information embodied in the behavioral requirement that the relation is between the two *actions*, i.e., the two total structures, and not just between the individual slices. For instance, information concerning the ways in which the slices are matched together is involved. We shall later state some relations which must exist between various slices. These will be examples of meaningful relations mentioned above among abstract structures which do not exist physically (different slices, for example, represent potential situations which can not actually exist at the same time).

An obvious property of Fig. 1 is that, given an initial position x of the object and an initial point in E, above x, one could furnish a rule specifying how to move to points in E which lie above continuously changing positions of the object. A rule of this type would be in effect a tabulation of classes of actions which could be performed by the system under various circumstances. Of course, many such rules are possible here but in the more complicated situations to be discussed, the existence of such rules will become significant.

Next, we may note that an even simpler structure would replace E in case the muscles did not respond with a continuous range of excitations, but exerted full strength, say $m = \pm1$ in either direction. Then E_1 and E_2 would each consist of two horizontal lines, and they would be fastened together with E_2 turned face down so that $+1$ matches -1 and -1 matches $+1$. This chart corresponds to a less differentiated structure, which might belong, say, to a "head" which always turned toward a stimulus or away from it, the ultimate extent of the turning being determined by factors external to the control system we are considering. For example, a baby's head might stop turning when the nipple came into contact with the mouth, but the control system initiating head movements need not "understand" this. Observe that the regions of the space X and the rules for joining E_1 and E_2 are the same as before. The difference lies essentially in the shape of a typical vertical slice of E, which is now merely two points, rather than a line segment. One of the aims of the present kind of analysis is to learn whether the structure of complicated actions, like those of a hand, can be learned more simply, and with more possibilities for adaptive modification, by building them out of less differentiated actions, like those of our hypothetical "head," than by constructing them directly. An understanding of the issues relevant to this problem is, for example, a prerequisite to continued progress in building the computer model of sensorimotor development proposed by Greene and Ruggles.

Finally, the utilization of common less differentiated precursors may, if understood, explain what it means to say that the "same" action can be performed by effector systems which work entirely differently. For instance, the very first time one signs one's name with a pencil held between the toes or in the mouth, the customary "handwriting" results, although the nerves, muscles, and kinematic mechanisms are entirely different. A psychologist might say that the correlations between the mechanisms have been "learned" through past experience. The present analysis aims at understanding precisely what it is that has to be learned.

The preceding lengthy discussion will serve as a continual source of reference enabling the abstract presentation to have meaning and useful associations for the reader. The properties which have been described, so obvious and trivial in our simple example, will have analogues which will enable us to extract useful information from system spaces of universal occurrence, which are in general infinite dimensional and difficult or impossible to visualize. This will sometimes be possible even when we do not know explicity what any of the mappings are, provided that we know that certain behavioral criteria are being met. We are unlikely to know the mappings explicitly if, for example, m is replaced by a multidimensional specification of the outputs of systems of thousands or millions of neuronlike elements, each satisfying nonlinear differential equations of high order, or x stands not for a point, but for a path through some configuration space, or if E might be not the simple space we have considered, but the space of all possible ways of fastening together all possible partial spaces (like our E_1 and E_2) of some other system space.

BIOLOGICAL ORGANIZATION OF SKILLED MOVEMENTS

Although there are mountains of data, there are few results analyzed or analyzable from our point of view. I shall only state a point of view held by some workers in this field in order to motivate the mathematical considerations and to show how they may help the biologist know what to look for and the engineer to build. Only those ideas will be stated which will be required for later reference.

J. Paillard[22] has presented an extensive review of research on the patterning of skilled movements. His organization of the material and interpretive remarks lay stress upon the fluidity of the means used to achieve a purposeful movement, depending in part upon the initial posture of the limb segments and the nature of the resisting forces. A physiologist may never observe a given movement being reproduced identically. A muscle which ordinarily participates in a movement may not act at all if under the particular circumstances (e.g., the particular action of gravity or inertia) that muscle action would be mechanically superfluous. The review emphasizes that the problem is not merely one of a simple classically studied form of innervation exerting antagonistic effects on extensor and flexor muscles groups, but also involves the problem of selecting particular combinations of muscles from a variety of possible combinations.

Paillard cites books by himself[21] and by P. Guillaume,[10] unavailable to me, which, according to his review, deal with the extent to which learning a new act does not just consist of creating a motor pattern from a sequence of activations of anatomical motor units, but requires disrupting of pre-existing functional units of action, selective choice of the useful motor combinations, and finally, their assembly into a new working unit. This procedure is said to require some sort of inventory of means available to reach the proposed goal, in other words a model something like the structure described earlier, in the central nervous system. (Our models can, of course, also represent our formulations of abstract structures which do not physically exist in the nervous system.)

Conceptualizations dating back to the beginning of the eighteenth century, and reviewed by Paillard, divide muscle groups participating in an action into *prime movers*, which directly carry the limb to a previously determined situation or attitude (but which are not necessarily the muscles acting earliest in time), *moderators*, such as antagonistic muscles, which counterbalance and modify the action of the prime movers, and *directors*, or *fixers*, which stabilize the limbs and articulations involved in the movement. Without the firmness produced, for example, by the fixing muscles of the shoulder, the delicate adjustments of the fingers would lose their purpose. Paralysis of the muscles of the wrist is said to interfere with prehension. There is said to be electromyographic evidence for preformed cerebral representation of these patterns of muscular activity, and not just a chain of events set off by the first muscle to move.

An example of progression from control of prehension by the shoulder to control by the hand, stabilized by the shoulder, and from grasping by the palm of the hand to grasping by the thumb and fingers is provided by H. M. Halverson's[11,12] extensive observations of grasping by infants.

Something of the use of centrally produced patterns is suggested by the following ideas. In a theoretical paper, D. M. MacKay[18] considers why it is that the environment appears to move if we push our eye with our finger, but not during voluntary eye movements performed by the visual system itself. MacKay rejects proposed explanations of oculomotor-induced transformations of the visual image which exactly compensate for retinal image displacements, as requiring too much accuracy of the oculomotor system. He reformulates the problem by associating perception not so much with a filtered and transformed incoming signal, but with structures actively produced by the organism. Incoming signals are compared with the internally produced signals (cf. also MacKay[19]. Voluntary eye movement entails a modification of the internal model, and the retinal changes which result exactly match what is expected, so no perception of environmental motion results. Pushing the eyeball causes a change in the retinal image without a corresponding change in the internal model, and the mismatch between incoming and outgoing signals leads to perception of movement. MacKay has nothing to say about how all this could be accomplished, and part of the present task is to gain some understanding of what an internal model could be. According to one of MacKay's metaphors in verbal discussion, the observer is like a submarine navigator who has an atlas open to what he thinks is the appropriate chart. So long as the reports from the man at the periscope are consistent with what the navigator finds on his chart, the navigator keeps the atlas open to that chart. The "percept," identified with the chart, rather than with the transformed information coming through the periscope, remains unchanged. If, however, someone has moved the prism at the top of the periscope, the resulting disparity between signals and chart, or the resulting collisions, lead the navigator to turn the page to another chart. There may, of course, be a cartographer on board who revises charts and draws new ones.

The use in perception and action of structures, some innate and some learned, which are evoked by stimuli, and which are fitted together to form models for perception and action is precisely the subject matter to be elucidated through mathematical methods to be presented here. The discussion will not deal with the methods which have been studied in learning theory, switching theory, and control system theory, only because the discussion presupposes that the system is built out of elements which already use these methods, and it will deal only with their coordination.

A COMPUTER MODEL

Some features of a baby's sensorimotor development have been incorporated into a program for the Philco 2000 digital computer at System Development Corporation, Santa Monica, California.[8]

The approach was based upon Jean Piaget's[23,24] interpretation of sensorimotor development. Since we did not feel that an attempt at a realistic simulation of the details of infant behavior would be instructive, we needed to work with a simple model which we hoped would retain some of the essential features in skeleton form. Such a model was suggested by the pattern recognizer of Uhr and Vossler.[26] Their program was given, or it evolved, a collection of templates which it matched to stimulus patterns, and it weighted the templates according to their usefulness in distinguishing patterns. We considered Piaget's infant to be a collection of half a dozen or so Uhr-Vossler machines, generalized in various ways. A machine corresponds to each basic activity like moving the head, sucking, moving the arms, or grasping. The Uhr-Vossler templates are numerical patterns which are fitted to a stimulus object. Our patterns are numerical configurations describing movements or nerve or muscle excitations, and are adjusted to fit the environment. The present theory is the beginning of an attempt to make this model grow into a means to experiment with developing adaptive structures, and not be just a collection of gadgets.

The patterns and templates of these models correspond to the charts mentioned previously, and will correspond in what follows to some structures in analogues of the spaced E_1 and E_2 of the Introduction.

SENSORIMOTOR SPACES

ABSTRACT SPACES

Some examples will suggest the range of possibilities open to mathematical treatment. While occasionally a space will be the physical space in which a system operates (as was the space X in the example given above), or the configuration space of the system (e.g., M in that example), usually, the space will be an abstract space which represents one's conception of the total behavior of the system under a variety of situations. For instance, in that example the vertical slices corresponded to different potentialities (the various possible positions of the object) which could not simultaneously be realized, and within a slice, different heights corresponded, via the mapping into H represented by the sloping lines, to different purposes of the system. We saw that an act could be represented by more than one space, depending upon what one wished to analyze, and that different acts might correspond to different spaces. The entire space might, in a more comprehensive analysis, be regarded as a single point of a larger space representing a wide range of activities of a system.

For many purposes, only certain topological properties of a space are relevant, and in such cases we may represent the space in any way which preserves these properties. For instance, suppose that the angular velocity of an electric motor depends upon the phase of an alternating-current signal to a thyratron, or that the luminance threshold for perception of a dim flash of light depends upon its phase relative to the alpha rhythm of the brain. These are two mechanisms, with highly specific features, which actually occur in some situations, and which might have significance in some particular analysis of control systems. For the purposes of the kind of analysis which will be pursued in this paper, both mechanisms might be divested of their specific features, and regarded simply as mappings of a circle into a straight line. The circle represents phase angle, since an angle of 360° is the same as an angle of 0°, and the straight line represents all possible values of the angular velocity or the threshold. The circularity, rather than eccentricity, of the former, and the straightness of the latter, may be as irrelevant to the analysis as the specific electronic and physiological features of the mechanisms. What makes these figures adequate representations of phase and intensity or threshold is solely that the former is connected in such a way that following it one returns to one's starting point, while the latter is not. The purpose of this explanation is to make it possible in what follows to refer simply to mappings of circles into lines, or lines into other spaces, and the like, knowing that the reader will appreciate that the discussion is not limited to simple geometrical figures, and that he will be able to supply his own interpretations of physical interest. A mapping of a line segment into the system space might stand for a desired time course of change of state. A mapping of one system space into another is a functional relationship between the structures represented by the two spaces.

Typical examples of the spaces which will be referred to are the cylindrical phase space of the electric motor (angular position and angular velocity); the $2N$-dimensional dynamical phase space of N particles; a plane, $X \times Y$, representing the fact that something depends upon two variables x and y; the $2N$-dimensional vector space of normal modes of an RLC-network with N terminals; the infinite-dimensional space of all paths in physical three-space; the two-dimensional space of a family of paths in three-space which are specified by two parameters; the $2TW$-dimensional ball of radius $\sqrt{2WE}$ corresponding to signals of duration T, bandwidth zero to W cycles per second, and total energy less than E; an algebraic surface which is the locus attainable by a point of a kinematic linkage; an integral manifold of a set of differential equations; an organized combination of many such spaces, as in the example previously given, or a space in which each point represents a transformation of such an organized combination which is an isomorphism when restricted to some neighborhoods of points in the space upon which the transformation acts.

This paper deals with functions defined on regions in spaces such as these, and this is to be kept in mind when viewing the illustrations, in which all such spaces will be represented pictorially merely as outlines of nondescript form.

SENSORY SPACES AND EXPERIENCE

It is important to understand how the meaningful relationships in spatial perception may sometimes exist in an abstract space of actions, but not exist at the level of the sense data or any mere transformation of the sensory signals by the receptor systems. A significant feature of the examples to be presented is that the relationships are not highly sophisticated and technical, but are the simplest geometrical relations of the ordinary physical space in which a perceiving organism moves, for instance, the relation of moving along a straight line, or of perpendicularity, or of associating a point of view with an object from which the view exists. The examples, due to J. Nicod,[20] are of hypothetical organisms, granted various limited forms of sensation, but endowed with the logical power and imagination of a mathematician. Nicod investigates the forms of geometry which these organisms could perceive. The first organism possesses only an external sense and a recognition of the order of temporal succession. In his example the sense is that of hearing, and the organism is imagined to be walking on the keyboard of a generalized organ, which may be multiply connected, and in which more than one key may emit the same note. It is obvious that this organism will learn the order relations of points on lines and some of the topological properties of the keyboard. What is important for the present discussion is that the order relations do not obtain among equivalence classes of similar sounds (the immediate sense data). They obtain only among constructs which penetrate to the individuality of the keys, despite the duplication of sounds. In this simple example, the only construct of this type is that of a class of identical sounds, any two of which are separated by symmetric sequences of sounds, signifying departure from and return to the same key. In this way, the perception depends upon a sequence of actions, and is thus richer than the individual sensation.

The previous example was too obvious to be very interesting. Nicod's second organism exhibits more remarkable properties. This creature, first of all, possesses only an internal sense, a kinesthetic sense which enables it to distinguish only that an arbitrary pair of its motions are exactly the same or are not exactly the same, together with a sense of temporal succession. This organism can only deduce the possible transitions in its state space, but grant it a single external reference signal, perceptible only if the organism is in a particular bodily attitude at a particular point of space, and, amazingly, it has enough information to derive a theory which enables it to recognize movements corresponding to *all* the elements of Euclidean geometry. These include such things as rectilinearity and equality of distances of translation in different directions, despite the fact that the sense data tell nothing of these things. The reader may consult Nicod to learn how this is accomplished.

The third and fourth examples concern an organism possessing a visual sense. Whereas the previous organisms remembered the order of succession of sensations, but regarded each sensation as an unanalyzed whole, the visual organisms are able to analyze the contents of individual views, but do not pay any attention to their order of succession. The third organism immediately apprehends every point in a space which is supposed to be entirely filled with points, each having a different quality. It is able to form equivalence classes of sense data in different views having the same quality (which correspond to the same object, viewed differently) and of data in different views having the same location in the visual field. This organism is able to construct Euclidean geometry four times over: a geometry of the *sense data*, a geometry of *objects* (in which points are quality classes), a geometry of *visual places* (in which the points are equivalence classes of data having the same locations in the visual field), and a geometry of *views*, in which each point is an entire view, with all its contents. It is possible for the organism to choose an arbitrary reference view, and to represent each different view by data in the reference view. We shall return to this problem of representation in succeeding sections. Of all Nicod's illuminating remarks about this situation, it will only be noted here that no way exists for this creature to identify any view with any object class corresponding to an object from which that view could be had. In fact, no hypothesis relevant to this could even be formulated by this organism to be affirmed or negated by experience.

The fourth organism possesses the same faculties, except that it receives sense data equivalent to the central projections of the objects upon a movable sphere, successive positions of which correspond to successive viewpoints. Moreover, there are now supposed to be only six objects, three of them collinear, and an object can obscure another object which happens to have the same projection in a particular view. Once more passing over Nicod's elegant mathematical analysis, only the following points will be noted. First of all, the organism is able, rather directly, to form equivalence .classes of visual places corresponding to great circles on the (to it unknown) sphere. From these and other constructs which utilize only the available information, it constructs a theory isomorphic to the spherical geometry of great circles. Using further contructs which, remarkably, are a systematic form of information which a real organism might possess in more haphazard form, this organism can formulate the Euclidean geometry of the positions of the center of its sphere, despite the fact that the immediate sense data are directly related to spherical geometry. The outcome is that, of the four Euclidean geometries attainable by the third organism, the present organism is unable to perceive a Euclidean geometry of immediate data, nor can it perceive a Euclidean geometry of object classes, because there are no longer objects and their accompanying qualities at every point of space, but only six objects. The Euclidean geometry of visual places has likewise vanished, for, while there are still an infinite set of these, they are arranged according to the laws of spherical geometry, not Euclidean. The only Euclidean geometry which persists is that in which the points are entire views. However, the interesting feature now appears that, while the objects no longer form a space, they have become perceptually locatable in space—i.e., it is possible for this creature, as it was not for the previous creature, in a natural way to assign views to the objects from which they may be experienced.

It is apparent from these examples that *the fact that the raw data possess a particular structure is not necessarily equivalent to the organization of perceptual experience according to that structure.* The organism with only a kinesthetic sense was able to construct Euclidean geometry. The third organism, which seemed to have Euclidean geometry handed to it intact, could not formulate any notion of space as a framework for objects, while the fourth organism, which had infinitely less information, and that organized according to spherical geometry, was able to attain the concept of the location of objects in Euclidean space and the assignment of viewpoints.

These examples illustrate the thesis that *percepts are not just transformed copies of some world of external facts or sensations.* They reveal, in a highly schematized and mathematical form, that dependence of perception upon activity which one would like to understand in the more natural, complicated and piecemeal development of spatial and object concepts investigated by Piaget. The remainder of this paper will be a beginning attempt to find concepts with which to do so.

ADAPTIVE SYSTEMS AND FINE ADJUSTMENTS

A loose distinction is often made between changes in a system which result in a new structure, and changes within a given structure, which modify this structure in a gradual way—as for example, by continuously varying parameters. While a gradual variation of parameters may sometimes lead to a drastic, discontinuous, and irreversible change in the behavior of a system, it is still true that the notion of the gradual and reversible modification of the behavior of a given structure is frequently a natural one. It is easy to state examples which need no elaboration. In adaptive feedback systems, artificial or biological, one is frequently concerned with the variation of parameters to optimize response according to some criterion, such as to minimize energy consumption, maximize output, maintain a variable at a desired level, or to modify a filter so that it will transmit only a desired signal. In psychological learning theory there are many examples of modification of behavior by continuous variation. One may learn by gradually adjusting the intensity or the probability of a response; one may learn by gradual adjustment to respond to a particular intensity or other numerical characteristic of a signal; or one's behavior may change in innumerable ways by the gradual change of parameters. In artificial devices which recognize input patterns by comparing them with stored templates, the relative weights assigned to the fact that the input matches a particular template are in general gradually changed by experience. In devices which attempt to discriminate among patterns by means of physical networks, the conductivities of the pathways and their thresholds are in general gradually changed.

The starting point for the present analysis is the basic assumption that all these mechanisms, and many more, do their job perfectly. It will simply be supposed that, wherever the existence of means to optimize behavior by continuous variation of parameters would be beneficial to the functioning of a control system, such means will be present. Nothing will be implied as to the nature of the optimizing process. It may be a simple feedback loop, or it may be an involved learning process which depends upon a long and complicated history of experience of the system. From our point of view, we only care about the fact that if a fine adjustment is needed, the system can make it. If this is the case, we may study the task of an adaptive control system to provide suitable structure up to the point where it can be optimized by continuous modifications. If we desire to build adaptive and intelligent systems, then *our program is to assume that the many learning and optimizing systems which are now the subject of much engineering research have all been made to work perfectly, and to try to learn what to do with these systems.*

The remainder of this section will introduce standard mathematical definitions which will be required throughout, and present some interpretations of them in terms of control systems. The previous examples showed that we are concerned with mappings between spaces of various sorts. Mappings will be assumed continuous, unless the contrary is stated. In accordance with what has been assumed above about the possibility of making fine adjustments, we shall not, at times, distinguish between mappings which may be continuously deformed into one another by varying parameters. We shall say that a family of mappings $h_s : X \to Y$, $s \in S$, is *parametrized by the set S* if the mapping $h : X \times S \to Y$ defined by $h(x,s) = h_s(x)$, $x \in X$, $s \in S$, is continuous. In case S is the closed unit interval, i.e., all real numbers $0 \leqslant t \leqslant 1$, we shall call h_t (and also h) a *homotopy*, and we shall call h_0 and h_1 the *initial and terminal maps of the homotopy*. Two mappings $f, g : X \to Y$ are called *homotopic* ($f \simeq g$) if there is a homotopy $h_t : X \to Y$ such that $h_0 = f$ and $h_1 = g$. The relation $\simeq$ is an equivalence relation which partitions all mappings from X to Y into disjoint *homotopy classes*. We shall denote the set of all mappings from X to Y by Y^x and the set of all homotopy classes of mappings from X into Y by $[X,Y]$. This set may be discrete, even if Y^x is not. The elements of $[X,Y]$ are classes of mappings which we may sometimes consider the same because of the assumed fine adjustment systems. Although these adjustments involve only a single real parameter t, they are no less general in effect than adjustments corresponding to any arcwise-connected parameter set S, for any two mappings f_s and $f_{s'}$, where s, $s' \in S$, are connected by an obvious homotopy f_t, where t is a parametrization of any arc joining s and s'.

It will be noted in passing, but not developed in this paper, that if one wishes to assign information measures to all mappings of one space into another, and one is interested only in the additional information over and beyond the work of the optimizing systems, which are always taken for granted, then the homotopy classes may provide a natural way of breaking up a continuum of functions into a set of information classes. These classes correspond to essentially different functions from our point of view, and may form a discrete, possibly small, set.

Two spaces X and Y are said to be *of the same homotopy type*, or to be *homotopically equivalent*, in case there exist mappings $f : X \to Y$ and $g : Y \to X$ such that $gf \simeq Id_X$ and $fg \simeq Id_Y$, where Id_X and Id_Y are the identity mappings on X and Y. For a simple example, let X be a circle (coordinate θ) and let Y be a circular cylinder (coordinates (θ, z)). These are easily seen to be homotopically equivalent under the mappings $f(\theta) = (\theta, z_0)$, where z_0 is a fixed value of z, and $g(\theta, z) = \theta$. Then $gf = Id_X$, and $Id_Y \simeq fg$ under a homotopy which slides each point of the cylinder an increasing proportion of the way towards the circle (θ, z_0), for instance, $h_t(\theta, z) = (\theta, tz_0 + (1 - t)z)$.

Suppose that X and Y represent behavior spaces of two control subsystems, and it is desired that space Y contain a model of space X. One direct way to accomplish this is to use as model the image of a mapping of X into Y. An example of this situation might occur in case a control system "wished" to store part of its information, X, in some storage medium having a structure given by Y. Will the control system be able to retrieve the information when it is needed? Or is the structure of the storage medium such that the information will necessarily be degraded to an extent that it cannot be recovered? Our standing assumption is that it is good enough to get the information back in a distorted form which can be restored to its original form by continuous deformations. Hence, the necessary condition is that the composite mapping $X \xrightarrow{f} Y \xrightarrow{g} X$ be homotopic to Id_X, Y is then said to *dominate* X. The definition of homotopy equivalence between X and Y said, in these terms, that each dominated the other.

Information might be lost in this type of storage. For instance, if X is a cylinder and Y a circle, then the composite mapping $X \to Y \to X$ has discarded information about the z-coordinate of the cylinder. However, an optimizing system which can provide one parameter and adjust its value can restore the information, and we have assumed such systems to be available. If the cylinder X (or the circle Y) were mapped, instead, into a line segment Z, there would exist no mapping which would retrieve the information in a form which could be patched up by continuous deformations. X and Y are not dominated by Z.

Later we shall see that criteria of system operation at the behavioral level can determine possibilities for information storage of this type.

During the course of gradual differentiation of behavior in an adaptive system, it may frequently occur that the system has found a mapping between two behavior spaces which is defined in a restricted portion of the space containing its domain. Will the system be able to find a continuous mapping defined upon the whole space which coincides with the original mapping on the restricted portion? In many important and typical mathematical situations, it can be shown that if this *extension* can be performed up to homotopy—i.e., in distorted form which can be repaired by an adjusting system, then it can be performed exactly. The possibility of extension then depends only upon the homotopy class of the mapping to be extended. Moreover, it is always true that extension up to homotoyp depends only upon the homotopy type of the spaces involved, i.e., if there is a solution, and all the spaces are replaced by homotopically equivalent spaces, then the new extension problem will have a solution. It is therefore very natural for many purposes to group mappings into their homotopy classes, and physically, this means that it is natural to study the additional problems faced by an adaptive system, granted that sufficient continuous adjustment mechanisms exist.

Related elementary definitions may be found in texts such as Hocking and Young,[14] and more information and references concerning deformations and extensions may be found in Hu,[16] especially Chaps. I and VI.

FIBER SPACES

The example previously given of mechanical hands illustrated a general situation which may arise when one views a space representing a total pattern of behavior. In that example the space E could be mapped onto the space X simply by projecting downward in the diagram. The set of points mapped onto any particular point of X comprised the vertical line representing different muscle configurations and their effects, corresponding to the situation in which the object was at that particular value of x. In another example, that set might be a more complicated abstract space. It was remarked that one could find a path in E which projected onto an arbitrary path in X and began at any preselected point in E which projected onto the initial point of the path in X. It was also noted that E could be regarded as the union of spaces E_1 and E_2, projecting onto overlapping sets which covered X, with certain points in E_1 regarded as coinciding with certain points in E_2. Different acts, or different ways of looking at the same act, corresponded to different ways of joining E_1 and E_2. In addition, all the vertical slices of E were images of a space H, and the difference between the two ways of mapping H into E_1 and E_2, where they overlapped, was one of a group of possible transformations of H, in this case, the group of all translations and reflections of H. The last two properties may be of some interest, but will not exist in most of the spaces which will be discussed in this paper.

We have already given examples of spaces to which the present discussion applies. These instances, together with the earlier example of mechanical hands, should enable the reader to supply interesting interpretations of the following definitions, which deal with mappings between spaces regarded from a point of view like the above.

Fiber spaces, fiberings, or *fibrations,* which all mean the same thing, are pairs of topological spaces, with a mapping from one to the other, possibly having additional structure, depending upon the definition employed, and regarded from a point of view exemplified by the preceding paragraphs of this section. One of the earliest notions to be formulated, which constitutes an important example of all current versions of fiber spaces, in the *fiber bundle*. This is a space which one would obtain if one started with a collection of spaces homeomorphic to product spaces of a fixed space (like H in our previous example) with open sets of another space (like parts of X in that example), and fastened them together, as in that example, so that on the overlap of two pieces, the two maps of the total space into H differed by an element of a group of transformations of H (all rigid motions of H, in that example). The mapping onto X is obtained from the natural projections of all the product spaces. Many important examples exist in mathematics. It was eventually found that many of the interesting theorems could be proved starting with just a few of the properties of fiber bundles, and combinations of these properties were used to define the situations to be studied. Most of the examples in this paper concern these more general situations. Motivation for the study of fiber bundles and some of their elementary properties may be found in Auslander and MacKenzie,[1] and the more detailed standard treatment in Steenrod,[25] which also deals with homotopies and extensions of mappings. Information on fiber spaces of various kinds, and related problems, may be found in Hu,[16] Holmann,[15] Deheuvels,[2] and Grothendieck.[9]

Most generally (Grothendieck), all that remains is a mapping between two spaces, and the distinguishing mark of the theory is the point of view from which it is regarded, by paying attention to spaces of operators on the given space, sets of locally isomorphic spaces, and other related notions. A *fiber space* over a space B is at least a triple (E, p, B), of topological spaces E and B, and a continuous mapping p of E into (often *onto*) B. More restrictive definitions will be introduced when required. The fiber space (E, p, B) will sometimes be denoted simply by E, but the space B and map p will be understood to be present. B is called the *base*, E is called the *total space*, and p is called the *projection*. If b is any point in B, the subspace $p^{-1}(b)$ of E is called the *fiber over b*. In case, in some instance, a particular point of b is singled out as a point of reference, the fiber over that point may be called *the* fiber; and if all the fibers are homeomorphic to the same space, that space may be called the fiber.

In the earlier example, X is the base, E is the total space, and the mapping of any point of E onto the point of X directly below is the projection. The fiber over any point x is what was referred to as a "slice" of the action space, and since all these vertical slices are homeomorphic images of H, the space H is the fiber. There is additional structure in the example, which will not be considered at present.

If Y is an open set contained in B, then the fiber space $(p^{-1}(U), p\,|\,p^{-1}(U)$, $U)$, where $p\,|\,p^{-1}(U)$ means the restriction of p to $p^{-1}(U)$, is called the *restriction* of E to U, and may be written $E\,|\,U$ for short. In the earlier example, the spaces E_1 and E_2 were restrictions of E to the sets $x > -1$ and $x < +1$, respectively.

A number of basic definitions and elementary propositions are given in the first pages of all the references. It is worthwhile to be familiar with these, since they help crystallize one's thinking, provide a standardized terminology, and perhaps, remind one of some of the operations that might have to be put into a computer program which handles these spaces and mappings. A review of these will not be attempted here, and only the minimum number of definitions actually needed in this paper will be introduced, when required.

It will generally be useful to represent a fiber space by a simple picture like that of Fig. 2, which schematically depicts E, p, B, two points b_1 and b_2 of B and the fibers over them, and a path ω from b_1 to b_2, together with a path α which starts at e_1 in the fiber over b_1, travels to e_2 in the fiber over b_2, and *covers* ω, i.e., points in α project onto corresponding points of ω. (A *path* f in X is a map $f : I \to X$, where I is the unit interval $0 \leqslant t \leqslant 1$. A path is here represented pictorially by its image, and α covers ω in case $p\alpha = \omega$, i.e., $p(\alpha(t)) = \omega(t)$ for all $t \,\epsilon\, I$. We may also say that ω is *lifted* to

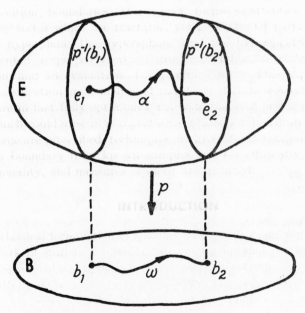

Figure 2

a path α which starts at e_1. The pictures are purely schematic, and represent the kinds of objects described under ABSTRACT SPACES. They will be employed in preference to symbolism whenever the symbolic expression is a purely mechanical transcription of the geometrical idea of the picture, as is, for instance, the homotopy written explicitly in the example of homotopically equivalent spaces.

PATH-LIFTING PROPERTY

In some of the examples which concern us, B will be physical space, a space of possible occurrences in physical space, or it may be a space of configurations or possible configurations of a control system; and E will be a space similarly related to the behavior of another control system. It was noted above that the two-hand control system could follow a continuously moving object by making appropriate changes in the muscle settings, and this was reflected in the obvious fact that one could cover a moving point in the base by a moving point in the total space. This is certainly a desirable property of the example, for without it, the system would not be able to handle objects skilfully in all positions. If we jump from this extremely simple system to the complicated control system which guides an infant's hand in relation to objects, we see that any abstract structure which faithfully represented the early behavior would not enjoy this property. The desirable covering property is eventually attained through a long history of experience. The physical mechanisms which actually execute the requisite adjustments may be numerous and involved, but we shall assume that they work and only discuss conclusions which follow as a consequence of the formal property.

We therefore define this property (see Hu,[16] Hurewicz,[17] and Fadell.[3]) The idea of the definition is that a map $p : E \rightarrow B$ has the *path-lifting property* if, for each $e \in E$ and each path $\omega : I \rightarrow B$ with $\omega(0) = p(e)$, there exists a path $\alpha : I \rightarrow E$ such that $\alpha(0) = e$, $p\alpha = \omega$, and such that α depends continuously on e and ω. This means one can lift the entire path, starting from any lifting of its initial point. More precisely (and, incidentally, in terms closer to a computer program), if $p : E \rightarrow B$ is a map (i.e., a continuous function), let Ω_p denote the subset of $E \times B^I$ (where B^I means all maps of the unit interval I into B, i.e., the space of paths in B) consisting of ordered pairs (e, ω) such that $p(e) = \omega(0)$. Then if to each path α in E we let correspond the pair consisting of its initial point and its projection, we have thereby defined a map $\tilde{p} : E^I \rightarrow \Omega_p$ given by $\tilde{p}(\alpha) = (\alpha(0), p\alpha)$. Then $p : E \rightarrow B$ is said to have the *path-lifting property* if there exists a map $\lambda : \Omega_p \rightarrow E^I$ such that $\tilde{p} \lambda$ is the identity map on Ω_p. Such a map λ is called a *lifting function*.

A lifting function is, in effect, a unified "policy" for changing the state of the system represented by the total space so as to follow changes in the situation represented by the base space. Of course, a complicated adaptive device may have arrived at its method of following such changes by piecemeal adjustments, so that each point in B has an open neighborhood such that the fiber space over that neighborhood has the path lifting property. This *local path-lifting property* is, however, sufficient to ensure the existence of a single lifting function defined throughout, under very general conditions (Hurewicz[17]). It is sufficient for this that B be metric. (More generally, B need only be *paracompact*, which means that it is Hausdorff (given two points of B, there are disjoint open sets, each containing just one .of the two points) and that every covering by open sets has a refinement which consist of open sets, and which is such that every point has a neighborhood intersecting only a finite number of sets of the refinement.)

If a policy of this type exists at all, there may be many of them. However, all of the lifting functions in this case form a single homotopy class, and, moreover, the entire homotopy λ_s connecting any two distinct lifting functions λ' and λ'' may lie within the family of lifting functions. To lift a path ω in B by means of the lifting function λ_s, $0 \leqslant s \leqslant 1$, will mean to lift ω by λ' from its initial point to the position $\omega(1 - s)$ and then to lift the remainder of ω, starting in E from the endpoint of the first lifted segment, by means of λ''. Then, $\lambda_0 = \lambda'$, and as s increases, longer and longer terminal segments are lifted by λ'', until finally, $\lambda_1 = \lambda''$.

This homotopy will be explicitly exhibited as a sample, solely in order to demonstrate how the precise symbolic expression of these operations can be written down mechanically from the geometric picture.

$$\lambda_s(e,\omega)(t) = \begin{cases} \lambda'(e,\omega)(t) & \text{if } 0 \leqslant t \leqslant 1 - s \\ \lambda''(\lambda'(e,\omega)(1-s),\omega')\left(\dfrac{t+s-1}{s}\right) & \text{if } 1 - s < t \leqslant 1 \end{cases}$$

where $\lambda_s(e,\omega)$ (t) may be read "λ_s of e and ω, evaluated at t," and likewise for similar expressions, and ω' is a path in B defined by $\omega'(t) = \omega(1 - s + st)$. The definition of ω' is one of many ways to represent the tail end of ω as a path, i.e., a mapping defined on the interval $[0,1]$. The transformation of the path parameter could have been any monotonic continuous function that changed $[1 - s, 1]$ into $[0,1]$. When all this is decoded, it expresses the desired geometrical idea.

The path ω in B may be regarded as a homotopy of a mapping of a single point onto $\omega(0)$; the homotopy is defined by $\omega_t(0) = \omega(t)$. Now ω can be lifted to a path α starting at an arbitrary point e over $\omega(0)$, and this path may be regarded as a homotopy $\alpha_t(0) = \alpha(t)$, which covers the homotopy

ω_t, i.e., $p\alpha_t = \omega_t$. Suppose that this *covering, homotopy property* applies to all homotopies in the following fashion: for every space Y of some class of spaces, every map $f : Y \to E$, and every homotopy $g_t : Y \to B$ of the map $g = pf$, there exists a homotopy $f_t : Y \to E$ of f which covers the homotopy g_t, i.e., $pf_t = g_t$ for all $t \in I$. Then the map $p : E \to B$ is said to have the *covering homotopy property relative to the class of spaces* Y, and if Y may be any space, p is said to have the *absolute covering homotopy property*. The larger the class of spaces Y, the smaller is the set of maps p with the corresponding covering homotopy property.

A covering homotopy property has at least one interesting behavioral interpretation. Let E and B represent behavior spaces of two parts of a control system. As before, E will represent possible configurations of an effector system, and B will represent situations in the external world. Other interpretations are possible. Let Y represent a structure in a central control system, like the central nervous system. Regard each mapping from Y into E as a composite specification of signals sent under a variety of circumstances by the central control system to the effector system. Suppose, as is plausible, that the central control system, at some moment of its history, possesses a repertoire of signals which it can send, and let these be represented by the mapping $f : Y \to E$ of the preceding paragraph. The environmental situations to which they are related, or which they produce, will then be represented by the mapping $g = pf$. For example, in our case of the mechanical hands, the image of a mapping into the base space X might be regarded either as various positions of an object, for which the internal configurations of the total space E were adopted; or else as positions of an object resulting from these internal configurations, under the interpretation that another control system was causing the hand to grasp the object. Suppose it beneficial if the effectors could act under a family of environmental circumstances, or produce a family of physical effects, related to the original circumstance or effect by continuous changes. Could the central control system find a family of signal specifications, $f_t : Y \to E$, which correspond to the desired family of environmental mappings? According to the covering homotopy property, these mappings are there to be found.

The path-lifting property and the *absolute* covering homotopy property (i.e., holding for *all* spaces Y) are equivalent properties (Hurewicz, 1955). For, suppose that the path-lifting property obtains. Then for each $y \in Y$, the mapping $g_t(y)$, regarded as a function of t, is a path ω_y in B, and all these paths may be lifted to define the paths in E corresponding to $f_t(y)$, the covering homotopy. Conversely, assuming the covering homotopy property, we have already seen that the path-lifting property follows by regarding a path as a homotopy of a mapping of a point.

If the mapping p has these two equivalent properties, the triple (E, p, B) is said to be a *Hurewicz fiber space*. In what follows, the word *fibration* will arbitrarily be reserved for Hurewicz fiber spaces. (Hu[16] deals extensively with fiber spaces which form a broader class, because the covering homotopy property is only required to hold relative to the class of triangulable spaces Y.

EXAMPLES

Now we may see some simple examples in which these properties hold or do not hold. One example in which one *can* lift paths is the two-hand control system previously described. Another example is the path space of any topological space mapped onto that space by mapping any path onto its final point. More precisely, let $B \subset X$, and let $E(X, B)$ denote the subset of X^I consisting of all paths $\alpha(t)$ for which $\alpha(1) \in B$. Define $p : E(X, B) \to B$ by $p\alpha = \alpha(1)$. Then $(E(X,B), p, B)$ is a fibration. This is plausible on intuitive grounds, for if we start with a point in B and any path $e \in E(X, B)$ which ends at that point in B, then as we move along a path ω in B, we can cover the moving point $\omega(t)$ with continuations of e by the initial portion of ω extending from $\omega(0)$ to $\omega(t)$, and the resulting paths all belong to $E(X,B)$. A fibration similarly results from the projection of paths starting within $A \subset X$ onto their initial points in A. Most generally, the space $E(X; A, B)$, consisting of paths $\alpha \in X^I$ for which $\alpha(0) \in A$ and $\alpha(1) \in B$, is a fibration over $A \times B$ by the projection $p(\alpha) = (\alpha(0), \alpha(1))$.

Observe that the central control system example which illustrates the covering homotopy property enjoys this property because of regulatory activities of some hypothesized control system, while the path space is a fibration by virtue of purely mathematical considerations.

A simple example of a situation in which paths *cannot* all be lifted is shown in Fig. 3, in which points of E are projected vertically onto points of B. No lifting function can be continuous at the point (e, ω), where e is the point indicated in the picture, and ω is any path which starts at $b = pe$ and goes to the left. The slightest difference in the starting point of the lifted path will change that path discontinuously from one which enters the upper branch of E to one which enters the lower branch. In terms of the covering homotopy property, suppose that f maps a space Y onto the indicated vertical line segment through e, and therefore, $g = pf$ maps Y onto b. Then any homotopy g_t, starting at g, which maps Y onto a single point that is carried to the left cannot be covered by a homotopy f_t, starting at f. This situation by no means typifies the myriad ways in which a map can fail to be a fibration.

A simple physical example of the last situation is the following: Imagine a two-bar plane linkage representing a simple arm. The bars are each of

Figure 3

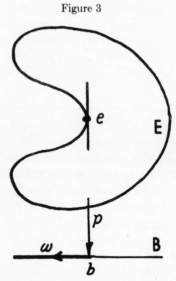

length L, and one bar is attached to a fixed frame by a "shoulder" pivot, while the second bar is attached to the first by an "elbow" pivot. Let ϕ denote the counterclockwise shoulder angle from the direction straight ahead of the frame to the first bar, let ψ denote the counterclockwise elbow angle from the first bar to the second, and let θ denote the counterclockwise angle at the shoulder from the forward direction to the radius from shoulder to free end of the second arm (the "hand"). Suppose that the hand must always slide along the radius vector θ, and that from the point of view of the control system in which we are interested, ϕ changes actively, while ψ passively changes so as to maintain contact between the hand and the line θ. This means, for instance, that our control system regulates ϕ, while some other mechanism (e.g., a feedback loop), not of current interest in this particular representation of behavior, maintains a suitable ψ. The line θ could represent the edge of some moving object, or it might represent the line of vision of a system which is currently learning how to move its hand so as to keep it in the line of sight. Then, for any fixed value of θ, we may plot ϕ as a function $\phi_\theta (r)$ of the distance r from the shoulder to the location (r, θ) of the hand on the line θ. We have $r = 2L \cos (\phi - \theta)$, and there are in general two values, ϕ_1, and $\phi_2 = 2\theta - \phi_1$, for each value of θ. For $r = 0$, however, any value of ϕ is suitable, so long as $\psi = 0$. The plot of $\phi_\theta(r)$ will therefore have the shape shown in Fig. 4a, in which the ends of the vertical line corresponding to $r = 0$ are joined to identify 180° with $-180°$, thereby producing a configuration topologically like Figure 4b.

The projection maps points vertically onto the r-axis. It is clear that most points on the curve corresponding to $r = 0$ cannot serve as starting points for paths which cover changes in r. If the arm is in these configurations, it must first swing through a large angle before the hand can begin to follow the desired path. Dead center positions like this would arise if a mariner's compass or telescope were to be supported by gymbals containing the minimum number of pivots allowing freedom to assume all positions. There would be certain positions in which stabilization of the device against the least rolling of the ship would require some supporting ring to oscillate wildly through angles of 180°, and therefore, additional links are added to the mechanism to eliminate this phenomenon. These very elementary examples have been belabored in order to make clear that what is being proposed is a point of view applicable to conventional devices. Of course, in these examples, this approach yields nothing more than a uniform terminology.

To conclude this discussion, we shall exhibit the behavior space of the act of maintaining the hand of the two-bar linkage in the line of sight, *when regarded from the point of view adopted above*, with respect to the variables considered relevant. This will be the only behavior space outside of our earlier example of mechanical hands to be exhibited explicitly in this paper. This illustrates once more how the space depends upon the action and the purpose of the analysis.

The choice of coordinate system and the peculiar appearance of the final product will reflect a simple, but important, observation. If the position of a point in a plane is specified by polar coordinates (r, θ), and r and θ are controlled by two different devices, then the configuration space of the devices is a cylinder, bounded at one end ($r = 0$), and going to infinity at the other. For the point, all positions $(0, \theta)$ are the same, so we have the usual polar plot with radii and concentric circles for the coordinate net, but for the controlling devices, $(0, \theta)$ depends upon θ. The space of the point is topologically equivalent to the space of the devices modulo the equivalence relation identifying all points on the lower rim of the cylinder. The action space to be described will be the space of the parameters, and not the space of the resulting positions.

We may imagine the loci of Fig. 4a, for all values of θ, to be embedded in 3-space in the following way. First, represent (r, ϕ_θ) for fixed θ as a point in a plane with a hole in the middle (a less bulky homeomorph of the cylinder of the preceding paragraph). This is easily done by representing (r, ϕ_θ) by the point $(r + r_0, \phi_\theta)$ of a polar coordinate system, where r_0 is any fixed positive number. This has already been done in Fig. 4b. The graph of the equations relating r and ϕ_θ consists of the curve obtained by drawing a circle passing through the origin with center (L, θ), and shifting all its points radially outward a distance r_0, together with a circle of radius r_0 centered at the origin. All these θ-cross-sections may be assembled into the complete surface by orienting each one in a vertical plane that passes through a common center C. The origin of each θ-cross-section lies on a circle with center C and arbitrary radius exceeding r_0, and is located at the point of the circle having angle θ relative to C and some reference direction. The result of all this will look like an automobile tire (assumed to be a torus) which has a "safety air chamber," (or which has an inner tube glued to it along a strip going all around the long way), and which has been chopped through (so that the tire is like a cylinder), and which finally has had the cut ends rejoined with a 360° twist. The twisted safety tire is the action space. The projection maps points onto pairs of their coordinates (r, θ).

Such spaces may be the domains or ranges of mappings. In particular, a system like those discussed above under perception and action models and computers has a collection of devices activated on various regions of the configuration space. Thus, a collection of sets which cover the configuration space may be mapped into other action spaces, each set corresponding to the product space of all the devices active throughout that set. It then becomes a matter of interest to understand these mappings in order to learn how more complex forms of behavior can be developed from simpler forms by increasing the number of covering sets and by mapping them into more elaborate spaces.

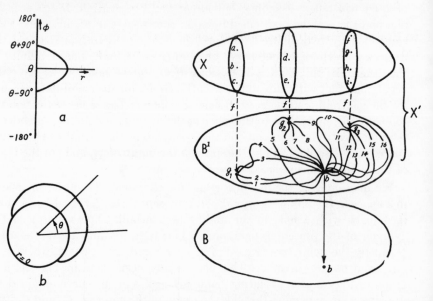

Figure 4   Figure 5

GENERAL REMARKS

In the next section we learn some of the reasons why the path lifting property is interesting. It should be pointed out here that the path lifting property does not imply that all maps may be lifted. For example, let E be the real line, and let B be the unit circle. The projection is given by $p(x) = e^{2\pi x i}$, where $x \in E$, e is the base of natural logarithms, and i is the imaginary unit. Then $p(x)$ is the point on the circle having the angle $2\pi x$ (mod 2π). E may be regarded as having the form of a helix with unit radius and vertical axis, with the map p projecting points vertically onto a circle with its center on the axis. This picture suggests correctly that p has the path lifting property. (The unit interval which is the domain of the path is simply laid out along the helix over its image in B.) Suppose now that a circle S of unit radius is mapped onto B by simply laying it on top of B. This map cannot be lifted into E, because, as the picture will show, an attempted lifting cannot be a continuous mapping of S into E. (Once again to emphasize the point that mappings of helices onto circles, etc., can have physical significance, refer to the example previously given of phase-shift control of a motor, using a thyratron. S could represent the grid signal phase angle, E the power delivered by the motor, and B the angular position of the rotor after a fixed time interval under these conditions.)

It should finally be remarked that the situation which has been described is an interesting one, but by no means the only interesting one. We shall use it solely to illustrate how a new point of view can suggest new issues in adaptive control theory, and new concrete opportunities for experimentation. Furthermore, any truly adequate theory from this point of view will require intimacy with the type of reasoning exemplified here. The end of this paper briefly deals with situations in which the path-lifting property need not hold.

BEHAVIORAL FIBRATIONS AND SOME ELEMENTARY PROPERTIES

EXAMPLES

We have already considered examples in which the path lifting property was an intrinsic characteristic of the spaces we chose to consider. These were spaces of paths, projected onto their initial or terminal points, or both. Incidentally, a homotopy may be regarded as a path in a space of mappings. Another example is the space of all k-dimensional frames (ordered sets of k linearly independent vectors) in n-space. This space is projected onto the space of all k-dimensional subspaces of the n-space, by projecting each frame onto the k-space which it spans (many sets of k vectors span the same k-space). This fibration has many additional properties, resembling the properties discussed in our first example. It could conceivably be of interest (aside from its mathematical interest) in the study of linear physical systems in which, for example, one might require output patterns to be synthesized from linear combinations of normal modes which were modified by changing the parameters of the system. Finally, if (E, p, B) is a fibration, so is $(\Omega(E, e_0), \Omega p, \Omega(B, b_0))$, where $e_0 \in E$, $pe_0 = b_0 \in B$, $\Omega(E, e_0)$ is the space of *loops* in E at e_0—i.e., all paths in E beginning and ending at e_0, $\Omega(B, b_0)$ is the loop space of B at b_0; and if $\alpha \in \Omega(E, e_0)$, then (Ωp) (α) $(t) = p(\alpha(t))$. If F is the fiber over b_0, and if $\omega_0 \in \Omega(B, b_0)$ denotes the constant loop $\omega_0(t) = b_0$ for all t, where $0 \leqslant t \leqslant 1$, then the fiber over ω_0 is $\Omega(F, e_0)$.

All these examples could have been stated without any reference to control systems, and it is time to give an example which, although well known in pure mathematics, has a more specific behavioral interpretation. Suppose that $f : X \to B$ is any map between the topological spaces X and B. X and B may have any of the interpretations we have given to spaces so far. In particular, suppose that X is a space representing internal configurations, and that B represents positions in external space, as previously indicated. More generally, X and B could represent configurations of two successive internal subsystems in a chain of subsystems. For convenience, under either interpretation, configurations in X will be said to be *proximal*, and configurations in B will be said to be *distal*. A system performing purposive actions must furnish whatever proximal events may be needed under the circumstances to produce a desired distal effect. The mapping f might map onto a distal event all proximal configurations which correspond to it, or which correspond to different purposes relative to the distal event.

Suppose that the system must find a way to get to a desired distal position. Further, suppose that the situation is complicated enough that the system needs some kind of internal model of events, for example, the models postulated by MacKay which we should like to understand. Here is one possibility, arbitrarily chosen for illustrative purposes only. We agree that possession of a model means that the system is prepared to reach any possible goal position in the region B. We suppose that the system need be interested in exactly two types of event: paths in distal space (because it might have to allow for things it might meet on the way) and final proximal configurations after following the paths (because they have to be matched to the configurations which are required for the next act). This is an arbitrary, but plausible, choice of information to put in the model. For each specified pair consisting of distal path and final proximal configuration, some control system tries to maintain the proximal configuration on a proximal path which leads to the desired final configuration, while covering the distal path, if this is possible. This is not necessarily possible, for we are assuming no properties of f beyond continuity.

If the above information must be contained in a model, then for each point $b \in B$, let us imagine the space X'_b, defined schematically as follows:

$$X'_b = \underset{\text{GOALS:}}{\text{ALL}} \left\{ \begin{array}{c} \text{FOR EACH GOAL:} \\ \hline \underset{\omega,\, x:}{\text{ALL}} \left(\begin{array}{cc} \text{distal path } \omega, & \text{internal configuration} \\ \text{from } b \text{ to goal } g,x & \text{over goal } g\epsilon B \end{array} \right) \end{array} \right\}$$

$$= \bigcup_{g \epsilon B} \{(\omega,x)|\omega \epsilon B^I,\ \omega(0) = b,\ \omega(1) = g,\ x\epsilon X,\ fx = g\}$$

$$\subset B^I \times f^{-1}(g) \subset B^I \times X$$

Define

$$X' = \bigcup_b X'_b$$

Then X' may be depicted crudely in some fashion like Fig. 5.

Since there is no way to draw this space accurately, and yet a visualizable model aids the understanding, a remark is required concerning the conventions used in Fig. 5. The bottom region represents the space B in our usual fashion. The middle region is intended to represent the space of all paths in B, in which each point stands for a path. Since this cannot be drawn, B itself has been shown, together with some representative paths in B which all start at b and go to three representative goals g_1, g_2, g_3. The space at the top is X, together with an indication of $f^{-1}(g_1)$, $f^{-1}(g_2)$, and $f^{-1}(g_3)$, and their mapping onto g_1, g_2, and g_3. Finally, the two spaces at the top, taken together in the following sense, are intended to depict X'. Since the cartesian product cannot be conveniently drawn, it is intended that a set $f^{-1}(g_i)$ in X and the subset of paths in B consisting of all paths from b to g_i be taken together as a cartesian product, rather than as the union which is actually drawn. Thus, if the only paths starting at b were those labeled $1, 2, \ldots, 16$, and the only points in the $f^{-1}(g_i)$ were $a, b, \ldots, i$, as indicated, then X'_b would consist of the following set of 144 pairs: $(1,a)$, $(1,b)$, $(1,c)$, $(2,a)$, $(2,b)$, $(2,c), \ldots, (4,c)$, $(5,d)$, $(5,e)$, $(6,d), \ldots, (9,e)$, $(10,f), \ldots, (16,i)$. The union of all such sets, corresponding to all starting points b, is the space X'.

Define a mapping $p : X' \rightarrow B$ by $p(X'_b) = b$. One may now easily verify the following well known facts:

(a) (X',p,B) is a fibration, i.e., p has the path-lifting property.

(b) $X \subset X'$ (more accurately, an isomorphic image of X is contained in X').

(c) X (i.e., its embedded image in X') is a strong deformation retract of X', and hence, X has the homotopy type of X'. (To say that X is a *retract* of a space X' which contains X, means that there is a mapping (called a *retraction*) $r : X' \rightarrow X$ such that r restricted to X is the identity mapping of X, i.e., all of X' may be "projected on X." To say that X is a *deformation retract* of X' means that the retraction r is homotopic to the identity on X', i.e., X' may be continuously deformed into its retraction on X. Finally, X is a *strong deformation retract* if this continuous deformation leaves X unchanged at all stages of the deformation in addition to the final one.)

(d) The following diagram *commutes*, that is to say, $Id_B f = pi : X \rightarrow B$, where Id_B is the identity mapping of B onto itself and i is the inclusion mapping of X into X' demonstrated in assertion (b).

$$
\begin{array}{ccc}
X & \xrightarrow{\ i\ } & X' \\
{\scriptstyle f}\uparrow & & \downarrow{\scriptstyle p} \\
B & \xrightarrow{\ Id_B\ } & B
\end{array}
$$

This implies that any two points of X which are mapped by f onto the same point of B will correspond to two points of X' which are projected by p onto the same point of B, i.e., that fibers of X (in the sense of inverse images, since f is an arbitrary map) and the points beneath them are mapped by the pair (i, Id_B) into fibers of X' and the points beneath them.

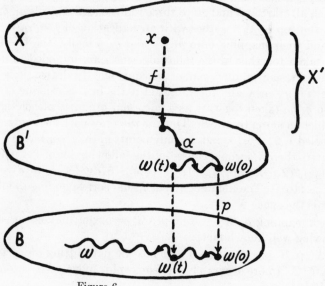

Figure 6

Hence, the mapping $f : X \to B$ is replaced by a fibration $p : X' \to B$ in a way which preserves the integrity of the "slices" discussed earlier. Since, by assertion (c), $X' \simeq X$, and of course, $B \simeq B$, the construction illustrates one way in which any mapping whatsoever may be converted into a homotopically equivalent fibration.

The four assertions may be demonstrated as follows. The reason for presenting these routine details is to illustrate the way of thinking about such problems, and to enable a reader to see for himself whether the specific operations involved seem to him like plausible ones for a natural or artificial system to perform.

Demonstrations:

(a) (p has the path-lifting property):

Figure 6 illustrates the intuitive meaning. Given $\omega : I \to B$ and (α, x) $\epsilon\ p^{-1}(\omega(0)\ )$, where $\alpha \in B^I$, $x \in X$, $\alpha(0) = \omega(0)$, and $f(x) = \alpha(1)$, we are required to find a lifted path $\lambda\ ((\alpha, x), \omega) \in X^I$, such that $\lambda((\alpha, x), \omega)(0) = (\alpha, x)$ and $p\lambda = \omega$. To accomplish this, define $\lambda((\alpha, x), \omega)(t) = (\beta, x)$, where $\beta \in B^I$ is the composite path consisting of the portion of the path ω starting at $\omega(t)$ and proceeding in reverse direction to $\omega(0)$, followed by the path α. Explicitly, define

$$\beta(s) = \begin{cases} \omega(t - s), & \text{for } 0 \leqslant s \leqslant t \\[2mm] \alpha\left(\dfrac{s - t}{1 - t} \right), & \text{for } t \leqslant s \leqslant 1 \\[2mm] \alpha(1), & \text{for } t = 1. \end{cases}$$

(According to this formula, as s increases, the point $\beta(s)$ moves backwards along ω "at normal speed" and then "speeds up" so as to complete all of α in the remaining "time" $1 - t$. Any other way of completing the composite path in unit "time" would simply yield a lifting function homotopic to this one. The parameters s and t are, of course, not really "time.")

(b) ($X \subset X'$):

X may be embedded in X' by the 1–1 correspondence $x \leftrightarrow (c_{f(x)},\ x) \in X'$, where $c_{f(x)}$ is the constant path at $f(x)$, i.e., $c_{f(x)}(t) = f(x)$, $0 \leqslant t \leqslant 1$.

(c) (X is a strong deformation retract of X', and hence $X \simeq X'$):

First of all, if any space X is a deformation retract of any space X', then $X \simeq X'$. For, if $i : X \to X'$ is the inclusion map $i(x) = x \in X'$, and $r : X' \to X$ is a retraction such that $r \simeq Id_{X'}$, then $ri = Id_X$ and $ir \simeq Id_{X'}$.

To show that X is a strong deformation retract of X', we must construct a homotopy $r_t : X' \to X'$, such that $r_0 = Id_{X'}$, $r_1 : X' \to X$ is a retraction of X' upon the subspace $X = (c_{f(x)}, x)$, and $r_t(x) = x$ for all $x \epsilon X$ and $0 \leqslant t \leqslant 1$. For this purpose, define $r_t(\alpha, x) = (\alpha_t, x)$, where $\alpha_t : I \to B$ is given by $\alpha_t(s) = \alpha(s - st + t)$, i.e., $\alpha_t(s)$ traverses the final segment of α

starting at $\alpha(t)$. The required properties are immediate consequences of this definition.

It may be pointed out, as an immediate corollary of the fact that X is a retract of X', that any mapping $g : X \to Y$, where Y is any space, defines a mapping $g' = gr : X' \to Y$, such that g' coincides with g on the subspace X.

(d) $(Id_B f = pi : X \to B)$:

This is immediate, for we have $Id_B f(x) = f(x)$, and $pi(x) = p(c_{f(x)}, x) = c_{f(x)}(1) = f(x)$. This completes the demonstration.

SOME PROPERTIES OF FIBRATIONS WITH POSSIBLE BEHAVIORAL SIGNIFICANCE

We can at present consider only a few elementary properties which are true of fibrations in general, because detailed analyses of specific control systems from this point of view are not yet available. A review of some of the results of Fadell,[3] however, demonstrates how conclusions which may be of some interest in control theory follow from the formal properties we are assuming. Fadell's proofs will be presented in geometrical language which can be automatically transcribed into the formal symbolic expression. These proofs are given here because the purpose of this exposition is to make this type of reasoning more widely accessible, and also because part of each proof is needed just to define the mappings referred to in the statements of the propositions. These propositions are not surprising, once pointed out. Still, they could not be thought of by one who did not have this way of looking at systems.

Recall that the mapping $\tilde{p}$ defined earlier mapped a path α in the total space E onto a pair consisting of the initial point e of that path and the projection $p\alpha$ of that path, lying in the base space B. Now, this pair lies in the domain of the lifting function λ, which may be applied to the pair to obtain a new path starting at the same place as α, but going somewhere else. Let $\tilde{\lambda}$ denote the composite mapping $\lambda\tilde{p}$, which we have just defined. The lifting function λ and the "dropping and relifting" function $\tilde{\lambda}$ will be used in the following propositions:

PROPOSITION 1. $\tilde{\lambda}$ is homotopic to the identity mapping of E^I, and there exists a homotopy $\tilde{\lambda}_s$ such that $p\tilde{\lambda}_s\alpha = p\alpha$ for each s, $0 \leqslant s \leqslant 1$.

Proof. To perform the homotopy, follow the given path α until "time" s, and for the remainder of the unit time, follow $\tilde{\lambda}$ of the remainder of α. That is to say, as s increases one drops and relifts decreasingly long pieces of the end of α. Figure 7 shows α, $\tilde{\lambda}\alpha$, and the intermediate stages of the homotopy.

PROPOSITION 2. If B is pathwise connected, then all the fibers have the same homotopy type.

Proof. The condition means that there exists a path joining any two points in B. Let F and F' be the fibers over b and b', respectively. Draw any path ω from b to b'. Then we may define a mapping $\phi : F \to F'$ as follows: for any point $x \in F$, let $\phi(x) \in F'$ be the endpoint of the lifting of ω which starts at x. Let x' denote $\phi(x)$. Define a mapping $\psi : F' \to F$, similarly, using ω traversed in the opposite direction (call this ω^*) for the path from b' to b. These are the two mappings of the homotopy equivalence. Consider once again the lifting of ω starting at x and going to x'. Let α denote this path traced in the opposite direction. Now examination of $\tilde{\lambda}_s \alpha$, where $\tilde{\lambda}_s$ is the homotopy defined in Proposition 1, will reveal that $\tilde{\lambda}_0 \alpha(1) = \alpha(1) = x$, while $\tilde{\lambda}_1 \alpha(1) = \psi(x') = \psi\, \phi(x)$. Therefore, $Id_F \simeq \psi\phi$, and, in a similar manner we have $Id_{F'} \simeq \phi\,\psi$. Figure 8 shows all these paths and the intermediate stages of the homotopy. Another way to see this result is to map x into the fiber over $\omega(1 - s)$ by a mapping analogous to ϕ, except that it lifts a shorter path in B, and then map the image in this fiber back into F by the analogue of ψ. The resulting mappings of F into itself as s increases from 0 to 1 form a homotopy connecting Id_F and $\psi\phi$.

PROPOSITION 3. If the total space E is pathwise connected, all path components (i.e., maximal pathwise connected subsets) of any fiber F have the same homotopy type.

Proof. Draw any path α from a point x_0 in path component $C \subset F$ to a point x_0' in path component $C' \subset F$. Then $p\alpha$ is a path in B which begins and ends at pF. As in Proposition 2, map each $x \in C$ onto $\phi(x)$, defined to

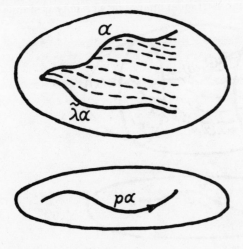

Figure 7

be the endpoint of the lifting of $p\alpha$ which starts at x. To show that this lifting actually travels into the other path component C', so that $\phi(x) \in C'$, note that the points of any path joining x_0 and x must be carried by ϕ into the points of a path joining x_0' and $\phi(x)$, so that $\phi(x)$ is in the same path component as x_0'. This is shown in Fig. 9. The remainder of the argument is the same as for Proposition 2.

PROPOSITION 4. If the fiber F over some point b is contractible in E to a point $x_0 \in E$, then F is dominated by the space Λ of loops based at b.

Proof. The condition means that the identity map on F is homotopic to the constant map $F \to x_0$, and that the images of points of F during the homotopy are not restricted to F but may range through E (so that F need not be contractible in itself). The loops at b are those paths which begin and end at b. Then we may define a map $\phi : F \to \Lambda$ as follows: Because of the homotopy implied by contractibility, each point $x \in F$ is the endpoint of a path α_x in E which starts at $x_0 \in F$ and terminates at x. The projection of this path is a loop based at b, which we define to be $\phi(x)$. In the reverse direction, given a loop ω based at b_0, we may define $\psi(\omega) \in F$ to be the endpoint of the lifting of ω which starts at x_0. Figure 10 shows these mappings. The same arguments as in Proposition 2 show that $\psi \phi \simeq Id_F$ (the endpoint of $\tilde{\lambda}_0$ of the lifted path is x, and the endpoint of $\tilde{\lambda}_1$ of the lifted path is $\psi \phi(x)$). Hence Λ dominates F. However, this argument cannot be reversed to show that F dominates Λ so that the two would be homotopically equivalent. For example, F might be a single point, while Λ might have several components (e.g., if there were holes in B).

Proposition 2 tells us, for instance, that the mapping of Fig. 3 is not a fibration. Of course, that particular mapping was only a simple example

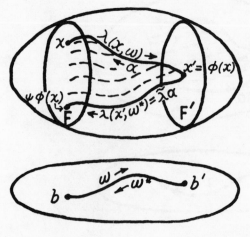

Figure 8

used to illustrate a definition, and this way of looking at it is of no value. Information of this type becomes significant when, as in Fig. 5 and more complicated instances, one cannot visualize the spaces.

One of the simplest examples illustrating the hypothesis of Proposition 3 is the previously mentioned helix which has a vertical axis, and which is projected vertically onto a circle. In this case, the proposition would be of interest only if a complicated space were "bent around" to form a helix, e.g., some space $\cup_x X_x$ projected onto x (mod 2π), where x ranges over the real numbers.

An ordinary helix is again an example of the hypothesis of Proposition 4, since any of its points can spiral up or down to the position of any other point. To define a homotopy h_t that moves all points in a fiber to the position of a single one of them, x_0, let $h_t(x) = x_0 + (x - x_0)\, e^{-t/(1-t)}$. for $0 \leqslant t < 1$ and $h_1(x) = x_0$.

It has already been pointed out that a space may be mapped into a space that dominates it, and the information retrieved, subject only to distortion which we assumed could be removed by a system which can adjust parameters.

It cannot be claimed that these particular propositions are necessarily representative of the kinds of results which will be most useful. They were

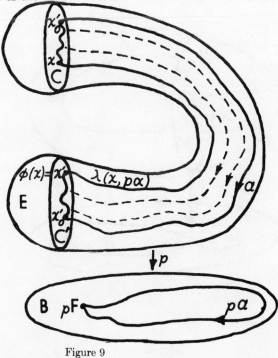

Figure 9

presented as samples of things that can be said even when very little specific information is available. In addition, they illustrate how properties formulated at the level of overall adaptive behavior can lead to new conclusions, provided that the structure of the entire action space, not just its "slices," is taken into account. For example, Proposition 2 asserts a relation between different fibers. If, as is generally the case, different points in the base space represent incompatible potentialities (e.g., different possible positions of the object in the controlled-hands example), different fibers contain structural information about events which cannot possibly occur together. Furthermore, as in that example, different points in the same fiber may represent incompatible purposes or potentialities. Nonetheless, the additional structural information obtained by viewing all these elements in a coherent whole, characterized only by the behavioral assumption that certain fine adjustments could be made, allowed us to deduce relations among the different events.

It should be mentioned to provide perspective, but only as a hopeful source of future applications which do not exist at present, that computational methods exist for obtaining certain types of relations between structures of the total space, fibers, and base space of fibrations (Hu,[16], Hilton and Wylie[13]).

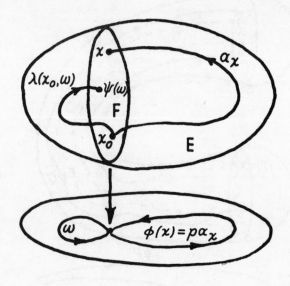

Figure 10

ACTIONS DEFINED ON BEHAVIOR SPACES

This review has attempted to bring together known information which concerns ways of viewing the structure of behavioral spaces, but which has generally not been brought together in this connection. The last two sections, however, illustrate only one part of the mathematical treatment for which the previous sections were formulated. The first three sections following the Introduction reviewed material emphasizing two problems in addition to the questions of fine adjustments which were treated mathematically. The first problem was that of forming new actions out of old ones by breaking the behavior space into pieces and rejoining these pieces in a different way. We saw an example of this in transferring pencils from left to right hand, in the simplified model, which corresponded to different ways of joining two partial action spaces. The second problem was that of forming actions out of additional spaces of behavior that became activated whenever the state of the system and its inputs entered certain regions of a behavior space. This problem is a general formulation of the computer models described, in which sensorimotor patterns could be activated and fitted to stimuli and desired movements, and of the notion, of models and "charts" which are selected by the system on the basis of incoming information.

We have also defined fiber spaces in greater generality than was actually used; the unused portions, presented for future reference, were those which concerned a possible basis for mathematical analysis of the two problems just stated. For instance, it was stated, but not developed further, that the most general fiber spaces were those in which any mapping might be studied with emphasis upon the analysis of local isomorphisms of spaces, and of spaces of functions defined on regions of a given space. These topics, when defined with a greater precision that requires introducing additional mathematical notions (see, for example, Holmann,[15] Grothendieck,[9] and Deheuvels[2]), provide mathematical formulations of the two problems, but it is not yet known whether they merely provide a convenient language or actually can lead to useful conclusions.

The two problems are closely related. Suppose that a fiber space E' is locally isomorphic to a fiber space E. One may think, for instance, of the space E described above. This means that E' is composed of subspaces E_i' which are isomorphic to subspaces E_i of E, but the E_i' and the E_i are put together differently so that E' and E are not "globally" isomorphic. Call the local isomorphisms $\phi_i : E_i \rightarrow E_i'$. On the intersection of subspaces $E_i \cap E_j$ there are thus two isomorphisms, ϕ_i and ϕ_j, both mapping $E_i \cap E_j$ into $E_i' \cap E_j'$. Then we may define a mapping v_{ji} of $E_i \cap E_j$ onto itself by mapping each $x \in E_i \cap E_j$ by ϕ_i into E' and back again into E via ϕ_j^{-1}.

This mapping is an isomorphism of $E_i \cap E_j$, onto itself. Thus, the set of all fiber spaces locally isomorphic to a given fiber space E may be put into correspondence with all possible sets v_{ji} of automorphisms of intersections of pairs of neighborhoods of E, and the techniques for doing this are presented in the references cited. We see, then, that the general problem is to characterize spaces and operations defined on neighborhoods of the fiber spaces.

All that can be done in this review is to call attention to these problems, which motivated the choice of topics in previous sections. Their behavioral meaning is not sufficiently well formulated to justify more than the following general statement of the problems.

As previously noted, the very first time one holds a pen between one's teeth and writes one's signature, the result, though crude, is essentially in one's own "handwriting." How is this possible, when the nerves, muscles, and kinematics of the neck are entirely different from those of the arm, hand, and fingers? The answer is, of course, that in a sense one is not doing the new action for the first time, because throughout life, one has learned the correlations between elements of motion of the hand and of the neck, and one is now merely applying this information to assemble the elements into the same total pattern produced by the neck as by the hand. What could this (correct) answer possibly mean? We must ask ourselves at least the following questions:

1. What does this learning mean, and what mechanisms might be required for its accomplishment? The one thing, at least, that this paper should have made clear is that there is much more to the action spaces than can be stated solely in terms of local strengthening of connections, even though this strengthening may indeed be the physical mechanism involved.

2. In particular, how can one characterize the common elements of structure within the system which cause entirely different patterns of movements to constitute the "same" action?

3. Suppose that the control system had somehow acquired information about all the correlations. In what form could it be stored and retrieved? If, for instance, the control system possesses a model which is completely like the activity it models, then it will be just as hard for the system to learn how to manipulate the model as to learn how to manipulate the actual effector systems. At the other extreme, if the control system possesses elaborate numerical tables correlating each movement of one effector with each movement of every other effector, for each pattern of activity that the system must perform, the number of entries in these tables will exceed the notorious 2^{2^N}, against which we are so frequently warned. In addition, some of our

problems would already have to be solved in order for the system to know how to look up the information. Finally, if possible, we would like a system which can make the necessary adjustments in a relatively noncomputational fashion by a technique which is composed of simple adjustments that one might expect a nervous system to make. It should not have to solve problems in spherical trigonometry or simultaneous differential equations.

4. How does differentiation of complex behavior take place? Guided by analogy with the development of sensorimotor skills in infancy (Piaget[23,24] Greene and Ruggles[8]), we may suppose that the crude behavior of the early stages is not just an unfortunate necessity imposed by the natural limitations of the building materials. Suppose that we imagined a different kind of infant, just like a real one except that some of the clumsy motor patterns of the real infant which later became more precise and easily regulated were replaced with motor patterns which were precise from the start. There are reasons to believe that the imaginary infant would not develop as well as the real one. The imaginary one would have a collection of isolated perfect patterns, while the real one, by learning to perform all sorts of elementary pattern ingredients and to make adjustments in them, somehow comes to build complex patterns out of simple precursors, and individual patterns stand related through their common precursors (Greene[4]). Even if this metaphorical description is an apt one, how is it possible to make precise sense out of it? How can one action be built out of another?

Certain indications come from the mathematics of the type found in the references, which suggest a program of research, currently underway. So far at best, they provide only a way to conceive of some of the issues and keep them in mind. We shall conclude by briefly seeing what some of these directions are. They can actually be explained more precisely, but to do so would require too much preliminary mathematical exposition of the concepts required.

The main problem is to understand what it means to say that one action is built up out of others. For instance, to cause a hand to move skilfully in space takes an elaborate computer program which is of an "unbiological" nature. But causing a head to perform simpler motions like turning left or right, and causing a hand to approach the mouth, and the eyes to watch the hand, and so on, through a variety of simple patterns of behavior, is a program which evidently can be carried out extremely well biologically. In what way can the highly differentiated hand movement behavior utilize the structures of the simpler head behavior and other such patterns?

There are a few mathematical hints as to how to study this. One was suggested at the beginning of our discussion, when it was shown that one could imagine a head behavior space that consisted of subspaces of simpler structure than the hand subspaces, but were fastened together by the same pattern of joining. In that example, a line H was mapped into the space E in two different fashions on the two subspaces E_1 and E_2 of the hand space, while a space consisting merely of two points was mapped into the two subspaces in the same two fashions to obtain the head space. So one problem is to characterize how knowledge of how to assemble patterns of one type can be transferred to learning how to put different patterns together the same way. Technically, this problem concerns principal and associated fiber spaces.

Suppose that the control system does not immediately learn all useful patterns, but remembers only a few precise patterns defined on a few regions of some space, and somehow interpolates rough approximations of what to do at positions in between. For instance, suppose that the two-bar arm linkage as outlined above must move so that the hand describes a straight line going from right to left, and passing through a point somewhere in front of the shoulder joint. Imagine the arm to remain in configurations in which $0 \leqslant \psi \leqslant 180°$, so that it resembles a person's left arm, held in a horizontal plane. Moving from right to left means doing the following things: at the extreme right one must increase ϕ and decrease ψ, but decrease ψ more and more slowly as the hand moves leftward, until in a region about the point of the path directly ahead, a good approximation to the path is obtained by increasing ϕ alone. Progressing still further, ϕ and ψ must both increase, with ϕ slowing down, until a region is reached in which ψ alone need change significantly to obtain a good approximation, and finally, a region is reached at the leftmost end of the path in which ψ continues to increase, but ϕ must decrease. It would seem, then, that an economical description of a process like this might be attained by first specifying a space of a simple action like keeping ϕ constant but small on the right side, and constant but large on the left, and, likewise, a simple rule for ψ, and then specifying another simple space of operators on the first space: on the right side the system must keep touching up the original pattern by decreasing ψ as it moves, perhaps linearly; next, specifying a simple space of operators on that space (e.g., the system must change the coefficients in the rule for decreasing ψ), and so on. To understand procedures like this as applied to the more complicated types of behavior space means understanding fiber spaces with fiber spaces of operators on them.

The last example is concerned with the use of patterns which are activated when the system enters various regions of its behavior space. Suppose that we have a progressive differentiation of the patterns which can be used. For instance, suppose that at first, no matter where an object is sighted, the arm just reaches out, because at this stage the only thing common to the responses to stimulation of various subsystems like sight and prehension is that the systems are all turned on. After a little more development, perhaps the left arm reaches out undirectedly if the object is toward the left, and the right arm if it is toward the right. Later, within the left arm region, in some subregion, the hand might perform one of a collection of movements in some behavior space, and still later in subregions of these sets the fingers might perform patterns in more elaborate spaces, and so on. This procedure may be characterized mathematically by saying that one has a covering of a space X by sets $\{U_i\}$ and to each set U_i corresponds a set of functions $f : U_i \rightarrow S_i$, and to each intersection $U_i \cap U_j$ corresponds a set of functions $g : U_i \cap U_j \rightarrow S_{ij}$, where S_i and S_{ij} are certain fiber spaces; and so on, perhaps for intersections of several sets. The resulting behavior may become more highly differentiated in at least two ways: one can increase the number of regions of definition of the functions, i.e., replace the covering $\{U_i\}$ by a finer covering $\{V_j\}$ (in our last example of grasping, the first covering consisted of a single set, while the next one had two), or one can enlarge the spaces S_i, etc., or otherwise make them more complex.

Now, suppose that this structure has become so highly differentiated that it includes the motions of the hand and of the neck needed to sign one's name in normal fashion and with pen held between the teeth. Imagine some detail of finger motion, defined on some tiny set of a refinement of an early covering, and imagine some detail of neck motion, defined on another tiny set, which "does the same thing" in relation to the pattern of the signature. What do these two motions have in common? They differ in physiology and kinematics. It is that they accomplish the same purpose, and one way to interpret this in terms of the model is to say that the two tiny sets are both included in some larger set of an earlier covering that corresponds to some easily definable "purpose," e.g., "reaching leftwards." It is assumed that the system has become satisfactorily adaptive at crude levels of definition of the actions, so that it is meaningful to talk of these "purposes," and the procedures of relating the finer subdivisions to the cruder ones can (in a way we want to understand) gradually extend these purposes to the finer acts. Then we must, at least, have a way of mapping sets of functions defined on the finer coverings into sets of functions defined on the coarser coverings.

This projection of sets of the refinement onto sets of the coarser coverings may not be uniquely defined, because a small set may belong to many overlapping large sets. However, in certain cases the resulting mappings of certain structures associated with these sets, such as spaces of continuous functions and spaces of all local isomorphisms (technically, certain co-homology groups of the nerve of the covering) map back uniquely, no matter how the projection is performed (see the references).

There were two reasons for presenting this final discussion of a topic which obviously has not been worked out. First of all, this paper is a review paper which has tried to point to areas where problems exist that have generally not been considered. Therefore, it may be useful to point to the fringe of possibilities surrounding what is actually known, so as to see the type of knowledge at which one might aim. Second, this last example is an object lesson in the thesis of this paper that even if all the mechanisms work by adjusting connections and probabilities, the meaningful laws may not exist at this level. In the example of mapping complex actions onto simpler ones, the actual mappings may be different each time it is done, and the choice of mapping may be completely haphazard and lawless. Therefore, the person who tried to measure what was going on inside the system would have entirely different data each time he measured it. It is only certain structural features, such as the space of local isomorphisms, which are lawfully mapped, and these are characterized in mathematical terms which are entirely different from those of the paths and probabilities.

CONCLUSION

This paper has described elements of sensorimotor structure at the behavioral level of actions, as distinguished from mechanical, electronic, or physiological processes, or individual movements which must be organized into these actions. It deals with questions which arose in designing a computer model of sensorimotor development. Others have looked at these questions from many different points of view, but in all these approaches, the mathematically describable elements are far removed from the struc-tural organization at the behavioral level. Such studies either tell about subbehavioral events (e.g., path weightings, or synaptic changes), in which case one can only assert his faith that the behavioral items are somehow recoverable, given enough of the subbehavioral events; or else (as in learning theory) they tell how often or how strongly behavioral items occur, but not what they are. Is there anything equally precise which can be said about the behavioral structures themselves, the acts as a whole?

The need for such a formulation is generally being overlooked in the torrent of papers appearing on the subjects of self-organization and artificial intelligence. If one is describing the elements of composition, perspective, and style in a painting, descriptions of juxtapositions of individual dots of paint become meaningful only insofar as they can be stated in terms of concepts at the compositional level. Similarly, in understanding skillful human or machine behavior, the rules for connection strengths and the like between individual elements have meaning only in relation to the behavioral structures which are to be achieved. All current research efforts on logical networks, synaptic strengths, parameter optimization, and so on, are, like any form of circuit theory, indispensable tools when you want to build something — but first you must know what you want to build. This paper, in short, presupposes the continued success of these efforts and attempts to review some of the issues which must be examined in learning what to build.

REFERENCES

1. Auslander, L., and R. E. MacKenzie, *Introduction to Differentiable Manifolds,* McGraw-Hill, New York, 1963.
2. Deheuvels, R., "Espaces fibrés," In *Seminaire d'analyse Pierre Lelong, Année 1957/58,* Faculté des Sciences de Paris, mimeographed, 1959.
3. Fadell, E., "On Fiber Spaces," *Trans. Amer. Math. Soc.,* vol. 90, pp. 1-14, 1959.
4. Greene, P. H., "An Approach to Computers that Perceive, Learn, and Reason," *Proc. Western Joint Computer Conf.,* 1959, pp. 181-186.
5. ———, "On the Representation of Information by Neural Net Models," in M. C. Yovits, G. T. Jacobi, and G. D. Goldstein (eds.), *Self-Organizing Systems 1962,* Spartan, Baltimore, 1963.
6. ———, "On Looking for Neural Networks and 'Cell-Assemblies' That Underlie Behavior; I, A Mathematical Model," *Bull. Math. Biophys.,* vol. 24, 1962, pp. 247-275.
7. ———, "On Looking for Neural Networks and 'Cell-Assemblies' That Underlie Behavior, II, Neural Realization of the Mathematical Model," *Bull. Math. Biophys.* vol. 24, 1962, pp. 395-411.
8. ———, and T. Ruggles, "CHILD and SPOCK (Computer Having Intelligent Learning and Development; Simulated Procedure for Obtaining Common Knowledge)," *IEEE Trans. on Military Electronics,* vol. MIL-7, 1963, pp. 156-159.
9. Grothendieck, A., *A General Theory of Fibre Spaces With Structure Sheaf,* 2d ed., University of Kansas, Lawrence, Kan., 1958.
10. Guillaume, P., *La Formation des Habitudes,* Alcan, Paris, 1936.
11. Halverson, H. M., "An Experimental Study of Prehension in Infants by Means of Systematic Cinema Records," *Genetic Psychol. Monogr.,* vol. 10, 1931, pp. 107-286.
12. ———, "A Further Study of Grasping," *J. General Psychol.,* vol. 7, 1932, pp. 34-64.
13. Hilton, P. J., and S. Wylie, *Homology Theory,* Cambridge U. P., Cambridge, 1960.
14. Hocking, J. G., and G. S. Young, *Topology,* Addison-Wesley, Reading, Mass., 1961.
15. Holmann, H., *Vorlesung über Faserbündei. (Ausarbeitungen mathematischer und physikalischer Vorlesungen, Band XXVI).* Münster, Westf., Aschendorffsche Verlagsbuchhandlung, 1962.
16. Hu, S. T., *Homotopy Theory,* Academic, New York, 1959.
17. Hurewicz, W., "*On the Concept of Fiber Space,*" *Proc. Nat. Acad. Sci. U.S.A.,* vo. 41, 1955, pp. 961-964.
18. MacKay, D. M., "Theoretical Models of Space Perception," in *Aspects of the Theory of Artificial Intelligence,* Plenum, New York, 1962, pp. 83-103.

19. ———, "Psychophysics of Perceived Intensity: a Theoretical Basis for Fechner's and Stevens' Laws," *Science*, vol. 139, 1963, pp. 1213–1216.
20. Nicod, J., *Geometry in the Sensible World*, in *Foundations of Geometry and Induction*, translated by P. P. Wiener, Humanities Press, New York, 1950.
21. Paillard, J., *Réflexes et Regulations d'Origine proprioceptive chez l'Homme*, Paris, Arnette, 1955.
22. ———, "The Patterning of Skilled Movements," in *Handbook of Physiology*, Sect. I, Vol. III, American Physiological Society, Washington, D.C., Williams and Wilkins, Baltimore, pp. 1679–1708, 1960.
23. Piaget, J., *The Origins of Intelligence in Children*, translated by M. Cook, International Universities Press, New York, 1952.
24. ———, *The Construction of Reality in the Child*, translated by M. Cook, Basic, New York, 1954.
25. Steenrod, N., *The Topology of Fibre Bundles*, Princeton U. P., Princeton, N.J., 1951.
26. Uhr, L., and C. Vossler, "A Pattern Recognition Program that Generates, Evaluates, and Adjusts Its Own Operators," *Proc. Western Joint Computer Conference, 1961*, pp. 555–569

19

THOUSAND-GATE-COMPUTER SIMULATION OF A BILLION-GATE COMPUTER*

ROBERT S. LEDLEY

National Biomedical Research Foundation
Silver Spring, Md.

THE PROBLEM

FEASIBILITY OF A MANY-BILLIONS-OF-GATES COMPUTER

It may soon actually be possible to construct an electron circuit having many billions of gates. Assuming that this feat is technically possible, the problem still remains of exactly what can be accomplished with such an array of gates. A computer with a billion gates would be difficult to "design" in the conventional sense, because, among other reasons, no draftsman could draw a billion lines. Clearly, then, such a computer must be "self-organized." Further, if a component breaks, it will not be possible to replace it, and hence the computer must be self-correcting and self-adaptive.

Can such a system actually be realized? Can it do "more" than present day computers? The answer to both of these questions is "Yes, of course." We need not prove an existence theorem with mathematical rigor or formalism; we need merely display such a computer: namely the brain. Clearly the brain has billions of "gates." It is self-organizing. "Gates" break, but the brain continues to operate; so it is called self-correcting and self-adaptive. However, we do not know how the brain is designed, because, in spite of the exceedingly vast knowledge we have about the brain, certain basic facts remain unknown—such as the detailed connections between cells, the site of the memory, and so forth.

*This work supported by Contract No. Nonr 3265(00).

THE PROBLEM POSED

Armed with at least knowledge of the existence of an example of a billion-gate computer, but without any idea of the "design" of our example, the problem arises: can we design or "organize" a billion-gate computer? We pose this problem for ourselves in a realistic sense; we will not try to utilize the brain as an example because we know so little about it. The solution must be feasible—if the fabrication of a billion gates is realized as a technically feasible operation, then our design and organization of the computer must be realizable, and possible to carry out in an economically feasible manner. In addition, the solution must produce a computer that utilizes the billion gates to do more than present-day computers can accomplish—indeed, to accomplish tasks that could not be done without the availability of these billion gates.

FOUR TYPES OF COMPUTERS

In this paper we will discuss basic concepts for the organization and design of a billion-gate computer that we believe satisfy the criteria set forth above. In building our concepts we will use four types of particular computer designs as concrete examples. The first is a multiple-parallel-access computer store, which is conceived of as a computer in itself. The second example is that of a large-systems processor and simulator. The third example is for that of a many-unit simultaneous processor and the final example utilizes the other three as subcomponents, and attempts to portray an "intelligent" machine, in the sense of its being capable of deduction and induction as well as concept formulation, concept learning, and concept recognition. By this time it probably has become clear to the reader that in the present brief paper we will not really accomplish our stated objectives; we do hope, however, that we can indicate a feasible technique for organizing a billion-gate computer which can accomplish far more than present-day computers by taking advantage of the unique capabilities offered by the availability of many billions of gates.

AN ASSOCIATIVE MEMORY WITH THOUSANDS OF SIMULTANEOUS ACCESSES

CONCEPT OF A DIPSOME

A multiple simultaneous-access memory is well suited as a context in which to introduce many of the concepts to be employed in the structuring of billion-gate computers. Let us begin by using a department store as an analogy to a multiple simultaneous-access memory. In a department store, thousands of people can all simultaneously locate merchandise they desire according to some complicated criteria, and bring the merchandise out of the store. In our analogy, the merchandise is the information stored, and the act of locating and retrieving the merchandise is the act of accessing the memory. The people who can use the store have an analogy in the so-called "Dipsomes" of our multiple-access computer. Thus a dipsome is an organization of computer processing potential that can move about in the billion gates, sensing and reacting to the immediate environment, that can record and dispose of information, and that can be programmed (in the conventional sense) with rules to regulate both the motion and the information handling. (The word dipsome is derived from "Dynamic Intra-Propogating Self-Organizing Modular Entity.")

ORGANIZATION OF COMPUTER NETWORK

The billion-gate computer is organized in a fixed, repetitive, two-dimensional pattern of gates, where each entity in the pattern is actually a complete conventional computer. Each such computer has, in addition, a special "state memory" that can be accessed by the adjacent computers' memories. Suppose there are 1,000,000 gates in a conventional computer and 10^{12} gates in the billion-gate computer*; then we can expect to have 10^6 conventional computer entities. This is a conservative estimate, since for some applications we can have as few as 10,000 gates in a computer entity, resulting in a total of 10^8 such computer entities in the system.

The relation between a dipsome and a computer entity is as follows: The dipsome is the computer program and associated data which may reside in a computer entity, where the computer program embodies the characteristics of that particular dipsome. The dipsome "moves" when the memory contents of the computer entity in which it resides is transferred to an adjacent computer entity. Of course the dipsome has control over its own movements. In addition, a dipsome can sense the state of an adjacent computer entity, and under ordinary circumstances should not move into it unless that entity is empty or not occupied by another dipsome. The state memories are utilized in this process, and as a dipsome enters a new computer entity it must load the state memory with an appropriate code to inform other dipsomes of its residence in that entity. (See Fig. 1.)

ORGANIZATION OF A SIMPLE MULTIPLE-SIMULTANEOUS ACCESS MEMORY

Let us illustrate some of the points made above by means of a description of how the dipsomes could be utilized in a multiple simultaneous-access

* If there is one gate in each 10^{-10} cm² (i.e., gates composed of 10^{-6} cm diameter wires in an area of 10^{-5} cm on a side) and if the billion-gate computer has an overall area of 100 cm² (10 cm on a side), then there will be $100/10^{-10}$ or 10^{12} gates available.

memory. Possibly the simplest such computer memory that can be organized must include the following four kinds of places (Fig. 2). First there must be the places for the storage of the information to be retrieved. Second there must be places for discharging and loading information to and from the outside world. Third, for flexibility in storage method, there must be some type of registry or index to the locations at which the information is stored. And finally there must be pathways through which the dipsomes can move to and from the storage locations.

As an example, let us trace the course a dipsome might take in solving an information retrieval problem (arrows in Fig. 2). Let us say that our dipsome is initially in the seventh input-output bin from the left. Criteria of as complicated a nature as desired concerning the information to be retrieved is given to the dipsome in the form of a conventional computer program. The dipsome would first move to the registry or index where it would attempt to determine if possible the approximate location of the desired information (double line in Fig. 2). Suppose the information was located somewhere in the second aisle from the bottom in Fig. 2. Then the dipsome would attempt to move to that aisle (arrows). We have indicated a possible path, where a slight detour had to be made to go around another dipsome. Each box in this aisle is searched according to the criteria until the information is found (double lines). Having found the proper information, the dipsome moves back to the original bin, again having to go around

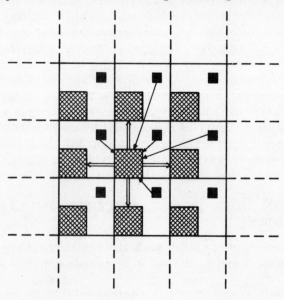

Figure 1

another dipsome. Note that we have provided two lanes in the paths to handle the traffic. Clearly this is a minimum, and the dipsome traffic control problem in such an organization can be approached through standard operations-research methods.

TYPES OF DIPSOMES

We have not discussed the important topic of how the information got into the computer to begin with. For this process we again utilize the dipsome concept, except that this time instead of *retrieval dipsomes* we will use *placement dipsomes*. The only difference is in the computer program that characterizes the properties of any particular dipsome. A placement dipsome would receive information from the outside world in an in-out bin. To determine in some systematic manner where to put the information, the dipsome would consult the registry.

Many other types of dipsomes would also be required. For instance, a *registry* or *index dipsome* is required, the duties of which are to keep track

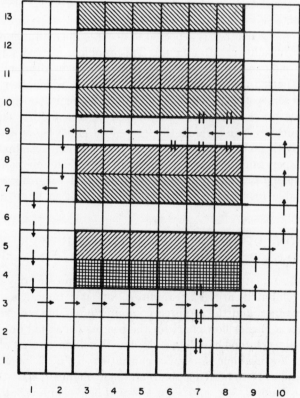

Figure 2

of the approximate location of the information, just like the "information desk" of a department store. These registry dipsomes would also be required to assist in determining the proper location for new or additional information. The actual "information sites" themselves are dipsomes. At their sites they can assist in the information search as well as hold data, just as a sales clerk assists a buyer. In addition, provision must be made for the efficient storage of information, for overloads, and other special circumstances. Here a "managerial" type of dipsome is required, that roves generally throughout the memory looking for such special circumstances.

From the above discussion it becomes clear that all dipsomes must have two basic kinds of subroutines, which can generally be described as *intrinsic* and *extrinsic* programs. The intrinsic programs are common to all dipsomes and are concerned solely with its movement and other basic capabilities, such as communication with other dipsomes, sensing the state of adjacent boxes, and so forth. The extrinsic programs are concerned with the specific mission of the dipsome itself. These programs depend on the type of dipsome, on the data being handled, and on the particular circumstances of the moment.

One of the problems that is expected to occur is the malfunction of some gates, either initially or after aging. This problem can be solved if we postulate a *maintenance* dipsome type. This type of dipsome makes a duplicate of itself in an adjacent computer entity, which then tests the entity with a series of test programs. If nothing wrong is found, it can erase itself from its previous entity, and proceed to test another entity. If a serious malfunction is discovered, the state of the entity is marked "closed" and that entity is no longer used. Of course, the maintenance dipsome must report to a supervisor dipsome that keeps track of the number and location of malfunctioning or closed computer entities, and when necessary may order a suitable rearrangement of the system to keep it operating successfully.

SIMULATION OF A BILLION-GATE COMPUTER WITH A THOUSAND-GATE COMPUTER

In order to simulate a billion-gate computer on a present-day computer, each of its computer entities is examined, one at a time in a systematic sequential manner, and the required computer programs are executed. In Fig. 3 we give a master flow chart for the process. In actual practice three tapes are used, each tape handling every fourth column so that all columns are handled. For example, for our organization in Fig. 2, numbering the columns from left to right, Tape A would hold columns 1, 4, 7, 10, Tape B would hold columns 2, 5, 8, and Tape C would hold columns 3, 6, and 9. In this way both computer entities on either side of the entity under consideration can be obtained for their state data without searching the tapes. By winding and unwinding the tapes appropriately, and by having the entities of each column in the proper order on the tapes, the process can easily be carried out. Figure 4 summarizes the tape motion and the order of the entities for each column on the three tapes. Note that Tape A is initially positioned so that it starts by turning backwards. Tape B starts at the same time turning forwards. Tape C comes into play only after the entities in the first column are covered. In a normal cycle the tapes go forward, backward, and forward three times over the same column. In the first cycle, column, on Tape A is gone over only twice, first backwards and then forwards, and in the last cycle column 10 on Tape A is gone over only twice, first forwards and then backwards. Note that the tape with the entity under consideration will be "looking ahead" for the state data of the next entity. When all the entities have been examined, and the dipsome programs executed, the process is restarted from the beginning, and so forth. The only other general remark that need be made is that by "loading a dipsome" (Fig. 2), we mean transferring the dipsome programs into another entity area on the tapes.

1. Read next computer entity and state data, that is advance all the tapes by one record.
2. If dipsome is in entity, perform dipsome programs, otherwise go to 1.
3. Locate entity into which dipsome will go next.
4. Load dipsome into this entity.
5. Load new state data.
6. If last computer entity then start over, otherwise go to 1.

Figure 3. Master Program for Billion Gate Simulation

TAPE A*	TAPE B	TAPE C
1, 13→ 1	2, 1→ 13	
4, 1 → 13	5, 13→ 1	3, 13→ 1
7, 13→ 1	8, 1 → 13	6, 1 → 13
10, 1 →13		9, 13 → 1

* STARTS TURNING BACKWARDS

Figure 4

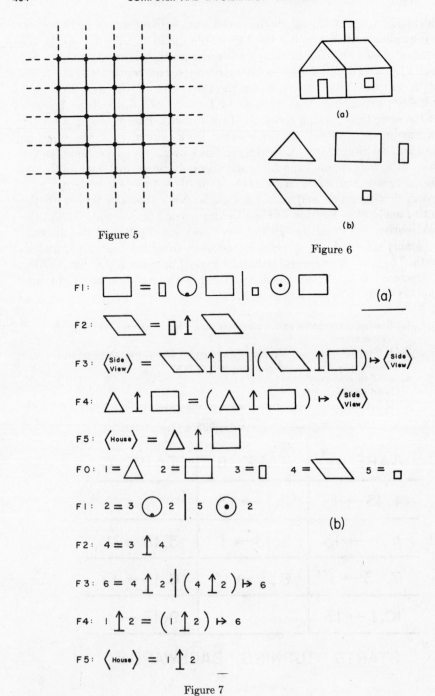

Figure 5

Figure 6

Figure 7

SUMMARY

The main points that we intend to portray in the above discussion are as follows: A dipsome is a programmable entity that can be moved from computer entity to computer entity within the billion-gate computer organization. Being programmable, the dipsome will embody the ideas of the programmer; the billion-gate computer, by having a multitude of such dipsomes, is capable of concentrating the efforts of many different talents into a single system.

A LARGE SYSTEMS PROCESSOR AND SIMULATOR

CONCEPTS

Because each dipsome is an entire computer program, the behavior of a dipsome can be made quite complex. Thus the dipsome can in effect be programmed to behave like a clerk with somewhat well defined duties. With this idea in mind, its easy to see how a billion-gate computer can be organized to perform many types of control processes and simulations involving systems that in the real world would utilize many such clerks. Examples are control systems where data from many sources is processed, sorted, and analyzed at various levels and stages, and subsequent control decisions made and implemented. Inventory systems are well suited to this process, where new stock depletion is recorded in almost the exact manner that a large room full of clerks would carry out, except that actual items would of course be represented by their names in the computer. Such a system would be of great use only for very extensive and complicated inventory problems, where the computer would be able to prepare all types of summary reports, and utilize many kinds of reordering and stock control techniques. Logistics systems could also be handled, planned or simulated by these means. All types of special cases could be taken care of by specially programmed dipsomes that could rove throughout the computer on their special missions.

Communication within the computer can be accelerated by utilizing specialized "telephone lines" over long internal distances. Standard switch-board techniques could be used, and at either end of the line one dipsome could call another to the "phone." In the billion-gate computer the phone could have the additional advantage that, since a dipsome is in reality only coded information, the dipsome could actually travel itself through the phone line and come out the other end, if it so desired. Thus the telephone lines would serve as high-speed pathways. To be more flexible, there could be a telephone crew type of dipsome that would be programmed to lay telephone lines and install telephone communications to any desired location in the billion gate computer. Special networks could be designed into the billion-gate entity pattern to facilitate this type of operation.

HIGHER-LEVEL ORGANIZATION

One of the most important advantages of the billion-gate computer organized in terms of dipsomes is that of the capability of higher-level organization. The programs of dipsomes could be controlled, changed and new programs inserted by other special high-level dipsomes. For example, a self-optimizing system can be made by having some of the dipsomes collect data on the operation of the system; this data would be analyzed by the higher-level dipsomes and optimization procedures installed if required. The techniques used by these higher-level dipsomes will be the optimizing methods that abound in the field of operations research. In a more complex system, the higher-level dipsomes can even determine exactly what data should be collected for any modification of the system they are considering at the moment. For instance, competing optimization methods may be tried in different parts of the system, and the best one adopted. In fact, a whole society of dipsomes will result from their complex interaction with each other. As soon as dipsomes are programmed to produce by themselves other dipsomes, certain rules and regulations must be established to avoid chaos and assume a smoothly working operation.

A MULTIPLE-UNIT SIMULTANEOUS PROCESSOR

APPLICATIONS

Let us now change our concept of the billion-gate computer in the following two senses. First, let each computer entity be a very greatly simplified computer, with a very limited memory and only a few basic logical and arithmetic instructions. This change means that there will now be many more such computers for a given number of total gates in the billion-gate computer. Second, let us dispense with the concept of the moving dipsome, and let every computer entity be itself a dipsome of the same type as all the others. Of course, we are not throwing away our original concept of a dipsome, for in a later section of this paper we consider both kinds of dipsomes in the same billion-gate computer. But for our present purposes, let us limit ourselves initially to consideration of this simpler type of dipsome.

Each of these simplified dipsomes can communicate with the adjacent dipsomes by simple memory exchanges. They can operate independently of each other in an asynchronous manner. Figure 5 shows such a network of simplified dipsomes. In most applications each dipsome has the same programs but may have different initial conditions. For same applications each dipsome knows its coordinate location in the network. It may sometimes be desirable to have communication between a dipsome and other dipsomes further away than its immediate neighbors. However, this may be accomplished without actual predesigned connections by communication from one dipsome through its immediate neighbors.

As an example of the application of such a simplified dipsome network, consider the solution of a partial differential equation by a relaxation method. The boundary dipsomes would initially be given the boundary values. For the Laplace equation, for instance, each dipsome would then try to compute a value of the function at its network, or lattice point as the average of the values at the neighboring points. All dipsomes would do this over and over again, asynchronously with each other. The surface of solution would be formed rapidly, somewhat like the formation of a three-dimensional plastic map by a vacuum technique pulling the surface into shape. Of course, there are many mathematical circumstances that may occur which have been neglected in this brief discussion. For instance, it is possible that wave oscillations may result and prevent a solution from being obtained, and so forth. These considerations must be taken into account in the dipsome programs.

Another example is that of two-dimensional pattern recognition and interpretation. Here let the each dipsome be given the grey level of the picture at its network or lattice point as the initial conditions. It is instructive to dwell at length on this application, as it introduces several important concepts associated with the effective utilization of a billion-gate computer.

PATTERN RECOGNITION AS A TWO-STAGE PROBLEM

A preliminary discussion is necessary before describing a process of pattern recognition by a billion-gate computer. We will approach pattern recognition as a two-stage problem. The first stage is the recognition of the parts of the pattern and the spacial relationships between the parts.

The second stage is the actual pattern-identification step itself, which is accomplished by a definitional reduction of the parts and their relationships to the finally desired recognition statements.

To be more concrete let us consider the picture of a house as in Fig. 6. The house is composed of five types of component parts: a triangle, a large square, a small rectangle, a small square, and a parallelogram. We can symbolize the picture by using the special relationships: $\uparrow$ on top of; $\mid\rightarrow$ on the side of; $\odot$ inside in the middle of; and $\odot$ inside on the bottom of. Then our picture can be symbolized as

$$\{ \triangle \uparrow (\square \odot \square)\} \vdash \{(\square \uparrow \diagdown) \uparrow (\square \odot \square)\}$$

Let us further suppose that for our purposes a house was defined simply as $\triangle \uparrow \square$. Utilizing the "reduction formulas" of Fig. 7 we can operate on our original picture of a house and actually show it to be equivalent to $\triangle \uparrow \square$. The work is as follows: where in terms of numbers (See Fig. 7) our original formula becomes

$$\{1 \uparrow (3 \odot 2)\} \mapsto \{(3 \uparrow 4) \uparrow (5 \odot 2)\}$$

Applying F 1	$\{1 \uparrow 2\} \mapsto \{(3 \uparrow 4) \uparrow 2\}$
Applying F 2	$\{1 \uparrow 2\} \mapsto \{4 \uparrow 2\}$
Applying F 3	$\{1 \uparrow 2\} \mapsto 6$
Applying F 4	$1 \uparrow 2$
Applying F 5	$\langle House \rangle$

The method is quite general, and for instance, several classes of houses can be recognized, as shown in Fig. 8. Of course more complex cases require many more reduction formulas (See, for example, R. S. Ledley, *Programming and Utilizing Digital Computers*, McGraw-Hill, New York, 1962, p. 320–321.)

From the above example we see that the second-stage recognition process is a relatively straightforward application of, in general, a sequence of recursive reduction formulas. However, this second stage assumes that the parts and their relationships have already been determined through the first stage of the process. Let us now proceed to discuss this first stage.

Many ways have been described in the literature for analyzing a picture by a computer for basic parts or two-dimensional pictographic structures. One may trace the outlines of the object, and keep track of curves, corners, and so forth; one may investigate areas for basic shapes, such as circles, ovals, rectangles, etc.; one may examine centers of gravity, radii of gyration, or higher-movement functions of the area; one may measure branching, follow connectivity, map boundaries; one may take intersections, unions, etc., of sets of points and determine dichotomous distance functions, and so forth. Any of all of these methods may be applied to the picture in order to determine the parts and their relationships in the first stage. All of these methods have one concept in common, however: they depend on multiple iteration of *local* operations—and this is the main point that we wish to emphasize. Hence each lattice-point dipsome can determine if it is a part of a boundary, area, line, rectangle, triangle, etc.—that is, can determine if it resides in or helps make up a basic part. In addition, since dipsomes can communicate with other dipsomes in different parts, the relationship between the parts can also be determined. Hence the formula for the picture can be compared.

USE OF BILLION-GATE COMPUTER

A conventional computer can be utilized successfully for the first stage of the recognition process. But because of the nature of conventional computers, a serial mode of approach must be taken for a problem that is basically parallel in nature. However, the parallel operations can rapidly be performed by the dipsome network, leading to an extraordinarily rapid parts and relationship analysis. It is to be noted that all the dipsomes in any one part will become aware of the fact that they are in that type of part; in addition, any two dipsomes in different parts of the same type will also sense this. Thus the dipsomes in the same part can act collectively as a single unit of information, using one of their member dipsomes to represent

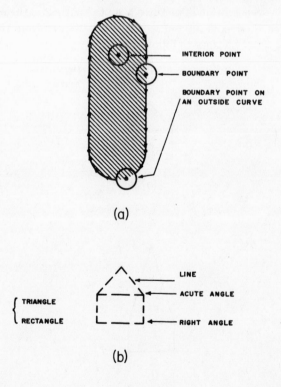

Figure 9

the collection. Then, the different collective units can note the relationship between their collective parts. Hence a hierarchy of parts and relationships will result in the construction of the final formula. Note that each dipsome must be aware of (i.e., have programmed in its memory) all possible parts and relationships.

For instance, consider Fig. 9a in which we show an oblong figure. Any black dipsome surrounded by black dipsomes immediately knows that it is an interior point. Any black dipsome with a white neighbor knows it is a boundary dipsome. The boundary dipsomes will draw arrows between each other, and if the arrows into and from a dipsome have about the same slope, then the dipsome knows it is on a straight line. If the differences in the slopes of successive arrows are about the same, then the dipsome knows it is on a curve; and so forth. In this way the dipsomes determine which "parts" they are in and also the relationships between the parts. In Fig. 9b we show the parts that the dipsomes can utilize to determine if they are in triangles or rectangles. Of course in this short discussion we have left much unsaid, but we hope that the reader can glean at least the idea we intend to portray. The recognition of pictures from the parts and their relationship is analogous to the recognition of words and sentences from the juxtaposition of characters or letters as follows:

$$\text{parts} \leftrightarrow \text{structures} \leftrightarrow \text{pictures}$$
$$\text{characters} \leftrightarrow \text{sentences} \leftrightarrow \text{paragraphs}$$

(a)

(b)

Figure 10

AN INTELLIGENT MACHINE WITH COMPETENCE IN CONCEPT FORMULATION AND RECOGNITION

INGREDIENTS OF INTELLIGENCE

For our purposes we will consider intelligence as concept formulation, concept learning, and concept recognition. By "concept" we mean a generic term which names or denotes a particular class of objects or situations, where the objects in the class satisfy certain criteria, which in general are recursive in nature. We hasten to point out that our use of the term "concept" is not the meaning of the term as used in relation to the powers of the brain, but we do feel that our use of the term may in some respects mimic what the brain does in the area of concepts. For if asked to tell what he means by a certain concept, a person can often verbalize in terms of particular criteria what he believes to be the concept; he may have to revise this criteria when challanged with examples that may not meet his original criteria. For example, he may define "living" as "something that reproduces itself," but when challenged with a crystal which can reproduce itself, he will add further more distinctive criteria. Hence the rules he states as characterizing the concept clearly are not necessarily the concept since he is able to revise the rules in many cases; however, we will consider these rules as good enough approximations to the concept, and will utilize them for our purposes *as if* they did indeed embody the concept.

We consider concept formulation, concept learning, and concept recognition as three separate aspects of concept analysis. It is best to start with with concept recognition; by this we mean the ability to identify the generic or class name for a particular realization of the concept in question. Hence the process of identifying the pictures of Fig. 8a as "houses" according to the rules of Fig. 7 is an example of a concept-recognition process. By concept learning we mean the process of being taught an already formulated concept by being exposed to many realizations of the concept with reinforcement and punishment, modes. During this process of exposure, reinforcement, and punishment, the computer learning the concept is attempting to formulate a collection of rules, such as given in Fig. 7, that enable the recognition process to be passed most frequently. By concept formulation we mean the original formulation of a useful generic class through experience with the environment. We consider this the most difficult to accomplish primarily due to the use of the word "useful." However, for our purposes it is not appropriate to dwell on this point at length.

We shall first discuss mechanisms for each of these aspects of concept analysis, and then indicate how the billion-gate computer organizations discussed above can be applied. Our discussions will be incomplete, but we hope to inpart at least the general ideas involved.

CONCEPT RECOGNITION

In the previous section we briefly noted how a formula of parts relationships could be identified as a "house" by means of a collection of reduction rules. In this section we wish to assert that this process may be equated to that of recognizing a concept. For instance, if one asked a four year old boy to draw a house, he may draw the diagram of Fig. 10a; this then presumably is his concept of a house. When asked to identify a real building as a house our assertion claims that the little boy does so successfully by utilizing reduction rules to reduce the more complex structure with windows, doors, chimneys, etc. to his simple concept of a house. Such reduction rules can be

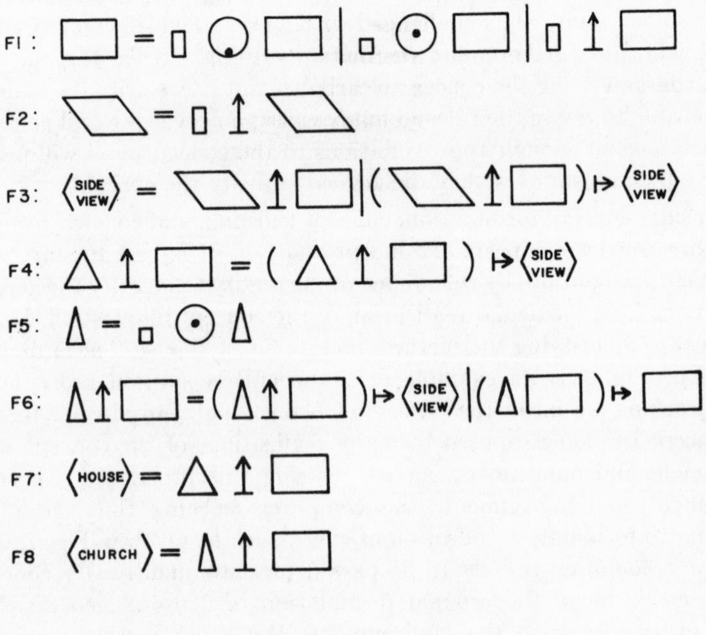

Figure 11

utilized to distinguish a house from a church, where the concept of a church is given in Fig. 10*b*, and the combined house-church is given in Fig. 11.

Let us examine the more closely the actual process of utilizing the reduction rules. Figure 12 presents a rough flow diagram of one systematic procedure that might be used. The formula for the real structure to be identified (called the realization formula) is examined symbol by symbol with respect to the reduction rules from, say, left to right. Consider for example the leftmost symbol of the realization formula: we look down the right-hand side of the reduction rules to see if it occurs, and if so we see if that reduction rule can be applied to simplifying the formula. If it can be applied; we apply it, otherwise we continue to look for another applicable reduction rule. When we have exhausted this process for the leftmost symbol of the formula, we go on to the next symbol, and so forth. If the structure is a house or church of the type that can be recognized by our simple reduction rules, we will have deduced its identification by this process. Further details of the process are given in the references, but the point we wish to make is that the process can be thought of as a deductive method for concept recognition.

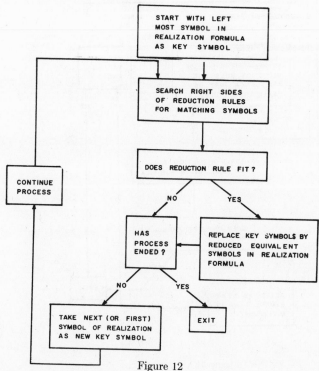

Figure 12

On the other hand, an entirely different systematic technique can be used, which in a sense embodies *induction*. Figure 13 gives the flow chart for this procedure (see also reference below). Here the idea is first to guess at the identification of the structure, then to try to confirm this guess by attempting to reduce the realization formula to the concept formula through the reduction rules. This method has often been called "heuristic" programming. In any case, the same reduction rules are utilized.

As an example of induction, consider the rules of Fig. 11 applied to the following realization formula by means of the flow chart of Fig. 13:

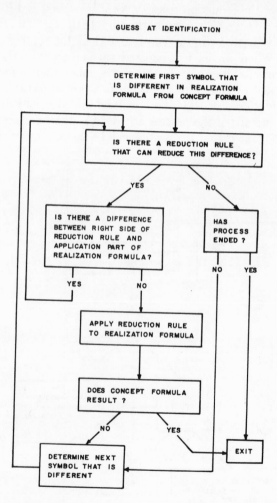

Figure 13

This is the picture of Fig. 14. We will guess that this is a church (see concept formula Fig. 8); the work is shown in Fig. 15.

CONCEPT LEARNING

There are two levels for concept learning as conceived for our purposes. First there is the learning for recognize the parts and their relationships. Second, there is the learning of the reduction rules associated with a concept that embodies particular criteria for identification of a realization of the concept. For the first level of learning many systems have been proposed in the literature, most often under the titles of "pattern recognition," learning, or adaptation. The training, reinforcement, and testing processes utilized in, for instance, a perceptron approach, or a Bayesian approach, are relatively well known, and we will not go into them here except to point out that they can be admirably carried out utilizing a billion-gate computer.

The more interesting problem from our point of view is the learning of the concept formula and reduction rules. Again a process of training and testing must be utilized. However, here the idea of using probabilities or reinforcement weights does not apply. Given a collection realizations of a concept—that is, given a collection of realization formulas—two stages of analysis are required. First, an attempt must be made to learn the concept formula itself by identifying common elements throughout the realization formulas. For instance, in our concept of a church, all realization formulas for churches must include a steeple ($\triangle$) on top of a wall ($\square$). The fact that steeples on top of walls always occurs will be noted by taking the intersection of all symbol sets of each of the formulas. However, this in itself is not sufficient, for the concept formula must also distinguish churches from structures that are not churches. Hence a set of realization formulas must

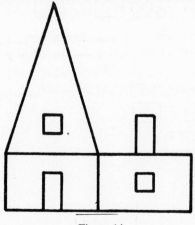

Figure 14

be given for structures that are not churches, and the set of, for instance, pairwise differences noted between churches and these structures. Not only must such operations be carried out for the basic symbols themselves, but also for combinations of symbols and relationships, starting from the simplest to the most complex. In this way the concept formula is learned.

The second stage of the analysis is to formulate the reduction rules themselves. This is accomplished by noting the differences between the concept formula and the realization formulas, and making an attempt to structure these differences with greatest efficiency. It must be realized however, that one or two concepts are not learned in isolation. In a realistic system, many concepts are involved, and in learning a new concept, already

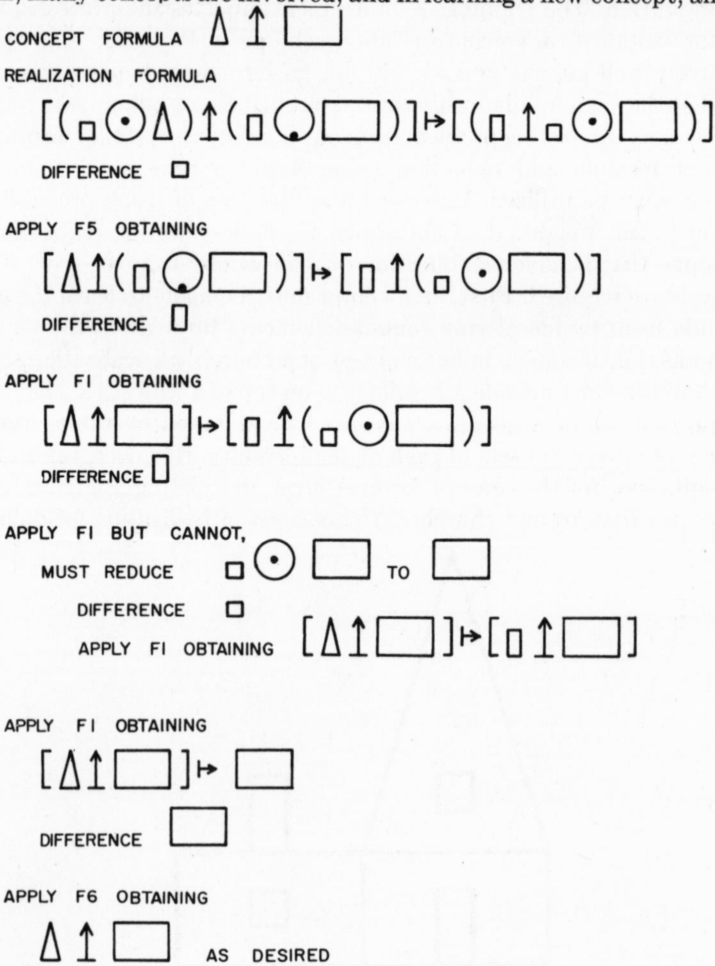

CONCEPT FORMULA   △ ↑ ☐

REALIZATION FORMULA

$$[(□ ⊙ △)↑(□ ◔ ☐)] ↦ [(□ ↑ □ ⊙ ☐)]$$

DIFFERENCE   ☐

APPLY F5 OBTAINING

$$[△↑(□ ◔ ☐)] ↦ [□ ↑ (□ ⊙ ☐)]$$

DIFFERENCE   ☐

APPLY FI OBTAINING

$$[△↑ ☐] ↦ [□ ↑ (□ ⊙ ☐)]$$

DIFFERENCE ☐

APPLY FI BUT CANNOT,

MUST REDUCE   □ ⊙ ☐ TO ☐

DIFFERENCE   ☐

APPLY FI OBTAINING $[△↑ ☐] ↦ [□ ↑ ☐]$

APPLY FI OBTAINING

$$[△↑ ☐] ↦ ☐$$

DIFFERENCE ☐

APPLY F6 OBTAINING

△ ↑ ☐   AS DESIRED

Figure 15

learned concepts are used continuously. For example, in the reduction rules for a church and house as given in Fig. 11, use is made of the concept of a wall (F1) and of a sideview (F3), and so forth. Thus in formulating the reduction rules for a new concept being learned, there must be a striving to utilize, as much as possible, old reduction formulas for already learned concepts.

CONCEPT FORMULATION

Concept formulation involves the interaction of system function and environment. The system, be it a control system, monitoring system, or storage system, etc., must have certain functions, which may be called more picturesquely, "motivations." In satisfying these motivations, or performing its functions, it must interact with the environment, sampling its features, controlling some of its parameters, noting and reacting to its changes. During these processes various structures in the environment can be classified according to the motivation or function with which it is involved. The formulation of a concept is the observation of common structural relationships within each of the classes and the making of trial-concept formulas. Once this is done the methods of concept learning are utilized to formulate the reduction rules leading to the trial concept formulation. However, whether or not a trial concept is retained as a true concept depends on its utility. Criteria for usage may simply be the frequency of use, or they may be more complex. Also note that there must be some heuristic guidelines for identifying functions and subfunctions, or motivations, upon which the original formulation of a trial concept is based. In addition, it is important to note that a concept is not formulated once and for all, but rather a concept is formulated, revised, and rerevised according to continuing experience with the changing environment and altered motivations. Hence a new concept may merely be an adaptation of previously known concepts. Concept formulation is a building up process, and attempting such formulation in isolated cases has little chance of resulting in successful demonstration of the ideas involved.

USE OF A BILLION-GATE COMPUTER

We have sketched above some of the ideas involved in concept recognition, learning, and formulation. Actual implimentation of these ideas can be greatly facilitated by use of a billion-gate computer, and in particular, by use of the three billion-gate computer organizations discussed in the previous sections. Concept recognition would make use of the parallel processor described above, because a major aspect of concept recognition is the initial interpretation of, for instance, a pictoral input in terms of its component parts and their relationships. Concept learning would, in addition, require the capabilities of the large-memory computer organization as well, because the learning of concepts utilizes a building-up process based on previously learned concepts, and the resulting plethora of reduction rules and concept formulas demand a large memory facility.

Finally, concept formulation will require the use of the large-systems simulation computer, in addition to the parallel processor and the large-memory computer. These latter two types of billion-gate organizations are needed for the handling of the concept recognition and learning capabilities required in association with concept formulation. In addition, the simulator is needed in order to produce a means of interaction of the billion-gate computer with its environment. Here the dipsome will gain experience in the simulated environment, and will be the vehicle for suggesting trial concepts for the concept-formulation process in the simulated environment.

SUMMARY AND CONCLUSIONS

The purpose of this paper has been to describe a simulation of a multi-billion-gate computer, where the simulation is intended to be run on a present day "thousand-gate computer." In the discussion of such a simulation we cannot hope to describe the many details of the computer program—this would be too lengthy and would imbed the reader in a plethora of minute points that could make him lose sight of the main ideas. Hence to cover the material with any perspective, we were forced to utilize a descriptive technique for this presentation.

Two main criteria were used for guiding the formation of the billion-gate computer model. These criteria are: (i) only the logical design skills presently required for the current technology are to be used; (ii) only the programming skills presently required for the current technology are to be used. These criteria reflect the fact that our purpose is to demonstrate the organization of a billion-gate computer which can be realized utilizing current capabilities in logical design and programming and which can be successfully accomplished at the present time.

Of course it would be useless to organize a billion-gate computer unless such a computer would have vastly increased capabilities not presently available in current machines. Hence, in addition to our above stated criteria, we have a goal—namely that the organization of the billion-gate computer provide these increased capabilities, and in particular, be capable of "intelligence" in the sense of being able to formulate, learn, and recognize a concept.

The purpose of this paper has been to describe the approach used and how the simulation was organized. The method of performing the simulation is secondary to the model itself and hence we have not emphasized this aspect of our work. However, in summary we might remark that the concept of the dipsome and the fact that a dipsome is essentially a complete present-day computer, lends itself naturally to our method of simulation. The method was to sequence through the dipsomes one at a time, where the "thousand-gate computer" represented one dipsome at a time. As observed above, special tape-handling methods were developed for this purpose so that efficient operation can result when a dipsome communicates with the adjacent dipsomes.

Since our intelligent computer is a complex system, in the description of the model we have used three steps in working up to the complete system. These steps are (i) the description of a large-scale memory system, (ii) the description of a multiple-unit simultaneous processor, and (iii) the description of a large-systems simulator. The intelligent computer utilizes all of these subsidiary organizations and integrates them into an over-all system which has the advanced capabilities of concept formulation, concept learning, and concept recognition.

Our formulation of the model, which borrows from methods in automatic-programming-language translation, is considered by us to be a new innovation in the theory of concept analysis in the sense, for example, of an alternative approach to the problems discussed by Banerji.[6]

An interesting corollary of our ideas which we have noted above is that techniques of heuristic programming and of automatic-programming-language translation[5] are closely related, and that the heuristic difference operators can be considered as being identical to the syntax definitions of the automatic-programming-languages.

However, this is not an expository paper on our theory of concept analysis; rather our prime concern here is the mechanics of concept analysis. It is these mechanics that the billion-gate computer is to perform; it is these mechanics with which the subsidiary computers are concerned. The recognition of a realization of a concept is the most fundamental operation; concept learning and concept formulation become relatively straightforward extensions of the methods of concept realization. Thus, the mechanics of concept realization were principally described.

These mechanics involved a two-stage approach: (i) the recognition of simple component parts of a pattern, such as points, lines, curves, angles, etc., and the relationship of one part with another; (ii) the identification of the pattern through an analysis of hierarchical syntactical definitions involving parts and their relationships. The mechanics of the parts and relationship recognition makes use of the multiple-unit simultaneous-processor subsidiary; the mechanics of the pattern identification through syntax analysis makes use of the large-memory-system subsidiary. These mechanics were discussed in some detail.

The mechanics of concept learning and concept formulation require, in addition, the systems simulator, so that the necessary environmental factor can be introduced into the over-all system. It is not currently feasible to have input and output transducers with capabilities that rival those found in nature; hence, we have pointed out how the environment can nevertheless be sampled and manipulated by means of the systems simulator in the manner required for the learning and formulation of concepts.

The integrated billion-gate system as formulated in this paper is different from the ideas of Holland and others. We have attempted to be concrete in describing precisely the organization we desired, we have explicitly described the subsidiary computers in terms of the computer entities, and we have attempted to sketch briefly the programming methods utilized for such a billion-gate computer. It is difficult to cover with any thoroughness any single aspect of our computer organization, for many and diverse problems had to be solved in order to form a complete and self-consistent model. The concept of the dipsome—namely, that of a computer program which can move itself from one component computer entity to another—helped unify these solutions. For example, the self-organizing problems were solved by means of this movement capability of the dipsomes, the self-adapting problems were met with the idea of higher-level dipsomes which can monitor and change other dipsomes (programs) as may be required, and the self-maintaining problems were met by the concept of maintenance dipsomes that roam through and test entity computers and close those with serious malfunctions.

Although in this paper we could not dwell at any length upon the great range of topics that had to be covered in the description of our model, we do hope that we have imparted to the reader, in some measure, our belief that the next major breakthrough in computer technology will come with the realization, in some form, of such a multibillion-gate computer.

REFERENCES

1. Shoulders, K., "On Micro-electronic Components, Interconnections, and System Fabrication," *WJCC*, May 1960.
2. Holland, J. H., "On Iterative Circuit Computers Constructed on Microelectronic Components and Systems," *WJCC*, May 1960.
3. Ledley, R. S., "Organization of Large Memory Systems," Chap. 2 in M. Yovits (ed.), *Large-Capacity Memory Techniques for Computing Systems*, Macmillan, New York, 1962.
4. ———, *Programming and Utilizing Digital Computers*, McGraw-Hill, New York, 1962.
5. ———, "Automatic-Programming-Language Translation Through Syntactical Analysis," *Communications ACM*, vol. 5, no. 3, March 1962.
6. Banerji, R. B., "The Description List of Concepts," *Communications ACM*, vol. 5, no. 8, August 1962.

20

NOOLOGY—THE SCIENCE OF INTELLIGENCE

Louis Fein

Consultant
Palo Alto, Calif.

INTRODUCTION

There are objections to the use of the popular term, "Artificial Intelligence," as the "scientific" name of a field of study. English-speaking persons are disposed to say that an inanimate processor is an artificial intelligence if it can do those tasks requiring (natural) intelligence when performed by animate processors—the presumption being that psychologists, if not the general populace, have defined (natural) intelligence, either operationally or by extension. But even psychologists—let alone the general populace—do not know quite to what concept the word "intelligence" refers. So-called intelligence tests measure a person's ability to perform such tasks as solving problems, perceiving analogies, and abstracting concepts. Stanford-Binet, for example, may be measuring an important attribute, but it is not clear that this attribute is validly called intelligence, i.e., that a high test score always indicates that the individual will behave intelligently in any one of the popularly accepted senses of the term. Thus, to utter the term (natural) intelligence, is not to know quite to what one is referring (talking about). It follows that to utter the term "artificial intelligence" is not to know quite what one is talking about, either.

There is a second objection to the use of "Artificial Intelligence" as the name of a field of study. The difficulty lies in the lack of parallelism. It can be illustrated by the fact that the science that deals with the intelligence of animate processors is not called "Natural Intelligence" (as opposed to Artificial Intelligence)—"psychology" is the name of that science.

Because science and society are especially interested in the performance of cognitive tasks whether by persons, machines, or in combination, a close

481

coordination is urgent between the studies of natural intelligence on the one hand, and artificial intelligence (*sic*) on the other. In meeting this requirement, it will be necessary to give to the concepts Psychology and Artifical Intelligence valid names and definitions that derive from a common doctrine. I will next propose such a doctrine; indeed, it will turn out to be the outline of a taxonomy of the newly identified and named noological sciences.

The taxonomy and nomenclature of the biological sciences provide a paradigm for developing the taxonomy and nomenclature of the noological sciences.

BIOLOGY

Biologists can't quite distinguish the living from the nonliving, even as psychologists have trouble discerning intelligence. Biologists don't quite know what they are talking about when they refer to the living which they define as a discrete mass of matter that is both metabolic and reproductive.* (Is a virus living or not?) Nevertheless, despite the fact that occasionally biologists can't make conclusive tests for life, science has usefully and conveniently dichotomized the structures of the universe assigning the biological sciences to deal with living things—*biota*, and the physical sciences to deal with nonliving things—*physica*. The biological sciences are divided according to three fundamental structural plans of living things— plants, animals, and bacteria (studied in botany, zoology, and bacteriology, respectively); each such plan is further subdivided into phyla, orders, classes, families, varieties, breeds, genus, species, etc. Organisms that resemble living things—i.e., that are metabolic or reproductive or have properties that living things ordinary possess—are called zooids. Where individual biota combine to live advantageously, the phenomenon is called symbiosis; each partner is called a symbiont. Each biological science has a common set of branches, such as (bio)morphology, (bio)ecology, and (bio)physiology dealing with forms, environments, and functions of living things, respectively. One kind of function—the cognitive function—is the subject matter of a specialty of (bio)physiology. In particular, the study of the adaptive-cognitive functions of human beings (psychology) is properly under (anthropo)physiology. (See Table 1.)

---

* "The necessary and sufficient condition for an object to be recognizable as a living organism, and so to be the subject of biological investigation is that it be a discrete mass of matter with a definite boundary, undergoing continual interchange of material with its surroundings without manifest alteration of properties over short periods of time and as ascertained either by direct observation or by anology with other objects of the same class originating by some process of division or fractionation from one or two preexisting objects of the same kind. The criterion of continuous interchange of material may be termed the metabolic criterion, that of origin from a preexisting object of the same class, the reproductive criterion." Taken from *Encyclopaedia Britannica*, article "Biology" by Charles Singer.

If we selected the name noology* (from the Greek *nous* = mind +
logos = discourse) for this specialty of physiology—i.e., the science of
intelligent (*sic*) functions, then the *biological* science psychology would be a
synonym of (anthropo)noology. By the same token, the intelligent (*sic*) or
cognitive functions of nonliving structures like computers would be the
subject matter of the *physical* science called computer noology. (See
Table 1.)

But this would be awkward and inconvenient for a society and science
that are currently interested in structures that are "intelligent"—living
or not. Fitting our knowledge about intelligent structures into a framework
that best accommodates a distinction between the living and the nonliving
is bound to be forced. Considering *psychology* as a *biological* science, and
artificial intelligence as a *physical* science is a poor way to accommodate and
exhibit our knowledge of intelligence. We must try to make a new dichotomy
of structures into intelligent and nonintelligent and then develop a tax-
nomy and nomenclature that will most conveniently accommodate our
knowledge of intelligence and will also facilitate its display, communication,
organization, learning, understanding, and recall or retrieval. Noology will
be selected, not as the name of a specialty of physiology, but as the name
of the science dealing with intelligent things. (Noo)physiology will be the
name given to the branch of noology dealing with the functions of intelligent
things. (The reader is asked to compare the parallelism between the following presentation under noology and the above presentation under biology.)

NOOLOGY

Even as biologists can't quite tell the living from the nonliving, psychologists can't quite discern the attributes of intelligence. Nevertheless,
just as science found it useful and convenient to dichotomize the structures
of the universe into living and nonliving, the current interests and purposes
of science and society guarantees that it will be useful and convenient to
dichotomize these structures into intelligent and nonintelligent by assigning
the noological sciences to deal with intelligent things—*noeta*, and the sum
of the other sciences, the anoological sciences, to deal with nonintelligent
things—*anoeta*.

INTELLIGENCE

It is now essential that we define "intelligent."
Intelligence, like beauty, hasn't yet been defined operationally, although

* An early nineteenth-century name for the science of intuitive truths or reason; now
rare.

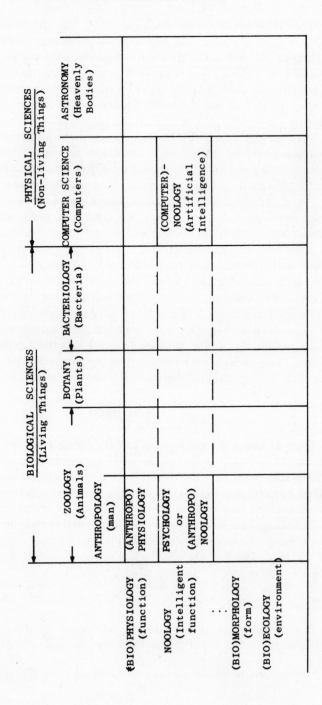

Table 1.
Outline of classification showing how we consider that psychology is a biological science and that artificial intelligence is a study in the physical sciences

there is popular concurrence on whether specific examples of things are intelligent (or beautiful). From such examples, let us try to ascertain that combination of distinguishing features which by such popular concurrence qualify a thing as intelligent. (Attempts to find that combination of distinguishing features of objects or phenomena as a basis for their classification or for generalization is usually one of the more formidable of intellectual tasks. Our specific task here is a relatively simple one.)

COGNITIVITY

We are inclined to call persons intelligent, if by inherited aptitude, or by learning and practice, they have acquired certain "mental" (as opposed to physical) skills and information. Over the years, society has changed its mind about what "mental" skills and information belong on the qualifying list of intelligence. Even the ranking of the items on the list depends on the times. Currently, items on the list include, but are not limited to, reading, writing, verbalizing, teaching, translating, calculating, induction, deduction, hypothesizing, deciding, predicting, and planning. We will call these cognitive skills. Whereas, cognitive skills cannot be defined operationally, they can be defined (and arbitrarily redefined with the season) by extension, as indeed they are here.

We will say that if a thing (living or not) has cognitive skills, it is a cognitive thing. Thus, persons, analog computers, mechanical calculators, digital-computer programs, perceptrons, dolphins, mechanical counters, and electronic multipliers are cognitive things since each has one or more of the cognitive skills enumerated above. But to be cognitive is necessary but not sufficient to qualify a thing as intelligent. And even if we were inclined to consider cognitivity alone sufficient, we would not put a mechanical counter or an electronic multiplier in the same "intellectual" class with persons or even perceptrons. And the reason we wouldn't is that unlike counters, multipliers, and desk calculators—persons, perceptrons, dolphins, and digital computer programs can alter themselves or be altered by external agents so that they maintain their acquired cognitive skills and information in the face of changing or hostile environments or of their own deteriorating structures. Also, if required, they can improve on the cognitive skills and information they already possess or they can acquire new cognitive shills and information by appropriate self-alteration or alteration by an external agent, i.e., they are adaptive. Thus to qualify as intelligent, i.e., as a noeton, a thing must be both cognitive and adaptive. It may be noted that adaptivity, unlike cognitivity, is operationally defined. Another difference between cognitivity and adaptivity is noteworthy. In carrying out a cognitive process, a noeton is playing the role of an active agent that processes something else, a passive patient. This something else, we call the *cognitia*; singular *cognitum*. In the items on the list of cognitive processes given above, cognitia are transformed, transferred, or stored. On the other hand, when a noeton is adapting either to maintain or to improve or change its cognitive skills and information, it is playing the role of a passive patient whose distinguishing features are being altered by an active agent which we call the *adapter*. Thus a noeton is one part of a trinity: (1) the always passive cognitia, (2) the active noeton as a cognizer of the cognitia, and (3) the adapter of the cognizer. We call the trinity a noetum.

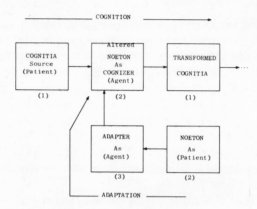

Fig. 1. The Noetum Trinity.

THE COGNIZER

If a noeton performs a cognitive task unaided, it is called an *autoneoton* (in parallel with automaton). If a noeton is following the directions of another autonoeton, the follower is called a *servonoeton* (not quite in parallel with a servomechanism). If two or more noetons are of mutual aid in performing a cognitive task, the combination is called *synnoeton*; each noeton is called a *synnoent* (in parallel with a *symbiont*); such a *phenomenon* (or more properly *noumenon*) is called *synnoesis* (in parallel with *symbiosis*).

THE ADAPTER

Furthermore, we should also distinguish among adaptation of a noeton by itself (self-adaptive); by an external agent (other-adaptive); and together with an external adapter (co-adaptive).

THE COGNITIA

Finally, the cognitia of a noeton may be outside the noeton, inside it, or partly inside and partly outside. Extra-, intra-, and inter- cognitiative, respectively will be terms adopted to denote these three possibilities.

A noetum (and a noeton as well) may thus be represented by one of 27 types with the descriptors obtained from the following nine items:

Table 2.   Descriptors of a Noetum

Cognitiative	Adaptive	Noeton
Intra-	Self-	Auto
Extra-	Other-	Servo
Inter-	Co-	Syn

For example, there may be an intracognitive, self-adaptive, autonoeton of which an isolated, introspecting student would be an instance, as would be a wired-program "computer" translating stored text. To recapitulate: The necessary and sufficient condition for an object to be recognizable as an intelligence (noeton) and so to be the subject of noological investigation is that it be a discrete mass of matter with a definite boundary alternately undertaking to perform certain (arbitrarily defined) cognitive processes without manifest alteration of its distinguishing cognitive features during this time and as ascertained by direct observation or by analogy with other objects or models of the same class, maintaining, improving, or changing its cognitive skills by virtue of alterations made by an agent in its distinguishing cognitive features. The criterion of performance of cognitive functions may be called the *cognitive criterion*; that of maintenance, improvement, and changes in skills by virtue of alterations in distinguishing features, the *adaptive criterion*.*

COMBINATIONAL NOETON

The function performed by a combinational circuit is to map an input into a desired input with a nominal delay. The combinational structure is a spatial *organization* or connection of certain types of *parts* each with particular *values* of relevant characteristic part parameters. The *organization, parts,* and *values* are the three inter dependent features that characterize a combinational structure. Varying one or more of these three features will, in general, alter the mapping it performs. A hostile physical *environment*, such as temperature can cause variations in *values*, and thereby in *organization*. Thus altering the *physical environment* can have the indirect effect of varying *organization, parts,* or *values* and thus of altering the mapping.

* Compare with definition of living thing given in footnote on page 000.

Furthermore, the mapping may be altered if the *input* or the *output* is changed. An interfering *signal environment* (such as noise) can change the *input* or *output* and hence the mapping.

If the combinational processor is a noetum, then *organization, parts, values, cognitive input, cognitive output, physical environment,* and *signal environment* are interdependent intellectual features of a noetum.

SEQUENTIAL NOETON

The task performed by a sequential circuit is performed by virtue of individual functions being carried out in a certain sequence, called a *program,* which may be "wired-in" (and thus possibly affected by a hostile *physical environment*) or stored as *program cognitia* (and thus possibly directly affected by an interferring *signal environment* or indirectly by an altered structure—*organization, parts, values.*)

Thus we add *program* to the list of intellectual features of a noeton giving a total of eight; and note that programs may be algorithmic or heuristic.

The adapter has the same eight intellectual features as does the cognizer. However, we know specifically what the input (cognitia) and output (cognitia) of the adapter are. They are the eight features of the cognizer.

ADAPTATION

DISTINGUISHING PARAMETERS

When a noeton is to carry out a particular cognitive task—e.g., translating—its distinguishing cognitive features are those isolable parameters whose variation could render the noeton incapable of acceptably carrying out that particular task. It is only these parameters that the noeton's adapter needs to vary in order to have it either maintain or improve its performance on the task, or perform another cognitive task altogether. We call these the intellectual parameters of a noeton. (It will be seen that all combinational and sequential curcuits have the same distinguishing parameters as other combinational and sequential circuits, whether or not the tasks performed are designated as cognitive). For our purposes it will be useful to consider first the distinguishing features of cognizers that are combinational circuits and then to consider the sequential operations. Thus adapting-programs are sequences only of alterations of one or more of these eight features of cognizers. (Cognitive programs, on the other hand, are sequences of functions performed on certain cognitia which may differ from instance to instance, specifically, an adapting program consists of some sequence of *adjusting* values; *replacing, adding,* or *deleting* parts; *organizing* or *reorganizing* the structure of the cognizer; *mixing* with the cognitiative input, *correcting* the cognitiative output; *controlling* the environment; *composing* or *recomposing* the cognizer program.

PURPOSES AND MODES OF ADAPTATION

We distinguish two purposes for adaptation: (1) a structure currently performing a function is required either to improve its performance on this function: *accommodation*, or (2) a structure that first performed a certain function is currently malfunctioning and it is required that the structure resume performance of the original function. We will call adaptation to this requirement *restoration*.

Instances of accommodation are: (*a*) persons learning new skills by practice without a teacher, and (*b*) Pavlov's conditioning of dogs. The person is self-accommodative; the dogs were other-accommodative.

Instances of restoration are: (*a*) computers repairing their own hardware faults or correcting their own errors, and (*b*) systems controlling the temperature of a room in the face of a changing external temperature.

Often, accommodation is accomplished by virtue of redesign, reprogramming, or teaching.

We can now elaborate the general description of a noetum. (Table II; Adaptive Column). A noeton may be self-, other-, or co-accommodative or restorative for each of which several examples may be identified. To repair faults or correct errors are restorative processes; to teach, condition, reprogram, or redesign may be accommodative processes. However, whether accommodative or restorative, a noeton may be self-, other-, or co-, adjusting, replacing, organizing, mixing, correcting, controlling, or composing.

REMARK. It is unfortunate that the English language has the term "learner" for a system that is being taught by an adapting agent named a teacher, but it has not terms for systems that adapt by virtue of similar alteration processes whose altering agents are named. For example, during restoration, we say that a system is being repaired by a repairer; the "repairee" is unnamed. Nor is there a verb for what the "repairee" is doing, as it is being repaired, like the verb "learning" for describing the system being taught. The same can be said for conditioning; the altering agent is the conditioner and the "conditionee" is unnamed. What's unfortunate about this situation is that the word 'learner' and the verb "to learn" (being the only ones available to describe the system as it is adapting) have been used indiscriminately as epithets for *all* adapting neota. Thus, an

---

* All indiscriminately called "learning machines" if the adapting patient is a machine.

adaptive system, a student, a "repairee," a "conditionee," a "designee," a "self-organizing" system, are all indiscriminately called *learning machines*, which has taken on such a broad connotation that by now it conveys little information.

	Adapter	Adaptive Function	Adapting Patient*	Adapting Function
Restorative	Repairer	Repairs	—	—
	Corrector	Corrects	—	—
	Therapist	Treats	Patient	Heals
Accommodative	Teacher	Teaches	Pupil	Learns
	Consultant	Advises	Client	Heeds
	Conditioner	Conditions	—	—

COGNITION AND THE TAXONOMY

A taxonomy for noology should include the identification of discrete intelligent structures as the subject matter of particular ones of the noological sciences and a list of the cognitive and adaptive functions and tasks as the subject matter of (noo)physiology. Clearly, humans, dolphins, flatworms, computers, perceptrons, automatons and chimpanzees are discrete intelligent structures and take places in the taxonomy of the noological sciences parallel to the places taken by particular plants, animals and bacteria in the taxonomy of the biological sciences. Furthermore, the cognitive and adaptive functions studied in (noo)physiology take a place parallel to the metabolic and reproductive functions studied in (bio)-physiology.

We can now write an outline of a taxonomy for the noological sciences (Table 3).

This partial taxonomy and the nomenclature developed in this paper provides us with a doctrine for naming, classifying, and defining the subject matter of fields that have heretofore been variously and ambiguously designated as artificial intelligence, man-machine relations or symbiosis, self-organizing systems, learning machines, etc. In particular, the fields of artificial and natural intelligence combined are common names for the science of noology; the fields of man-machine symbiosis, and hybrid computers are common names for the science of synnoetics; the field of natural intelligence is the common name for the science of bionoology; the field of artificial intelligence is the common name of the science of physico-noology. This is not to suggest that vernacular names such as artificial intelligence should be disused and always displaced by physiconoology, any more than chemists insist on exclusive use of the chemical name sodium chloride instead of the common name *salt*, or biologists insist on the exclusive use of the name Diptera Cullicidae instead of the common name

Table 3. Outline of a Taxonomy of the Noological Sciences

	N O O L O G I C A L S C I E N C E S (Intelligence)				
	BIO-NOOLOGICAL SCIENCES Natural (Intelligence)			PHYSICO-NOOLOGICAL SCIENCES (Artifical Intelligence)	
	HUMANS	DOLPHINS	. . .	COMPUTERS	AUTOMATONS	. . .
(NOO) PHYSIOLOGY Cognitive functions Induction Translation Theorem proving Composition Recall					
. . .					
Adaptive functions Accommodative					
. . .					
Restorative Adjust Replace Mix					
. . .					
(NOO) MORPHOLOGY (NOO) NOTOMY (NOO) ECOLOGY					

mosquito. Common names and scientific names each have their distinctive roles.

The purpose of a complete taxonomy and nomenclature of science, in general, and of noology in particular is much more than to provide a few scientific names for common ones. Its purpose is to provide a vehicle for conveniently accommodating and clearly exhibiting and conveniently making knowledge available—for noology, knowledge of cognitive-adaptive structures. In a new field, its most important role may be to guide and interpret research. Charles Singer stated in his article "Biology" in the *Encyclopaedia Britannica* "The whole course of biology may be represented as the history of ideas on the classification of living things." Will a future historian of science say that the whole course of noology may be represented as the history of ideas on the classification of intelligent things?

APPENDIX A

SOME CONCEPTS OF NOOLOGY

Just as the taxonomy of biological sciences and their branches provided a paradigm for constructing a taxonomy of the noological sciences and their branches, the concepts and nomenclature of biology together with those of zoology and psychology provide a paradigm for identifying important concepts and terminology in the noological sciences and their branches. We have already noted the correspondence between sym*bio*sis and syn*noe*sis. The author has examined the Webster's New Collegiate Dictionary definitions of terms prefixed by *bio-*, *zoo-*, and *psycho-*; substituted the prefix *no-*, *noo-*, or *noe-*; and asked if the resulting terms would denote parallel significant concepts in noology. Remarkably, the following list of concepts and their names were derived. (Bold-face entries are Webster's; light faced cap entries are the author's.)

> **Psy′che** 1. Class. Myth. A beautiful princess of whom Venus became jealous. Cupid, Venus's son, fell in love with Psyche and Venus imposed many hardships on her, but Psyche was finally reunited with Cupid and made immortal. 2. The human soul; also, mind; mental life.
>
> **Psyche knot** A style of wearing hair in a projecting or conical coil at the back of the head.

NOE 1. Modern Mythology. An ugly genius whom the world contemptuously rejected but ultimately grudgingly accepted. Noe was known as a "longhair" on account of his hair style nowadays referred to as a *Noe's knot*. 2. A noetum's intellect; the intellectual activity.

Bio' sis   Biol. A combining form denoting a (specified) mode of living, as in symbiosis.

-Noesis   Nool. A combining form denoting a (specified) mode of thought, as in synnoesis.

Psycho' sis   Psychiatry. Mental disease; any serious mental derangement; a purely psychiatric term without the legal implications of the word insanity. Syn., see *Insanity. Psychot' ic,* adj. & n.

No' osis   No' iatry. Intellectual disease; any serious intellectual deficiency; a purely noiatric term without the educational implications of the word idiocy. *nootic,* adj. & n.

Biotic   A combining form for biotic, denoting having a (specified) mode of life. Cf. **Biosis**

-Noetic   A combining form for noetic denoting having a (specified) mode of thought. Cf. Noesis.

Psy' chical   adj. 1. Psychic. 2. Of or pertaining to the mind; mental; contrasted with physical. *Psy' chically,* adv.

Noical   adj. 1. Noic. 2. Of or pertaining to the intellect—*Noically,* adv.

Psy'chic   adj. 1. Of or pertaining to the psyche, or soul or mind. 2. Not physical; lying outside the realm of known physical processes; as, psychic forces. 3. Sensitive to nonphysical forces; as a psychic medium. n. 1. A person apparently sensitive to nonphysical forces; esp., Spiritualism, one capable of serving as a medium. 2. The field of psychic phenomena.

Noic   adj. 1. Of or pertaining to the noe or intellect. 2. Not in the realm of known physical processes; as *noic forces.*

Psychi' atry   n. The medical speciality dealing with mental disorders, esp. with psychoses, but also with neuroses. *psychiatrical, psychiatric,* adj. *psychiatrist,* n.

No' iatry   n. The medical specialty dealing with intellectual disorders, especially with no' oses, *noiatrical, no' iatric,* adj. *no' iatrist,* n.

Psychopathol' ogy   n. The scientific study of mental disorders from the psychological point of view.

Noopathology   n. The scientific study of intellectual perturbances from the noological point of view.

Psychoanal' ysis n. A method of psychotherapeutic analysis resting on the theory that abnormal mental reactions are due to desires consciously rejected but subconsciously persistent. *Psychoanalytic, psychoanalytical,* adj. *Psychoanalytically,* adv.

NOOANALYSIS n. A method of nootherapeutic analysis resting on the theory that abnormal intellectual activity is due to repression of intellectual values and a set consciously rejected but subconsciously persistent. *Nooanalytic,* adj. *Nooanalytically,* adv.

Psychosur' gery n. Cerebral surgery employed in treating psychic symptoms, specif., leucotomy.

NOOSURGERY n. Cerebral surgery employed in treating noic symptoms.

Psychop' athy n. 1. Mental disorder in general. 2. More commonly mental disorder characterized by eccentricity, emotional instability, perversity of conduct, undue conceit and suspiciousness, or lack of common sense, social feeling, self-control, truthfulness, energy, or persistence. 3. Incorrectly, psychotherapeutics.

NOOPATHY n. Intellectual disorder in general.

Psychother' apeutics n. Science and art of psychotherapy.

NOOTHERAPEUTICS n. Science and art of nootherapy.

Psychother' apy n. Mental treatment of illness, esp. of nervous diseases and maladjustments, as by suggestion, psychoanalysis, or reeducation.

NOOTHERAPY n. Intellectual treatment of illness, esp. of nervous diseases, as by intellectual-work therapy.

Psychopath' ic adj. 1. Of, pertaining to, of the nature of, or characterized by psychopathy. 2. Designating, or relating to, abnormal sensitiveness to spiritual phenomena; characterized by extreme susceptibility to religious emotion, conscientious doubts and fears, etc. 3. Incorrectly, of or pertaining to psychotherapeutics.

NOOPATHIC adj. Relating to abnormal sensitiveness to nooidal influences.

Bi' o (bi' o) [Gr. *bios,* life, mode of life.] A combining form denoting relation to, or connection with, life, vital phenomena, or living organisms; often, biological; physiological; as in:

biocentric	biolinguistics	biophysiology
bioclimatic	biomagnetism	biopsychic
bioclimatology	biomicroscopy	biopsychology
bioeconomic	bio-osmosis	bioreaction
bioelectric	biophysics	biosocial
biogeography	biophysiography	biosociological

No′ o- (*no′ o*) [Gr. *nous* - understanding.] A combining form denoting relation to, or connection with, intelligence, intellectual phenomena (or noumena), cognizing noeta, often noological as in:

noocentric	noolinguistics	noophysiology
nooeconomic	noomagnetism	noosocial
noogeography	noomicroscopy	

Bio-assay′ n. Estimation of the strength of a drug, etc., by testing its effects on a living organism, as by feeding to rats.

Noo-ASSAY n. Estimation of the strength of a drug etc. by testing its effects on a thinking noetum, as by feeding to chimpanzees.

Biocat′ alyst n. A substance which activates or stimulates a biochemical reaction, as insulin; a coenzyme, a vitamin, or a hormone.

Noo-CATALYST n. A substance which activates or stimulates a noochemical reaction, as an intellectamin.

Biosyn′ thesis n. Biochem. The synthesis of a chemical compound by a living organism.

Noo-SYNTHESIS n. Noochem. The synthesis of a chemical compound by a noeton.

Bio-chem′ istry n. Chemistry that deals with the chemical compounds and processes occurring in organisms (plants and animals). *biochemic, biochemical*, adj. *biochemically*, adv. *biochemist*, n.

Noo-CHEMISTRY n. Chemistry that deals with the chemical compounds and processes occurring in intellectuals; *noochemic, noochemical*, adj. *noochemically*, adj. noochemist, n.

Psychophys′ ics n. The scientific study of the relations between mental and physical processes.

NOOPHYSICS n. The scientific study of the relations between intellectual and physical processes.

Biodynam′ ics n. Physiology treating of the active vital phenomena of organisms; opposed to biostatics.

NOODYNAMICS n. Physiology treating of the active intellectual phenomena or noumena of noeta; opposed to noostatics.

Bio-stat′ ics n. Physiology treating of the structure of organisms in relation to their functions; opposed to biodynamics.

Noo-STATICS n. Physiology treating of the structure of noeta in relation to their functions; opposed to noodynamics.

Zoot′ omy   n. The science dealing with the anatomy of animals, esp. other than man.

Nootomy   n. The science dealing with the anatomy of intellectual organs.

Psycho–dra′ ma   n. A drama in which actors extemporize in meeting a given situation, thus exhibiting their natural psychological reactions, used esp. in treating the mentally ill; *psychodramatic*, adj.

No′ o-dra′ ma, n. A drama in which bionoeta extemporize in noological tendencies, used esp. in treating the intellectually stumped; *noo′ dramatic*, adj. sometimes referred to as "brain-storming."

Zooph′ ilous   adj. [zoo- + -philous.]   animal-loving;   specif., Bot., adapted to pollination by animals.

Noophilous [noo + Ophilous] Intellectual-loving; specif., Politics, adapted to influence by intellectuals.

Zo′ ophyte   n. Zool. Any of numerous invertebrate animals resembling plants in appearance or mode of growth, as the corals, sea anemones, hydroids, bryozoans, sponges, etc.

Noophyte   n. Nool. Any of numerous invertebrate intellectuals resembling plants.

Psychogen′ esis   n. 1. Genesis through an internal force, as opposed to natural selection. 2. Psychol. The origin and development of the mind.
Biogen′ esis   n. 1. The development of life from preexisting life. 2. The supposed tendency for stages in the evolutionary history of a race to briefly recur during the development and differentiation of an individual of that race.

Noogenesis   n. Nool. The origin, design, and development of the intellect.

Psychogen′ ic   adj. Originating in the mind; caused by mental influences; as, psychogenic nervous disorders.

Noogenic   adj. Originating in the intellect; caused by intellectual influences; as noogenetic digestive disorders.

Zoo   (zo͞o)   n. A zoological garden or collection.

Noo (no͞o) n.   A noological collection.

Zoological Garden   A garden or park where wild animals are kept for exhibition.

Noological collection.   A place where intellectuals collect for exhibition in a synthetic environment; such as think factories and Espresso coffee houses.

Biol' ogy n. 1. The science of life; the branch of knowledge which treats of living organisms. 2. Plant and animal life, as of a region; also biological history laws, or phenomena; as the biology of a wasp.

Zool' ogy n. 1. The science which treats of animals; the branch of biology dealing with the animal kingdom and its members (as individuals and classes) and with animal life. Cf. *classification, 2.* 2. A treatise on zoology. 3. Animal life, as of a region.

Psychol' ogy n. 1. The science which treats of the mind in any of its aspects; systematic knowledge and investigation of the phenomena of consciousness and behavior. 2. the traits, feelings, actions, and attributes, collectively, of the mind; as the psychology of a criminal. 3. A treatise on the science of psychology.

NOOLOGY [*noo* + -logy] The science that deals with intelligent things.

Zoologist n. One who is versed in zoology.

NOOLOGIST One who is versed in noology.

Biological warfare Warfare involving the use of living organisms, esp. disease germs, and toxic substances produced by them, against men, animals, or plants; also, warfare involving the use of synthetic chemicals harmful to plants.

NOOLOGICAL WARFARE Warfare involving the use of nootogens to render an enemy nootic; so that he loses his intellectual faculties temporarily.

Biom' etry n. (*a*) Calculation of the probable duration of human life. (*b*) Also biometrics.

Psychom' etry n. 1. Occult. Divination of facts about an object or its owner through contact with, or proximity to, the object. 2. Psychol. Also Psychometrics. Mental measurement, as a speed and precision of mental processes.

Zoom' etry n. Scientific measurement of animals.

NOOMETRY n. The science of measurement of the distinguishing parameters of noeta and intellectual behavior.

Zoomor' phism n. The representation of God, or of gods, in the form, or with the attributes, of the lower animals.

NOOMORPHISM n. The representation of God or of gods, in the form or with the attributes, of the lower intellectuals.

Zoogeog' raphy   n. Study or description of the geographical distribution of animals; esp. determination of the land and marine areas characterized by special groups of animals and the study of the causes and significance of such groups.

NOOGEOGRAPHY   n. Study or description of the geographical distribution of intellectuals, . . .

Zo' oid   n. Biol. An entity which resembles but is not wholly the same as a separate individual animal; specif., (a) an organic body or cell having locomotion, as a sperm cell, (b) Zool. A more or less independent animal produced by fission, proliferation, or the like, and not by direct sexual methods. Cf. *zoon*, a. (c) Zool. Any of the individuals which, in alternation of generation come between the products of true sexual reproduction, as the free-swimming medusa of a hydriod colony.

No' OID   Nool. An entity which behaves like but is not wholly the same as a separate individual intellectual.

Biog' raphy   n. 1. The written history of a person's life. 2. Biographical writings collectively or as a literary genre.

Zoog' raphy   n. Description or depiction of animals, esp. their forms and habits.

Psy' chography   n. A psychological biography or analysis of a person.

NOOGRAPHY   A documentation of a noetum's intellectual history, form, and unique capabilities; as to document digital computer programs is to write its noography.

Biog' rapher   n. A writer of biography.

NOOGRAPHER   n. A writer of noography.

Biol' ogism   n. A system or doctrine formulated from the biological point of view, or based on biological modes of explanation; also, adherence to such a doctrine or point of view.

NOOLOGISM   A system or doctrine formulated from the noological point of view, or based on noological modes of explanation; also adherence to such a doctrine or point of view.

Psychol' ogize   v.i. To engage in psychological thought or investigation.

NOOLOGIZE   To engage in noological thought or investigation.

Psychomo' tor   adj. Of or pertaining to muscular action ensuing directly from a mental process.

NOOMETER   adj. Of or pertaining to muscular action ensuing directly from an intellectual process.

Zo' oplasty   n. Surg. Act or process of grafting animal tissue into the human body.

NOOPLASTY   Surg. Act or process of grafting intellectual tissue into the human body.

Bi' opsy   n. Med. The removal and examination (usually microscopic) of a piece of tissue from the living body, esp. for diagnosis.

No' OPSY   n. Med. The removal and examination (usually microscopic) of a piece of the intellect or noe from a noetum, esp. for diagnosis.

Psychog' nosis   n. Any penetrating study of the psyche.

No' OGNOSIS   n. Any penetrating study of the noe.

Psychosomat' ic   adj. Pertaining to the functional interrelationship between mind and body, as in psychosomatic medicine, which deals especially with bodily disorders induced by mental or emotional disturbances. *Psychosomatics*, n.

No' OSOMAT' IC   adj. Pertaining to the functional relationships between intellect and body, as in noosomatic medicine, which when inaugurated will deal especially with bodily disorders induced by intellectual perturbances. *Noosomatics*, n.

Bios' ophy   n. A system of spiritual self-education developed by Dr. Frederick Kettner, of New York.

NOOSOPHY   n. A secular religion devoted to the worship of the intellect.

Bio' ta   n. The flora and fauna of a region.

NOO TA   n. A certain class of intellectuals in a community; as in a university community.

Bi' otype   n. Biol. A genotypic race or group of organisms.

No' OTYPE   Noology. A genotypic group of intellectuals.

Bi' osphere   n. The sphere of living organisms penetrating the lithosphere, hydrosphere, and atmosphere.

NOOSPHERE   "Outside and above the biosphere, there is the noosphere" (Teilhard de Chardin); the "thinking layer."

Bi′ otin n.　[Gr. *bios,* life + *-in* (with euphonic *t*).] A member of the vitamin-B complex. See *Vitamin.*

Nootin　n.　(Gr. nous mind + -in (with euphonic *t*)] A member of the intellec-amin -B complex. See *Intellectamin.*

Vi′ tamin n.　[L. vita life + amine]　Any of a number of con-stituents of food (once thought to be composed of amines) of which minute quantities are essential to the maintenance of life.

Intellectamin　n. [L. *intellectualis* + *amine*] An amine present in minute quan-tities in most foods; will be found to be essential to the maintenance of the intellect.

21

PRINCIPLES OF LEARNING SYSTEM CONSTRUCTION FOR COMPLEX PROCESSES CONTROL

A. G. Ivakhnenko

Academy of Science, Kiev, U.S.S.R.

INTRODUCTION

The combined control systems which include open-loop (feed-forward) and feedback (correcting) couplings are the most efficient.

In principle, a system may be of the pure feedback type, but the more precisely the feed-forward part is designed (according to the invariance conditions), the less the power of the corrector and the shorter the control processes.

Eventually, the combined cybernetic control systems which possess determined and self-organizing parts are the most efficient, too. In principle the system can be self-organizing only, but to make its volume less and to speed the learning processes the designer has to introduce into the determined part all reliable information (mainly to point out the purposes of the control, the prototypes and algorithms, the list of sensitive units, etc.). Then the self-organizing part will generate all additional information, make the control more detailed and correct the mistakes of the human-designer.

Until now the main efforts of the scientists and engineers were directed to the design of purely determined systems. It is necessary to know the algorithms of processes for this. We will pay more attention to design of the nonalgorithmic or self-organizing part of the systems for complex-process control, because this part is not as yet satisfactorily elaborated.

ELEMENTS OF INDUSTRIAL SITUATION COGNITION THEORY

The process can be characterized by the same output control variables $\varphi_1, \varphi_2, \ldots, \varphi_\alpha$ and by input variables. The latter can be divided into the dependent variables manipulated by us, $\mu_1, \mu_2, \mu_3, \ldots, \mu_\beta$ and independent disturbances $\lambda_1, \lambda_2, \lambda_3, \ldots, \lambda_\gamma$. In the state-determined systems *the state of the process* corresponds to the point in the n-dimensional space of the coordinates mentioned above (to the end of the characteristic vector). A set of the states gives us *the situation.*

The geometric meaning of the situation is the set of points in the n-dimensional space of the coordinates, in the same way as the stimulus corresponds to the set of the points in the n-dimensional space of properties. It seems appropriate to use the methods of the dichotomy of the n-dimensional space that are used in the theory of stimulus cognition,[1,2] in order to build the theory of industrial-situations cognition. We will use the following analogy system:

Table of Analogy

Theory of the stimulus cognition	Theory of the situation cognition	Letter
Complete set of the stimuli (alphabet)	Complete set of the situations	W
Stimulus (letter)	Situation	S_i
Pattern	State	V_i

There is no problem about the use of individual letters, which are established as definite points in the space of properties. These points, of course, are to be the centers of the given stimulus regions. In the process of learning, the human operator points out the boundaries of these regions. In the process of self-learning, the systems find them out spontaneously.[3] How may we use this result of the cognitive theory to evaluate the situations? Very often there are no definite standards of the situations, and eventually the dichotomy of the coordinate space is more subjective than the dichotomy of the properties space.[3] It is necessary to clarify the question of the possible classification of the situations. Different approaches are possible. Let us examine some of these.

CLASSIFICATION BY INPUT VARIABLES

In the quick-response systems where we can neglect the transients and where it is easy to measure the disturbances, the situations are determined by the disturbances themselves. The complete set of coordinates should be distinguished from the set of coordinates defining the situations. The space defining the coordinates is to be divided into parts in which it is not necessary to vary the manipulated variables to get the optimum regime. These partsrepresent the situations.

Let us consider the example of the hydroturbine control.[4] To keep efficiency high, the angle of turbine blades is to be changed according to the generator load and water pressure. In this problem there is one output variable, the efficiency of generator φ_1, and two disturbances—the generator load λ_1 and the water pressure λ_2.

For every two values of disturbances we can find the maximum of qualitative index (or figure of merit) and optimum value of manipulated variable. So, point after point, the entire plane of defining coordinates λ_1 and λ_2 can be covered by the values of qualitative index and manipulated variable. The corresponding table or curve or analytical formula expresses the so-called astatic characteristic of the given system.

To define the boundaries of the situations we are to find the curves of equal values of the manipulated variable. We can consider these curves as the ground relief. Beginning with the highest place, we cover all the working range of the change of defining coordinates with the horizontal square terraces to get the minimum of the *excavation*.* When all situations are equally possible, the steps between the terraces are to have the same value, defined by the accuracy of the control. By such construction we find the optimum number of the discretization units and optimum irregularity of scales. This construction is to be made twice if there are two manipulated variables, and the resulting nets are to be superimposed.

Therefore, by *situation* is understood the region in the space of defining coordinates, in which, under the given accuracy of control, it is unnecessary to do anything to improve the performance of the system.

CLASSIFICATION BY OUTPUT VARIABLES

In some systems the disturbances are only the starting impulses, not the constantly acting factors. For such systems classification by output variables, which are the indirect measure of the disturbances, is more suitable. For example, such classification evidently will be used in machines for the treatment of ill people. The space of the defining coordinates is to be divided on the situations (i.e., the parts where the optimum values of manipulated variables are constant), as shown above.

---

* If the relief is such that in order to get the minimum of the *excavation* it is better to transform coordinates, we can use the special device elaborated by V. I. Vasiljev[1].

COMBINED CLASSIFICATION BY INPUT-OUTPUT VARIABLES

This classification is the combination of the two, considered above. The cognitive system "alpha" (we suppose, the readers are acquainted with it from Ref. 1) can be used to make any classification mentioned above.

DIGITAL CONTROL SYSTEMS FOR STATE-DETERMINED PROCESSES

To control many processes in the simpler cases considered here, extremum controllers can be used—for example, the classical problem of the hydro-turbine control mentioned above. A second example is the furnace using oil and air.[5] The furnace is used to warm the water flowing in the heating tubes. In this problem φ_1 is the temperature of the water, μ_1—the quantity of the oil, coming to the furnace, μ_2—the quantity of the air and λ the production of warmed water.

The function of the schemes designed below is not to replace the extremum controllers but to help solve more complex problems in which there are a number of the coordinates. For example, the problem of the extremum control of hydroturbines has been solved by means of the nonlinear converters or conoids.[4] If we meet more than two disturbances it is impossible to use analog converters because the conoids are more than three-dimensional.

Let us consider the basic schemes of state-determined control systems, to clarify the complexity (volume) of them and the methods of investigation. One limitation is necessary: we shall consider only such processes where it is possible to show the main generalized *figure of merit*. The cost function of finite product by constant (its production and quality) can often serve as such figure of merit. In the first example considered above, the purpose is to get the maximum hydroturbine efficiency, but in the second example the problem is to use a minimum of oil and air expenditure for the required temperature of the heated water.

THE DETERMINED (ALGORITHMIC) SYSTEMS

The possible realization of the digitally determined system is shown in Fig. 1. For purposes of simplification only two disturbances and two manipulated variables are shown. The only output—the figure of merit—is not used for control. The last property is very characteristic for the openly determined systems. The situations become distinguishable from the input variables, and for this the cognitive system "alpha"[1] is used. The setting of the cognitive system can be given by a subject (learning) or can be obtained automatically, by the system itself (self-learning).

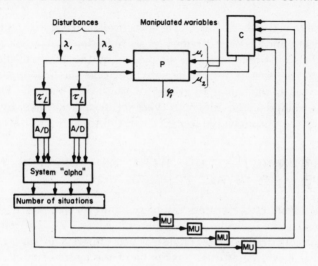

Figure 1

The subject chooses the definite values of the manipulated variables or "move" for every situation. He points out the corresponding settings of controllers R by means of memory units MU. To compensate for the inertia the definite delay time τ_L is to be introduced; it is equal to the time of the process delay. Clearly enough, the setting can be made only when the algorithm of the process is known and, moreover, when it is constant (for example, when the optimum value of the hydroturbine blade angle is known for all the combinations of load and pressure).

To choose the scheme and optimum values of the coefficients (parameters) of the open systems, the theory of invariance can be successfully used. For the analog extremum system the invariance method is given in Ref. 5. The conditions of invariance of the sampled data system are deduced by Yu. V. Krementulo and V. M. Kuntzewich.[6] An attempt is made by them to deduce the invariance conditions for the digital cognitive system and for the determined control system (Appendices 1 and 2).

"SEARCHING SYSTEMS" HAVING THE PROPERTY OF SPONTANEOUSLY DECREASING ENTROPY

It is easy to prove that the determined system and the system of simple statistical searching until the first satisfactory answer (the homeostat, for example) have a constant value of entropy. The degree of the organization is constant, i.e., nothing can be learned without the help of the operator. Only some feedback systems have the property of self-learning (or can "generate new information"). These are the systems of (1) the testing of the complete set, (2) self-improving statistical search until the first satis-factory result and (3) the extremum positive feedback. The self-improving statistical search differs from the simple one by the use of memory units, which force the system to try the most moves at the first opportunity or (what is almost the same) to get rid of the useless moves.[7] These three principles comprise the different types of feedback links by reacting because of the output variables. We shall call them the *searching systems*.

SELF-LEARNING SYSTEM—WITH THE TESTING OF THE COMPLETE SET OF ALL POSSIBLE MOVES

The algorithm of the process can be unknown or variable, if we use the system testing the complete set of all possible moves—i.e., the combinations of the manipulated variable values—which are tried in turn and values chosen that correspond to the maximum of the figure of merit. The tests are repeated periodically.

THE SELF-LEARNING SYSTEM OF SELF-IMPROVING STATISTICAL SEARCH UNTIL THE FIRST SATISFACTORY RESULT

When, for the given move, the figure of merit reaches the satisfactory level, the gates turn on the integrating memory units (Fig. 2). Then the indicator of highest voltage, comparing the outputs of the integrators, shows us the move by which the satisfactory result has been obtained most often and recommends trying this move at the first opportunity. When it fails, the system tries the next move, based on the probability of the success move. The search stops just as the figure of merit reaches the satisfactory value, but the learning (evaluation of the probability of successes of each possible move) proceeds continuously.[1] The time of the search decreases.

THE COMBINED (DETERMINED + SELF-LEARNING) SYSTEM

The combined system, joining both previous principles, is the most efficient. We shall get the combined system if we add directly the scheme of Fig. 1 to that of Fig. 2. This system will have the determined part and the part of self-improving statistical search. Another way of building the combined system is shown in Fig. 3. Here there is a combined system joining the determined part and the system with the testing of the set of the most perceptive moves.

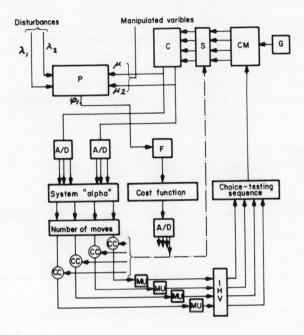

Figure 2

The basic logical formula for the construction of all combined systems for the state-determined processes is:

$$(N \text{ of situation}) \wedge (N \text{ of move}) = \left(\begin{array}{l} \text{state of the system} \\ \text{and mark of the result} \end{array} \right)$$

A move is selected not because it is workable for all possible moves but only for those moves which are possible in the given situation. The decrease of the search volume is the main advantage of these combined systems.

The general quantity of the possible states having a single system is equal to the sum $\sum\limits_{i=1}^{i=l} m_i$ where l = number of the situations, m = number of the moves in each situation. When the m_i are the same, $m = m_1 = m_2 = \ldots$, then, the number of the states is equal to the product $(m \times l)$. The duration of each test is Δt and the duration of the complete set of the state tests is

$$T_{\text{f.b.}} = m \times l \times \Delta t$$

But in the combined system this time is $T_c = m\Delta t$, i.e., l times shorter.

The characteristic property of the combined system is the presence of the parallel gates, which compare the number of the situation and the

number of moves. The outputs of parallel gates switch on the memory
units MU, which check the result of the move-up in every situation. The
outputs of memory units are switched into the indicator of highest voltage
IHV to clarify which of the moves in the given situation gives us the best
result. The controllers C translate this move into action. The deterministic
part of the scheme is that the initial settings of the memory units can be
given by the operator. But the longer the system acts the better are the
settings. However, when constructing the system of the complete set of
tests it is necessary to use the additional checking system, which cuts out
the memory unit until the neighboring ones are taught (i.e., through
compulsory learning of the given layer of the memory units).

It is possible to design a self-learning system which, after having tried
different coordinates, selects those corresponding to the minimum of the

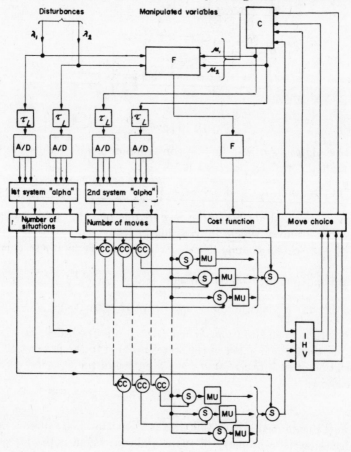

Figure 3

dispersion (differences) of evaluations of the qualitative index or figure of merit. The basic coordinates of the system can be found automatically in this way.

The range, number of levels and nonlinearity of the scales can also be found, using the criteria of the minimum dispersion of evaluations.

SYSTEM VOLUME CALCULATION AND HOW TO DECREASE IT

DISCRETIZATION OF THE COORDINATES

To construct the systems in accordance with Figs. 1, 2, 3, and r it is necessary to transform the coordinates into discrete numbers. The question of how to choose the range of the coordinate change and the number of the levels demands special consideration, and is solved by purely practical means. The difference of the figure-of-merit values, which we get at one and the same situation, is to be small. In another case we can conclude that by the scheme synthesis some important coordinates are missed or that the characteristics are indefinite (bivalued). Except for this, the difference mentioned depends on the quantity of the discretization levels— the more levels, the less is the difference. Practically the difference will be no more than a few percent.

To calculate the volume of the system we must have the following values:

number of states: $f = f_1 \cdot f_2 \cdots f_\alpha \cdot m_1 \cdot m_2 \cdots m_\beta \cdot l_1 \cdot l_2 \cdots l_\gamma$
number of moves: $m = m_1 \cdot m_2 \cdots m_\beta$,
number of situations: $l = l_1 \cdot l_2 \cdots l_\gamma$

(The last number is calculated under the classification of the situations on input variables). Here f_i, m_i, l_i are the numbers of the levels for corresponding coordinates. Let us calculate, for example, the volume of the combined system in Fig. 3, in the case having five disturbances, three manipulated variables, and one figure of merit of the process. Each coordinate is transformed into the binary number. Let us choose the definite method of discretization. Suppose, the coordinate μ can change within the range 0 to 1. The present value of μ is μ_i. Let us divide the complete diapason of the possible change into ten equal parts. Suppose, the output $+1$ gives us only one part within limits of the present value of the variable. For example, if $\mu = 0.38$, then:

$$\mu = -1 - 1 - 1 + 1 - 1 - 1 - 1 - 1 - 1 - 1$$

The number of the association units in the first system "alpha" (under such discretization as an example) is equal to the product of the number of disturbances multiplied by the number of situations and the number of discretization levels.

The number of gates and memory units is equal to the product of the number of situations and the number of moves. Therefore we shall get:

$$f = 10^8, m = 10^3 \quad \text{and} \quad l = 10^5$$

discretizators $D = 5 + 3 = 8$
association units in the first system "alpha" $= 50 \cdot 10^5$
association units in the second system "alpha" $= 30 \cdot 10^4$
parallel gates $= 10^8$
switches $\quad = 10^8 + 10^5$
memory units $= 10^8$

The example shows that the problem of large volume is difficult when constructing such systems as hardware. W now turn to ways of decreasing the volume.

SERIES ACTION INSTEAD OF PARALLEL

All operations can be programmed for the usual computers if they have a sufficiently large memory, and be realized in sequence. Because the time of the optimal move estimation increases rapidly, it is better to get more units acting in parallel, if possible. For example, in order to preserve the unit structure of the system we can make one complete set of gates and integrators serve every situation in turn, but to do so it will be necessary to design memory units that will remember all initial settings. It is clear that the general-purpose computers are to be used only for control of the major plants, where speed of control is not important.

The observation of the manual control, the increasing of the initial degree of organization, the extremum positive feedback, and, finally, the optimal choice of the coordinate discrimination method (including use of continuous signals and analog devices) enable us to construct a simple, self-organized control system for use with less important processes.

OBSERVATION OF MANUAL CONTROL

We obtain a strong decrease in the system volume when the process can be realized by use of manual control over short periods. For the first phase the system observes the manual control and finds out what situations can be met practically in the process. It occurs usually that only a small part of the possible situations is realized. We can say exactly the same about the moves. Only the most probable moves used by the operator are to be compared for every situation. The special automatic-device switches the association unit groups on for the self-learning in the cognitive system "alpha."[1] If the situations repeat, the new groups remain empty. Thus it establishes automatically how many groups are really necessary.

The analysis of the manual control gives us the possibility of establishing the minimum volume of the control system. For instance, the possibility of out-performing the operator in control remains when using the searching system, because it does not copy the man blindly, but precisely evaluates every move he made (including moves made occasionally) and, in addition, can try the neighboring moves.

The system acts without the operator for the second phase, realizing elaborated recommendations. It continues to evaluate every move in the process of observation of its own control. When the properties of the plant change the system relearns itself.

INCREASING THE DEGREE OF INITIAL ORGANIZATION (DEGREE OF DETERMINISM)

The first phase of learning considered above can be accomplished by the man himself. Using his experience, the man can also force the system to keep a definite relationship among its coordinates, which also decreases the volume of the system. When we add the controller to the process, connecting two of the coordinates, we decrease the whole quantity of the coordinates by one. The region of the optimum search decreases correspondingly. The less limitations we use the more complete the optimum, but the volume of the system increases.

THE EXTREMUM CHARACTERISTIC FORMATION

Sometimes it is possible to find a line of system states to be tried where an extremum characteristic is present. For example, let us suppose that by building the definite order of the gates we can find an order such that the figure of merit always first increases and then decreases. Then we can use the extremum controller to find the optimum move instead of the schemes of the complete set of tests or the self-improving statistical search. The system is that of the optimum move search by the extremum positive feedback,[1] namely in the cases when the extremum is out of the range of the plant.

Considering different ways of decreasing the volume of the combined system we come to the conclusion that they are all based on slowing down the tempo of the search, or on increasing the degree of initial organization (of determinism). The smallest volume has the completely determined system of Fig. 1, but being open it can be used only in cases when the algorithm of the process is well known and constant. The combined system is bigger, but it is free from the last limitation.

CENTRAL SYSTEMS FOR STATE-DETERMINED PROCESSES WHEN CONSIDERABLE INERTIA IS PRESENT

When the inertia of the process is considerable, a combined classification of situations, using disturbances as well as output variables, is necessary.

It is necessary to detain signals from disturbances or to speed up signals from output to compensate for the inertia. The delay lines τ_L in the open links are shown in Figs. 1, 2, and 3. On the other hand, we can use the *predictive filters* in the measuring links to speed up processes in closed loops. Often they are based on the *theory of the statistical forecasting* which is of the great importance for modern control.[12]

DIGITAL CONTROL SYSTEMS FOR PERIODIC (NON-STATE-DETERMINED) SYSTEMS

In this section we shall consider the processes which continue for some periods and can be evaluated only at the end of the process. At any other time the figure of merit cannot be measured; it is shown in Fig. 4 by the switch K at the output of process. The examples are: producing of metal, cooking, treatment of ill people, growing corn, etc.

In the considered processes it is possible to find one repeated coordinate N_1 such as time, or way, or number of the process period. To achieve a finite result it is necessary to keep definite and accurate note of the states.

The logical formula for the constructing of the combined system to control periodical processes is:

(N of the situation) Λ (N of the move) Λ (N of the period) = (the state and the mark of result).

The choice is made not from all possible moves but only from the moves that are possible in the given situation and given period of the process. For this purpose the outputs of the matrix "number of the situation—number of the move" are switched to one more matrix of the gates, which takes into account the number of the process period.

Each of the gates and memory units corresponds to the given state of the system. So the whole process is characterized by one representative curve (instead of a representative point for state-determined systems). The example is shown in Fig. 4. This evaluation is to be applied to each result of every state; i.e., to every one of the representative curves. The third system, "alpha," with self-switching of the groups, is used to interpret the representative curves. One additional layer of the memory units is used to evaluate the marks of these curves.

Suppose, for example, the output product is evaluated by the five-grade scale. If the system always comes to the mark "five" along the given representative curve, then the given memory unit will get the maximum grade "five." But if the system using the given curve comes to the mark "three" once, and to the mark "five" three times, then the average mark of the representative curve will be "four and a half," and so on. Within finite limits the mark has an excellent accuracy probability for any given representative curve.

Evaluation of the given representative curve is very similar to evaluation of the pupils' works at school. The teacher gives an average mark at the end of a year. There is the deterministic part of the system because the

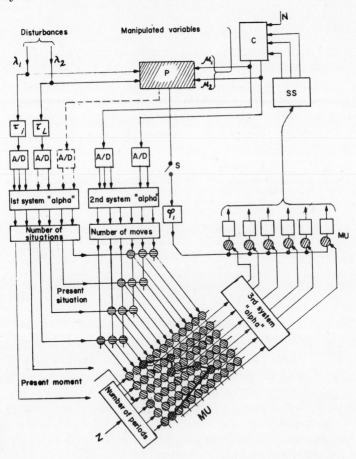

Figure 4

initial values of the memory units' settings are given by the operator, but the system continuously changes them by its experience and even corrects certain mistakes of the operator. Now, having in the memory units the evaluation of each representative curve, we can use this information to choose the move that is most likely to succeed, using one of the three searching systems considered above.

Some difficulties connected with discretization of the coordinates: the marks of some states or representative curves can be precisely equal. Then the rule of middle choice can be recommended—the move which is in the middle of the group of equal highest marked moves is to be chosen.

THE USE OF THE COGNITIVE SYSTEM FOR THE CLASSIFICATION OF PROCESSES BY OUTPUTS

Charges of one line of the memory unit matrix enable us to recognize and evaluate each state of the system by its figure of merit. This can be stated when processes change slowly enough ("theory of compactivity"). Only then the analogy between the theory of stimulus cognition and the theory of situation cognition (see the table above) is valid. When the stimulus is applied, the voltages of the sensory units correspond to letters (A or B). When the situation is known, voltages of one line of memory units present the mark of the situation. It can be easily evaluated by the five-grade scale like the output product itself. The cognitive system is to be constructed with five groups of association units, each calculating the possibility of the "excellent" output mark.

The indicator of the highest voltage compares the results of calculations and shows the mark of the present situation.

Figure 5 shows that the predictive filter can be added to the output of the cognitive system. The possibility of predicting the results of the choice of the move is essential to satisfy the conditions of invariance (Appendices 1 and 2).

CONCLUSION

When the controlling processes have many coordinates, the digital technique has an advantage because it enables us to use the theory of stimuli cognition to solve the problem of situations cognition.

Recognizing the situation, the move, and the period of the process, we use a simple logical formula to determine the state of the system and to evaluate the quality of the move. Eventually the "searching system" (i.e., the system with the complete set of tests or the system of self-improving statistical search or the system with positive extremum feedback, at least) determines the optimal move. Only these principles of the search mentioned here give the system the property of self-learning when it can outperform its operator in the skill of control.

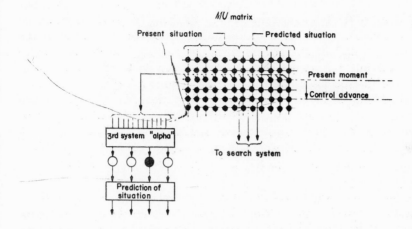

Figure 5

As in the common systems, the combined systems joining both open deterministic and self-learning feedback (realized by the searching systems mentioned above), are the most efficient. The deterministic part is to be designed according to the invariance conditions, but the searching systems according the rules of compromise settings (the "by parts" method[5]).

APPENDIX I

THE INVARIANCE CONDITIONS FOR THE COGNITIVE SYSTEMS

The theory of invariance developed by Profs. G. V. Shchipanov (acad.), V. S. Kulebakin (acad.), B. N. Petrov and many others[13] enables us to find the conditions by which the error of the system is equal to zero and the transients do not influence the controlled variable. Sometimes these conditions cannot be fulfilled precisely, but nevertheless they show us the relationship of the parameters we are to seek. Suppose, for example, the system is described by linear differential equation $a_c(p)\ \varphi_1 = b_c(p)\ \lambda$ where φ_1 controlled variable, λ — the basic disturbance $a_c(p)$ and $b_c(p)$ — the polynomials of $p = \dfrac{d}{dt}$. The general solution according the Heaviside formula is:

$$\varphi_1 = h + \Sigma e^{-c_{12}T}(a_1 \cos \beta\ T + b_1 \sin \beta\ T) + \Sigma a e^{-c_3 T}$$

The coefficients h, a_1, b_1, a and damping coefficients c_{12}, c_3 are the functions of the system parameters. When the invariance is absolute, $\varphi_1 \equiv 0$. Reducing these coefficients to zero we get the conditions of invariance, which can be satisfied by the choice of the transfer functions of disturbance couplings. It means that to get the invariance we vary the "equivalent" initial conditions, but do not change the damping. If we shall define the duration of the process as the time of the amplitude decreasing by the definite times, we come to the conclusion that the disturbance couplings do not influence the process duration. On the contrary, if we define the duration as the time of the amplitude decreasing to the definite value, we shall state that the considered time is strongly decreased (when the invariance conditions are completely satisfied, the duration of the processes is equal to zero).

This conclusion is valid for the cognitive systems as well. Let us consider the cognitive system "alpha", which has open feed-forward coupling from the input variables and the feedback connections.[1] The open couplings connect the sensitive units and association units directly and therefore the former control the latter. If the coupling acts very quickly and precisely it means the absolute invariance of the cognitive system because the processes of self-learning become short and precise. In the presence of invariant feed-forward coupling, the action of the feedback is unnecessary. Analogous to this, when the compound coupling of the generator acts precisely, the corrector of voltage is no longer necessary. In both of the examples given, the feedbacks begin to work only when the open couplings are not invariant, or when disturbances act.

Suppose that the consequence of the input properties slowly changed so that "K" open couplings work incorrectly. The function of the feedback is to improve these inaccuracies. The duration of self-learning remains constant (because all association units are to be tried). But the voltage error at the output of the association unit group will be smaller (compared to the absence of the open feed-forward couplings), particularly by the number $\dfrac{K}{n_1}$, where n_1 = the number of units in the group. Thus, the synthesis of feed-forward coupling according to the invariance conditions brings us the same results from the physical point of view—it decreases the error of the transient process.

Open coupling in the cognitive system does not differ from the servomechanism. The invariance condition for the servomechanism, described by the dynamic equation $a_3(p) \; \varphi = b_3(p) \; \psi$, can be written in the form $\varphi = \psi$ or $\dfrac{b_3(p)}{a_3(p)} = 1$. The invariance conditions for the open coupling in the cognitive system described by the equation $a_3(p) \; \alpha_i = b_3(p) \; V_i$ has almost the same form $\alpha_i = V_i$ or $\dfrac{a_3(p)}{b_3(p)} = 1$ where V_i — the sequence of the voltages of sensitive units and α_i — the sequence of output voltages of the given group. Let us consider two cases.

CASE 1

The stimuli are transformed into the binary voltages of the sensitive units which have existed a sufficient time, having two values $+1$ and -1 volt. Each member of the sequence is switched to its corresponding association unit. To get the invariance of the whole system it is enough to get the invariance of each coupling. The last includes the following units: sensitive unit-correcting filter $K_g(p)$ — the inertial part of the coupling $W(p)$ non-linear coupling-association unit. The equation of dynamics is

$$K_g(p) \ W(p) \ \alpha_i = V_i$$

To get absolute invariance it is enough to construct the correcting filter
$K_g(p) = \dfrac{1}{W(p)}$.

CASE 2

Stimuli are transformed into impulses. For example, voltages of the system reading a printed text are impulses. This case can be explained by switching a key at the beginning of the open coupling mentioned above. This key acts periodically with the time of repetition T and the breadth γT. The invariance conditions for this impulse system were deduced by Yu. V. Krementulo.[6] For the open system we find:

$$K_g(p)W(p) = \frac{\alpha(p)}{K_T(p) \ \alpha^\circ(p)}$$

where $\alpha(p)$ = Laplace transform of input voltages — impulses
$\alpha^\circ(p)$ = its discrete transform
$K_T(p)$ = Laplace transform for the impulses
We find the operator of the correcting filter:

$$K_g(p) = \frac{\alpha(p)}{K_T(p) \ \alpha^\circ(p) \ W(p)}$$

where

$$\alpha(p) = \frac{1}{q} \qquad \alpha^\circ(p) = \frac{e^{q-1}}{e^q} \qquad K_T = \frac{1 - e^{-q\gamma}}{q}$$

Practically, the solution means the use of the lead components (differentiators) in the open coupling.

APPENDIX 2

THE INVARIANCE CONDITIONS FOR OPEN DETERMINISTIC CONTROL SYSTEM FOR CONTINUOUS (STATE-DETERMINED) PROCESSES

The system shown in Fig. 1 possesses two clearly seen channels for processing disturbances. According to the well-known theorem of B. N. Petrov[13] this system means that it is possible to satisfy the conditions of invariance. Let us consider the case where only two disturbances λ_1, λ_2 and two manipulated variables are present. The characteristic of the process in this case will be: $\varphi = f(\mu_1, \mu_2, \lambda_1, \lambda_2)$.

The number of the situation l is defined by the matrix of the discrete values of λ_1 and λ_2: $l = l_1 \cdot l_2$. The number of system moves μ is defined by the matrix of μ_1 and μ_2: $\mu = \mu_1 \cdot \mu_2$.

The first necessary condition of invariance is obviously

$$m = l \tag{1}$$

For each two values of λ_1 and λ_2 there exist a definite pair of values μ_1 and μ_2 when φ_1 becomes the extremum, particularly where

$$\frac{\partial \varphi}{\partial \mu_1} = 0; \qquad \frac{\partial \varphi}{\partial \mu_2} = 0 \qquad \lambda_1 = \text{const. and } \lambda_2 = \text{const.}$$

From these two equations we find the second and the third invariance conditions, determining settings of memory units,

$$\mu_1 = \mu_{1\max} \qquad \text{and} \qquad \mu_2 = \mu_{1\max} \tag{2, 3}$$

Conditions 1, 2, and 3 received in such way enable us to get the maximum when the process has no inertia. To outperform the inertia we are to use the lead differential units, the transfer function of which is to be chosen according to the fourth invariance condition.

$$K_g(p) = \frac{1}{W(p)}$$

Thus we obtain

$$K_g(p) \, W(p) = 1$$

where $W(\rho)$ is the transfer function of the process and of the controller.

22

ON THE DESIGN OF LEARNING SYSTEMS FOR CONTROL

V. I. IVANENKO

Institute of Cybernetics, Kiev, U.S.S.R.

and

J. T. TOU

Northwestern University

INTRODUCTION

At the core of the theory of automatic control lies the problem of the synthesis of the control automaton. Within the body of literature available on automatic control are to be found many fundamental papers based on both the classical method and the newer method employing variational techniques.[1-10] Yet, on the important aspect of the synthesis of the control automaton, little work has been done. The areas of treating such a synthesis problem, particularly control automata for a process with nonlinear properties and for a process with either partially known or unknown mathematical descriptions, have been neglected almost completely. The most common difficulty met with by an investigator in the field is the lack of formalized principles resulting from the fact that the problem of synthesis cannot be fitted into the general framework of variational methods. This is particularly true if the mathematical presentation of the objective is either partially known or unknown and believed also to be nonlinear.

The absence of formal mathematical methods for the solution of the synthesis problem does not mean, however, that it is absolutely impossible to control such a process. It is well known pragmatically, from practical observation, that a human operator acting as controller of a process very frequently achieves a quite satisfactory control of his objective. From this observation can be deduced a significant reason for such success: a human operator can control the entire system due to his ability to be taught, or, in other words, to *learn*. Further, depending on the intelligence and adaptability of the human controller, he can also be self-taught—that is, he can make judgments.

To put it more succinctly: the synthesis of a human operator into the system as a control automaton depends on the *learning process* and on the *methods of learning*. However, since at present knowledge of the learning process and of learning methods is still in the formative and gathering stage, there is no formalized system of principles in the discipline. Therefore it might be said that the entire problem of the synthesis of the control automaton for nonlinear processes with an unknown mathematical presentation cannot yet be formulated and does not yet have a true solution. It is possible, nonetheless, to investigate the phenomenon and to attempt some conclusions. The results of this investigation may prove to be of interest.

It has been found, after theorizing and experimenting, that it is possible to synthesize, for certain systems, a control automaton in one or another class of algorithm by methods of learning which are similar to those used in teaching, or imparting data to a human operator who is to act in the capacity of an automatic controller. This solution to the problem may provide some guidance for an important generalization which leads in the direction of a more precise formulation. In the consideration of the problem, the newness of the concept, the lack of clearly defined terminology, the absence of previously formalized principles will all have to be taken into account. We shall begin by examining the problem through investigation of the simplest system of automatic optimization, applying a new terminology (i.e., learning) to concrete, physically extant concepts and phenomena.

SOME CONCEPTS OF LEARNING OF A CONTROL AUTOMATON

Let us examine Fig. 1, in which

P = control process

YA_1 = control automaton which can teach

YA_2 = control automaton which can learn

$\bar{y}$ = state vector of the process in space Y

$\bar{x}$ = control vector of the process in space X

$\bar{z}$ = disturbance vector

$\bar{e}$ = error vector

$\bar{u}$ = vector of learning effects

The components of vectors $\bar{y}$ and $\bar{x}$ are designated by indices:

$$i = 1, \ldots, n \quad \text{and} \quad j = 1, \ldots, r$$

Now we introduce the sampling period τ and then examine the behavior of the system. The sampling instants are defined by

$$\nu = \frac{t}{\tau} = 1, 2, \ldots$$

For instantaneous values of all variables, we introduce vectors in terms of sampling instants $\bar{y}(\nu)$, $\bar{x}(\nu)$ and $\bar{z}(\nu)$,

$$\bar{y}_\nu[\bar{y}(\nu - \xi), \bar{y}(\nu - \xi + 1), \ldots, \bar{y}(\nu - 1), \bar{y}(\nu)]$$

$$\bar{x}_\nu[\bar{x}(\nu - \xi), \bar{x}(\nu - \xi + 1), \ldots, \bar{x}(\nu - 1), \bar{x}(\nu)]$$

$$\bar{z}_\nu[\bar{z}(\nu - \xi), \bar{z}(\nu - \xi + 1), \ldots, \bar{z}(\nu - 1), \bar{z}(\nu)]$$

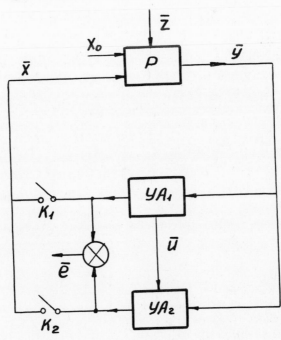

Figure 1

Let the control process P and the control automaton YA_1 form an optimum system characterized as follows:

$I(\bar{y})$ is a specified performance criterion describing the quality of control which has one extreme value at $\bar{x} = \bar{x}^0 \, \epsilon \, X$, so that

$$I^0 = \min_{\bar{x}} I(\bar{y}) = \min_{\bar{x}} I\{F[\bar{x}(\nu), \bar{z}(\nu), \bar{y}(\nu), x_0]\} \tag{1}$$

Let us assume that $z(\nu)$ is a one-dimensional, stationary, random function identified as noise. The mathematical characterization of the process $F[\bar{x}(\nu), z(\nu), \bar{y}(\nu), x_0]$ is unknown. For the purpose of simplification, assume the process has zero memory. For some random and arbitrary initial displacement x_0, control automaton YA_1 must find the optimum control vector $\bar{x} = \bar{x}^0$ at each sampling instant.

Assuming that the components of the control vector $\bar{x}$ are independent, the effect along one of them must now be further examined. The algorithm of the control automaton YA_1 is built on the basis of determination of the gradient of the function $I(\bar{y})$ under conditions of disturbances with the following aspect for the most simple case

$$x(\nu) = x(\nu - 1) + d(\nu - 1) \tag{2}$$

where the increment of control effect $d(\nu - 1)$ can assume only two values:

$$d(\nu - 1) = [-\text{sgn grad } I(\nu - 1)] \, d \tag{3}$$

and

$$\text{grad } I(\nu - 1) = \sum_{i=1}^{n} \frac{\partial I(\nu - 1)}{\partial y_i(\nu - 1)} \cdot \frac{dy_i(\nu - 1)}{dx(\nu - 1)}$$

$$\approx \sum_{i=1}^{n} \frac{\Delta I(\nu - 1)}{\Delta y_i(\nu - 1)} \cdot \frac{\Delta y_i(\nu - 1)}{\Delta x(\nu - 1)} \tag{4}$$

Let the selection of the experimental increment Δx be limited by certain condition:

$$\Delta x \leq D \ll d \tag{5}$$

The control automaton YA_1 while performing the searching process at each instant $(\nu - 1)$, determines the sgn of constant increment $d(\nu - 1)$ of the control effect $x(\nu)$ according to conditions set up by Eqs. (2), (3) and (4). In these conditions the search can be characterized by the time spent in search—or, in other words, the number of steps T in the process of searching. It can be seen that the algorithm indicated above gives the minimum number of steps T^0 in the searching process when the disturbance $z(\nu)$ is absent:

$$T^0 = \frac{x_0 - x^0}{d} \tag{6}$$

This is evident from the fact that Eq. (4) determines exactly

$$\text{grad } I(\nu - 1)$$

Where disturbance $z(\nu)$ exists commensurate with D, the accuracy of the determination of grad I is considerably decreased: at each step the grad I is determined by the realization of the unmeasured disturbance, and the number of steps in the search for T increases accordingly. This increase may be conveniently characterized by

$$\varphi = \frac{T^0}{T} < 1 \tag{7}$$

To increase the accuracy of the computation, the method of statistical synthesis is generally applied here, and consists of smoothing out disturbances by summation in time of elements of the vector grad I_ν, with some weighting coefficients a_ξ where

$$\text{grad } I_\nu = \sum_\xi \sum_i \frac{\partial I(\nu - \xi)}{\partial y_i(\nu - \xi)} \; \frac{dy_i(\nu - \xi)}{dx(\nu - \xi)} \, a_\xi$$

Good smoothing out results in an increase of the index φ whose limit approaches unity.

Such a method is easily applied, however, only where the statistical properties of the disturbance at the output of the process are independent of x. Otherwise, as is usual with a nonlinear process, it is very difficult to apply the statistical method of synthesis to the determination of an algorithm which would yield the automaton YA_1.

The following hypotheses are used as a basis for further considerations.

HYPOTHESIS I

If a human operator acts as the control automaton YA_1 then his ability to control is based on his memorizing the correct controls for one or another state of the process. Storage of information is achieved in this manner.

HYPOTHESIS II

For a multidimensional control process, there is a definite correlation between components of the vector grad $I(\nu)$ determined by the properties of the process dynamics.[11]

If this correlation is determined, and if the levels of disturbance are such that the correlated connections cannot be destroyed, then the smoothing out of the disturbances is realized by the determination of these indicated correlations and, even more important, by the measured data of $\bar{y}(\nu)$, $x(\nu)$ at the sampling instant ν, that is, instantaneous information as differentiated from $\bar{y}_\nu$, $\bar{x}_\nu$, which take into account previous values. This is known as the principle of instantaneous weighting and is demonstrated in Ref. 11.

The more complex the character of indicated correlations, as in the case of a nonlinear process, the greater their stability with reference to disturbances and therefore it is easier to determine them. This latter conclusion suggests many interesting ramifications for further exploration in the field of nonlinear problems.

From the foregoing it is possible to assume now that the value of the index φ characterizing the work of a human operator is proportional to the accumulation of experience obtained from the study of these correlations and will approach unity. If the number of possible states of the process in spaces X and Y is finite, then the ideal operator, as regards his proficiency, has an index φ_1 equal to unity since for every further sampling instant the sgn of $d(\nu - 1)$ is determined correctly and positively.

Applied to the problem basic to this discussion, the foregoing may indicate that for any combination of input data $(x, \bar{y})$ for all possible values of the disturbance z with any x_0, the operator knows in which direction he should move to reach the extreme point. This operator YA_1 may now be designated as the ideal teacher-operator.

Returning to Fig. 1, now assume that the control automaton YA_1 is a perfect teacher-operator. When switch K_1 is closed, switch K_2 is automatically disconnected and automaton YA_1 is in control of the searching process. If the contrary situation occurs—that is, when switch K_2 is turned on, switch K_1 is automatically disconnected—control passes to the learning-automaton, YA_2. The process may now be restated thus: it is essential to teach the learning-automaton YA_2 to behave in a manner that varies as little as possible from that of the teaching automaton YA_1 in the course of controlling a given system. Let the evaluation of the behavior of the teaching automaton be determined by index φ_1 and the evaluation of the behavior of the learning-automaton be given by index φ_2. It may then be assumed that the measurement of learning is determined by the difference between φ_2 and φ_1. If the assumption is that φ_1 characterizes a perfect teacher-operator and is equal to unity, then it may be stated that in going to the limit in the process of learning, index φ_2 approaches unity.

In the process of training, the teaching automaton on the basis of an analysis of the error $\bar{e}$, communicates a learning effect $\bar{u}$ to the learning automaton. The graph shown in Fig. 2 illustrates the method used in the evaluation of index φ_2, with regard to the error $\bar{e}$. The abscissa π represents the amount of information absorbed in the process of learning. The index φ_2 may be referred to as the *index of learning*. From these preliminary statements, it is now possible to proceed to the formulation of the problem.

FORMULATION OF THE PROBLEM OF LEARNING

First introduce the discrete control signal x_k so that

$$x_{k+1} = x_k + d \qquad k = 1, 2, \ldots, K \tag{8}$$

Now examine a certain state of the control process for a fixed displacement $x_o = x_{om}$, and a certain value of control $x = x_k$. In the state space at the sampling instants $\zeta = 1, 2, 3, \ldots$, the process is characterized by the vector $\bar{y}_k(\zeta)$. In this state space the point of interest is grad $I_{mk}(\zeta)$ or its components $\sigma_{ikm}(\zeta)$ from the n components:

$$\bar{\sigma}_{km}(\zeta) = \{\sigma_{1km}(\zeta), \ldots, \sigma_{nkm}(\zeta)\} \tag{9}$$

If it is known that the inequality exists at all conditions, then

$$|\sigma_{ikm}(\zeta)| \leq B \tag{10}$$

The quantization level q_0 is now introduced for all σ_i such that as a result of the measurement, σ_i may have one of the multiude Q values

$$\sigma_i \,\epsilon\, Q = \{q_1, q_2, \ldots q_l \ldots q_s\} \tag{11}$$

and

$$q_{l+i} = q_l + q_0 \tag{12}$$

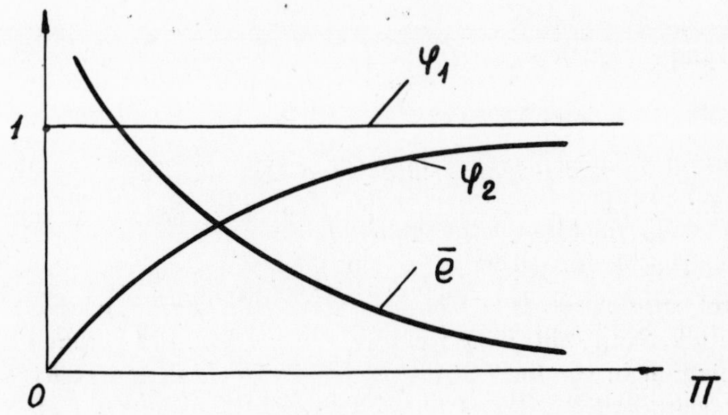

Figure 2

Next is introduced the vector $\bar{v}_i$ with components v_l of the same dimension s and construct the vector $\bar{v}$ to an $(s \times n) = H$ dimension. Then

$$\bar{v}(\bar{v}_i(v_l)) = \bar{v}(v_\eta), \quad \eta = 1, \ldots, H \tag{13}$$

Equations (9), (11), and (13) are then related in the following manner. If as a result of measurement the value of σ_1 is q_l, then the vector $\bar{v}_i$ will appear as

$$\bar{v}_i(v_i = 0, \ldots, v_l \neq 0, \ldots v_s = 0)$$

which means that with the exception of l all components are equal to zero. If $\bar{v}_i$ is a zero vector, then in each i group of components there is one unit which corresponds to the measured value $\sigma_{imk}(\zeta)$. Where such condition exists, the definite aspect of the vector $\bar{v}_{mk}(\zeta)$ may be considered a certain code pattern of measurement represented by the vector $\sigma_{mk}(\zeta)$. The vector $\bar{v}(\zeta)$ is designated as the *information-pattern vector*. An information pattern is illustrated in Fig. 5, where $\bar{v}_{km}(\zeta)$ is shown in a network with the dimensions $n = 4, s = 10, H = 40$. It is evident that the total number of patterns connected with such a vector may be equal to

$$N = s^n \tag{14}$$

Where this holds true, the number N_1 of patterns $\bar{v}_{mk}(\zeta)$ may be related to the observed state of the process $(x = x_k, x_o = x_{om})$

$$N_1 < N, \quad \zeta = 1, 2, \ldots N_1 \tag{15}$$

All possible states of the process should now be examined and to this consideration be introduced the finite number M of possible values of the displacement $x_{om}(m = 1, 2, \ldots, M)$. The number of such possible states is N_2 and

$$N_2 = (MK) \tag{16}$$

In certain specified instances, however, N_2 may be selected as much smaller than would appear from Eq. (16). The total number of information patterns is $N_1 \times N_2$ which forms the multitude S.

Referring to the earlier definition, it may now be stated that an ideal control automaton YA_1 has a positive distribution p over the entire multitude S. In controlling the process P, the control automaton receives information in the form of one of the members of the multitude S and must coordinate it with one of the values of the increment d of the control signal x. For example, if

$$\bar{v}(v) = \bar{v}_{km}(\zeta)$$

then

$$d_{km}(\nu) = +1$$

Let the learning-automaton YA_2 perform a linear transformation $\overline{W}$ of the vector $\bar{v}$ such that

$$\overline{W}\bar{v} = (w_1, w_2, \ldots w_H) \begin{bmatrix} v_1 \\ \vdots \\ v_H \end{bmatrix} = \sum_{\eta=1}^{H} w_\eta v_\eta \qquad (17)$$

Introducing additionally the components W_0 and $\eta_0 = 1$ and summing up Eq. (17) from 0 to H, the problem of learning can be formulated in the following manner:

It is required to determine the linear transform $\overline{W} = \overline{W}^0 \epsilon W$ so that it will satisfy the system of inequalities

$$\sum_\eta W_\eta v_{mk\eta}(\zeta) \gtrless 0 \qquad \begin{matrix} m = 1, 2, \ldots, M \\ k = 1, 2, \ldots, K \\ \zeta = 1, 2, \ldots, N_1 \end{matrix} \qquad (18)$$

which encompass the entire multitude S of the states. Then the sign $>$ is established for $d = -1$, and the sign $<$ for $d = +1$.

If the solution $\overline{W} = \overline{W}^0$ exists for the inequalities of Eq. (18), then after determining it the automaton must be designed to respond to such solution, i.e., it must fulfill the linear transform W^0 over the entire multitude of information patterns S. The most elementary automaton of this type is that of the artificial neuron discussed in the literature[12-15] and referred to as the threshold logic element. A schematic diagram of such an element is shown in Fig. 3: the learning effects $\bar{u}$ are applied to the weighting coefficients $\overline{W}$. Various methods can be applied to determine the solution of

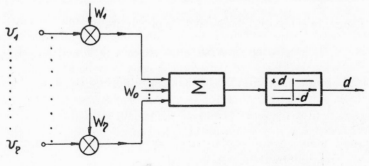

Figure 3

the system of inequalities in (18), including those worked out especially for problems of pattern recognition and general mathematical methods as, for example, linear programming.

If the solution $\overline{W} = \overline{W}^0$ does not exist for the inequalities of (18) then the quantization level q_0 must be decreased by increasing the dimension H of each inequality in (18) or, choosing another direction, by the introduction of combinations of neurons to form a neural net. This leads to a host of new problems which will not here be discussed since the aim of this investigation is to demonstrate an approach to only one particular problem.

ILLUSTRATIVE EXAMPLE

The process of learning may now be illustrated by way of a numerical example. For a certain process, $n = 4$ and $r = 1$. It is assumed that the state variables $y_i(i = 1, \ldots, 4)$ and the control signal x can be measured. The equations of the process are

$$y_i = |[x - (c_i + x_0)] \frac{a_i}{b_i} + z|, \qquad i = 1, 2, 3, 4 \tag{19}$$

where z is the noise with a normal distribution for which the mean square value equals unity and the mathematical expectation is zero. Equation (19) will not be used in the process of teaching, since it is assumed that mathematical description of the process is not available; but it will only be used in the simulation of the behavior of the entire system.

Values of the coefficients in Eq. (19) are:

$a_1 = 2$ for $x \leq (c_1 + x_0)$; $\quad a_1 = 1$ for $x > (c_1 + x_0)$;

$a_4 = 1$ for $x \leq (c_4 + x_0)$;

$a_4 = 2$ for $x > (c_4 + x_0)$; $\quad b_i = 1; i = 1, \ldots, 4, \quad a_3 = a_2 = 1$

Figure 4a shows the characteristics of the process for

$$c_1 = 60, c_2 = 80, c_3 = 90, c_4 = 110, \text{ and } x_0 = 0$$

The performance criterion of the control process is

$$I = \sum_i y_i$$

and is shown in Fig. 4b. To set up the multitude S of patterns $\bar{v}_{km}(\zeta)$, the following information is to be used:

$$x_{\min} = 5, x_{\max} = 165 \text{ and } X = 160$$

Introduce quantization according to Eq. (8), and select $d = 5$ and $K = 33(k = 1, 2, \ldots, K)$. Only one value will be examined: $x_0 = 0$, i.e., $M = 1$.

The tested increment is chosen as $\Delta X = 1$. In each of the K steps of control can be determined the information pattern $\bar{v}_{km}(\zeta)$ in discrete time ζ, by means of the method given above. Consequently, for the point $x_k = 50$ a certain pattern resulting from the disturbance $z(\zeta)$ will be obtained, as shown in Fig. 5. The quantization level of $q = 0.5$ is introduced here for each component of the gradient $\sigma_{kmi}(\zeta)$ where the index of the component is on the abscissa and its measured value on the ordinate. If it is also assumed that $B = 2.5$, then $H = 40$. Examining all sampling instants $\zeta = 1, 2, \ldots, N_1$, the resultant submultitude of patterns S_{km} is obtained, differing from each other because of the disturbance $z(\zeta)$. For $k = 1, 2, \ldots, 33$, the result is that the entire multitude is given by

$$S = \{S_{im}, S_{2m}, \ldots, S_{33m}\}$$

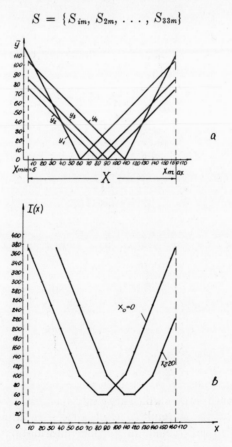

Figure 4

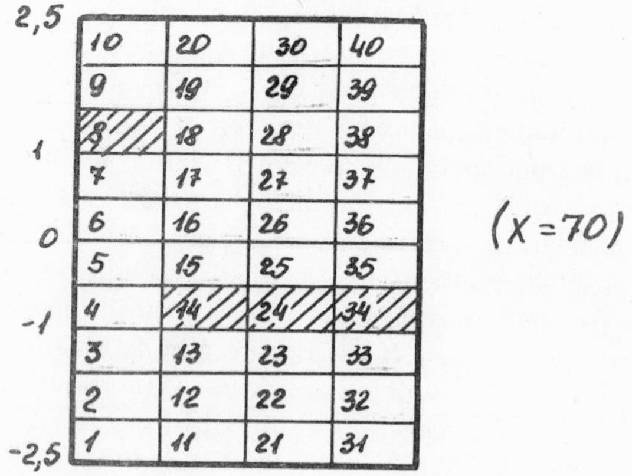

	10	20	30	40
9	9	19	29	39
	8	18	28	38
	7	17	27	37
0	6	16	26	36
	5	15	25	35
-1	4	14	24	34
	3	13	23	33
	2	12	22	32
-2,5	1	11	21	31

(Left axis: 2,5 ; 1 ; 0 ; −1 ; −2,5)

$(x = 70)$

$$\bar{v}(\zeta) = (v_1(\zeta),\ v_2(\zeta),\ \ldots\ v_{40}(\zeta))$$

$$v_8(\zeta)=1,\quad v_{14}(\zeta)=1,\quad v_{24}(\zeta)=1,\quad v_{34}(\zeta)=1$$

Figure 5

For this particular case, taking into account the piecewise linear characteristics, only 5 values of k will be considered: for $x = 50$, $x = 70$, $x = 85$, $x = 100$, and $x = 120$ ($k = 1, 2, \ldots, 5$, respectively). From this it is not difficult to see that states adjacent to these points will yield, over the entire length of the segment, the same basic characteristics of the pattern.

Then the multitude S is given by

$$S = \{S_1,\ S_2,\ S_3,\ S_4,\ S_5\}$$

The perfect-operator is aware that for $x_0 = 0$, the first and second states are to the left and the fourth and fifth to the right of the extremum; the third state is in the extremum. Now the rules for decision making can be written down in the following manner:

(1)   For all $\bar{v}_k(\zeta) \in S_1 \cup S_2$ choose $d = +5$

(2)   For all $\bar{v}_k(\zeta) \in S_4 \cup S_5$ choose $d = -5$

(3)   For all $\bar{v}_k(\zeta) \in S_3$ choose $d = 0$

If a sufficiently large N_1 is selected, it can be ascertained that any pattern connected with the states which are analogous to states at $k = 1$ and $k = 2$, will be found in the submultitudes S_1 and S_2. In addition, the conditions expressed above will include all possible information patterns which are found in the process of controlling $\bar{v}_k(\nu)$. The learning-automaton YA_2 is characterized by the threshold-logic elements which determine a certain relationship between the sum $\sum_\eta W_\eta v_\eta(\zeta)$ and the increment of the controlling effect d for each pattern $\bar{v}(\zeta)$. In the process of teaching the learning automaton YA_2, the coefficients $\overline{W}$ must be chosen so that they will satisfy the following conditions which may be written in the form of a system of inequalities, for $= 1, 2, \ldots, N$

$$\sum_{\eta=0}^{40} W_\eta V_{\eta k}(\zeta) < (-\delta) \qquad \begin{aligned} k &= 1, 2 \\ \zeta &= 1, \ldots, N_1 \end{aligned}$$

$$\sum_{\eta=0}^{40} W_\eta V_{\eta k}(\zeta) > \delta \qquad \begin{aligned} k &= 4, 5 \\ \zeta &= 1, \ldots, N_1 \end{aligned} \qquad (22)$$

$$\sum_{\eta=0}^{40} W_\eta V_{\eta k}(\zeta) < \delta \qquad \begin{aligned} k &= 3 \\ \zeta &= 1, \ldots, N_1 \end{aligned}$$

where δ is a certain zone of insensitivity. The values of weighting coefficients $\overline{W} = \overline{W}{}^0$ correspond to the completion of the training of automaton YA_2 and are determined through the general methods indicated above.

After the coefficients $\overline{W} = \overline{W}{}^0$ are made known to the learning automaton YA_2, switch $K_{1/2}$ is disconnected and switch $K_{1/2}$ is closed (Fig. 1), and the process P and the control automaton YA_2 form an automatic control system.

Some of the properties of this system with regard to its simulation on a digital computer are now discussed. The behavior of the system during the process of searching is described by the following system of equations:

(1) $\qquad y_i(\nu) = |\{x(\nu)[c_i + x_0(\nu)]\} \dfrac{a_i}{b_i} + z|, \qquad i = 1, 2, 3, 4$

(2) $\qquad x(\nu) = x(\nu - 1) + d(\nu - 1)$

(3) $\quad d(\nu - 1) = +5 \qquad$ if $[\Sigma w_\eta^0 v_{\eta k}(\nu - 1) < (-\delta)]$

$\qquad d(\nu - 1) = -5 \qquad$ if $[\Sigma w_\eta^0 v_{\eta k}(\nu - 1) > \delta]$

$\qquad d(\nu - 1) = 0 \qquad$ if $[|\Sigma w_\eta^0 v_{\eta k}(\nu - 1)| < \delta]$

(4) $\quad v_k(\nu - 1) = 1$ or 0, according to Refs. 12-15. $\qquad (23)$

Assume that x_0 is constant for one searching process. Then select $x_0 = 0$. The effect of the number N_1 on the learning index φ_2 of the system is first investigated. The results of computer simulation are plotted in. The index φ_2 increases with the growth of experience, approaching $\varphi_1 = 1$, as expected.

The index φ_2 was determined as the average from the multitude P of searchings at every fixed N_1, that is,

$$\varphi_2 = \frac{T^0}{T} = \frac{T^0}{\dfrac{\displaystyle\sum_{i=1}^{} T_i}{P}} \tag{24}$$

If the initial displacement is now changed, as for example, by taking $x_0 = 20$, then by repeating the entire sequence of experiments, it would be found that the index $\varphi_2(N_1)$, shown in Fig. 6, curve b, is practically invariant in relation to the displacement. Hence the control algorithm is to find the extreme value of the performance criterion of the process for any displacement x_0 over the entire segment X.

If at a certain N_1 a portion of the coefficients W_η is made equal to zero, with a view to verifying the reliability, then that system is stable with regard to such disturbances. Thus the value of φ_2 at a chosen N_1 is reduced and later increases again; but it reaches $\varphi_1{}^{16}$ as N_1 becomes considerably greater (Fig. 6, curve c). This property of the stability of a parallel algorithm with regard to destruction has been previously discussed by von Neumann.[18]

DECISION THEORY APPROACH

The learning problem in control systems may be formulated as a problem of statistical decision. Referring to Fig. 1, the densities of conditional probability distributions are

$$P_1[\overline{y}(\nu) = \overline{y}'(\nu)/\overline{x}(\nu) = \overline{x}'(\nu)]$$

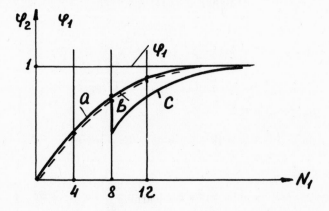

Figure 6

and

$$P_2[\bar{x}(\nu) = \bar{x}'(\nu)/\bar{x}(\nu - 1) = \bar{x}'(\nu - 1), \bar{y}(\nu - 1) = \bar{y}'(\nu - 1)]$$

for the process P and the control-automaton YA_2, respectively. As before, the control process is assumed to have no memory. Introduce the loss function

$$c(\nu) = c[\bar{y}(\nu), \bar{y}^0(\nu), \nu]$$

where $\bar{y}^0(\nu)$ denotes the desired value of $\bar{y}(\nu)$. The total loss is defined by

$$C = \sum_\nu c(\nu)$$

The learning problem in a control system may be formulated as the problem of minimizing a risk function, which is defined as the mathematical expectation of the total loss function

$$R = E\{C\} = E\{ \underset{\nu}{\Sigma} c(\nu)\} = \sum_\nu E\{c(\nu)\} = \sum_\nu R(\nu) \qquad (25)$$

Following Refs. 6, 16, and 18, the risk function may be written as

$$R(\nu) = \int_\Delta \int_x \int_y P_4[\bar{x}(\nu - 1), y(\nu - 1)]$$

$$P_2[\bar{x}(\nu) = \bar{x}'(\nu)/\bar{x}(\nu - 1) = \bar{x}'(\nu - 1), y(\nu - 1) = \bar{y}'(\nu - 1)]$$

$$P_1[\bar{y}(\nu) = \bar{y}'(\nu)/\bar{x}(\nu) = \bar{x}'(\nu)] \, c(\nu) \, d\Delta \, dX \, dY \qquad (26)$$

where $P_4[\bar{x}(\nu - 1), \bar{y}(\nu - 1)]$ is the joint density of probability distributions.

If the functions P_1 and P_4 are known, the problem of synthesizing the control-automaton reduces to the determination of function P_2 which minimizes the risk function given in Eq. (26). The important problem in the determination of functions P_1 and P_4 for a given process will ultimately depend on whether the statistics of the disturbance $P_3[\bar{z}(\nu)]$ is given.

Two problems can be evolved:
(1) $P_3[z(\nu)]$ is given and the functions P_1 and P_4 can be determined a priori;
(2) $P_3[\bar{z}(\nu)]$ is not given at all; or P_3 is given but the functions P_1 and P_4 cannot be determined a priori.

The first problem is designated the problem of statistics synthesis. The second one has various names, the best known of which is the problem of synthesis of a self-adjusting or self-organizing system.

The problem formulation of the synthesis of the automaton for the recognition of patterns [16] shall now be reviewed. Assume that a certain pattern $\bar{v}$, in a given space V belonging to the multitude L is composed of submultitudes L_i. Due to the effect of disturbances, the observed pattern is a distorted pattern $\bar{y}$ in the space Y. It is required now to determine to which of the submultitudes L_i the observed pattern $\bar{y}$ belongs.

The following expressions are introduced:

$P_i(\bar{v})$ = density of probability distribution of patterns in space V;

$P_2(\bar{y}/\bar{v})$ = conditional density of probability distribution that the pattern $\bar{y}$ will be observed when the actual pattern is $\bar{v}$. A cost is incurred if the observed pattern belongs to classification L_2 when the actual pattern lies in classification L_1. The loss function provides a measure of the cost of accepting a distorted pattern.

$P_3(\bar{x}/\bar{y})$ = the rule for the selection of solution which must be determined so that the average risk

$$R = \int\limits_v \int\limits_x \int\limits_y P_1(v) \, P_2(\bar{y} = \bar{y}'/\bar{v} = \bar{v}') \, P_3(\bar{x}/\bar{y}) \, c(\bar{v},\bar{x}) \, dV \, dX \, dY$$

(27)

will be a minimum. In this case there arise also two problems:

(1) $P_1(v)$ is given, and $P_2(\bar{y}/\bar{v})$ is also given or can be determined *a priori*;

(2) $P_2(\bar{y}/\bar{v})$ is not given or cannot be determined *a priori*.

It is customary to designate the first problem of synthesizing automata for the recognition of patterns as the training problem and the second one as the problem of self-learning or self-organization. It can be seen that from a mathematical point of view these problems are indentical to the problems of synthesis of the control-automaton formulated above. Investigation of problems concerning the recognition of geometrical patterns, in particular letters of the alphabet, has entailed the study of a special, degenerated case of the first problem. In this case, for each one of the submultitudes L_i in the entire multitude of observed patterns there exist at least several patterns about which it is known with certainty that the given pattern is

$$\bar{y} \, \epsilon \, L_i$$

It must be assumed with regard to these patterns that

$$P_2(\bar{y}/\bar{v}) = 1, \, P_3(\bar{x}/\bar{y}) = \delta, \text{ and } c(v,\bar{y}) = 0$$

or, in other words, the average risk R for both is equal to zero. In the above expression, δ is the Dirac delta function. These patterns are used by the teacher for training a certain automaton to recognize. The remaining portion of the patterns is recognized automatically by this learning-automaton, depending on its ability to interpolate. This ability for interpolation is based on a certain correlation inherent in the elements of the patterns belonging to the same submultitude L_i. This method is used in Refs. 12, 14, and 15 and in the majority of other investigations for the recognition of visual patterns.

The problem of "degenerated" learning problems was examined earlier in the example given above, in which was discussed the problem of training a control-automaton. The assumption that an ideal operator has a positive knowledge of the distribution p over a multitude of patterns S is equivalent to the condition

$$c(\nu) = 0$$

Further steps in the training of control-automata are related to the solution of the two non-degenerated problems stated above, the solution of which will probably open new avenues of research in automatic control.

ACKNOWLEDGMENT

The work covered by this paper was supported in part by the National Science Foundation and the Office of Naval Research. The research opportunity was made available to V. I. Ivanenko through the Exchange Program in Sciences and Culture organized by the Ministry of Higher Education of the U.S.S.R. and the Inter-Universities Committee of the United States.

REFERENCES

1. Tou, J. T., *Optimum Design of Digital Control Systems*, Academic, New York, 1963.
2. Tou, J. T., *Digital and Sampled-data Control Systems*, McGraw-Hill, New York, 1959.
3. Newton, G. C., Gould, L. A., and Kaiser, J. P., *Analytic Design of Linear Feedback Controls*, Wiley, New York, 1958.
4. Letov, A. M., *Analytical Design of Controllers*, Automatika i Telemekhanika, 1961–62.
5. Chang, S. S., *Optimum Synthesis of Control Systems*, McGraw-Hill, New York, 1961.
6. Fel'dbaum, A. A., *Dual Control*, Automatika i Telemekhanika, nos. 9, 11, 1960; Nos. 1, 3, 1961.
7. Wiener, N., *Extrapolation, Interpolation and Smoothing of Stationary Time Series*, Technical Press, Cambridge, 1949.
8. Wald, A., *Statistical Decision Function*, Wiley, New York, 1950.
9. Pontryagin, L. S., et al., *Mathematical Theory of Optimum Control Processes*, Wiley, New York, 1960.
10. Bellman, R., *Dynamic Programming*, Princeton U. P., Princeton, N. J., 1960.
11. Ivanenko, V. I., *On Information Patterns of Controlled Objectives*.

12. Rosenblatt, F., *Principles of Neurodynamics*, Spartan, Baltimore, 1961.

13. Sebestyen, G. S., *Decision-making Processes in Pattern Recognition*, Macmillan, New York, 1962.

14. Winder, R. O., *Threshold Logic in Artificial Intelligence*, Winter Meeting of AIEE, 1963.

15. Widrow, B., *Pattern Recognition and Adaptive Control, Proc. JACC*, June 1962.

16. Middleton, J., *An Introduction to Statistical Communication Theory*, McGraw-Hill, New York, 1960.

17. Neumann, J., *The Computer and the Brain*, Yale U. Press, New Haven, 1958.

18. Tou, J. T., and Fu, K. S., *Digital Control Concepts for Nervous System Synthesis and Simulation, Proc. Third Int. Congress on Cybernetics, 1961*.

INDEX